THE GOOD HOTEL GUIDE

46ᵀᴴ EDITION

GREAT BRITAIN & IRELAND

Editors
Jane Knight
Nicola Davies
Kate Quill
Jane Anderson

THE GOOD HOTEL GUIDE LTD

The Good Hotel Guide Ltd

This edition first published in 2022 by
The Good Hotel Guide Ltd

Copyright © 2022 The Good Hotel Guide Ltd
Maps © 2022 David Perrott

Chief executive: Richard Fraiman

Contributing editors:
Rose Shepherd
Helen Pickles
Bonnie Friend

Production: Hugh Allan
Managing editor: Alison Wormleighton
Designer: Stuart Sutch
Text editor: Daphne Trotter
Computer consultant: Vince Nacey
Digital agency: Umi Digital
Researcher: Cristina Recio-Corral

A CIP catalogue record for this book may be found in the British Library.

ISBN 978-0-9932484-7-4

PHOTO CREDITS
Front cover – The Felin Fach Griffin, by Paul Massey.
Main-entry chapter openers – Shutterstock: p11 lunamarina, p25 James Ratchford, p323 Scotland's Scenery, p373 Pajor Pawel, p401 Gary Le Feuvre, p407 Greg Fellmann.
Other photos supplied by the hotels.

Printed and bound in Malta by Gutenberg Press Ltd

*'A good hotel is where
the guest comes first'*

Hilary Rubinstein, founding editor
(1926–2012)

The Bell at Skenfrith, Wales

CONTENTS

goodhotelguide.com

Our website has many handy features to help you get the most out of your Guide.

- **Explore offers and discounts**
- **View special collections**
- **View the annual Césars and Editor's Choice winners**
- **Read the latest news**
- **Search for a hotel near you**
- **Search for a hotel near a particular destination**
- **Submit a review**
- **Join the Good Hotel Guide Readers' Club**
- **Order a copy of the printed Guide**

DESKTOP

TABLET

SMARTPHONE

Make it even easier to get on the Good Hotel Guide website while you're on the go: add an icon to the home screen of your iPhone or iPad for one-touch smartphone access. Go to **goodhotelguide.com** on your mobile browser. Tap on the rectangle with an arrow pointing upwards, at the bottom of the screen. Then tap on the + sign ('Add to Home Screen') that pops up.

INTRODUCTION

Welcome to the 46th edition of The Good Hotel Guide. We bade farewell to Adam and Caroline Raphael this year, as they decided to take well-earned retirement. Caroline had edited every edition of the Guide and had a deep intuitive knowledge of the hotel world. Adam, with his energy and savvy, was its public face and media presence, responding to readers and hoteliers with grace, wit and the occasional barb.

It was my great pleasure to work on the Guide with both Adam and Caroline for several years, and, as the Guide's new owner, I am committed to upholding its cherished values of independence and impartiality. Although the Raphaels have gone, the editorial team, led by Jane Knight, former travel editor for The Times, is unchanged. The team's detailed knowledge of hotels and hospitality, and their ability to convey the essence of a place, from intimate B&B to five-star hotel and gastropub, have again done us proud. This edition features a Michelin-starred restaurant with only two guest bedrooms (possibly Britain's smallest) in Herefordshire, a practically perfect pub in the Cotswolds, and a fun hotel in York with a working train set in the bar and vinyl to spin.

While the Guide's principles of honesty and independence remain fundamental, I shall continue to seek to make improvements for you, the reader. The print Guide is designed for pleasurable armchair browsing and to accompany you on your travels, but it can only ever be a single snapshot in time. It is for this reason that, in the dynamic and evolving world of travel, we encourage you to reach out to hotels directly to verify that details are as we state in the Guide. We provide multiple ways for you to contact them.

The Guide's website, meanwhile, will continue to evolve. You can now see our coveted Césars and Editor's Choice awards only online, along with other useful information, such as hotels with good facilities for the disabled, hotels with tennis courts and swimming pools, even our choice of hotels for a Christmas break. Recent years have been challenging for the hospitality industry, requiring hoteliers to be ingenious in adapting to survive. Against a background of rapid innovation, the fluid nature of our website enables us to update more swiftly, to ensure that write-ups are as useful as possible.

Some things may change, but others are constant, and you, our readers, are the bedrock of our operation, as important and valued by us as ever. So please tell us about your hotel experiences, both good and less good. You can file reports with us via our website, or by using the form at the back of this Guide. We respond to every single review that we receive. They are the beating heart of The Good Hotel Guide, the best and most trusted guide to the UK and Ireland's finest hotels, inns and B&Bs.

Wishing you all happy travels.

Richard Fraiman
July 2022

HOW TO USE THE GOOD HOTEL GUIDE

MAIN ENTRY

The 413 main entries, which are given a full page each, are those we believe
to be the best of their type in Great Britain and Ireland.

Colour bands identify each country;
London has its own section.

An index at the back lists hotels by county;
another lists them by hotel name.

Hotels appear
alphabetically
under the name
of the town or
village.

The maps at the
back of the book
are divided into
grids, with a small
house indicating a
main entry, and a
triangle a Shortlist
entry.

If a hotel is making
its first appearance
or is returning after
an absence, this is
indicated by a 'new'
emblem.

The panel provides
useful information,
such as contact
details, number
of bedrooms and
facilities.

We try to indicate
whether a hotel is
wheelchair-accessible
or is unsuitable for
the disabled. It's
always worth calling
the hotel to check the
details of this.

We name readers
who have endorsed a
hotel; we do not name
inspectors, readers
who ask to remain
anonymous, or those
who have written a
critical report.

If the Shortlist (see opposite) also has
one or more entries for this village or
town, a cross-reference to the Shortlist
appears here.

We give the starting
price for room, bed-
and-breakfast and/
or dinner-bed-and-
breakfast prices.
The price for dinner
is for a set meal, or
the average cost of
three courses from
an à la carte menu.

---

320   ENGLAND   goodhotelguide.com

YORK Yorkshire   MAP 4:D4

NO. 1 YORK   NEW

This Georgian town house with cool styling and
a playful vibe offers comforting Yorkshire food,
a cocooning spa and a sunny welcome to all, dogs
and children included. Step through the porticoed
entrance and 'you know this place is going to be
fun', reports a Guide insider. A black-painted hall
is lined with violins; a drawing room is full of art;
a clubby bar 'buzzes with a toy train, Johnny Cash
spinning on a turntable'. The handsome house,
a five-minute walk from the city walls, has had
a 'radical and daring make-over' while retaining
its Georgian good looks: sash windows flood
rooms with light, the dining room has a modern
elegance. Minimalist bedrooms of milk-coloured
walls, floaty muslins and painted floorboards
'make the most of often small-ish spaces' while
'the treats made me smile': a turntable (vinyl
library downstairs) and a guest pantry of sweets,
cakes, soft drinks. Bathrooms with under-floor
heating are 'bright and well thought-through'.
Dinner is stylish Yorkshire comfort food such
as smoked venison with rhubarb, pork cutlet
with herb polenta. Breakfast's 'excellent choice'
includes omelette and mushrooms on toast. (HP)

1 Clifton
York YO30 6AA

T: 01904 644744
E: no1.reservation@
guesthousehotels.co.uk
W: guesthousehotels.co.uk

BEDROOMS 39. 1 suitable for disabled.
OPEN all year.
FACILITIES bar, lounge, dining room,
private dining room, spa (5 treatment
rooms), kitchen pantry, in-room TV
(Freeview), terrace, parking, EV
charging, public rooms wheelchair
accessible, adapted toilet.
BACKGROUND MUSIC in public areas.
LOCATION central York.
CHILDREN all ages welcomed, under-
4s free, extra bed from £25.
DOGS allowed in designated bedrooms
(£25 per night, welcome pack), public
rooms apart from dining room and
spa.
CREDIT CARDS Amex, MC, Visa.
PRICES B&B doubles from £167.
À la carte £37. Occasional 2-night
min. at weekends.

Prices may change – check with hotel.

SEE ALSO SHORTLIST

HOW TO USE THE GOOD HOTEL GUIDE

SHORTLIST ENTRY

The Shortlist complements our main section by including interesting
new entrants and a selection of places in areas in which we have limited choices.
It also includes some hotels that have previously been in the Guide but have
not had sufficient feedback this year.

This hotel is
making its first
appearance in
the Shortlist or is
returning after
an absence.

Shortlist hotels
are included in
both indexes at
the back of the
book, where (S)
indicates that it is
a Shortlist entry.

Many readers
tell us they find
background music
irritating. We say
whether music
is played and
where you might
encounter it.

We list the principal
credit cards accepted
by the hotel (with
MC standing for
Mastercard).

We give the starting
price or range of
room, bed-and-
breakfast and/or
dinner-bed-and-
breakfast prices.
The price for dinner
is for a set meal, or
the average cost of
three courses from
an à la carte menu.

LONDON

Trafalgar Square and Big Ben

LONDON

ARTIST RESIDENCE LONDON

Eccentric, fun and colourful, this Pimlico town house in a leafy residential street is as much a neighbourhood hang-out and art gallery as a place to sleep and eat. Part of Justin and Charlotte Salisbury's small collection of Artist Residences (see index), the public areas are a seamless blend of café, bar, brunch and supper spot, the walls hung with original and limited-edition artwork, and neon pop art. There are tan leather chairs, velvet-covered armchairs, reclaimed timber walls and shelves of pot plants; outside the pavement terrace is shaded with stripy awnings; downstairs there's a speakeasy-style cocktail bar. An all-day brunch offers dishes such as kedgeree, scrambled egg with avocado, feta and chilli, and pancake stack; come evening (Thursday to Saturday), the short-choice menu might include fish pie, Balinese vegetable curry, and steak with chimichurri sauce. Bedrooms, with wood floors and pale-grey walls, are furnished with vintage and reclaimed pieces, limited-edition prints, Roberts radios, espresso machines and organic toiletries; the suites have freestanding bathtubs and walk-in showers.

52 Cambridge Street
Pimlico
London SW1V 4QQ

T: 020 3019 8610
E: london@artistresidence.co.uk
W: artistresidencelondon.co.uk

BEDROOMS: 10.
OPEN: all year, evening meals Thurs–Sat only.
FACILITIES: restaurant/café/bar, cocktail bar/lounge, private dining/events, in-room TV (Freeview), terrace, car parks (charge) nearby, unsuitable for disabled.
BACKGROUND MUSIC: in public areas.
LOCATION: Pimlico, underground Pimlico.
CHILDREN: all ages welcomed, free cot, extra bed £30.
DOGS: in some bedrooms (£15 a night, welcome pack), and all public spaces.
CREDIT CARDS: Amex, MC, Visa.
PRICES: room-only doubles from £190. Cooked breakfast dishes £6.50–£12, à la carte £35. 1-night bookings sometimes refused weekends.

Prices may change – check with hotel.

SEE ALSO SHORTLIST

LONDON

MAP 2:D4

BATTY LANGLEY'S

Inside a Georgian house in a trendy corner
of East London, once home to Huguenot silk
weavers, Peter McKay and Douglas Blain set out
to weave a fantasy of their own. And to whom
should they turn but that great, eccentric arbiter
of 18th-century style, Batty Langley, with his
'Great Variety of Grand and Usefull Designs'.
As at London sister properties Hazlitt's and The
Rookery (see entries), to enter is 'like walking
into another century'. Interiors are filled with
antiques, books, paintings, rich velvets, tapestries.
Kitty Fisher's boudoir has a carved four-poster,
a balcony, a Victorian canopy bath. The Earl of
Bolingbroke suite has a canopy bed built for a
bishop, a Tuscan marble bath, a 'secret throne
toilet behind a bookcase'. Some rooms have 'a
"theatre bath" behind a curtain'. A box-room
single is 'cosy and characterful'. Relax by the fire
in a book-lined library with a drink from the
honesty bar. Order chicken pie or a baguette
from a room-service menu. Despite the historic
feel, you have all mod cons here, and if you
want to know how life was without them, visit
neighbouring Dennis Severs' House, which reeks
of the 1700s. (RF)

12 Folgate Street
Spitalfields
London E1 6BX

T: 020 7377 4390
E: reservations@battylangleys.co.uk
W: battylangleys.com

BEDROOMS: 29. 1 suitable for disabled.
OPEN: all year.
FACILITIES: lift, library, parlour,
lounge, meeting rooms, in-room TV
(Freeview), small courtyard, ground
floor (except courtyard) wheelchair
accessible, adapted toilet.
BACKGROUND MUSIC: none.
LOCATION: 5 mins' walk from
Liverpool Street Underground and
rail stations.
CHILDREN: all ages welcomed, extra
bed under-13s free, 13–16s £45.
DOGS: assistance dogs only, by
arrangement.
CREDIT CARDS: Amex, MC, Visa.
PRICES: room-only doubles from £229.
Breakfast baker's basket (pastries,
yogurt) £11.95, bagels from £9.95.
Occasional 2-night min. stay if busy.

Prices may change – check with hotel.

SEE ALSO SHORTLIST

LONDON   MAP 2:D4

THE BEAUMONT

The elegance is timeless, the style is Jazz Age
glamour, the feel is New York fun – all of which
makes The Beaumont, in the heart of Mayfair,
one of London's leading luxury hotels. Art
Deco interiors of glossy panelling, opaque-glass
lampshades and mirrored pillars together with
black-and-white photographs of legendary stars
create the feel of a private members' club. Staff are
'suited and booted', yet the hotel has 'a warmth'
and 'light-heartedness' that makes it ideal 'for
a romantic escape'. Bedrooms are sleek with
1930s-style furniture, floor-to-ceiling windows
and mosaic-and-marble bathrooms. Even entry-
level rooms are spacious; all have complimentary
snacks and soft drinks. Take coffee on the terrace,
afternoon tea in Gatsby's Room, cocktails in the
walnut-panelled American bar before dining in
the glamorous Colony Grill restaurant. With its
red-leather booths and speakeasy vibe, it features a
New York-influenced menu of classic dishes such
as grilled Dover sole and steak tartare. Breakfasts
are decadent affairs including muffins, pancakes,
salt beef hash, and eggs how you want them, as
well as a full grill.

Brown Hart Gardens
Mayfair
London W1K 6TF

T: 020 7499 1001
E: reservations@thebeaumont.com
W: thebeaumont.com

BEDROOMS: 72. Some rooms suitable
for disabled.
OPEN: all year, restaurant closed Sun
eve.
FACILITIES: bar, restaurant, restaurant/
lounge, private dining room, spa,
outdoor dining terrace, electric shuttle
limousine, in-room smart TV (free
movies), nearby car parks (charge),
public rooms wheelchair accessible,
adapted toilet.
BACKGROUND MUSIC: in public areas.
LOCATION: Mayfair, mews parking,
underground Bond Street, valet
parking.
CHILDREN: all ages welcomed, free
cots, extra bed £80.
DOGS: by arrangement.
CREDIT CARDS: Amex, MC, Visa.
PRICES: B&B doubles from £490
(with continental breakfast). Cooked
breakfast dishes £8–£25, à la carte
dinner £60.

Prices may change – check with hotel.

SEE ALSO SHORTLIST

LONDON

MAP 2:D4

DURRANTS

If you're looking for afternoon tea after trawling Marylebone's chichi emporia, you'll find freshly baked cakes and pastries in a clubby atmosphere at this much-loved bolt-hole. Owned by the Miller family since 1921, it occupies four former Georgian town houses as one seamless whole. 'The staff are unfailingly welcoming, with old-fashioned courtesies such as bags swept in a moment from the taxi.' Bedrooms have period and contemporary furniture, a Savoir bed, L'Occitane toiletries. 'Those at the quieter rear', overlooking Manchester Mews, are snug; if you want lots of space, suites have a sitting room. Fires burn in cosy lounges, while in the Grill Room menus range from comfort food (liver and bacon, shepherd's pie, roasts from the trolley) to more innovative dishes (wild mushroom ravioli, chicken tagine). Readers who love the place are indulgent of occasional shortcomings. 'Unfailingly my bathroom sink is blocked or slow on my arrival, but this is swiftly cleared.' 'Breakfast is very grand, with pots of this and that crowding the table, and the menu full of specially cooked calorific dishes.' (Robert Cooper, Keith Salway)

26–32 George Street
Marylebone
London W1H 5BJ

T: 020 7935 8131
E: enquiries@durrantshotel.co.uk
W: durrantshotel.co.uk

BEDROOMS: 92. 7 on ground floor.
OPEN: all year, restaurant closed 25 Dec evening.
FACILITIES: lifts, bar, restaurant, lounge, meeting/events rooms, in-room TV (Freeview), use of nearby fitness club, public areas wheelchair accessible, no adapted toilet.
BACKGROUND MUSIC: none.
LOCATION: off Oxford Street, underground Bond Street, Baker Street.
CHILDREN: all ages welcomed, extra bed (in larger rooms only) £50.
DOGS: allowed in George bar only.
CREDIT CARDS: Amex, MC, Visa.
PRICES: B&B doubles from £245, singles from £195. À la carte £42.

Prices may change – check with hotel.

SEE ALSO SHORTLIST

LONDON

MAP 2:D4

11 CADOGAN GARDENS

A home away from home in the heart of
Chelsea is the aim of these red brick Victorian
town houses, which have been converted into
a luxurious hotel of dazzling individuality. A
warren of corridors and staircases leads to a
sprawl of bedrooms, sitting rooms and private
retreats. There are gilt-framed portraits around
the black-painted staircase, a wall of art in
the drawing room with its smart armchairs
and purple sofas, a sultry cocktail bar, leather
armchairs in the library, and a plant-filled
conservatory. The 'buzzy and busy' Hans' Bar and
Grill has flavourful dishes such as grilled chicken,
pan-fried hake and falafel burgers. Breakfast
dishes include French toast with berry compote,
omelettes, and slow-cooked mushrooms with
poached egg. Bedrooms have a modern elegance,
with soft shades, button-back armchairs and
jewel-bright splashes in headboards and cushions.
Top-end suites are dramatic with sumptuous
fabrics and marble bathrooms. All have coffee
machines, and views over Cadogan Gardens or
rooftops. Staff are 'a real highlight' with their
'very polite' but 'super-friendly' manner. A
member of Relais & Châteaux.

11 Cadogan Gardens
Chelsea
London SW3 2RJ

T: 020 7730 7000
E: reservations@11cadogangardens.
com
W: 11cadogangardens.com

BEDROOMS: 56 (incl. 25 suites). Plus
6 apartments.
OPEN: all year.
FACILITIES: small lift, drawing room,
library, cocktail bar, Hans' Bar and
Grill (wine room, conservatory),
private dining/events rooms, in-room
TV (Sky), civil wedding licence, gym,
decked terrace, 24-hr secure parking
(charge), grill and public rooms
wheelchair accessible, adapted toilet
by Grill.
BACKGROUND MUSIC: everywhere
except the library.
LOCATION: Chelsea, underground
Sloane Square.
CHILDREN: all ages welcomed, cots
free, extra bed in suites £72.
DOGS: only assistance dogs.
CREDIT CARDS: Amex, MC, Visa.
PRICES: B&B doubles from £340, singles
from £304. À la carte £45.

Prices may change – check with hotel.

SEE ALSO SHORTLIST

LONDON

MAP 2:D4

THE GORING

'Traditional with a capital T', The Goring epitomises grand Edwardian luxury from its silk-lined walls and liveried footmen to its brass-trimmed lift and secret garden. Owned by fourth-generation Gorings and in a peerless position in Belgravia close to Buckingham Palace, it's reassuringly expensive with service to match. Cases are whisked to rooms, polished shoes are returned wrapped in tissue, suites have dedicated butlers. Public rooms dazzle: carved wall-panels in the gold-and-red bar and lounge, Swarovski chandeliers in the dining room. 'But it's not affected,' says a Guide insider; current owner, Jeremy Goring, 'is frequently present' ensuring guests 'feel at ease'. The garden 'is an oasis of calm, the perfect place for afternoon tea'. Top-tier bedrooms overlook the lawn; all have a low-key glamour of silk wallpapers, bespoke furniture and marble bathrooms. Dine in the Michelin-starred restaurant on classics such as beef Wellington and Dover sole, or in the colourful veranda on lighter dishes such as the signature lobster omelette. Both have vegetarian options. Breakfast is a royal feast; service throughout impeccable. (JK)

15 Beeston Place
Grosvenor Gardens
London SW1W 0JW

T: 020 7396 9000
E: reception@thegoring.com
W: thegoring.com

BEDROOMS: 69. 2 suitable for disabled.
OPEN: all year.
FACILITIES: lifts, lounge, bar, restaurant (veg. menu), private dining rooms, gym, in-room TV, civil wedding licence, veranda, 1-acre garden, parking, EV charging, public rooms wheelchair accessible, adapted toilet.
BACKGROUND MUSIC: pianist in lounge Thurs, Fri, Sat eves.
LOCATION: Belgravia, mews parking, underground Victoria.
CHILDREN: all ages welcomed, under-12s extra bed £80.
DOGS: small dogs allowed in bedrooms (£200 cleaning charge), garden, not in public rooms.
CREDIT CARDS: Amex, MC, Visa.
PRICES: room-only doubles from £590. Breakfast from £32 (continental). À la carte (3 courses) dining room £80, veranda £56.

Prices may change – check with hotel.

SEE ALSO SHORTLIST

LONDON

THE GRAZING GOAT

A country pub feel close to the bustle of Oxford Street sounds unlikely but this pub-with-rooms with its popular pavement terrace in a quiet backwater manages it with unpretentious style. A first-floor dining room of beams and stripped floorboards, Georgian sash windows and giant lampshades is lively and relaxed, 'not for an intimate occasion'. While our Guide insider found the menu 'a bit limited', the modern pub dishes are 'perfectly cooked and presented' and might include fresh oysters, steak pie and mash with Guinness sauce, and fish and chips as well as smarter options such as bream with pistachio and mint pesto, and a range of steaks. Staff are 'exceptionally pleasant and efficient'. Bedrooms, spread over three floors, are neat and 'perfectly comfortable' with oak-wood floors and panelling, pale-coloured walls, a king-size bed and industrial-style lighting. Bathrooms, with bathrobes and botanical toiletries, are compact and shower-only. Breakfast, charged à la carte, offers 'lots of choice' including home-made granola and yogurt, flamenco eggs with nduja, plus three versions of a full grill. (See also London sister pub, The Orange.)

6 New Quebec Street
Marble Arch
London W1H 7RQ

T: 020 7724 7243
E: reservations@thegrazinggoat.co.uk
W: cubitthouse.co.uk/the-grazing-goat

BEDROOMS: 8.
OPEN: all year.
FACILITIES: bar, dining room, patio, in-room TV, car park nearby (charges), ground-floor bar and toilet fully wheelchair accessible.
BACKGROUND MUSIC: all day in bar and restaurant.
LOCATION: central, underground Marble Arch.
CHILDREN: all ages welcomed, free cot, extra bed £30.
DOGS: allowed in ground-floor bar, not in dining room or bedrooms.
CREDIT CARDS: Amex, MC, Visa.
PRICES: room-only doubles from £250. Breakfast items from £5, full English £16.75, à la carte dinner £50.

Prices may change – check with hotel.

SEE ALSO SHORTLIST

LONDON

MAP 2:D4

HAZLITT'S

You can imagine nodding off in an armchair over the latest issue of Samuel Johnson's Idler, or William Hazlitt's polemics in the Tatler, when you step into this time-warp hotel and close the door on trendy Soho. It was here, on a Georgian terrace in the 1820s, that essayist Hazlitt penned his final diatribes, and antiques and furnishings keep faith with a bygone age. Bedrooms have a carved oak or four-poster bed, Victorian bathroom fittings. A suite has a sitting room with working fireplace, a garden with sliding glass roof. All have air conditioning, a minibar, modern plumbing, Land & Water toiletries (no chamber pot, Denmark wash or wig powder). The staff are 'welcoming and friendly'. Public rooms are 'cosy, with fireplaces, immaculately presented'. Venture out to a local coffee house, or sit tight with a drink from the library honesty bar, comestibles from a 24-hour room-service menu. At breakfast, send for cereal and croissants, a Buck's Fizz and one of those new-fangled bread-and-meat confections so lately made popular by the Earl of Sandwich. (See also London sister ventures The Rookery and Batty Langley's.)

6 Frith Street
Soho
London W1D 3JA

T: 020 7434 1771
E: reservations@hazlitts.co.uk
W: hazlittshotel.com

BEDROOMS: 30. 2 on ground floor.
OPEN: all year.
FACILITIES: lift, library, private lounge/meeting room, in-room TV (Sky, Freeview), public rooms wheelchair accessible, adapted toilet.
BACKGROUND MUSIC: none.
LOCATION: centre of Soho, underground Tottenham Court Road, Leicester Square.
CHILDREN: all ages welcomed, under-13s free, extra bed £45.
DOGS: not allowed.
CREDIT CARDS: Amex, MC, Visa.
PRICES: room-only doubles from £279. Breakfast £12, limited room-service menu, dishes from £7.

Prices may change – check with hotel.

SEE ALSO SHORTLIST

LONDON

THE LOST POET   `NEW`

'In a discreet building that could be a private residence', this 'beautifully designed' guest house is at the end of Portobello Road. Guide inspectors failed to find the poet, but did discover suites with 'living-room-type seating, a large bed with interesting headboard, snazzy fabrics, alluring art, an espresso machine, a mini-fridge with complimentary drinks, and exquisite bathroom'. Up 'a tight staircase for the fit and able', the Muse, painted in soft blue, has a freestanding bath in the bedroom, stairs to a lounge area and roof terrace, a bathroom with walk-in shower. The ground-floor Quarters suite, in soft-hued green, has a window seat from which to watch the hurly-burly in the world's largest street antiques market. A lower-ground-floor suite has a private patio. 'Guests are served a continental breakfast, hung in a bag outside their room', though you won't have to venture far to find a full English. If you fancy a cool hang-out in a hip postcode from which to come and go without fuss, it is for you. There is a daytime concierge, but with keyless self check-in, you are left to your own devices.

6 Portobello Road
Notting Hill
London W11 3DG

T: 020 7243 6604
E: info@thelostpoet.co.uk
W: thelostpoet.co.uk

BEDROOMS: 4.
OPEN: all year.
FACILITIES: concierge 9 am–6 pm, keyless self check-in, 24-hour phone support, in-room TV.
BACKGROUND MUSIC: none.
LOCATION: Notting Hill, underground Notting Hill Gate.
CHILDREN: not under 12, extra bed for stays of 5 days or more (additional charges apply).
DOGS: allowed only during exclusive hire.
CREDIT CARDS: Amex, MC, Visa.
PRICES: B&B doubles from £199.
1-night bookings sometimes refused.

Prices may change – check with hotel.

SEE ALSO SHORTLIST

LONDON

MAP 2:D4

THE MAYFAIR TOWNHOUSE

The designers have really gone to town on this city
sister to Cliveden House, Taplow, and Chewton
Glen, New Milton (see entries), spread over a row
of Georgian town houses on Half Moon Street
in swanky W1. 'It has a playful personality and
oodles of eccentricity,' says our inspector, with
'nods to Oscar Wilde', who set The Importance of
Being Earnest on Half Moon Street. In reception,
Clarita Brinkerhoff's peacock sculpture, made
from 25,000 Swarovski crystals, is called Alfie
after Wilde's lover, Lord Alfred Douglas. The
'flamboyant and theatrical' Dandy bar is ideal for
a spot of Bunburying over cocktails. Bedrooms
and suites, some with garden terrace, are
'decorated in seductive shades' and supplied with
'plenty of treats', including an espresso machine
and tipples in a minibar. 'Ours, in Art Deco style,
had a gold statement lamp standing out against
navy furnishings.' You can graze on large and
small plates the whole day in the bar, and in
the lower-ground-floor Club Room, hung with
'quirky takes on the usual ancestral portraits'.
'The burger was enormous, with delicious sweet-
potato fries.' Dogs, allowed in the bar, get 'treats,
meals, a bed, even a bathrobe'.

27–41 Half Moon Street
Mayfair
London W1J 7BG

T: 020 8138 3400
E: reservations@
   themayfairtownhouse.com
W: themayfairtownhouse.com

BEDROOMS: 172. Some suitable for
disabled.
OPEN: all year.
FACILITIES: lifts, cocktail bar, dining
room, events/meeting rooms, in-room
TV, room service, meeting/function
facilities, fitness suite, bar and (by
lift) lower ground floor wheelchair
accessible, adapted toilet.
BACKGROUND MUSIC: in public areas.
LOCATION: central, underground
Green Park 3 mins' walk.
CHILDREN: all ages welcomed.
DOGS: smaller breeds (up to 30 lb)
allowed in some bedrooms (blanket,
bowl, toy, no charge), in bar until
6 pm.
CREDIT CARDS: Amex, MC, Visa.
PRICES: room-only doubles from £277,
singles from £252. Breakfast £25,
à la carte £32.

Prices may change – check with hotel.

SEE ALSO SHORTLIST

LONDON

MAP 2:D4

THE ORANGE

On the corner of a leafy Pimlico street, close to
Sloane Square, this handsome cream-coloured
stucco building has relaxed and smart interiors
that make it a popular neighbourhood eatery
topped with four airy bedrooms. The ground-
floor bar with its pale-washed walls, sturdy
wooden tables and striped banquettes is lively
with locals, who often spill on to the pavement in
summer. Eat here such punchy dishes as cumin-
spiced lamb meatballs and pizzas. For a smarter
menu – perhaps roast turbot with Swiss chard and
wild garlic, and steak with rosemary and Pecorino
fries – choose the elegant first-floor dining room
with its floor-to-ceiling sash windows. On the
top floor, high-ceilinged bedrooms with beams,
light-oak floors and panelling continue the fresh,
countryside theme with vases of dried flowers,
soft colours and simple linen curtains. Bathrooms
are on the small side, only one with a bathtub;
all rooms have bathrobes, coffee machines and
botanical toiletries. An à la carte breakfast offers
tempting dishes such as smoked salmon and
scrambled egg with crème fraîche, grilled focaccia
sandwiches and the full English.

37 Pimlico Road
Pimlico
London SW1W 8NE

T: 020 7881 9844
E: reservations@theorange.co.uk
W: theorange.co.uk

BEDROOMS: 4.
OPEN: all year.
FACILITIES: restaurant, bar, private
dining room, in-room TV, rooftop
terrace, pavement seating, civil
wedding licence, ground-floor pub/
dining area wheelchair accessible,
adapted toilet.
BACKGROUND MUSIC: in public areas.
LOCATION: Pimlico, underground
Sloane Square.
CHILDREN: all ages welcomed, extra
bed £30.
DOGS: allowed in ground-floor bar, not
in bedrooms or dining room.
CREDIT CARDS: Amex, MC, Visa.
PRICES: room-only doubles from £200.
Breakfast items from £5, cooked
from £13. À la carte £31 (bar), £53
(restaurant).

Prices may change – check with hotel.

SEE ALSO SHORTLIST

LONDON

MAP 2:D4

PORTOBELLO HOTEL

Beyond the Doric portico of a white stucco neo-classical mansion, this boutique hotel captures the eclectic charms of glamorous and bohemian Notting Hill. Acquired by Peter and Jessica Frankopan's Curious Group of Hotels in 2014, it has been styled by Jessica with a mix of heritage chic, '60s pizzazz and Portobello Road finds. Rooms are painted in bold colours – from rusty reds to minty greens – or feature designer wallpapers. Doubles range from 'cosy', with an exotic de Gournay mural, to grand signature rooms with a garden view, a shower and freestanding roll-top bath. No two are alike. The most desired has a circular bed with diaphanous drapes. Two lower-ground-floor 'roomy rooms' have a private patio, while two attic box rooms are singles. All have a minibar, a coffee machine, fine porcelain and own-brand natural Green & Spring bath products. There is an honesty bar in the sitting room, where you can take breakfast (juices, pastries, charcuterie, cheeses) – or have it brought to your room. Spa-and-stay breaks include access to partner venture Cloud Twelve Wellness Spa, five minutes away.

22 Stanley Gardens
Notting Hill
London W11 2NG

T: 020 7727 2777
E: stay@portobellohotel.com
W: portobellohotel.com

BEDROOMS: 21.
OPEN: all year.
FACILITIES: lift, sitting room/breakfast room with honesty bar, in-room TV (Freeview), street parking (fees), unsuitable for disabled.
BACKGROUND MUSIC: 'chill-out' in sitting room.
LOCATION: Notting Hill, underground Notting Hill Gate.
CHILDREN: all ages welcomed.
DOGS: allowed in 2 bedrooms, not in breakfast room.
CREDIT CARDS: Amex, MC, Visa.
PRICES: room-only doubles from £210, singles from £168. Continental breakfast £14.50, bacon or sausage sandwich £6, smoked salmon and scrambled eggs £8. 1-night bookings sometimes refused Sat, public holidays.

Prices may change – check with hotel.

SEE ALSO SHORTLIST

LONDON

MAP 2:D4

THE ROOKERY

Hip eateries and bars have supplanted hovels and
bawdy houses in this once-notorious area, but
behind the 18th-century facade of three shop-
houses Georgian London lives on. Peter McKay
and Douglas Blain had the property gutted and
refitted, with salvaged mahogany panelling
and old stair treads for an authentic creak,
then filled the interiors with antiques, books,
portraits, artefacts. Expect to find Bagheera the
cat snoozing by a fire in one of the cosy parlours.
Bedrooms have names, not numbers. Ground-
floor Dr Theophilus Garencières has a carved
oak four-poster, a separate sitting area. The
emerald-green Rook's Nest has a hand-painted
four-poster, an old-fangled bathing contraption
on a plinth, stairs to a sitting room with a lawyer's
writing desk. All rooms have vintage bathroom
fittings, a freestanding bath or powerful shower,
air conditioning, a minibar and TV (here, as at
London sister hotels Hazlitt's and Batty Langley's,
verisimilitude has its limits). You can order from
a room-service menu, maybe a charcuterie plate,
chicken pie or lobster ravioli, and take the sun in a
leafy patio garden among stone urns and cherubs.

12 Peter's Lane
Cowcross Street
London EC1M 6DS

T: 020 7336 0931
E: reservations@rookery.co.uk
W: rookeryhotel.com

BEDROOMS: 33. 1 on ground floor.
OPEN: all year.
FACILITIES: 3 sitting rooms, honesty
bar, gin bar, meeting rooms, in-room
TV (Sky), small patio garden,
unsuitable for disabled.
BACKGROUND MUSIC: none.
LOCATION: Clerkenwell, underground
Farringdon, Barbican.
CHILDREN: all ages welcomed, under-
13s sharing with parents stay free in
some rooms.
DOGS: not allowed.
CREDIT CARDS: Amex, MC, Visa.
PRICES: room-only doubles from £229,
singles from £209. Breakfast from
about £12, à la carte (from room-
service menu) £28.

Prices may change – check with hotel.

SEE ALSO SHORTLIST

ENGLAND

Seven Sisters, Sussex

ALDEBURGH Suffolk   MAP 2:C6

THE WENTWORTH

One of the hotels that have appeared in the Guide for the lengthiest time is also one of the most loved among long-standing readers – it's as dependable as the tides that wash over the sand and shingle beach opposite. 'My favourite destination in the UK,' writes one. 'Such a joy to be back there again,' relates another. 'Still a fantastic place, overseen by Michael Pritt, the caring owner.' The ground floor has new carpet, and the hotel prides itself on its updated wallpapers and fabrics, but the feel remains traditional, and the lounges, with open fires, retain their clubby atmosphere. Immaculate bedrooms, some with wheelchair access and a bath and wet-room shower, are in the main hotel and Darfield House annexe. Many have 'wonderful views of the sea'. There is a cosy bar with a wood-burner, access to sea-facing terraces. You can take afternoon tea indoors or out, dine in the restaurant (no shorts, please) where a wide menu, with plenty of meat-free options, includes dishes such as grilled Dover sole, caper and herb butter. 'Many of the staff are still there and remember us. The food is delicious, even better than before.' (Julian Landy, Simon Rodway)

Wentworth Road
Aldeburgh IP15 5BD

T: 01728 452312
E: stay@wentworth-aldeburgh.co.uk
W: wentworth-aldeburgh.com

BEDROOMS: 35. 7 in Darfield House opposite, 5 on ground floor, 2 in hotel and 1 in annexe suitable for disabled.
OPEN: all year except possibly 2 weeks in Jan.
FACILITIES: 2 lounges, bar, restaurant (veg/vegan menus), in-room TV (Freeview), 2 terrace gardens, courtyard garden, parking, public rooms wheelchair accessible, adapted toilet.
BACKGROUND MUSIC: none.
LOCATION: seafront, 5 mins' walk from centre.
CHILDREN: all ages welcomed, extra bed £15.
DOGS: allowed in bedrooms (£5 per night) and public rooms, not in restaurant.
CREDIT CARDS: Amex, MC, Visa.
PRICES: B&B doubles from £215, singles from £135. Set-price dinner £28–£34 (2/3 courses). 1-night bookings refused Sat.

Prices may change – check with hotel.

ALFRISTON Sussex

MAP 2:E4

THE STAR

Mother and daughter Olga and Alex Polizzi
have beautifully reinvented this picturesque
15th-century hostelry in a medieval South Downs
village. Beyond a welcoming oak-beamed bar
frequented by locals lies a hotel decorated in the
signature Polizzi style. In a modern block, dog-
friendly rooms have French windows to a patio;
those above, a Juliet balcony. A Guide insider
noted plenty of nods to nature with 'soft greens
and blues … lampshades with hand-painted
birds, door handles shaped as oak leaves'. Even
the more compact bathrooms have 'a sizeable
walk-in shower'. A secret door behind the library
bookshelves opens on to the restaurant, with its
'exquisite food, starting with the sourdough',
followed perhaps by 'a crab beignet full of flavour
or melt-in-the-mouth beef fillet wrapped in
coppa'. The portrait of an Elizabethan lady,
hanging above a Georgian carved oak table,
unnervingly blinks. In warm weather, you can eat
in the Mediterranean-style courtyard. 'Breakfast
is a treat, with fresh-squeezed orange juice',
and sets you up for walks from the door. See also
Hotel Endsleigh, Milton Abbot, and Tresanton,
St Mawes. (KS, JK)

High Street
Alfriston BN26 5TA

T: 01323 870495
E: thestar@thepolizzicollection.com
W: thepolizzicollection.com

BEDROOMS: 30. 1 bedroom suitable for
wheelchair-users (no wet room).
OPEN: all year.
FACILITIES: bar/lounge, library,
restaurant, courtyard (alfresco dining),
in-room TV, parking, EV charging,
restaurant wheelchair accessible,
adapted toilet.
BACKGROUND MUSIC: none.
LOCATION: centre of village.
CHILDREN: all ages welcomed, extra
bed £30.
DOGS: allowed in ground-floor
bedrooms (£25 a night with beds,
bowls) and inn, not in restaurant.
CREDIT CARDS: MC, Visa.
PRICES: B&B doubles from £190.
À la carte £54. 1-night stays refused
at weekends.

Prices may change – check with hotel.

SEE ALSO SHORTLIST

ALNWICK Northumberland   MAP 4:A4

THE COOKIE JAR

Guests find a jar of home-made cookies in their
rooms, which is just one of the fun quirks of this
intimate boutique hotel in a former convent,
a stroll from Alnwick Castle. Owner Debbie
Cook has created a 'charming hotel' with 'superb
service' and a modern country-house feel of
stripped-wood floors, leather armchairs and
chic shades-of-blue colour scheme. Geometric-
patterned fabrics are mixed with bright-orange
Penguin classics in the lounge. In the 'light and
elegant' dining room, framed collections of cutlery
hang on walls, while pieces of blue-and-white
glassware and pottery catch the eye. Bedrooms
continue the blue theme with an uncluttered style
that mixes vintage and modern. Some overlook
the castle, others have cosy sloping ceilings, while
the extraordinary Chapel Suite offers a copper
bath beneath stained-glass windows. All have
sharply modern bathrooms and, of course, a
cookie jar. Dine on Modern British food such
as home-cured salmon pastrami and venison
Wellington. An 'excellent breakfast', eaten
overlooking the garden, includes home-made
granola, poached egg and avocado, and a full grill.
(David Ganz)

12 Bailiffgate
Alnwick NE66 1LX

T: 01665 510465
E: hello@cookiejaralnwick.com
W: cookiejaralnwick.com

BEDROOMS: 11. 1 suitable for disabled.
OPEN: all year, bistro open daily Mar–
end Oct, restricted opening Nov–end
Feb (ring to check).
FACILITIES: lounge, bistro, drying
room, secure gunroom, in-room TV
(Freeview), lift, terrace with fire pit
(alfresco dining), garden, parking,
wheelchair accessible throughout,
adapted toilet.
BACKGROUND MUSIC: in public spaces.
LOCATION: near town centre.
CHILDREN: all ages welcomed, extra
bed £30.
DOGS: in some bedrooms (£30 per
stay), not in public areas, 5 kennels for
gun dogs.
CREDIT CARDS: MC, Visa.
PRICES: B&B doubles from £180. Set
dinner 2 courses £38, 3 courses £49.

Prices may change – check with hotel.

ALVESTON Warwickshire

MAP 3:D6

BARASET BARN

'Foodie heaven with the bonus of nearby culture,' was a Guide insider's verdict on this restaurant-with-rooms a short spin by loan bike from Stratford-upon-Avon. The centrepiece is 'an old barn, beautifully done out, with statement lights dangling from impossibly high, beamed ceilings'. In this 'spectacular setting', exciting small and large plates showcase local produce. 'My son decreed the jerk barbecue baby back ribs with watermelon, chilli, ginger and coriander the best he'd tasted, unusual but delicious. My scallops with sticky pomegranate and sesame pork belly zinged with flavour.' 'Wonderful, imaginative menus,' readers concur, and 'lovely, cheerful staff', but 'we disliked the awful music'. 'There is a slight US motel feel' about the new-build bedroom block, where rooms have a Juliet balcony or terrace. 'Our enormous room had a neutral palette, mustard and green chairs, an impressively large, powerful walk-in shower.' Fresh milk in a fridge, an espresso machine and posh toiletries are welcome extras. 'Breakfast was also particularly good, with plenty of fresh fruit and home-made yogurt.' (Wendy Hill, JK)

Pimlico Lane
Alveston
Stratford-upon-Avon CV37 7RJ

T: 01789 295510
E: barasetbarn@lovelypubs.co.uk
W: barasetbarn.co.uk

BEDROOMS: 16. In separate annexe, 1 suitable for disabled.
OPEN: all year, hotel closed Sun nights.
FACILITIES: restaurant, conservatory, bar lobby, in-room TV (Freeview), courtyard garden, patio, meetings/private dining, EV charging, hotel bicycles, public area and restaurant wheelchair accessible, adapted toilet.
BACKGROUND MUSIC: in public rooms at mealtimes.
LOCATION: rural, 2 miles NE of Stratford-upon-Avon.
CHILDREN: all ages welcomed, free cots, extra bed £20.
DOGS: allowed in garden and conservatory, not bedrooms.
CREDIT CARDS: Amex, MC, Visa.
PRICES: B&B doubles from £110 (with continental breakfast, cooked dishes £10). À la carte £37.

Prices may change – check with hotel.

AMPLEFORTH Yorkshire

SHALLOWDALE HOUSE

Guests are made to feel like old friends at this wisteria-clad, light-filled 1960s house with its peerless views over gardens to the Howardian hills. Hosts Phillip Gill and Anton van der Horst have the happy knack of creating rooms and an atmosphere that are 'deeply relaxing', helped in no small measure by the picture windows that ensure striking views at every turn. Large, luminous bedrooms are full of warm colours, brightly patterned fabrics and a classic country house style. They are filled with art and books, as are the two sitting rooms. Thoughtful touches include binoculars (great for birdwatching and rabbit-spotting), pot plants, chocolates and Penhaligon toiletries. Enjoy complimentary tea and home-made cakes while gazing over the 'mature and lovely gardens'. Phillip's cooking is 'out of this world', says a regular guest, with dinner (booked ahead) a treat of white napery, fresh flowers and four courses that might include smoked trout salad, duck breast with braised endive and Marsala, and 'delicious desserts'. The scrambled eggs at breakfast are legendary: 'Nobody does that better!' An 'utterly splendid' stay. (AW, FT)

West End
Ampleforth YO62 4DY

T: 01439 788325
E: stay@shallowdalehouse.co.uk
W: shallowdalehouse.co.uk

BEDROOMS: 3.
OPEN: all year except Christmas/New Year and 'occasional' other times.
FACILITIES: drawing room, dining room, sitting room/library, in-room TV (Freeview), 2½-acre gardens, unsuitable for disabled.
BACKGROUND MUSIC: none.
LOCATION: edge of village.
CHILDREN: not under 12.
DOGS: not allowed.
CREDIT CARDS: Amex, MC, Visa.
PRICES: B&B doubles from £150, singles from £135. Set dinner £55 (min. 72 hours' notice). 2-night min. stay, occasional 1-night availability.

Prices may change – check with hotel.

ARKENDALE Yorkshire

MAP 4:D4

THE BLUE BELL

This is a village inn you would like to keep a secret: real ales at the bar, high-quality food and a modern country style that still keeps the pub's character. A handy stop-over on the A1 near Harrogate – also useful for the races at Ripon, Thirsk or Wetherby – the Blue Bell has the rural pub essentials of flagged floors, beamed ceilings and wood-burner, but smartened with soft colours, leather chesterfields and wool-covered armchairs. Neat and fuss-free bedrooms have super-king beds, light-oak furniture, and headboards and throws in plaid wool. Two rooms have a bath as well as shower, one a romantic double-ended affair. Some rooms are small but 'we were very impressed', reports a reader. 'Everything was top quality.' Generous menus are a mix of pub classics – home-made fish pie, Yorkshire beef burger, say – and more elaborate dishes such as pan-seared salmon with lovage emulsion, or roast chicken with pancetta and mushroom fricassée. 'Our meal was delicious,' say readers who point out the 'good vegetarian options'. Breakfasts offer wild mushrooms on toast, eggs Benedict and poached haddock among the 'top-class' cooked dishes. (JC)

Moor Lane
Arkendale
Harrogate HG5 0QT

T: 01423 369242
E: info@thebluebellatarkendale.co.uk
W: thebluebellatarkendale.co.uk

BEDROOMS: 4.
OPEN: all year.
FACILITIES: bar, restaurant, patio, in-room TV (Freeview), parking, public areas wheelchair accessible, adapted toilet.
BACKGROUND MUSIC: in public rooms.
LOCATION: 4 miles NE of Knaresborough, 10 mins from A1(M).
CHILDREN: all ages welcomed, no charge for extra bed.
DOGS: in bar area only.
CREDIT CARDS: Amex, MC, Visa.
PRICES: B&B doubles from £110. À la carte £33.

Prices may change – check with hotel.

AUGHTON Lancashire

MAP 4:E2

MOOR HALL RESTAURANT WITH ROOMS

New arrivals at this Jacobean manor house and gastronomic hot spot in landscaped grounds with a lake can take a tour of the impressive kitchen garden to see the produce that will appear on their plate. The food is earthed in the landscape, with local, home-grown and foraged ingredients, and everything possible, even cheeses, made on the premises. In the beamed Barn, a Michelin-starred à la carte menu features dishes such as Herdwick lamb with purple sprouting broccoli and smoked anchovy; sourdough gnocchi with white asparagus, morels and hazelnut. The roast sirloin at Sunday lunch is a big attraction. But it is the two-star tasting menu in the glass-walled restaurant that truly showcases chef/patron Mark Birchall's stellar talents, in dishes such as turbot with salsify, mussel and roe sauce; guineahen with morel, ramson and white asparagus ragout, whey, liver and truffled honey; garden apples with woodruff, birch sap and apple marigold. There are five suites in the main house; two in the Gatehouse, on the lakeside. All have an emperor bed, a 40- or 50-inch smart TV and luxury bathroom. The full Lancashire breakfast should not be missed.

Prescot Road
Aughton L39 6RT

T: 01695 572511
E: enquiry@moorhall.com
W: moorhall.com

BEDROOMS: 7. 2 on ground floor in Gatehouse.
OPEN: hotel open all year Wed–Sun, except 26 Dec, 27 June–13 July (the Barn open Christmas/New Year).
FACILITIES: bar, lounge, 2 restaurants, in-room TV, 5-acre grounds, EV charging, ground floor public areas wheelchair accessible, lift to one restaurant, adapted toilet.
BACKGROUND MUSIC: in public areas.
LOCATION: on B5197, 2½ miles SW of Ormskirk.
CHILDREN: all ages welcomed, extra bed £50, no under-12s in Moor Hall restaurant in eve.
DOGS: not allowed.
CREDIT CARDS: Amex, MC, Visa.
PRICES: B&B doubles from £250. Moor Hall 4-course lunch £95, 8-course dinner £195, the Barn set lunch (Thurs–Sat) £32, set dinner (Wed, Thurs) £45.

Prices may change – check with hotel.

AUSTWICK Yorkshire

MAP 4:D3

AUSTWICK HALL

With its grandly furnished rooms, extravagant decorative style and sweeping Italianate garden, this Yorkshire Dales country house B&B has the flavour of a stately home. Run for many years by Eric Culley and Michael Pearson, the 'very beautiful' 16th-century manor house with 'lovely features' is not for the minimalist. Public rooms are filled with curios and art; logs burn in fireplaces (lovely for the welcoming tea and home-made scones); walls are richly coloured; and an 'imperial' staircase leads to well-appointed bedrooms with exotic rugs on 'pleasantly creaky' floorboards. Antiques, plump sofas and extravagant beds fill these large rooms, with equally palatial bathrooms boasting roll-top bath, bathrobes and a separate shower. All rooms overlook the 'really special' gardens, with a terrace and woodland sculpture trail. 'Beautifully cooked', leisurely breakfasts include home-made granola, eggs from their own hens, and local bacon. The hosts, who can advise on supper places – The Traddock (see next entry), a favourite with guests – are 'so kind and couldn't do more for us'. (SB, and others)

Townhead Lane
Austwick LA2 8BS

T: 01524 251794
E: info@austwickhall.co.uk
W: austwickhall.co.uk

BEDROOMS: 3.
OPEN: all year except 24–26 Dec.
FACILITIES: hall, drawing room, sitting room, dining room, in-room TV (Freeview), 14-acre gardens, hot tub, unsuitable for disabled.
BACKGROUND MUSIC: none.
LOCATION: edge of village.
CHILDREN: aged 16 and upwards welcomed.
DOGS: not allowed.
CREDIT CARDS: MC, Visa.
PRICES: B&B doubles from £160, singles from £145. Min. 2-night bookings throughout year.

Prices may change – check with hotel.

AUSTWICK Yorkshire

MAP 4:D3

THE TRADDOCK

'A lovely hotel in a lovely village,' says a fan of this Yorkshire Dales country house hotel that combines comfort and elegance with a homely atmosphere. This handsome Georgian and Victorian house, celebrating 20 years under the Reynolds family, retains a period feel with rooms of antiques, plump sofas and rich wallpapers. Inviting sitting rooms have fires in the grates, newspapers and magazines to browse; one has garden views. Bedrooms are spacious, in soft colours and pretty fabrics. 'Our room was pristine and very comfortable.' Most have a bath as well as a shower; all spoil with fruit and home-baked biscuits. Equally indulgent is the 'ambitious and well-executed food', which promises to continue under new chef Ryan Shilton. 'A memorable scallop with caramelised celeriac' impressed one reader who chose the taster menu. Alternative brasserie-menu dishes might include poussin with langoustine and shiitake. A big breakfast, with home-made bread, sets you up for one of many walks from the door. Guests report enjoying their stays enormously thanks 'in no small measure to the friendly and attentive staff'. (Frances Thomas, J and KP)

Austwick LA2 8BY

T: 01524 251224
E: info@thetraddock.co.uk
W: thetraddock.co.uk

BEDROOMS: 14. 1 on ground floor, unsuitable for disabled.
OPEN: all year. Taster menu Tues–Sat, brasserie menu all week.
FACILITIES: 3 lounges, bar, 2 dining rooms, function facilities, in-room TV (Freeview), 1½-acre grounds (terrace), ground-floor restaurant wheelchair accessible.
BACKGROUND MUSIC: in public areas except 1 lounge.
LOCATION: 4 miles NW of Settle.
CHILDREN: all ages welcomed, extra bed/cot £25.
DOGS: allowed in bedrooms (£10 a night) and public rooms except dining rooms, owners may eat in bar area with their dogs.
CREDIT CARDS: MC, Visa.
PRICES: B&B doubles from £110, singles from £100. Taster menu £65, à la carte 3-course £45. 1-night bookings refused Sat.

Prices may change – check with hotel.

AYLESBURY Buckinghamshire

MAP 2:C3

HARTWELL HOUSE

An equestrian statue of Frederick, Prince of Wales, marks your arrival at this glorious Jacobean-cum-Georgian mansion, a hotel since the late 1980s. 'A beautiful country house with personal service at its core', it gazes over an 18th-century landscape, with Ionic temple, obelisk, a lake spanned by an arch from the old Kew Bridge. Restored by Historic House Hotels and owned by the National Trust (see Middlethorpe Hall, York, and Bodysgallen Hall & Spa, Llandudno), it is beautifully presented, with perfectly judged antiques and spectacular original features. 'What a wonderful hotel, perfect in every way for all our requirements,' writes a reader this year. The 'lovely accommodation' ranges from classic double rooms with coffee machine and home-made biscuits to 'royal' rooms and suites, some with four-poster. There are further rooms and dog-friendly suites in a converted 18th-century riding school. Dress formally to dine on such elaborate dishes as pan-fried sea bream, chicken-braised pearl barley, caramelised chicory, pickled artichoke, roasted yeast sauce. 'Catering at the highest level made our stay a real treat.' (Ralph Wilson, CC)

Oxford Road
Stone
Aylesbury HP17 8NR

T: 01296 747444
E: info@hartwell-house.com
W: hartwell-house.com

BEDROOMS: 48. 16 in stable block, some on ground floor, 1, in main house, suitable for disabled.
OPEN: all year, closed for lunch weekdays.
FACILITIES: Great Hall, morning room, drawing room, library, 2 dining rooms, function facilities, in-room TV (Sky, Freeview), civil wedding licence, spa (indoor pool), 94-acre gardens and parkland, tennis, EV charging, public rooms wheelchair accessible, adapted toilet.
BACKGROUND MUSIC: none.
LOCATION: 2 miles W of Aylesbury.
CHILDREN: not under 6, no extra beds.
DOGS: allowed in stables suites (max. 2 small/1 large, no charge).
CREDIT CARDS: Amex, MC, Visa.
PRICES: B&B doubles from £260, singles £225. Set-price dinner £74.

Prices may change – check with hotel.

BABBACOMBE Devon

CARY ARMS & SPA

A cosy beamed pub is the warm heart of this hotel, in the shelter of wooded, red sandstone cliffs that reminded the young Queen Victoria of 'a ballet or a play where nymphs appear'. Designed by owner Lana de Savary, sea-view rooms and suites, at the inn and in former fishermen's cottages, have a cool beachside chic, some with a balcony or terrace for seal-watching. Welcoming touches include complimentary sloe gin on arrival, an espresso machine, chocolate and biscuits. Most luxurious are the blue-and-white 'beach hut' doubles and suites, with king-size bed, a waterfall shower or a bath and walk-in shower, bifold doors on to a decking area, music system, mini-fridge, under-floor heating. You can dine on pub classics and more sophisticated fare – pan-roasted venison haunch steak with juniper jus, say, or steak, ale and mushroom pie; Lyme Bay lobster; beer-battered Brixham fish with hand-cut chips; stuffed roasted red pepper, tomato and basil couscous and herb salad. Spa use for residents is £25. Blissful days can be spent in sheltered coves, walking the South West Coast Path or the surrounding downs, spotting roe deer and buzzards.

Beach Road
Babbacombe TQ1 3LX

T: 01803 327110
E: enquiries@caryarms.co.uk
W: caryarms.co.uk

BEDROOMS: 18. 6 beach huts, 2 beach suites, unsuitable for disabled. Plus 7 self-catering cottages.
OPEN: all year.
FACILITIES: saloon, bar/restaurant (vegetarian menu), in-room TV, civil wedding licence, spa (hydrotherapy pool, gym, steam room), garden, parking, EV charging, unsuitable for disabled.
BACKGROUND MUSIC: all day in inn, saloon and spa.
LOCATION: by beach, 2¼ miles N of Torquay harbour.
CHILDREN: all ages welcomed, extra bed £25.
DOGS: allowed in some bedrooms (£25 per night).
CREDIT CARDS: Amex, MC, Visa.
PRICES: B&B doubles from £230, beach huts from £355, singles from £184. À la carte £40, vegetarian/vegan £28, spa use £25. 1-night bookings refused at weekends.

Prices may change – check with hotel.

BABCARY Somerset

MAP 1:C6

THE RED LION

There's bags of olde worlde character in Clare and Charlie Garrard's thatched gastropub, with flagstone floors and exposed beams and plenty of cosy corners and crannies. Much loved by locals, this 17th-century village inn is also conveniently close to Glastonbury and makes a good stopping-off point between London and the West Country. Expect a welcome as warm as the interiors. You can dine in the bar, in the panelled restaurant with logs stacked floor to ceiling for the fire, or in the large and lovely garden, where wood-fired pizzas are cooked in summer. The menu mixes pub favourites with dishes such as grilled sea bass, crab fettucine, cockle popcorn, clam and white wine cream sauce. The bedrooms, in a separate, purpose-built 'barn', are contemporary in style, with pastel paint finishes, big, padded headboards, a bath and/or shower. A family room has a sofa bed to sleep one or two children. After a breakfast of free-range eggs, Wiltshire bacon and Sausage Shed bangers, you can take a stroll to see the wild flowers and butterflies in Babcary Meadows Reserve. Or make the 20-minute drive to see Glastonbury's mysterious tor.

Babcary
Somerton TA11 7ED

T: 01458 223230
E: info@redlionbabcary.co.uk
W: redlionbabcary.co.uk

BEDROOMS: 6. All in converted barn, 1, on ground floor, partially suitable for disabled.
OPEN: all year.
FACILITIES: bar, snug, restaurant, private dining room, seasonal outdoor pizza bar, meeting/function facilities, in-room TV (BT), garden (with play area), parking, bar wheelchair accessible, adapted toilet.
BACKGROUND MUSIC: in bar area.
LOCATION: 5 miles E of Somerton.
CHILDREN: all ages welcomed, family room.
DOGS: allowed in bedrooms (£15 a night) and public bars.
CREDIT CARDS: Amex, MC, Visa.
PRICES: B&B doubles from £110, singles from £100, family room from £150. À la carte £35.

Prices may change – check with hotel.

BAINBRIDGE Yorkshire

LOW MILL GUEST HOUSE

An 18th-century watermill on the River Bain
with most of its parts still operational makes
both a charismatic and peaceful B&B from
which to explore the surrounding gentle hills
of Wensleydale. When owners Neil and Jane
McNair first saw the mill on a visit from London,
they just had to have it; they brought the vision
of inspired amateurs, along with Neil's carpentry
skills, to the creation of something special.
Rooms are the quirkiest mix of rusticity and chic,
with stone walls, timbers, statement wallpaper,
antiques, fringed standard lamps, maybe a big
ceramic tiger or leopard – and why not? The vast
beamed living room has a massive grinding stone
along with a toasty range and colourful rugs. The
spacious Workshop bedroom contains the mill
machinery in the rafters, an emperor-size bed,
log-burner, freestanding copper bath and separate
shower room. The Kiln Room, overlooking the
river, has a sleigh bed and separate sitting room,
a walk-in shower, while the Store Room has a
wrought iron bed, a bath with a shower over.
A locally sourced breakfast with eggs from a
neighbour's free-ranging hens sets one up for a
walk to Aysgarth waterfalls.

Bainbridge
Leyburn DL8 3EF

T: 01969 650553
E: lowmillguesthouse@gmail.com
W: lowmillguesthouse.co.uk

BEDROOMS: 3.
OPEN: all year except 24–26 Dec.
FACILITIES: lounge, dining room, small
library, honesty bar, in-room TV
(Freeview), ¼-acre riverside garden
with seating, secure bicycle storage,
unsuitable for disabled.
BACKGROUND MUSIC: none.
LOCATION: 5 miles E of Hawes.
CHILDREN: not under 15.
DOGS: allowed in bedrooms (£10 per
stay), not in dining room, on lead in
other public areas.
CREDIT CARDS: MC, Visa.
PRICES: B&B doubles from £125, singles
from £105. 1-night bookings refused
Sat, bank holidays.

Prices may change – check with hotel.

SEE ALSO SHORTLIST

BARFORD ST MICHAEL Oxfordshire

MAP 2:C2

THE GEORGE INN

In an 'interesting village of honey-coloured stone, well off the beaten track', a beautifully renovated 17th-century thatched inn lives anew as a local gastropub-with-rooms. Manager Claire Lenkowiec and chef Valerio Grimaldi run the show for the owners and, by George, they get it right! Three chic bedrooms above the pub, and six in converted stables, have smart bathrooms with under-floor heating, a coffee machine, handmade truffles and botanical toiletries. Dog-friendly garden rooms, one fully accessible, open directly on to terrace and garden. In a beamed, flagstone-floored bar frequented by locals, horse brasses and Buddy Holly prints hang over the inglenook where a log-burner blazes. Fifties film posters and George V in ermine grace the walls. The mix of pub classics and blackboard specials on the menu are 'excellent' and there are 'delicious home-made brownies', accordng to our inspectors. You can eat in the dining room or on the all-weather terrace. Breakfast brings fresh pastries, butcher's sausages, sourdough toast, local jams, porridge with Transylvanian acacia honey.

Lower Street
Barford St Michael
Banbury OX15 0RH

T: 01869 338160
E: info@thegeorgebarford.co.uk
W: thegeorgebarford.co.uk

BEDROOMS: 9. 6 in converted stable, some suitable for disabled.
OPEN: all year.
FACILITIES: bar, restaurant, wine room/chef's table, in-room TV, civil wedding licence, covered heated terrace, parking, EV charging, public areas wheelchair accessible, adapted toilet.
BACKGROUND MUSIC: 'a mix' of music in public areas, depending on time of day.
LOCATION: in village, 8 miles SW of Banbury.
CHILDREN: all ages welcomed, no charge for extra beds, children's menu.
DOGS: allowed in 6 garden bedrooms (no charge at present).
CREDIT CARDS: MC, Visa.
PRICES: B&B doubles from £110. À la carte dinner £40 (small plates only, Sun).

Prices may change – check with hotel.

BARLOW Derbyshire

MAP 4:E4

THE PEACOCK AT BARLOW

The 'young, enthusiastic staff' extend a genuinely warm welcome at this 'large, modernised pub-with-rooms', in a rolling, pastoral north Derbyshire landscape. The 300-year-old building with a glass-fronted extension retains much of its original character while the bar does a brisk trade in ales from the on-site Collyfobble Brewery. Bedrooms, in the pub and a converted barn, are named after types of hops, from Fuggles to Phoenix. They have a boutique-hotel feel, with air conditioning and coffee machine, White Company toiletries, under-floor heated bathrooms, and dressing gowns. 'Our bedroom was spacious, modern, very comfortable, with lovely views,' a reader writes. 'Scones were there to greet us, with jam and fresh milk in the fridge.' The menu is long on staples such as burgers, fish and chips, steaks and pies, alongside seafood linguine, vegetable tagine, curries, confit pork belly and fishcakes. 'We dined outside on the terrace, which was very pleasant,' although the service was somewhat slow. 'Overall, a pleasant experience, and encouraging to see a large, flourishing pub in so small a village.' (Geoffrey Bignell)

Hackney Lane
Barlow
Chesterfield S18 7TD

T: 01142 890340
E: cheers@thepeacockatbarlow.co.uk
W: thepeacockatbarlow.co.uk

BEDROOMS: 8. 4 in barn conversion, 2 on lower floor with step-free access, 2-bedroom self-catering cottage.
OPEN: all year.
FACILITIES: orangery dining area, tap room (open fire and lounge area), brewery with tasting/function room, in-room TV (Sky), terraces, large car park, EV charging, wheelchair accessible, adapted toilet.
BACKGROUND MUSIC: in all public areas including upper terrace, not brewery.
LOCATION: on outskirts of village, 10 miles S of Sheffield.
CHILDREN: all ages welcomed, no extra beds, children's menu.
DOGS: in cottage bedrooms only (no charge) and all pub areas.
CREDIT CARDS: MC, Visa.
PRICES: B&B doubles from £109, singles from £99. À la carte £30.

Prices may change – check with hotel.

BARTLOW Cambridgeshire

MAP 2:C4

THE THREE HILLS

The Hills were alive with the sound of 'obvious customer contentment' when our inspector called at Chris and Sarah Field's pub in a village known for its Roman burial tumuli (the eponymous 'hills'). Customers were clearly enjoying themselves as they sat on the heated, covered patio and dined on dishes such as daube of venison, vegetable terrine or pizza from the outdoor oven. The 'friendly, prompt service', value for money, and 'beautifully cooked food' all won praise. This is a very family-friendly place, and dogs are welcome (bed, bowl and towel are provided). Inside, the 17th-century building has been stylishly refurbished, while retaining its character. Smart bedrooms – four in an annexe, two above the pub – have a muted palette, a coffee machine, and luxury toiletries. 'Our room was light and airy, privacy blinds with interior roman blinds giving a Scandi style.' 'The garden is basically a mown meadow with tables and attached benches, sloping gently towards the River Granta.' Cambridge is just 20 minutes away, Stansted Airport 40 minutes if you wish to pay a flying visit. (SH, and others)

Dean Road
Bartlow
Cambridge CB21 4PW

T: 01223 890500
E: info@thethreehills.co.uk
W: thethreehills.co.uk

BEDROOMS: 6. 4 in annexe, 1 on ground floor suitable for disabled, plus 2-bedroom flat.
OPEN: all year, restaurant closed Sun pm, Mon, Tues.
FACILITIES: bar, snug/library, restaurant, in-room smart TV (Freeview), function facilities, large covered patio, garden and meadow, public areas wheelchair accessible, adapted toilet.
BACKGROUND MUSIC: soft music (light jazz) in bar, restaurant.
LOCATION: in a small village, 12 miles SE of Cambridge.
CHILDREN: all ages welcomed, children's menu, extra bed £15.
DOGS: allowed in all bedrooms (£12.50 per stay), bar, snug.
CREDIT CARDS: Amex, MC, Visa.
PRICES: B&B doubles from £105. À la carte £32.

Prices may change – check with hotel.

BASLOW Derbyshire   MAP 3:A6

THE CAVENDISH

'A wonderful place for a stay in the Peak District', the Duke and Duchess of Devonshire's Derbyshire hotel offers a taste of country house living a stroll from their magnificent Elizabethan pile. Views across the Chatsworth Estate commend some standard bedrooms. Larger rooms have pieces of the fine art and antiques that are dispersed throughout the property, perhaps a four-poster. Rooms in the coach house have smart bathrooms with bath and walk-in shower. All have fresh milk in a mini-fridge, Chatsworth biscuits, luxury toiletries. A reader this year was disappointed that the duplex Redesdale Suite had no estate view, and found road noise was a problem through an open window. Others were more enthused by their choice. 'Our room was fabulously comfortable, very tastefully furnished, with lovely country views.' In the Gallery restaurant, menus include dishes such as Derbyshire beef fillet, cheek, truffle gnocchi, nasturtium, onion, or vegetarian options. On a day when only fish and chips will do, eat more casually and cheaply in the Garden Room. 'Staff VERY well trained, nothing too much trouble … Expensive but worth every penny.'

Church Lane
Baslow DE45 1SP

T: 01246 582311
E: reception@cavendishbaslow.co.uk
W: cavendishbaslow.co.uk

BEDROOMS: 28. 2 on ground floor, 4 in coach house, 2 suitable for disabled.
OPEN: all year.
FACILITIES: lounge/bar, 2 restaurants, 2 private dining rooms (vegetarian menu), in-room TV (Freeview), civil wedding licence, ½-acre grounds, EV charging, public rooms wheelchair accessible.
BACKGROUND MUSIC: none.
LOCATION: on edge of village.
CHILDREN: all ages welcomed, extra bed £10 (excl. breakfast).
DOGS: allowed in 1 bedroom (£20 per night), not in main house.
CREDIT CARDS: Amex, MC, Visa.
PRICES: B&B doubles from £200. Gallery restaurant, à la carte £55–£65 (2/3 courses), tasting menu £85, Garden Room à la carte £40. 1-night bookings sometimes refused at weekends.

Prices may change – check with hotel.

BASLOW Derbyshire

MAP 3:A6

FISCHER'S AT BASLOW HALL

An Edwardian homage to 17th-century style, this beautiful manor house with rich Jacobean-inspired interiors is run as a luxury hotel with fine-dining restaurant. House bedrooms have fine antique furniture, views to the Derbyshire Dales or over beautiful, well-tended gardens and arboretum. Annexe rooms in their own walled garden have a more contemporary look. Four, on the ground floor, have a bath and walk-in shower. All have an espresso machine, handmade biscuits and luxury toiletries. Readers on a return visit had a house room and, 'while we were very comfortable, we missed the spaciousness of the garden rooms'. New head chef Adam Thackeray's menus, for omnivores and vegetarians, make creative use of local, home-grown ingredients, in dishes such as sirloin of Baslow beef, oxtail ravioli, hen of the woods and chard; halibut, Chinese artichoke and sea aster; salt-baked beetroot, horseradish, yoghurt and beetroot balsamic. Tasting menus are available as well as the à la carte menu for dinner from Wednesday to Sunday. Activities include fly-fishing, foraging events and 'Meet the Maker' days. (J and KP)

Calver Road
Baslow DE45 1RR

T: 01246 583259
E: reservations@fischers-baslowhall.
co.uk
W: fischers-baslowhall.co.uk

BEDROOMS: 11. 5 in Garden House, 4 on ground floor.
OPEN: all year except 25/26 Dec, restaurant closed Mon, Tues.
FACILITIES: lounge/bar, main dining room (vegetarian menu), drawing room, wine room, function facilities, in-room TV (Freeview), civil wedding licence, 5-acre grounds, restaurant and lounge wheelchair accessible.
BACKGROUND MUSIC: in bar/lounge and dining rooms.
LOCATION: edge of village, 5 miles NE of Bakewell.
CHILDREN: all ages welcomed, cots £10 per stay, no under-8s in restaurant.
DOGS: not allowed.
CREDIT CARDS: Amex, MC, Visa.
PRICES: B&B doubles from £227. Set-price 4/5-course menu £78.50, tasting menu £105.

Prices may change – check with hotel.

BATH Somerset

MAP 2:D1

HOMEWOOD

A 'playful, quirky hotel', in a traditional honey-stone building, Homewood is 'full of eclectic eccentricity'. The beautiful grounds house animal hedge sculpture, reception has a plethora of clocks, and a seating area rows of copper kettles, while the dining room has a wall adorned with antique plates, another with dried flowers. 'Sometimes it works, others it doesn't,' says a Guide insider. Part of Ian and Christa Taylor's Kaleidoscope Collection (see Shortlist, The Bird, Bath), 'it is, above all, fun'. Bedrooms are all different but even the cheapest ones have mood lighting, an espresso machine and luxury toiletries, while some suites have their own hot tubs. In Olio restaurant and on the terrace, 'rather odd menus' offer 'pub classics such as excellent fish and chips alongside Mediterranean-influenced dishes, including grilled halloumi with lime and pomegranate'. Vegetable Wellington disappointed, but 'the glass dining pods looked fun'. 'The spa is a highlight', with its outdoor heated pool and hot tub. 'The complimentary pantry with jars of sweets, soft drinks and fresh milk was a nice touch.' (CJ, JK, and others)

Abbey Lane
Freshford
Bath BA2 7TB

T: 01225 580439
E: reservations@homewoodbath.
co.uk
W: homewoodbath.co.uk

BEDROOMS: 31. 8 with private hot tubs. 10 in annexe.
OPEN: all year.
FACILITIES: bar, lounge, restaurant, dining domes (up to 8 guests), meeting rooms, in-room TV (Freeview), civil wedding licence, spa, indoor hydrotherapy pool, outdoor heated pool, outdoor hot tub, 20-acre gardens, EV charging.
BACKGROUND MUSIC: in public spaces.
LOCATION: 5 miles S of Bath, on A36.
CHILDREN: all ages welcomed, children's menu, cots free, extra bed £35.
DOGS: welcomed in bedrooms (£25 per night, dog menu), bar, lounge, terrace, not in restaurant.
CREDIT CARDS: Amex, MC, Visa.
PRICES: B&B doubles from £205.
À la carte £45.

Prices may change – check with hotel.

SEE ALSO SHORTLIST

BATH Somerset

MAP 2:D1

NO.15 BY GUESTHOUSE

The three Guest brothers made their first bold foray into hospitality with this boutique hotel and spa occupying three Grade I listed town houses on a splendid Georgian terrace. All but the small attic bedrooms are dog-friendly, and all have an espresso machine, a turntable to spin some vinyl, 100 Acres toiletries, access to a pantry of treats. Touches of whimsy include a ceiling with exotic bird wallpaper inspired by the pergola in Henrietta Park opposite; a coffee-maker in a doll's house. Large rooms in the coach house have a lounge area, a working fireplace, stand-alone bath and rain shower. The basement spa has a circular copper bath for two. Adventurous menus feature dishes such as thin tart of leeks, wild garlic, smoked new potatoes, romesco sauce; beef medallion, beef cheek and bacon tart, nettle purée, hand-cut chips. Breakfast is similarly inventive (avocado on sourdough, spiced tomato compote, poached egg; wild mushrooms on toast, as well as the usual suspects). Children are indulged, with Sally Lunn buns for elevenses and picnics for the park. A new sister hotel, No. 1 York, has opened in York, and another is planned in Brighton.

13–15 Great Pulteney Street
Bath BA2 4BS

T: 01225 807015
E: no15@guesthousehotels.co.uk
W: guesthousehotels.co.uk

BEDROOMS: 36. 8 in coach house, 1 suitable for disabled.
OPEN: all year, restaurant Mon–Sat, Sun lunch.
FACILITIES: lift, bar, restaurant, private dining room, in-room TV (Freeview, Chromecast), spa (treatments), small garden terrace, bookable small private car park (£25 a night), public rooms wheelchair accessible, adapted toilet.
BACKGROUND MUSIC: all day in bar and restaurant.
LOCATION: central.
CHILDREN: all ages welcomed, extra bed free, breakfast charged for.
DOGS: allowed in most bedrooms (£25 per night), bar, not in restaurant.
CREDIT CARDS: Amex, MC, Visa.
PRICES: B&B doubles from £187. À la carte dinner £38. 1-night bookings sometimes refused at weekends.

Prices may change – check with hotel.

SEE ALSO SHORTLIST

BATH Somerset

MAP 2:D1

THE QUEENSBERRY

There's a huge sense of fun at this stylish hotel, whose logo is Vanity Fair's caricature of the 9th Marquess of Queensberry, Oscar Wilde's Nemesis. Laurence and Helen Beere's 'exceptional hotel' in a 'quirky combination of four town houses' has pugilism-themed jokes throughout; the decor is knockout too. Junior suites, in former drawing rooms overlooking Russel Street, have floor-to-ceiling windows, an original fireplace, maybe Divine Savages' Crane Fonda or Portobello Parade wallpaper. Some suites have a seven-foot-square four-poster, a large bathroom with double shower. Club rooms are small but chic, and the use of colour is ravishing. In the Michelin-starred Olive Tree restaurant, Chris Cleghorn's tasting menus pack a punch with dishes such as Wiltshire lamb loin, anchovy, celery, artichoke, Sarawak pepper; ruby beetroot, alliums, hen of the woods. 'Food and service were outstanding,' write readers 'bowled over by the warm and informative welcome'. Light bites are available in Old Q bar. Continental and cooked breakfasts include pastries, charcuterie, smoked haddock or salmon, a full English or full vegetarian. (Geoffrey Bignell)

4–7 Russel Street
Bath BA1 2QF

T: 01225 447928
E: reservations@thequeensberry.co.uk
W: thequeensberry.co.uk

BEDROOMS: 29. Some on ground floor.
OPEN: all year, restaurant closed Mon, midday Tues–Thurs.
FACILITIES: lift, residents' drawing room, bar, 2 sitting rooms, restaurant (vegetarian/vegan menus), meeting room, in-room TV (Freeview), 4 linked courtyard gardens, valet parking, unsuitable for disabled.
BACKGROUND MUSIC: in restaurant and bar.
LOCATION: near Assembly Rooms.
CHILDREN: all ages welcomed, extra bed £25 plus breakfast £25, children's menu.
DOGS: assistance dogs only.
CREDIT CARDS: Amex, MC, Visa.
PRICES: B&B doubles from £190. Tasting menus £95–£135, à la carte £75. 1-night bookings sometimes refused at weekends.

Prices may change – check with hotel.

SEE ALSO SHORTLIST

BATH Somerset

MAP 2:D1

THE ROYAL CRESCENT HOTEL & SPA

At the centre of a glorious Georgian crescent, two adjoining mansions are home to an elegant yet family-friendly hotel with oasis garden and beautiful spa. There is a touch of Versailles about the public rooms, with fine art and cascading chandeliers. From smart deluxe doubles with contemporary styling to master suites adorned with artwork, every room is individually designed. 'Roomy rooms, beautifully presented,' notes a reader. Dog-friendly rooms have outdoors access, and your best friend can now join you in the bar as you eat from the lounge menu. By day, relax in the garden or in the Georgian spa with its 12-metre pool. At night in the Dower House restaurant, Martin Blake's tasting menus cater to omnivores and vegetarians. 'The attention to detail and the attentive staff make this hotel very special,' writes our reader. Others also note the 'kind attention of the staff', especially the head hall porter, who collected them in his car when they couldn't get a taxi in the rain. Some guests are more prickly: when you're enjoying a drink outside, try to spot the resident rescued hedgehogs. (Annette Pickering, Peter and Anne Davies)

16 Royal Crescent
Bath BA1 2LS

T: 01225 823333
E: info@royalcrescent.co.uk
W: royalcrescent.co.uk

BEDROOMS: 45. 10 in Dower House, 14 in annexes, 8 on ground floor.
OPEN: all year.
FACILITIES: lift, bar, lounge, library, restaurant (vegetarian menu), in-room TV (Sky, Freeview), civil wedding licence, 1-acre garden, spa (12-metre pool), EV charging, parking, public rooms wheelchair accessible, adapted toilet.
BACKGROUND MUSIC: in library and restaurant.
LOCATION: ½ mile from High Street.
CHILDREN: all ages welcomed, under-7s free, extra bed 7–12s £50.
DOGS: allowed in some bedrooms (£35 per stay), public rooms, garden, not restaurant.
CREDIT CARDS: Amex, MC, Visa.
PRICES: B&B doubles from £360. À la carte (lounge menu) £45, tasting menu £85. Min. 2-night stay Sat.

Prices may change – check with hotel.

SEE ALSO SHORTLIST

BAUGHURST Hampshire   MAP 2:D2

THE WELLINGTON ARMS

Beyond massed ranks of pots and planters, a
former hunting lodge on the Duke of Wellington's
estate is now a dog-friendly gastropub of immense
charm, with its own Welli deli. Owned by Simon
Page and Jason King, it is a labour of love, from
the home-made jams and sourdough loaves to
the fluffy tea cosies knitted by Simon's mum. In
the bar, restaurant and garden, Jason's menus
include risotto of foraged mushrooms with roast
chicken and asparagus; baked potato gnocchi
with tomato, goat's cheese, basil and Parmesan;
Brixham cod with a preserved-lemon-and-olive
crust, marsh samphire; roast rack of home-reared
lamb. The food is 'excellent', readers report.
Bedrooms are a clever mix of rusticity and chic,
with oak furniture, an espresso machine and
minibar, home-made biscuits, a rainfall shower,
fine toiletries. The Apartment, above the pub,
has a sitting room with a cast-iron stove. The
beamed barn has an old fireplace and a chandelier.
At breakfast there are new-laid eggs, croissants,
Uig Lodge smoked salmon, smashed avocado, a
full English (full veggie on request). 'We had no
complaints; happily recommend it.' (John and
Elspeth Gibbon)

Baughurst Road
Baughurst RG26 5LP

T: 0118 982 0110
E: hello@thewellingtonarms.com
w: thewellingtonarms.com

BEDROOMS: 4. 3 in converted
outbuildings.
OPEN: all year, Tues–Sat, Sun breakfast
only.
FACILITIES: 2 dining rooms, in-room
TV (Freeview), 2-acre garden,
parking, dining room wheelchair
accessible.
BACKGROUND MUSIC: in bar and
restaurant.
LOCATION: equidistant between
Reading, Basingstoke and Newbury.
CHILDREN: all ages welcomed, no
extra beds.
DOGS: allowed in 2 bedrooms (£10 per
night), public areas.
CREDIT CARDS: MC, Visa.
PRICES: B&B doubles from £125.
À la carte £40.

Prices may change – check with hotel.

BEADNELL Northumberland

MAP 4:A4

BEADNELL TOWERS

An easy stroll from one of Northumberland's prettiest beaches and in 'an excellent area for walking', this family- and dog-friendly hotel offers a clever mix of boutique-smart bedrooms and a warm, unpretentious atmosphere. Interiors of the Georgian building have a 'chic and fun' style: denim-blue panelling, William Morris-style wallpapers, parquet flooring and quirky collections of Bakelite telephones and maritime paraphernalia. The bar-dining area has exposed stone, painted brick and mustard-yellow leather seats. A 'good upmarket gastropub-style' menu focuses on seafood with local oysters, scallops in their shells and a 'good, flavoursome' fish pie as well as classics such as shepherd's pie. Barking dogs during dinner irritated one reader. Bedrooms, some with beams, combine a town-house smartness of elegant headboards and designer lighting with a seaside practicality of polished floorboards and solid wood furniture. Most have a bath and shower. Breakfasts include porridge with cream and whisky, kippers, eggs and 'good coffee'. Throughout, staff are 'friendly and competent'. 'We really couldn't fault anything.' (Donald Reid)

The Wynding
Beadnell NE67 5AY

T: 01665 721211
E: info@beadnelltowers.co.uk
W: beadnelltowers.co.uk

BEDROOMS: 22. 4 in coach house, 7 on ground floor, 1 suitable for disabled.
OPEN: all year.
FACILITIES: lounge, bar/restaurant, in-room TV (Freeview), private dining room, terrace, public rooms wheelchair accessible, adapted toilet.
BACKGROUND MUSIC: in public rooms.
LOCATION: in Beadnell, 800 yds from the beach.
CHILDREN: all ages welcomed, extra bed £45, family room and interconnecting rooms.
DOGS: allowed in some bedrooms (£25 per stay, welcome pack), bar.
CREDIT CARDS: MC, Visa.
PRICES: B&B doubles from £129, singles from £119. À la carte £44.

Prices may change – check with hotel.

BEAMINSTER Dorset

MAP 1:C6

THE OLLEROD

The Ollerod (Dorset dialect for cowslip), with
boutique rooms and a dabster in the kitchen, is
the perfect place for a 'bit-an'-drap' when you're
hungry and thirsty. Silvana Bandini and Chris
Staines have created a restaurant-led hotel, where
'the food is the real attraction'. You can eat in the
bar, restaurant, or on a covered terrace. Chris,
who held a Michelin star at London's Mandarin
Oriental, uses locally sourced and home-grown
produce in dishes such as roast fillet of cod,
saffron, squid, mussels and pickled cucumber in
black garlic sauce. 'Vibrant flavours pinged off
the plate,' a reader relates, although they found
the attention to detail in their 'spacious, newly
renovated, restful soft grey' bedroom wasn't
quite up to the same standard. Another reader
disagrees: 'We had a lovely big ground-floor
room, an excellent, spacious bathroom with a
big bath and powerful shower.' A noisy party
in one of the conservatories was an unforeseen
hazard, and service lapses have been noted. But
'to keep everything in perspective, it's a very nice
hotel, comfortable, with good food and efficient,
accommodating staff'. (Peter Anderson, and others)

3 Prout Bridge
Beaminster DT8 3AY

T: 01308 862200
E: enquiries@theollerod.co.uk
w: theollerod.co.uk

BEDROOMS: 9. 1 on ground floor
suitable for disabled. 2 self-catering
apartments in coach house.
OPEN: all year.
FACILITIES: lounge, bar, 2
conservatories, restaurant (vegan
menu), in-room TV (Freeview),
treatment room, civil wedding licence,
walled garden, covered terrace,
parking, restaurant wheelchair
accessible, no adapted toilet.
BACKGROUND MUSIC: in public rooms.
LOCATION: 100 yds from centre.
CHILDREN: all ages welcomed, cots £10
per night, extra bed for ages 2–16 £25,
children's menu.
DOGS: allowed in 1 bedroom in house,
1 apartment (£15 per night), bar and
terrace, not restaurant.
CREDIT CARDS: Amex, MC, Visa.
PRICES: B&B doubles from £205.
À la carte £45, vegan £35.

Prices may change – check with hotel.

BEANACRE Wiltshire

MAP 2:D1

BEECHFIELD HOUSE

'It's like staying with friends in their country retreat,' said our inspectors on a visit to this ornate Italianate Victorian house in woodland and gardens, with the 'huge plus' of an outdoor heated pool. It is 'well set back' from the A350, though 'faint traffic noise' might travel on the breeze. Bedrooms range from the smallest, in a coach house, to a master room with a handsome four-poster. A 'good-sized' mid-price room had a super-king half-tester bed with 'dazzling white linen' and 'a guide to Buddhism as well as the usual Gideon Bible' in a bedside cabinet. Dual-aspect windows made it 'airy and light'. You can enjoy a lunchtime sandwich or afternoon tea on the terrace, in the bar, or by the fire in a 'spacious sitting room'. The pool now has a bar. In a low-lit blue dining room, our inspectors enjoyed 'pan-seared scallops, parsnip purée, tempura-fried courgettes, wild garlic', and sirloin steak with twice-cooked chips. Generous servings included 'heaps of veg and salad' from the kitchen garden. Breakfast on local free-range eggs, Wiltshire bacon, grilled kippers and freshly baked pastries, before visiting the lions at Longleat.

Beanacre
Melksham SN12 7PU

T: 01225 703700
E: reception@beechfieldhouse.co.uk
W: beechfieldhouse.co.uk

BEDROOMS: 24. 8 in coach house, 4 on ground floor suitable for disabled.
OPEN: all year (exclusive use only, New Year).
FACILITIES: morning room, bar, 4 dining rooms, in-room TV (Freeview), 8-acre grounds (12 by 6 metre heated pool, end Mar to early Nov), pool bar, EV charging, bar, reception rooms, dining rooms all wheelchair accessible.
BACKGROUND MUSIC: light music in public areas.
LOCATION: just outside a small village, 1½ miles N of Melksham.
CHILDREN: all ages welcomed, extra bed £50, children's menu.
DOGS: allowed by prior arrangement in bedrooms (£20 per night), public rooms.
CREDIT CARDS: MC, Visa.
PRICES: B&B doubles from £149. À la carte £35.

Prices may change – check with hotel.

BEAULIEU Hampshire

MAP 2:E2

MONTAGU ARMS

This handsome wisteria-covered Victorian building, in a picturesque village by the Beaulieu river on the edge of the New Forest, is a pleasing prospect. It is today a luxury hotel with a fine-dining restaurant and a pub, Monty's Inn. There is a wide choice of bedrooms, mixing contemporary and traditional style. Some overlook a Gertrude Jekyll-inspired garden, some have a four-poster, a bay window from which to watch free-ranging ponies and donkeys sauntering by. Dog-friendly, open-plan courtyard studios surround a courtyard garden, and have a private terrace, a marble bathroom with under-floor heating, a freestanding bath and walk-in shower, a minibar and decanter of gin. In the Terrace restaurant, New Forest-born chef Matthew Whitfield, with Michelin-star experience under his belt, uses local and organic home-grown produce for dishes such as Isle of Wight black garlic with roasted gnocchi, and line-caught pollack with Fowey mussels. Sunday lunch might bring roast rack of Hampshire pork with beef dripping potatoes. Or pop into the pub for a burger; your dog can join you. 'We greatly enjoyed our stay.' (GB, Tom and Sarah Mann)

Palace Lane
Beaulieu SO42 7ZL

T: 01590 612324
E: reservations@montaguarmshotel.
co.uk
W: montaguarmshotel.co.uk

BEDROOMS: 24. 2 in Hayloft suites.
OPEN: all year, restaurant closed Mon, Tues.
FACILITIES: lounge, conservatory, library/bar/brasserie, restaurant, in-room TV, civil wedding licence, 3-acre garden, EV charging, public rooms wheelchair accessible, adapted toilet.
BACKGROUND MUSIC: Classic FM in reception.
LOCATION: village centre.
CHILDREN: all ages welcomed, under-16s extra bed £35, no under-12s at dinner, welcome in Monty's Inn.
DOGS: well-behaved dogs welcome in Hayloft suites, Courtyard rooms (£35 a night), in grounds, Monty's Inn.
CREDIT CARDS: Amex, MC, Visa.
PRICES: B&B doubles from £219. À la carte £50 (restaurant), £28 (Monty's). 1-night stays sometimes refused Fri/Sat.

Prices may change – check with hotel.

BEESANDS Devon

MAP 1:E4

THE CRICKET INN

Twisty lanes and steep hills ensure this village inn, with its celebrated seafood and views over Beesands beach on Devon's south coast, still feels like a wonderful discovery. Despite the inn's name, it's the sea that's the focus here with breezy contemporary interiors in nautical colours, and vintage photographs celebrating Beesands' fishing heritage dotted around. The airy restaurant, in cool whites and with sea-facing glass sliding doors, serves 'delicious and imaginatively cooked' locally caught seafood, such as crab soup, seafood pancake and fish pie, as well as traditional fish and chips. A Josper grill turns out steaks and vegetarian dishes, too. When the weather's fine, take a table on the roadside terrace. New England-style bedrooms – most with sea views, three for families – are fresh in blues and whites with tongue-and-groove panelling and nautical nods in rope-framed mirrors and jolly ship's wheels. Bathrooms have walk-in showers. The Heath family ensure a friendly welcome while the South West Coast Path, which runs past the door, helps you work up an appetite for dinner, perhaps preceded by a local ale or cider.

Beesands
Kingsbridge TQ7 2EN

T: 01548 580215
E: enquiries@thecricketinn.com
W: thecricketinn.com

BEDROOMS: 7. 4 in extension.
OPEN: all year, except Christmas Eve night and Christmas Day.
FACILITIES: bar, restaurant, terrace (alfresco dining), private dining facilities, in-room TV (Freeview), parking, restaurant and bar wheelchair accessible, adapted toilet.
BACKGROUND MUSIC: all day.
LOCATION: in village, on South West Coast Path.
CHILDREN: all ages welcomed (extra bed £25), children's menu.
DOGS: allowed in bar and parts of restaurant only.
CREDIT CARDS: MC, Visa.
PRICES: B&B doubles from £135. À la carte £30. Min. 2-night stay preferred at weekends in high season.

Prices may change – check with hotel.

BEPTON Sussex

MAP 2:E3

PARK HOUSE, HOTEL & SPA

More than 70 years after the O'Brien family first opened their Edwardian country house to the Cowdray Park set, third-generation owner Seamus O'Brien presides over a thriving spa hotel. From standard rooms to family suites, the accommodation is a contemporary take on traditional English country house style. Some rooms have a balcony or patio. Dual-aspect master rooms have a bath and power shower. All have home-made biscuits, fine toiletries, 24-hour room service. With the South Downs on the doorstep, and golf, tennis, bowls, croquet and swimming on site, this is the perfect place for 'a restorative stay'. You can order from an all-day menu, enjoy a Sunday roast, take afternoon tea on the terrace, or horse around in a bar adorned with polo memorabilia. At dinner, locally sourced dishes might include fillet steak Rossini, market fish risotto, and guineafowl supreme with morel sauce. 'The crab soup and guineafowl were delicious,' writes a reader, who would have liked more choice of fruit at breakfast, before, say, kippers, a full English or smoked salmon with scrambled egg. (Frances M Thomas)

Bepton Road
Bepton
Midhurst GU29 0JB

T: 01730 819000
E: reservations@parkhousehotel.com
W: parkhousehotel.com

BEDROOMS: 23. 5 on ground floor, 1 suitable for disabled, 10 in cottages (2 self-catering).
OPEN: all year, except 24–26 Dec.
FACILITIES: drawing room, bar, dining room, conservatory, function rooms, in-room TV, civil wedding licence, 10-acre grounds, spa, heated indoor and outdoor swimming pools, tennis, EV charging, public rooms and spa wheelchair accessible, adapted toilet.
BACKGROUND MUSIC: in restaurants.
LOCATION: village centre.
CHILDREN: all ages welcomed, extra bed £25–£50.
DOGS: allowed in some bedrooms (£20 a night), not public rooms.
CREDIT CARDS: Amex, MC, Visa.
PRICES: B&B doubles from £208, singles from £203. Set-price dinner £50. Min. 2-night stay Fri/Sat.

Prices may change – check with hotel.

BEVERLEY Yorkshire

MAP 4:D5

NEWBEGIN HOUSE

It is a rare treat to stay in a fine Georgian town house that is still very much a family home, with personal photographs and heirlooms complementing the handsome original features. Walter and Nuala Sweeney's comfortably furnished house, minutes from Beverley centre, is full of antiques, books and curios set against shuttered windows, polished-wood floors and marble fireplaces. 'Our stay,' say readers, 'was an absolute delight from arrival to departure.' The well-upholstered feel, with plump chairs, pictures and Victorian rugs, continues in the bedrooms: 'Surely the largest, most eccentric and delightful room we have ever had the pleasure of sleeping in.' One has a rocking horse, another overlooks the walled garden. Bathrooms are spacious and traditional. Thoughtful extras, including sherry, fresh milk and flowers, are praised, as is the garden. 'A surprising oasis in the very centre of the town.' Breakfast includes omelettes, smoked salmon and 'delicious pancakes' as well as a full Yorkshire. Readers continue to be astonished by the exceptional value of a stay 'given the quality of the experience'. (Hannah and Andrew Butterworth)

10 Newbegin
Beverley HU17 8EG

T: 01482 888880
E: wsweeney@wsweeney.karoo.co.uk
W: newbeginhousebbbeverley.co.uk

BEDROOMS: 3.
OPEN: all year except when owners take a holiday.
FACILITIES: sitting room, dining room, small conference/function facilities, in-room TV (Freeview), ¾-acre walled garden, parking, EV charging, unsuitable for disabled.
BACKGROUND MUSIC: none.
LOCATION: central.
CHILDREN: all ages welcomed, no charge if own cot provided, variable charge for older children sharing with parents (contact for prices).
DOGS: not allowed.
CREDIT CARDS: none accepted.
PRICES: B&B doubles from £100, singles from £70. 1-night bookings sometimes refused during the Early Music Festival.

Prices may change – check with hotel.

BIGBURY-ON-SEA Devon   MAP 1:D4

BURGH ISLAND HOTEL

Pack your Schiaparelli gowns, beach pants and playsuits, and board the sea tractor for a trip back to the 1930s at this Art Deco hotel on a tidal island where the beau monde came to play. Bedrooms range from cosy doubles and deluxe to grand suites with a sea-view balcony. Agatha Christie's beach house, where she wrote of murder most foul, sleeps four. All rooms have Devon fudge and Burgh Island toiletries. Everything is retro, from a transistor radio to the Bakelite phone to call for tea or coffee. You can eat fish and chips at the atmospheric old Pilchard Inn, take a dip in the romantic sea-bathing Mermaid Pool, sip cocktails in the Palm Court lounge, enjoy a black-tie dinner in the ballroom, or eat more informally in the Nettlefold restaurant. Readers enjoyed 'an excellent taster menu in the ballroom, and an à la carte meal in the restaurant, with largely seafood on offer'. Breakfast brings 'ample choice'. 'The public rooms, and especially the Palm Court, are wonderful in their decor.' Even lapses in service and a bathroom 'in need of some refurbishment' could not dull the razzle-dazzle. (Anthony Bradbury)

Burgh Island
Bigbury-on-Sea TQ7 4BG

T: 01548 810514
E: reception@burghisland.com
W: burghisland.com

BEDROOMS: 25. 1 suite in Beach House in grounds, apartment above Pilchard Inn.
OPEN: all year.
FACILITIES: lift, bar, 2 restaurants, ballroom, sun lounge, billiard room, private dining room, spa, civil wedding licence, 26-acre grounds, sea bathing pool, tennis, mainland garage, EV charging.
BACKGROUND MUSIC: period in public rooms.
LOCATION: off Bigbury beach, private garages on mainland.
CHILDREN: no under-5s, no under-13s in ballroom, extra bed with breakfast £250.
DOGS: allowed in Beach House, Artist's Studio and Pilchard Inn (£25 a night).
CREDIT CARDS: Amex, MC, Visa.
PRICES: B&B doubles from £395. À la carte £75. 1-night bookings refused at weekends, some bank holidays.

Prices may change – check with hotel.

BIGBURY-ON-SEA Devon

MAP 1:D4

THE HENLEY

The 'spectacular views of the rugged coastline' over Bigbury-on-Sea's sands towards Burgh Island are what first impress about this former Edwardian holiday home, but guests also appreciate the 'inventive, tasty and well-cooked' food and the 'warm, jovial and friendly' owners. Petra Lampe and Martyn Scarterfield's seaside bolt-hole has the feel of a private home. Bedrooms, with rich colours and mix of vintage and contemporary furnishings, all have 'stunning views' and contain 'everything we would have expected and more, even binoculars'. There's a cosy lounge with green velvet sofas and books, an inviting decked terrace, plus a path down to the beach, where you can take the sea tractor to Burgh Island. Chef Martyn's short-choice daily-changing evening meals (advance notice required), served in the palm-filled garden room with more of those views, might include braised pork belly with seared scallops. 'We particularly enjoyed the monkfish and king prawn served with a lobster sauce.' 'Portions are generous.' Breakfast is equally handsome with fresh juice, eggs Benedict and a full Devonian. An 'idyllic place'. (Steven Hur, and others)

Folly Hill
Bigbury-on-Sea TQ7 4AR

T: 01548 810240
E: info@thehenleyhotel.co.uk
w: thehenleyhotel.co.uk

BEDROOMS: 5.
OPEN: Mar–end Oct, restaurant closed Sun eve.
FACILITIES: 2 lounges, dining room, in-room TV (Freeview), small terraced garden (steps to beach, golf, sailing, fishing), Coast Path nearby, unsuitable for disabled.
BACKGROUND MUSIC: jazz/classical in the evenings in lounge, dining room.
LOCATION: 5 miles S of Modbury.
CHILDREN: not under 15.
DOGS: allowed in bedrooms (not on bed, £10 per night), lounges, garden, terrace, not in dining room.
CREDIT CARDS: MC, Visa.
PRICES: B&B doubles from £159, singles from £117, D,B&B doubles from £220, singles from £152. 1-night bookings sometimes refused at weekends.

Prices may change – check with hotel.

BIGGIN-BY-HARTINGTON Derbyshire   MAP 3:B6

BIGGIN HALL

In a small rural village in the White Peak area, this Grade II* listed 17th-century country house is run as a hotel with warmth and heart. A reader, returning after a few years' absence, had 'a fantastic stay', finding everything 'even better than I remembered', and the service 'professional, brisk and assured'. Paintings and furniture have been chosen with care. 'The gardens, like the hotel itself, are quirky and enchanting.' The master suite has a four-poster. Another suite has a double and a single bedroom. Rooms in garden annexes are pet-friendly, and you can now dine with your dog in a glass garden pod. On Saturdays, come rain or shine, you can take afternoon tea alfresco or snug indoors by the fire. In the oak-beamed dining room and new conservatory, a nightly changing menu includes such dishes as slow-cooked feather blade of beef, chive mashed potato, spiced carrot purée, red wine jus. 'The evening meals were a delight with plenty of choice,' our reader continued, although another guest hated the background music. A free packed lunch is provided for a day's exploration of the Peak District. (Mike Craddock)

Biggin-by-Hartington
Buxton SK17 0DH

T: 01298 84451
E: enquiries@bigginhall.co.uk
W: bigginhall.co.uk

BEDROOMS: 21. 13 in annexes, some on ground floor.
OPEN: all year, lunch served on Sun only, afternoon tea served Wed, Fri, Sat and Sun.
FACILITIES: sitting room, library, dining room, conservatory, meeting room, in-room TV, civil wedding licence, 8-acre grounds, EV charging, restaurant wheelchair accessible, adapted toilet.
BACKGROUND MUSIC: in restaurant.
LOCATION: 8 miles N of Ashbourne.
CHILDREN: not under 12, extra bed £25.
DOGS: allowed in annexe bedrooms (no charge), dining pods, not in main house.
CREDIT CARDS: MC, Visa.
PRICES: B&B doubles from £110, singles from £95. Fixed-price menu £28.50–£34.50 (2/3 courses). 1-night bookings sometimes refused at weekends.

Prices may change – check with hotel.

BILDESTON Suffolk

MAP 2:C5

THE BILDESTON CROWN

With its slightly wonky windows, half-timbering and sunny yellow paintwork, this 15th-century coaching inn, in the heart of a lovely Suffolk village, has a cheerful appeal that continues inside. Low beams and log fires mix with deep-hued walls and brightly patterned fabrics. Owners Chris and Hayley Lee, chef and manager respectively, have created a place that feels inviting to all, but with a touch of style. Rooms are delightfully individual, many with low ceilings and exposed timbers. One has a silvered French-style bed and bright pink boudoir chair; another a vast sleigh bed and rich floral curtains. Some overlook the High Street, others the garden or courtyard with its planters of olive trees, bamboo and lavender. If it's warm, choose to dine in the latter; the same menu is served here as in the atmospheric bar and restaurant. Chris's food is a highlight and his menu should satisfy all tastes, from classics such as fish and chips and Red Poll cheeseburger to the more unusual, such as pork with scallop, apple and date, and bream with polenta and salsa verde. Breakfast includes freshly squeezed juice and hearty hot dishes.

104 High Street
Bildeston IP7 7EB

T: 01449 740510
E: reception@thebildestoncrown.co.uk
W: thebildestoncrown.com

BEDROOMS: 12. 1 suitable for wheelchair.
OPEN: all year, no accommodation 24–26 Dec, New Year's Day.
FACILITIES: 2 bars, restaurant, champagne lounge, 2 private dining areas, lift, in-room TV (Freeview), courtyard, walled garden and terrace, EV charging, parking, restaurant and bar wheelchair accessible, adapted toilet.
BACKGROUND MUSIC: in bar, restaurant and courtyard.
LOCATION: village centre, 10 mins' drive from Lavenham.
CHILDREN: all ages welcomed, extra bed £10.
DOGS: allowed in bedrooms (£10 per night), in bar, not in restaurant.
CREDIT CARDS: Amex, MC, Visa.
PRICES: B&B doubles from £110, singles from £90. À la carte £40.

Prices may change – check with hotel.

BINFIELD HEATH Oxfordshire   MAP 2:D3

THE BOTTLE & GLASS   NEW

Offering 'the perfect foodie escape', this thatched
gastropub is 'ideally located' just ten minutes from
Henley-on-Thames on the Phillimore estate. Our
inspector described the food, served in 'Tardis-
like dining spaces in the beamed pub', as 'little
short of superb'. Alongside haddock and chips,
menus include dishes such as venison haunch,
chorizo and cabbage purée, potato terrine, roasted
artichoke, red wine jus. 'I relished every mouthful
of the butternut squash agnolotti with charred
purple-sprouting broccoli and tahini dressing.'
You can eat flame-grilled burgers and wood-fired
sourdough pizzas in the barn, and co-owner and
former chef David Holliday holds simple outdoor
fire and butchery classes. Above the pub are 'three
rustic-chic rooms, their pastel walls adorned with
botanical prints'. All have a king- or super-king-
size bed, Bramley toiletries. 'Room 3 had sloping
ceilings, a gorgeous Victoria & Albert roll-top
bath in the bedroom, as well as a shower.' Cooked
breakfasts are 'spot on'. Take a 'boozy walk on
the estate' to the Loddon Brewery and onward
to the Henley Distillery, which makes a special
gin for the pub.

Binfield Heath
Henley-on-Thames RG9 4JT

T: 01491 412625
E: info@bottleandglassinn.com
W: bottleandglassinn.com

BEDROOMS: 3.
OPEN: all year, pub, restaurant closed
Sun pm, Mon, Tues (excl. bank
holidays), but barn open Mon, Tues
until 4 pm.
FACILITIES: bar, dining room/snug,
restaurant, terrace, in-room TV,
garden (alfresco dining), barn (pizzas,
burgers, cakes, etc), public areas
wheelchair accessible, adapted toilet.
BACKGROUND MUSIC: in dining room
and barn.
LOCATION: in village between Henley-
on-Thames and Reading.
CHILDREN: all ages welcomed, travel
cots, no extra beds.
DOGS: in public spaces, not in
bedrooms.
CREDIT CARDS: Amex, MC, Visa.
PRICES: B&B doubles from £142.50.
À la carte £35, set-price menu £15/£18
(2/3 courses).

Prices may change – check with hotel.

BISHOP'S CASTLE Shropshire

MAP 3:C4

THE CASTLE HOTEL

Built on the site of a Norman Marcher lord's castle, this 18th-century former coaching inn has dreamy views to the south Shropshire hills, as blue and memorable as you please. Like parent venture Pen-y-Dyffryn, Oswestry (see entry), it delights our readers. 'We have fallen in love with the hotel,' writes one. 'The setting is rather impressive.' Walkers are in their element (the Shropshire Way runs through the 'delightful little town'; Offa's Dyke is nearby). A welcome box awaits freeloading doggy guests who book ahead. Bedrooms are smart, contemporary and characterful. Two have an in-room bath. A new ground-floor suite with bath and walk-in shower is in the Elephant Gate House, a former stable, so named because it housed homeless circus elephants in WW2 (not because Clive of India once owned the inn – the elephant in the room). You can eat and drink in one of the bars with fire or log-burner, in the restaurant or outside, enjoying the vistas. The evening menu appeals to all tastes, with burgers, steaks, vegan options. The staff are 'highly professional and passionate about being part of a happy team'. (Jane Parkinson, and others)

Market Square
Bishop's Castle SY9 5BN

т: 01588 638403
е: stay@thecastlehotelbishopscastle.
co.uk
w: thecastlehotelbishopscastle.co.uk

BEDROOMS: 15. 1 ground-floor suite next door (small step), 2 suites in cottage and town house opposite.
OPEN: all year except 25 Dec.
FACILITIES: 3 bar areas, dining room, in-room TV (Freeview), in-room spa treatments, patio, terrace, garden, bars and restaurant wheelchair accessible, adapted toilet.
BACKGROUND MUSIC: in bar areas.
LOCATION: in small market town centre.
CHILDREN: all ages welcomed, extra bed £25.
DOGS: allowed in bedrooms (no charge, welcome pack), bar, at owner's side at mealtimes in dog-friendly areas, not in restaurant.
CREDIT CARDS: MC, Visa.
PRICES: B&B doubles from £125, singles from £115. À la carte £35. 1-night bookings sometimes refused Sat.

Prices may change – check with hotel.

BISHOPSTONE Wiltshire

MAP 3:E6

HELEN BROWNING'S ROYAL OAK

There is 'a sense of connection to the land' at this pub-with-rooms on an organic farm 'in a lovely and really rural village' on the Marlborough Downs. Helen Browning OBE, chief executive of the Soil Association, is a passionate advocate for animal welfare and wildlife conservation. Hearty pub fare includes flame-grilled burger, pork and leek pie, fish and chips, steak frites, veggie super salad and vegan ice creams. In a separate building, bedrooms are themed on different fields on the farm, with nods to rusticity. Some are dog-friendly, with a put-you-up bed for a child. Kate's Folly has an in-room bath, king-size bed and sofa bed. 'The outside spaces have an air of charming, almost festival-like, informality' (pull up a hay bale!) and 'gazebos strung with bunting and fairy lights'. A communal space, The Wallow, has books, tea and coffee, an honesty bar, fridge and record player. There is also a farm shop. Order a picnic of charcuterie, hams, artisan cheeses and home-baked bread, and head out to explore. 'Another great stay at this remarkable pub,' reports a returning reader. (Simon Orlik, Paul and Jenny Cheshire)

Cues Lane
Bishopstone
Swindon SN6 8PP

T: 01793 790481
E: royaloak@helenbrowningorganics.co.uk
W: helenbrowningsorganic.co.uk

BEDROOMS: 12. All in annexe, 100 yds from pub, 1 suitable for disabled.
OPEN: all year, lunch, dinner not served 25 Dec.
FACILITIES: lounge, pub (2 dining areas), restaurant meeting/function room, in-room TV (Freeview), ½-acre garden (rope swing, Wendy house, 'flighty hens'), EV charging, restaurant wheelchair accessible, partially adapted toilet.
BACKGROUND MUSIC: none.
LOCATION: on an organic farm, in village, 7 miles E of Swindon, 10 miles from Marlborough.
CHILDREN: all ages welcomed, extra bed £20.
DOGS: allowed in 3 bedrooms (£20 per dog stay), in public rooms 'at our discretion'.
CREDIT CARDS: MC, Visa.
PRICES: B&B doubles from £99. À la carte £35.

Prices may change – check with hotel.

BLAKENEY Norfolk

MAP 2:A5

THE BLAKENEY HOTEL

'A wonderful reminder of the delight a well-run, imaginative hotel can offer,' reads one of many good reports of this family-friendly hotel with shimmering vistas over estuary and salt marsh. There is a wide choice of fairly pricey, smart, contemporary rooms in three grades. The best have antiques, perhaps a four-poster, a patio or balcony. 'Our A+ room in the Granary annexe was charming, with a very comfortable bed, a small but pleasant bathroom with under-floor heating.' 'Our rooms were classed B, but we need not have been anxious … What we lacked in views was well compensated for by the magnificent first-floor lounge with picture windows over the salt marsh and treats for lunch – seafood platter and crab sandwiches especially.' In the restaurant, expect dishes such as seared cod with sweetcorn, ham hock, crab chowder, spinach and lemon. 'The food exceeded expectations by a wide margin.' 'A good choice' of breakfast dishes includes 'kedgeree, undyed smoked haddock'. A boat trip to see the seals at Blakeney Point is a must. (JK Chothia, David Sowden, Lady Elizabeth Akenhead, and others)

The Quay
Blakeney
Holt NR25 7NE

T: 01263 740797
E: reception@blakeneyhotel.co.uk
W: blakeney-hotel.co.uk

BEDROOMS: 64. 16 in Granary annexe, some on ground floor, 1 suitable for disabled.
OPEN: all year.
FACILITIES: lift, 2 lounges, bar, restaurant, in-room TV, function facilities, heated indoor pool, steam room, mini-gym, games room, terrace, ¼-acre walled garden, public rooms wheelchair accessible, adapted toilet.
BACKGROUND MUSIC: none.
LOCATION: on the quay.
CHILDREN: all ages welcomed, family rooms with bunk beds, cot £6, extra bed from £20, adult £45.
DOGS: allowed in some bedrooms (£20 per night), not in public rooms.
CREDIT CARDS: Amex, MC, Visa.
PRICES: B&B doubles from £306, singles from £132. Set-price 3-course menu £40. 1-night stays refused Fri, Sat, bank holidays.

Prices may change – check with hotel.

BLANCHLAND Northumberland

MAP 4:B3

THE LORD CREWE ARMS

'A truly peaceful place to stay, potter about and walk in unspoilt countryside', this hotel in a 'spectacular building' is in a conservation village surrounded by grass moors. Beyond a trefoiled arch Hobbit door, the building incorporates the west cloister range of the dissolved Blanchland Abbey. 'Quietly sophisticated' bedrooms blend the chic of the Lord Crewe's Cotswold cousins (see Calcot & Spa, Tetbury) with notes of rusticity. Most are across the road at The Angel which 'despite its antiquity had all mod cons including free lightweight travelling water bottles, as many capsules as you want for the Nespresso machine'. Suites in neighbouring miners' cottages have a log-burner, a roll-top bath for two. There are drinks, darts and dominoes in the barrel-vaulted Crypt bar, and hearty fare in three dining areas. 'Food was simple but excellent, for example rump of lamb with globe artichokes and beans.' 'No other spot brings me sweeter memories,' wrote WH Auden, who stayed in 1930, drank champagne, played Brahms on a honky-tonk piano and swam in the River Derwent. (Simon and Mithra Tonking, and others)

The Square
Blanchland DH8 9SP

T: 01434 677100
E: enquiries@
 lordcrewearmsblanchland.co.uk
W: lordcrewearmsblanchland.co.uk

BEDROOMS: 26. 7 in adjacent miners' cottages, 15 in The Angel across road, some on ground floor, 1 suitable for disabled.
OPEN: all year.
FACILITIES: reception hall, lounge, 3 dining rooms, bar, Gatehouse events space, in-room TV, civil wedding licence, beer garden, EV charging, 1 dining area wheelchair accessible with ramp, adapted toilet.
BACKGROUND MUSIC: in dining room, bar.
LOCATION: in Blanchland village on B6306, 9 miles S of Hexham.
CHILDREN: all ages welcomed, extra bed for under-13s £25.
DOGS: well-behaved dogs allowed in bedrooms (£20 per night), public rooms, not in dining room.
CREDIT CARDS: Amex, MC, Visa.
PRICES: B&B doubles from £209. À la carte £37. 1-night bookings refused Sat.

Prices may change – check with hotel.

BLEDINGTON Gloucestershire

MAP 3:D6

THE KING'S HEAD INN

Archie and Nicola Orr-Ewing have created a seamless blend of friendly village local and gastropub-with-rooms at their former 16th-century cider house overlooking the green. You can pop in for a pint of Hook Norton by the fire in the beamed bar with 'relaxed atmosphere', while the children feed the ducks on the brook or enjoy ice creams from the pub's shepherd's hut. In the dining room and courtyard, 'very good food' is served by 'excellent, warm and friendly staff'. Menus use free-range and organic local produce, running from pub classics to dishes such as haunch of venison with red wine jus or tiger prawn linguine. Smallish bedrooms, above the pub and in the courtyard annexe, are supplied with 'generous amounts' of bespoke Bantam toiletries. They have been styled by Mrs Orr-Ewing (aka Nicola de Selincourt, milliner), with Cole & Son wallpaper and junk-shop bric-a-brac. The shabby-chic style isn't to everyone's liking: one reader thought their room 'was in need of TLC', another that 'the furniture looked like something from a second-hand store'. That didn't put them off the whole experience though: 'Would certainly recommend.'

The Green
Bledington OX7 6XQ

T: 01608 658365
E: info@kingsheadinn.net
W: thekingsheadinn.net

BEDROOMS: 12. 6 in courtyard annexe, some on ground floor.
OPEN: all year except 25/26 Dec.
FACILITIES: bar, restaurant, snug, courtyard, in-room TV (Freeview), children's play area.
BACKGROUND MUSIC: most of the day, in bar.
LOCATION: on village green.
CHILDREN: all ages welcomed, cot £5, extra bed £25.
DOGS: allowed by arrangement in 3 ground-floor bedrooms (no charge), bar, not in restaurant.
CREDIT CARDS: Amex, MC, Visa.
PRICES: B&B doubles from £110, singles from £90 (Sun–Thurs). À la carte £36. 1-night bookings refused Sat.

Prices may change – check with hotel.

BOLTON ABBEY Yorkshire

THE DEVONSHIRE ARMS

This former 17th-century inn, which is part of the Duke of Devonshire's 30,000-acre estate at Bolton Abbey, is today an impressive country house hotel, with fine dining and a spa. Its notable luxuries – antiques, stylish contemporary furniture, works of art from the Chatsworth collection – are complemented by 'extremely helpful' staff. Prompt, efficient service included a 'fine glass of champagne' for a swiftly corrected shower problem. Bedrooms range from being 'quite small' in the new wing near the road-facing front of the property or overlooking the garden, to four-poster rooms, with larger ones in the original 17th-century, traditionally furnished wing. All have fresh milk and coffee machines, and modern bathrooms with bath and shower. After a 'beautiful country walk from the door' choose either the smart Burlington restaurant's creative taster-menu dishes such as cured sea trout and wasabi, and salt-aged Yorkshire mutton with salsa verde, or the colourful brasserie's more casual style of 'good-quality traditional meals such as steak and chips'. 'We will stay again.' (See also The Cavendish, Baslow.) (Max Lickfold, and others)

Bolton Abbey Estate
Bolton Abbey
Skipton BD23 6AJ

T: 01756 718100
E: reception@thedevonshirearms.co.uk
w: thedevonshirearms.co.uk

BEDROOMS: 40. Some on ground floor suitable for disabled.
OPEN: all year, restaurant closed Mon–Wed, brasserie open all week.
FACILITIES: 4 lounges/snugs, 2 restaurants (vegetarian menu), private dining rooms, in-room TV (Freeview), civil wedding licence, spa, gardens, helipads, EV charging, public areas wheelchair accessible, adapted toilet.
BACKGROUND MUSIC: in public areas.
LOCATION: 6 miles E of Skipton.
CHILDREN: all ages welcomed, extra bed £40.
DOGS: allowed in some bedrooms (£10 per night), public areas, brasserie, not spa or restaurant.
CREDIT CARDS: Amex, MC, Visa.
PRICES: B&B doubles from £270, singles from £250. Set menu £77 (restaurant), à la carte (for 2/3 courses) £30–£39 (brasserie).

Prices may change – check with hotel.

BOLTON BY BOWLAND Lancashire   MAP 4:D3

THE COACH & HORSES   `NEW`

Away from the crowds but close to good walking
in the Yorkshire Dales and Forest of Bowland,
this traditional coaching inn offers richly
decorated bedrooms and great food. With its
creeper-covered facade and window boxes, the
pub (with microbrewery) holds court in stone-
cottage Bolton by Bowland in the picturesque
Ribble valley. It has been carefully renovated with
a striking copper-clad bar, flagstone floor and
smart tartan carpets; its staff offer a 'warm and
friendly welcome'. Bedrooms have 'beautifully
rich and heavy furnishings' in a traditional,
country house style: lavish curtains, oversized
headboards, elaborate mirrors. One has a copper
bath on a dais, another a bath under the window.
All have robes, coffee machines, hair straighteners
and home-made biscuits, although, noted an
inspector, disappointingly no fresh milk. The two
dining areas, with hunting prints on the walls and
candlesticks on the tables, offer a short menu of
elevated pub classics, such as game pie with bacon
date purée, skrei cod and chips, and aged sirloin
with potato terrine. A 'comprehensive selection' of
breakfast dishes are 'cooked to perfection'.

Main Street
Bolton by Bowland BB7 4NW

T: 01200 447331
E: bookings@
   coachandhorsesribblevalley.co.uk
W: coachandhorsesribblevalley.co.uk

BEDROOMS: 7.
OPEN: all year incl. 25/26 Dec, 31 Dec/1
Jan, closed bank holidays, Mon, Tues.
FACILITIES: bar, 2 restaurant areas,
in-room TV (Freeview), beer garden,
parking, bar and one restaurant
wheelchair accessible, adapted toilet.
BACKGROUND MUSIC: 'easy listening',
jazz in bar, restaurant.
LOCATION: in village, off A59, 7 miles
N of Clitheroe.
CHILDREN: all ages welcomed, 2 family
rooms, 2 interconnecting rooms.
DOGS: allowed in 2 bedrooms (no
charge, welcome pack) and public
areas.
CREDIT CARDS: MC, Visa.
PRICES: B&B doubles from £155, singles
from £145. À la carte £36.

Prices may change – check with hotel.

BORROWDALE Cumbria

HAZEL BANK

For many guests, Hazel Bank is the epitome of a small country house hotel with the bonus of a picturesque valley setting, captivating fell views and walks from the doorstep. Sitting above Rosthwaite village 'in a quiet part of Borrowdale', the Victorian house has a warmth that is all thanks to owners Gary and Donna MacRae who create a homely atmosphere with a 'sense of indulgence'. The interiors are comfortable with soft carpets, polished wood and vases of flowers, but not too fussy; after all, why compete with those views! Bedrooms have a simple elegance with pretty wallpapers, handsome headboards, top-notch bathrooms and breathtaking views across the valley and fells. Spoiling touches include sherry and home-made biscuits. Donna's evening meals are equally spoiling: canapés in the lounge are followed by a four-course affair with dishes such as teriyaki mackerel with roasted watermelon, and Lakeland beef fillet with wild mushrooms and caramelised shallots. Breakfast is a feast of local produce including home-made muesli, Manx kippers, and a full Cumbrian (vegetarian option) – and maybe a red squirrel sighting in the garden.

Borrowdale
Keswick CA12 5XB

T: 01768 777248
E: info@hazelbankhotel.co.uk
W: hazelbankhotel.co.uk

BEDROOMS: 7. 1 on ground floor with walk-in shower.
OPEN: all year except Dec to end Jan.
FACILITIES: lounge, dining room, drying room, in-room TV (Freeview), 4-acre grounds (croquet, woodland walks).
BACKGROUND MUSIC: Classic FM at breakfast.
LOCATION: 6 miles S of Keswick on B5289 to Borrowdale.
CHILDREN: not under 16.
DOGS: not allowed.
CREDIT CARDS: MC, Visa.
PRICES: B&B doubles from £200, singles from £190. Set 4-course dinner £49 (£42 for residents booking ahead). Min. 2-night bookings except by special arrangement.

Prices may change – check with hotel.

BORROWDALE Cumbria

MAP 4: inset C2

LEATHES HEAD HOTEL

Many regard Borrowdale as the Lake District's most picturesque valley, and this comfortable Edwardian country house has one of its finest locations. Set back from the road it's 'quiet with splendid views of the hills', says a reader who also admired the gardens, 'the bird life a delight'. Guests report spotting red squirrels, too. Walks start from the hotel, so it's popular with hikers who like their creature comforts; a cup of tea by the log-burner in the lounge or on the terrace after a day on the hills. Bedrooms in the rear annexe are light and simple, perhaps with a feature wall; larger rooms in the original part are traditional with big windows. All have been recently refurbished, and boast views and modern bathrooms, some a bath under the window. The daily-changing set menu, with most items made from scratch, offers 'inventive dishes' such as butter-poached lobster claw with pickled beets, and wild mallard with hibiscus kombucha. Lamb from nearby Yew Tree Farm is always popular. 'Varied and very good breakfasts' set you up for the day. Staff are 'cheerful, efficient; nothing was too much trouble'. (Sir William and Lady Reid)

Borrowdale
Keswick CA12 5UY

T: 01768 777247
E: leathesheadhotel@icloud.com
w: leatheshead.co.uk

BEDROOMS: 11. Some on ground floor, 1 suitable for disabled.
OPEN: all year except 24–26 Dec, restaurant closed Sun, Mon.
FACILITIES: lounge, bar, conservatory restaurant, in-room TV (Freeview), drying room, terrace, 3-acre grounds, EV charging, public rooms wheelchair accessible.
BACKGROUND MUSIC: in public rooms.
LOCATION: 4½ miles S of Keswick.
CHILDREN: not under 15.
DOGS: not allowed.
CREDIT CARDS: Amex, MC, Visa.
PRICES: B&B doubles from £160. Set 4-course dinner £65, tasting menu £95. 1-night bookings refused Sat May–Sept.

Prices may change – check with hotel.

BOSCASTLE Cornwall

THE OLD RECTORY

'In some of the most beautiful inland scenery in Cornwall', Chris and Sally Searle's B&B is 'a time capsule of Victorian virtues, rich in associations with Thomas Hardy'. A reader, who was welcomed with tea and shortbread by the 'kind and helpful hosts', confirms the Guide's long-held view that this is a special place. It was here that Hardy hung his architect's hat when working on plans for the restoration of the church, and courted his first wife, Emma Gifford. Bedrooms have antiques and fresh cut flowers. Emma's Room, overlooking the garden (Sally's pride and joy), has the original 1870s thunderbox toilet. Mr Hardy's Room is slightly smaller, with an antique carved double bed and a view of the church. A self-catering suite in the old stables has an open-plan living space with log-burner. At breakfast there is 'a generous buffet, including delicious fruit from the gardens and an excellent cooked-to-order full English' with free-range eggs and home-grown tomatoes. At night you can enjoy a picnic or takeaway indoors or out; the Searles will supply napkins, plates, knives and forks – and do the washing-up. (Mike Craddock)

St Juliot
Boscastle PL35 0BT

T: 01840 250225
E: sally@stjuliot.com
W: stjuliot.com

BEDROOMS: 3. Plus 1 self-catering in stables (on ground floor, connected to house via conservatory and with separate entrance, 1 step).
OPEN: Apr–early Oct, but 'please check'.
FACILITIES: sitting room, breakfast room, conservatory, in-room TV (Freeview), 3-acre garden (croquet lawn, 'lookout', walled kitchen garden), EV charging, unsuitable for disabled.
BACKGROUND MUSIC: none.
LOCATION: 2 miles NE of Boscastle.
CHILDREN: not under 12.
DOGS: in stables room only (£10 per dog stay).
CREDIT CARDS: Amex, MC, Visa.
PRICES: B&B doubles from £110, singles from £99. 1-night bookings only accepted if there is a late vacancy or quiet period.

Prices may change – check with hotel.

BOSHAM Sussex

MAP 2:E3

THE MILLSTREAM

A little wooden bridge leads across the Bosham Stream into the rose-filled gardens of the Wild family's hotel, occupying three 17th-century workmen's cottages, a stroll from its own quayside. Bedrooms, in country-classics style, are supplied with a coffee machine and cookies, fresh milk in the fridge and good toiletries. They range from a single with a sleigh bed to a superior garden room with French doors to a private garden. A lift, installed this year, has improved access. Readers thought their room, over the car park, 'very nice and well equipped' but added that the price together with an evening meal was 'excessive'. There are two suites in a thatched cottage in the residents-only garden, each with a sitting room, a private garden and patio seating; one has a sofa bed. You can dine in the Sea School restaurant, on dishes such as cod fillet, dill potato purée, rope-grown mussels and leeks, or more informally in the brasserie. Chef Neil Hiskey has been here since 2001, and although this year a soufflé, among other things, failed to rise to expectations, we've heard many murmurs of quiet contentment over the years.

Bosham Lane
Bosham
Chichester PO18 8HL

T: 01243 573234
E: rec@millstream-hotel.co.uk
W: millstreamhotel.com

BEDROOMS: 31. 2 in cottage, 7 on ground floor, 1 suitable for disabled.
OPEN: all year.
FACILITIES: lounge, bar, restaurant, brasserie, conference room, in-room TV (Freeview), civil wedding licence, front lawn (alfresco dining), residents' garden, parking, EV charging, public areas wheelchair accessible, adapted toilet.
BACKGROUND MUSIC: 'gentle', in bar, lounge, restaurants.
LOCATION: 4 miles W of Chichester.
CHILDREN: all ages welcomed, cots free, extra bed for under-13s £20, children's menu (brasserie).
DOGS: not allowed.
CREDIT CARDS: MC, Visa.
PRICES: B&B doubles from £175, singles from £165. À la carte (restaurant) £45, (brasserie) £27. 1-night bookings sometimes refused Sat.

Prices may change – check with hotel.

BOWNESS-ON-WINDERMERE Cumbria   MAP 4: inset C2

LINDETH FELL

With rolling gardens, lakeside views, and elegant
and spacious interiors, this Edwardian home
above Windermere is more country house hotel
than B&B. Run by the Kennedy family for almost
40 years, now in the second generation, the house,
with its wood panelling and ornate ceilings,
is gracious yet never stuffy. There are fires in
the hall and two sitting rooms; books, garden
flowers and family photographs among the large
sofas; and a generous window seat to drink in
the views. It is a perfect setting for the 'treat of a
welcoming cream tea', and if it's sunny, you can
enjoy this on the terrace. Bedrooms hit a balance
'between traditional and contemporary' with bold
wallpapers, well-upholstered armchairs and soft
carpets. Well-designed bathrooms are spotless.
'Thoughtful extras' include sherry, iced water,
digital radio, robes and coffee machines. Eating
options include light snacks, afternoon tea and
savoury platters (to pre-order), while breakfast, in
the garden-view dining room, offers fresh juice,
omelettes, poached haddock, as well as a full (or
vegetarian) grill. Readers agree that the family
and staff know how to make you feel welcome.

Lyth Valley Road
Bowness-on-Windermere LA23 3JP

T: 015394 43286
E: kennedy@lindethfell.co.uk
W: lindethfell.co.uk

BEDROOMS: 14. 1, on ground floor,
suitable for disabled.
OPEN: all year except 23–26 Dec,
2 Jan–11 Feb.
FACILITIES: 2 lounges, bar, entrance
hall with seating, dining room, in-
room TV (Freeview), 7-acre grounds
(terrace, gardens, croquet lawn),
public rooms wheelchair accessible.
BACKGROUND MUSIC: classical in dining
room, bar.
LOCATION: 1 mile S of Bowness.
CHILDREN: 12 and over, extra bed from
£28.50.
DOGS: only assistance dogs allowed.
CREDIT CARDS: MC, Visa.
PRICES: B&B doubles from £186, singles
from £93. Evening platters £17.50
(with additional 2 courses, £30). Min.
2-night stay Mar–end Oct, 3-night
min. bank holidays (ring to check
1-night availability).

Prices may change – check with hotel.

BOWNESS-ON-WINDERMERE Cumbria   MAP 4: inset C2

STORRS HALL   [NEW]

With an enviable position on Windermere, this Georgian hall has a relaxed country house style, a choice of dining and bedrooms ranging from family friendly to seriously swanky. Public rooms are 'a delight', furnished with a mix of contemporary velvet seating, display cabinets of curios, gilt-framed art, and make the most of the lake views. The light-filled restaurant, with its smart napery, offers well-executed classic dishes such as local venison with braised red cabbage, local hogget with rösti potato and 'perfectly cooked halibut', as well as grills. More traditional 'pub' dishes – fish and chips, home-made burgers – are served in the fire-warmed bar with its deep-blue walls and Victorian carved bar fittings. Spacious bedrooms – most with lake views – are individual in furnishings but share a modern country house style of statement wallpapers, oversized headboards, upholstered armchairs, contemporary bathrooms. For romance, the vast Lakeside suites and Boathouse spoil with hot tubs and freestanding baths. Take a woodland walk, relax over afternoon tea – if warm, on the terrace – or drive to Bowness five minutes away. (Ralph Wilson)

Bowness-on-Windermere LA23 3LG

T: 01539 447111
E: reception@storrshall.com
W: storrshall.com

BEDROOMS: 35. 6 suites in separate building, 1 suitable for disabled, 1 boathouse suite.
OPEN: all year.
FACILITIES: bar, restaurant, drawing room, study, terrace, civil wedding licence, in-room TV, 17 acres of lakeside grounds, EV charging, ground-floor public rooms wheelchair accessible, adapted toilet.
BACKGROUND MUSIC: throughout ground floor.
LOCATION: on Lake Windermere, off A592.
CHILDREN: all ages welcomed, extra bed £40.
DOGS: not allowed.
CREDIT CARDS: Amex, MC, Visa.
PRICES: B&B doubles from £225, singles from £215. À la carte £58. Min. 2-night stay at weekends.

Prices may change – check with hotel.

BRADFORD-ON-AVON Wiltshire

MAP 2:D1

WIDBROOK GRANGE

A Georgian stone farmhouse filled with upcycled agricultural salvage might seem an odd sort of sister hotel for a Scottish hunting lodge, but here, as at Shieldaig Lodge, Gairloch (see entry), it's all about heritage. Owners Nick and Charlotte Dent have had a field day playing up the property's past as a model farm, pressing all kinds of vintage miscellanea into service – churns, handcarts, seed spreaders, weighing scales … Among the whackiness, there is a gin bar, an indoor pool and cosy lounge. Bedrooms in the main house have a fashionably muted palette, while those in converted stables and piggery have rustic beams and exposed stone. Some are dog-friendly; four-footed friends are extremely welcome here and can enjoy a special afternoon tea with their owners. A reader thought the shabby-chic decor 'tended towards shabby' and was 'really in need of decorating' but praised the 'friendly staff' and the 'very tasty' food. 'Large portions of belly of pork and rump of lamb were delicious.' At breakfast there are local pork-and-leek sausages and black pudding, thyme butter mushrooms, kippers, home-made baked beans. (CH, and others)

Bradford-on-Avon BA15 1UH

T: 01225 864750
E: stay@widbrookgrange.co.uk
W: widbrookgrange.co.uk

BEDROOMS: 19. 15 in outbuildings, 1 suitable for disabled.
OPEN: all year.
FACILITIES: gin bar, snug, restaurant, conservatory, in-room TV (Freeview), civil wedding licence, function facilities, 11-acre grounds, 11-metre indoor heated swimming pool, gym, giant chess, parking, public rooms wheelchair accessible, no adapted toilet.
BACKGROUND MUSIC: soft, all day in public rooms.
LOCATION: 2 miles S of Bradford-on-Avon.
CHILDREN: all ages welcomed, family rooms, children's menu.
DOGS: allowed in certain bedrooms (£15 per night), public rooms, not restaurant.
CREDIT CARDS: Amex, MC, Visa.
PRICES: B&B doubles from £155, family from £190. À la carte £40, tasting menu £59.

Prices may change – check with hotel.

SEE ALSO SHORTLIST

BRADFORD-ON-AVON Wiltshire

MAP 2:D1

WOOLLEY GRANGE

It may be a grand Jacobean manor but fun and frolicking for all the family is positively encouraged at Woolley Grange, which has all bases covered, from crèche and cinema to spa and pools. Part of the Luxury Family Hotels group (see Fowey Hall, Fowey, and Moonfleet Manor, Fleet), it has thought of most things to give everyone a break. For children, the hotel is a playground with games room, dressing-up box, tree swings, fairy garden, hens' eggs to collect and marshmallows to roast. Grown-ups can relax in the oak-panelled drawing rooms or in the spa. The crèche and baby-listening services are free, too. Interiors are rich but not precious, with fairground carousel animals in corridors, squishy sofas in the lounges. Bedrooms, in both the main house and cottages, are comfortably country house with floral curtains, tartan throws, the occasional antique. In summer, there are chic, two-bedroom glamping suites, with bathrooms, in the meadow. Children's high tea is available or evening menus offer burgers and pasta as well as smarter dishes such as monkfish tail with salsa verde; choose either a child-friendly or more intimate dining space.

Woolley Green
Bradford-on-Avon BA15 1TX

T: 01225 864705
E: info@woolleygrangehotel.co.uk
W: woolleygrangehotel.co.uk

BEDROOMS: 25. 11 in annexes, 2 on ground floor, 1 suitable for disabled, 8 summer glamping suites.
OPEN: all year.
FACILITIES: 2 lounges, restaurant, summer café, cinema, in-room TV (Freeview), crèche, spa, heated indoor and outdoor swimming pools, civil wedding licence, 14-acre grounds, EV charging, wheelchair accessible.
BACKGROUND MUSIC: in restaurants.
LOCATION: 1 mile NE of Bradford-on-Avon, 8½ miles SE of Bath.
CHILDREN: all ages welcomed, no additional charge for extra beds.
DOGS: allowed in bedrooms (£15 per night), public rooms, not restaurant.
CREDIT CARDS: Amex, MC, Visa.
PRICES: B&B doubles from £140. À la carte £40–£50. 1-night bookings sometimes refused at weekends.

Prices may change – check with hotel.

SEE ALSO SHORTLIST

BRAITHWAITE Cumbria

MAP 4: inset C2

THE COTTAGE IN THE WOOD

A whitewashed cottage on a steep woodland pass may seem an unlikely setting for Michelin-starred dining, but this restaurant-with-rooms charms both the eye and the palate. Liam and Kath Berney's former 17th-century drovers' inn, in Whinlatter Forest, enjoys views to Skiddaw and a rural environment that teems with birds and wildlife. It's 'immensely relaxing', as is Kath's warm welcome. With the minimum of fuss, she ensures cases are whisked to rooms and will suggest walks should you want to work up an appetite. Rooms have a neat, contemporary style with feature wallpapers, oak furniture and perhaps a brass bedstead. Some are 'small but well designed'. Modern bathrooms, some compact, have 'good lighting and a decent shower'. Nice touches include 'delicious home-made shortbread' and, for rooms with a tub, 'bath soak; perfect for easing walkers' limbs!' Ben Wilkinson's set menus offer dishes that are considered but never contrived: monkfish with burnt orange, beetroot and sweet potato, say, or venison with fennel and pine nuts. Breakfast includes home-made yogurt granola, omelettes and 'the creamiest of scrambled eggs'. (HP)

Magic Hill
Whinlatter Forest
Braithwaite CA12 5TW

T: 01768 778409
E: relax@thecottageinthewood.co.uk
W: thecottageinthewood.co.uk

BEDROOMS: 9. 1 in the garden with separate entrance.
OPEN: all year except 25/26 Dec, 2nd and 3rd week Jan, last week in June, closed Sun, Mon, Tues.
FACILITIES: lounge, restaurant (vegetarian menu), in-room TV (Freeview), secure bicycle storage, terraced garden, 2 acres of woodland, restaurant and public areas wheelchair accessible, adapted toilet.
BACKGROUND MUSIC: none.
LOCATION: 5 miles NW of Keswick.
CHILDREN: not under 10.
DOGS: not allowed.
CREDIT CARDS: MC, Visa.
PRICES: D,B&B doubles from £300, singles ring to check. Set dinner £75, tasting menu £100. Min. 2-night booking but ring to check 1-night availability.

Prices may change – check with hotel.

BRAMPTON Cumbria

MAP 4:B3

FARLAM HALL

In a quiet corner of Cumbria, close to Hadrian's Wall, this long-established hotel exudes the traditional comforts of a country house but with a modern elegance. Guests returning after several years were pleased the Victorian hall had been 'tastefully refurbished' while 'enhancing and retaining its original charm'. High-ceilinged rooms are comfortably traditional with fires in carved fireplaces, well-upholstered chairs and crisp napery in the dining room, but colours are soft, wallpapers lightly patterned and ornaments well chosen. Dinner's short-choice menu offers classic British dishes with a modern twist such as citrus-cured salmon with samphire and crème fraîche, and local lamb with lyonnaise potatoes. One reader considered the venison 'the best we have had for a long time'. Many fruit and vegetables come from the kitchen garden. Large bedrooms have a country house style of gentle colours, reproduction and antique furniture, and big armchairs; sofas in larger rooms. All have garden views and modern bathrooms, most with bath as well as shower. Staff are 'caring, attentive' and deliver a 'first-class service'. (Robert Henry)

Hallbankgate
Brampton CA8 2NG

T: 01697 746234
E: farlam@farlamhall.co.uk
W: farlamhall.co.uk

BEDROOMS: 13. 2 on ground floor, 1 in stables. 4 self-catering cottages in grounds sleep 2–6.
OPEN: all year.
FACILITIES: 2 lounges, restaurant, cocktail bar, in-room TV (Freeview), civil wedding licence, 6-acre grounds (stream, walled garden), EV charging, public rooms wheelchair accessible, adapted toilet.
BACKGROUND MUSIC: in public areas, restaurant.
LOCATION: on A689, 2½ miles SE of Brampton.
CHILDREN: all ages welcomed, interconnecting rooms, self-catering cottages.
DOGS: allowed in 2 bedrooms (not unattended, £30 per night), bar and grounds on lead.
CREDIT CARDS: Amex, MC, Visa.
PRICES: B&B doubles from £189, singles from £169. À la carte £54, tasting menu £65.

Prices may change – check with hotel.

BRANCASTER STAITHE Norfolk

THE WHITE HORSE

The superb setting of the Nye family's hotel overlooking salt marshes to the sea and Scolt Head Island is matched by a 'really good atmosphere', say readers, who visit year after year. 'It was wonderful to return to such a well-managed hotel,' runs a typical report. Food is served outside from noon till night, allowing diners to fully appreciate the big-sky landscape and spectacular sunsets. You can eat sea-fresh shellfish cooked over coals in an open-sided marquee (ponchos provided), dine under a parasol in the courtyard garden, or by the fire in winter. In the glass-walled restaurant, with 'excellent food and service', the menu ranges from fish and chips to lobster or marsh-grazed dry-aged sirloin steak. 'Extremely comfortable and nicely decorated' refurbished bedrooms have new carpets and linen, local artwork, a Norfolk seascape palette of green, blue, lavender and sand. The split-level 'Room at the Top' has a balcony and telescope to better appreciate the view. Spacious, dog-friendly garden rooms, built into the contours of the land, under a sedum roof, have a private terrace, a stroll from the Coast Path. (David Craig, SP)

Main Road
Brancaster Staithe PE31 8BY

T: 01485 210262
E: reception@whitehorsebrancaster.co.uk
W: whitehorsebrancaster.co.uk

BEDROOMS: 15. 8 on ground floor in annexe, 1 suitable for disabled.
OPEN: all year.
FACILITIES: open-plan bar, lounge areas, conservatory restaurant, dining room, in-room TV (Freeview), ½-acre garden (terrace, covered sunken garden), in-room therapies, EV charging, public rooms wheelchair accessible, adapted toilet.
BACKGROUND MUSIC: 'subtle' in restaurant.
LOCATION: centre of village.
CHILDREN: all ages welcomed, cot £5, extra bed £35, children's menu, high chair.
DOGS: allowed in garden rooms (£10 a night), bar.
CREDIT CARDS: Amex, MC, Visa.
PRICES: B&B doubles from £140, single occupancy discount available. À la carte £38 (Marshside £25). 1-night bookings may be refused.

Prices may change – check with hotel.

BRIGHTON Sussex   MAP 2:E4

ARTIST RESIDENCE BRIGHTON

Bohemian Brighton is artfully encapsulated in this Regency town house with its cool vibe, quirky furnishings and neighbourhood café-bar. In a seaward-facing square, with sea views but without the seafront traffic, it's the original hotel of Justin and Charlotte Salisbury's small collection of Artist Residences (see index). The café-bar and lounge boast G-plan furnishings, timber floors, industrial lighting and limited-edition artwork. Here you can laze over coffee and brunch – perhaps eggs Florentine or toasted sourdough with smoked salmon and avocado – G&Ts or a Peroni. Bedrooms of stripped-wood floors, pale-grey walls, often a bare-brick feature, are furnished with retro and reclaimed pieces; perhaps tea chests turned into bedside tables and vintage Anglepoise lamps. Most showcase work – including huge murals and framed pop art – by local artists. Smaller rooms are snug, and bathrooms can be compact; the largest rooms have freestanding baths. All have Roberts radios, espresso machines and organic toiletries; several have sea-view balconies. Come evening, try a cocktail from the basement 'secret' bar.

34 Regency Square
Brighton BN1 2FJ

T: 01273 324302
E: brighton@artistresidence.co.uk
W: artistresidence.co.uk

BEDROOMS: 27, incl. 2 bunkhouse rooms (sleeping 4–6). Plus 3 self-catering apartments next door.
OPEN: all year.
FACILITIES: small lift, bar and café, lounge, cocktail bar, ping-pong room/private events, in-room TV (Freeview), small terrace, car park opposite (charge), unsuitable for disabled.
BACKGROUND MUSIC: all day in public areas.
LOCATION: town centre.
CHILDREN: all ages welcomed, free cots, extra bed £30.
DOGS: allowed in some bedrooms (£15 per night, welcome pack), all public areas.
CREDIT CARDS: Amex, MC, Visa.
PRICES: room-only doubles from £129. Breakfast items £4.50–£12.50. 1-night bookings refused at weekends.

Prices may change – check with hotel.

SEE ALSO SHORTLIST

BRIGHTON Sussex

MAP 2:E4

DRAKES

Indulge in a Pornstar Martini in the sea-facing cocktail bar at this stuccoed, bow-fronted Georgian seafront hotel, for this is Brighton, after all – hip, tolerant and fun. Occupying two adjoining town houses, it counts among its glamorous past guests Sophie Dahl, Cate Blanchett and Kylie Minogue. Whether it's a city-facing attic hideaway with freestanding bath and wet room, or a feature room overlooking the Palace Pier with a roll-top bath under a floor-to-ceiling window, a super-king bed, chaise longue and monsoon-shower bathroom, the accommodation here is confident, chic and surprisingly affordable. At Amarillo, in the light and airy basement, Ian Swainson, who held a Michelin star at the Samling in Cumbria, creates six-course tasting menus for omnivores and vegetarians, with tempting accents of Spain. Dishes might include raw and pan-fried langoustine with heritage tomato and tarragon; venison tartare with jalapeño sauce and smoked pine oil; or spookily black cuttlefish with squid-ink rice and squid cracker. In the morning, pop down for a full English breakfast before browsing the boutiques in the Lanes.

43–44 Marine Parade
Brighton BN2 1PE

T: 01273 696934
E: info@drakesofbrighton.com
W: drakesofbrighton.com

BEDROOMS: 20.
OPEN: all year, restaurant Tues–Sat.
FACILITIES: lounge/bar, restaurant (vegetarian menu), meeting/private dining room, in-room TV (Sky), civil wedding licence, some off-road parking £15 a night, unsuitable for disabled.
BACKGROUND MUSIC: in bar and restaurant.
LOCATION: ½ mile from centre, on seafront.
CHILDREN: all ages welcomed, no extra beds, babies 'by prior arrangement'.
DOGS: only assistance dogs allowed.
CREDIT CARDS: Amex, MC, Visa.
PRICES: room-only doubles from £125. Breakfast £12 for overnight guests, £10–£15 for drop-ins, 6-course tasting menus £65. Min. 2-night stay Sat, but check availability.

Prices may change – check with hotel.

SEE ALSO SHORTLIST

BRISTOL

BROOKS GUESTHOUSE

Unlikely as it sounds, a 1950s office block in central Bristol is today a cool B&B with neat bedrooms, shiny rooftop caravans, a relaxed vibe and a courtyard garden. Ten minutes from the harbour, the three-storey building was converted by Carla and Andrew Brooks to provide bright, frills-free accommodation. Bedrooms are simply furnished with classy wallpapers, tongue-and-groove panelling, pale-wood bedsteads and colourful throws. Space is at a premium – wooden hooks replace wardrobes – and tiled bathrooms are compact. 'Older folk might want more creature comforts,' commented inspectors, though the 'good lighting' was appreciated. Alternatively, Airstream-style silver caravans in the rooftop garden, squeezing in double bed and shower, have a sense of 'pizzazz' and are a fun retreat for families. 'Freshly cooked' breakfasts, including home-made fruit compote, eggs Benedict, a full grill as well as daily specials, are served in the open-plan living area. Eclectically furnished with vintage and rustic furniture, it has large bifold glass doors open to the courtyard garden. 'Certainly good value' and surprisingly quiet given the location.

Exchange Avenue
St Nicholas Street
Bristol BS1 1UB

T: 0117 930 0066
E: info@brooksguesthousebristol.com
W: brooksguesthousebristol.com

BEDROOMS: 27. 4 in Airstream-style caravans on roof.
OPEN: all year except 24–26 Dec.
FACILITIES: lift, lounge/breakfast room, honesty bar, in-room TV (Freeview), courtyard and rooftop garden, discounted parking, unsuitable for disabled.
BACKGROUND MUSIC: in lounge and breakfast area.
LOCATION: central, next to St Nicholas Market.
CHILDREN: all ages welcomed, free cot, extra bed £20.
DOGS: only assistance dogs.
CREDIT CARDS: Amex, MC, Visa.
PRICES: B&B doubles from £69, caravans from £119. Min. 2-night stay Sat.

Prices may change – check with hotel.

SEE ALSO SHORTLIST

BRISTOL

NUMBER THIRTY EIGHT CLIFTON

'Our favourite stop-over when travelling to Cornwall', this twin-bayed Georgian merchant's house B&B sits atop one of Bristol's highest hills, with panoramic views. Choose a dual-aspect loft suite and look out to the fore across the green spaces of Clifton Down and, to the rear, across the city to the Mendips. Owned by Adam Dorrien Smith, it is a stylish mix of period and contemporary furniture, with a palette of taupe and duck-egg blue, deep teal and charcoal, coir flooring, velvet armchairs, perhaps a velvet-covered sleigh bed. While everything is tastefully uncluttered, it is 'warm and welcoming at the same time', with 'top-notch service'. All rooms have a fridge, a Roberts radio, waffle gowns and slippers, 'divine-smelling' 100 Acres toiletries; some bathrooms have a copper roll-top bath and large walk-in shower. 'The breakfast buffet is a highlight' while, for a small supplement, you can enjoy a full English or vegetarian, avocado on toast, smoked salmon with scrambled eggs. The 'friendly, helpful' staff stand down at 8 pm, as you head out to the nearby restaurants in Clifton. (J and KP, and others)

38 Upper Belgrave Road
Clifton
Bristol BS8 2XN

T: 0117 946 6905
E: info@number38clifton.com
W: number38clifton.com

BEDROOMS: 12.
OPEN: all year.
FACILITIES: lounge, breakfast room, meeting space, in-room TV (Freeview), terrace, limited number of parking permits on request, unsuitable for disabled.
BACKGROUND MUSIC: in public areas 8 am–8 pm.
LOCATION: 2½ miles from city centre.
CHILDREN: not under 12, no extra beds or cots.
DOGS: not allowed.
CREDIT CARDS: Amex, MC, Visa.
PRICES: B&B doubles from £145, singles from £130. Cooked breakfast £5 surcharge.

Prices may change – check with hotel.

SEE ALSO SHORTLIST

BRISTOL

MAP 1:B6

OLD CHURCH FARM

A Saxon royal hunting lodge in the Gloucestershire countryside, rebuilt over centuries, is run today as a private hotel by 'lovely hosts' Christopher Trim and Kathryn Warner. This was previously a hospitality venue for Rolls-Royce, and they cater to conferences, but the ambience is that of an intimate country house party and is not the least corporate. The 'beautiful and historic building' has stone mullion windows, a Tudor arched stone fireplace and 16th-century plasterwork ceilings. The ruins of medieval St Helen's church stand serene in the grounds. Bedrooms have fine antiques, home-made biscuits, views of the churchyard or rose garden and croquet lawn. The drawing room and snug have comfy sofas, rich fabrics, books, prints and pastoral landscapes. At 24 hours' notice (72 hours, for special diets), Cordon Bleu-trained Kathryn cooks a three-course dinner that is 'nothing short of exceptional' for assembled guests, with produce from the walled garden and local farms. Breakfast brings freshly baked pastries, maybe eggs Benedict, home-made jams, the full English or vegetarian if you wish. (Neil Bartlett, Mary Hills, and others)

Church Road
Rudgeway
Bristol BS35 3SQ

T: 01454 418212
E: stay@old-church-farm.co.uk
W: old-church-farm.co.uk

BEDROOMS: 5.
OPEN: all year (whole house booking only at Christmas), dinner Mon–Sat.
FACILITIES: snug, drawing room, breakfast room, dining room, in-room TV, conference facilities, 8-acre gardens, parking, EV charging, public rooms wheelchair accessible, adapted toilet in conference centre.
BACKGROUND MUSIC: in drawing room, dining room.
LOCATION: 12 miles N of Bristol, on the edge of a south Gloucestershire village.
CHILDREN: not under 12.
DOGS: not allowed.
CREDIT CARDS: Amex, MC, Visa.
PRICES: B&B doubles from £160. Set-price dinner (24 hours' notice) £27.50–£32.50 (2/3 courses). 1-night bookings refused at weekends May–Sept.

Prices may change – check with hotel.

SEE ALSO SHORTLIST

BROADWAY Worcestershire   MAP 3:D6

THE BROADWAY HOTEL

With its wisteria-covered honey stonework, medieval half-timbering and a lovely position overlooking the village green, The Broadway is film-set perfect. Standing in the centre of its namesake photogenic Cotswold village, it's popular with locals and visitors. In warm weather, people spill on to the front terrace; otherwise the Jockey bar with its oak panelling, double-height beamed ceiling, open fire and minstrels' gallery is the heart of the hotel. Throughout the building, there's a horse-racing theme (jockeys' colours, historic photographs) in homage to nearby Cheltenham. Creaky stairs lead to contemporary-style bedrooms, individual in shape and furnished with bright-patterned fabrics, headboards and feature wallpapers. Some have beams; most have baths as well as showers and all have a coffee machine and Roberts radio. Dine either in the bar or the glazed-roof restaurant on brasserie classics such as seafood chowder, West Country lamb with rösti potato and chargrilled Herefordshire burger. Breakfasts include home-made preserves, eggs Florentine, pancakes and a full Cotswold grill. After a day's exploring, relax in the quiet rear garden.

The Green
Broadway WR12 7AA

T: 01386 852401
E: info@broadwayhotel.info
W: broadway-hotel.co.uk

BEDROOMS: 19. 3 rooms on ground floor. 3 self-catering cottages nearby.
OPEN: all year.
FACILITIES: sitting room, bar, brasserie, in-room TV (Freeview), courtyard, garden and terrace (residents only), parking, EV charging, unsuitable for disabled.
BACKGROUND MUSIC: ambient in public areas.
LOCATION: village centre, 'best to request a parking space before you arrive, especially in summer'.
CHILDREN: all ages welcomed, under-13s on extra bed £20, children's menu.
DOGS: dogs allowed in dedicated bedrooms (ring for details/availability, welcome pack), in bar and on terrace.
CREDIT CARDS: Amex, MC, Visa.
PRICES: B&B doubles from £163, singles from £153. À la carte £43.

Prices may change – check with hotel.

SEE ALSO SHORTLIST

BROADWAY Worcestershire

THE LYGON ARMS

This sprawling honey-stone building with its tall chimneys and leaded windows offers history, grand rooms and antiques, along with a thoroughly modern spa and 21st-century luxuries. The Cotswold town former coaching inn, and favoured spot of royalty and Hollywood stars, is a maze of snugs and lounges that blend original panelling, inglenooks and beams with rich colours and contemporary and antique furniture. There's a chic bottle-green cocktail bar – try their rhubarb negroni – while the barrel-vaulted dining room with minstrels' gallery has been turned into a buzzy space with marble-top tables and modern grill menu: perhaps Cotswold lamb, beef Wellington or poached halibut. There is a good selection of plant-based dishes, too. Bedrooms range from quirkily shaped rooms in the main house and adjoining cottages, to contemporary annexe rooms and open-plan courtyard suites overlooking a landscaped terraced garden. All are furnished with bright coloured plaids, a mix of contemporary and antique Gordon Russell furniture, and original artwork. Modern bathrooms mostly have bath and shower. 'When we're there we feel very much at home.'

High Street
Broadway WR12 7DU

T: 01386 852255
E: reservations@lygonarmshotel.
co.uk
W: lygonarmshotel.co.uk

BEDROOMS: 86. 26 on ground floor, some in cottages, some courtyard suites, 2 suitable for disabled.
OPEN: all year.
FACILITIES: 7 lounge areas, bar/grill (vegetarian menu), cocktail bar, in-room TV (Freeview), civil wedding licence, 3-acre garden, indoor pool, spa, EV charging, public areas (not spa) wheelchair accessible, adapted toilet.
BACKGROUND MUSIC: in lounges.
LOCATION: village centre.
CHILDREN: all ages welcomed, under-5s free, extra bed for 5–16s £25.
DOGS: in some bedrooms (£25 a night, welcome pack), all lounges.
CREDIT CARDS: Amex, MC, Visa.
PRICES: B&B doubles from £210, singles from £195. À la carte £45. 1-night bookings sometimes refused Sat, bank holidays.

Prices may change – check with hotel.

SEE ALSO SHORTLIST

BROADWAY Worcestershire

MAP 3:D6

RUSSELL'S

In a gem of a Cotswold town, with its green verges, galleries and tea shops, a honeyed-stone house is home to this first-class restaurant-with-rooms. It was once a workshop for Sir Gordon Russell, pioneer of wartime utility furniture, who grew up at the Lygon Arms (previous entry). A lover of good design, food and wine, he would be in his element. The seven bedrooms here are as carefully crafted as the food which features on George Santos's eclectic modern menus downstairs, and blend original 17th-century features with modern comforts. The best are under the eaves, with original beams, exposed stone walls, wood floors, and views of the Cotswold hills, but all rooms are light and spacious. Even the smallest have window seats and armchairs, contemporary furnishings and splashes of colour in suede headboards and velvet armchairs as well as natural-stone bathrooms. In the stylish, beamed restaurant with sea-blue banquettes, or outside, you can feast on dishes that include pan-fried Cornish cod, with curried potato, spinach, pickled grapes, toasted almonds and korma sauce – or go for the more rustic version at Russell's Fish and Chips.

20 High Street
Broadway WR12 7DT

T: 01386 853555
E: info@russellsofbroadway.co.uk
W: russellsofbroadway.co.uk

BEDROOMS: 7. 3 in adjoining building, 2 on ground floor.
OPEN: all year, restaurant closed Mon/Tues, Sun dinner.
FACILITIES: bar, restaurant, private dining room, in-room TV (Freeview), patio (heating, meal service), parking, restaurant and bar wheelchair accessible, adapted toilet.
BACKGROUND MUSIC: in restaurant.
LOCATION: village centre.
CHILDREN: all ages welcomed, under-2s free, extra bed £15.
DOGS: allowed in 1 ground-floor bedroom (no charge), some areas of restaurant.
CREDIT CARDS: MC, Visa.
PRICES: B&B doubles from £165. À la carte £50. 1-night bookings refused at weekends.

Prices may change – check with hotel.

SEE ALSO SHORTLIST

BROCKENHURST Hampshire   MAP 2:E2

DAISYBANK COTTAGE

The name has an Enid Blyton ring to it, and it sits
in a dingley dell on the edge of the New Forest,
but this single-storey Arts and Crafts cottage is
home to an entirely grown-up B&B. Hosts Cheryl
and Ciaran Maher have the personal touch,
welcoming guests with home-baked cupcakes and
sharing their knowledge of the lovely area. All
bedrooms have a mini-fridge, a Roberts radio, an
espresso machine, fine toiletries, a king or super-
king bed. The decor is chic, with a muted palette
and works by local artists. The Courtyard Suite
has glass doors to an enclosed, tiled patio, a rattan
king-size bed, a power shower. The Marryat Suite
has a bath and walk-in shower and opens on to
a terrace with patio heater and barbecue; sit out
and read Captain Marryat's classic Children of the
New Forest. 'Everything in our spacious room
felt like luxury,' a reader wrote after a 'fantastic
stay'. Pop your order in a flowerpot outside your
door at bedtime, and awake to a full English or
full veggie, new-laid local farm eggs, American
pancakes. 'The breakfasts, delivered to our room,
were delicious.' (Alexandra Rodgers)

Sway Road
Brockenhurst
New Forest SO42 7SG

T: 01590 622086
E: info@bedandbreakfast-newforest.
co.uk
W: bedandbreakfast-newforest.co.uk

BEDROOMS: 8. 2 in Gardener's Cottage,
all on ground floor, 1-bed shepherd's
hut available Apr–Sept, some suitable
for disabled but not fully adapted.
OPEN: all year, except 1 week over
Christmas.
FACILITIES: 2 sitting rooms, breakfast
room, in-room TV (Freeview), 5-acre
grounds, front and back garden,
parking, EV charging.
BACKGROUND MUSIC: none.
LOCATION: ¾ mile S of Brockenhurst
village.
CHILDREN: over-7s welcomed, extra
bed £40.
DOGS: not allowed.
CREDIT CARDS: MC, Visa.
PRICES: B&B doubles from £120,
single occupancy from £110. Min.
2-night stay, 3 nights at weekends and
bank holidays, but check for 1-night
availability.

Prices may change – check with hotel.

BROCKENHURST Hampshire

NEW PARK MANOR

NEW

Charles II might not recognise his old royal hunting lodge today but, as the father of at least 11 children and a great lover of his spaniels, the Merry Monarch would enjoy the dog-friendly, inclusive ethos. The 18th-century mansion, built around an older core, served as a residence for the Duke of Bedford, Lord Warden of the New Forest, and is today part of the Luxury Family Hotels group (see Fowey Hall, Fowey; Woolley Grange, Bradford-on-Avon; and Moonfleet Manor, Fleet). Bedrooms are a mix of period and contemporary styling and range from cosy and classic to two-bedroom and deluxe suites (one with handsome carved four-poster). The deer park suite has a master bedroom, twin bedroom, French doors to a roof terrace, a bathroom with bath and walk-in shower. There's plenty to keep the kids occupied here, with a crèche, cinema room and games room. Flexible dining includes a lounge menu and Matilda afternoon tea, Sunday lunch served family style. For the grown-ups, à la carte dining includes dishes such as Sopley Farm risotto, fennel and lemon, or Owton's Farm beef trio with swede mash and cabbage roulade. Cycle hire with toddler seats can be arranged for two-wheel tootles around the forest.

Lyndhurst Road
Brockenhurst
New Forest SO42 7QH

T: 01590 623467
E: info@newparkmanorhotel.co.uk
W: newparkmanorhotel.co.uk

BEDROOMS: 25.
OPEN: open all year.
FACILITIES: 2 lounges, 2 restaurants, crèche, cinema, games room, in-room TV, civil wedding licence, spa, spa café, indoor pool, outdoor pool (May–Sept), terrace, gardens, children's play area, EV charging, Vinery restaurant and spa wheelchair accessible.
BACKGROUND MUSIC: 'light modern instrumental' in dining areas.
LOCATION: 2 miles N of Brockenhurst.
CHILDREN: all ages welcomed, no charge for extra bed, children's menu.
DOGS: allowed in bedrooms (£15 a night), on lead in public areas, not in crèche, restaurants or spa.
CREDIT CARDS: Amex, MC, Visa.
PRICES: B&B doubles from £120.
À la carte £40. 1-night bookings may be refused at weekends.

Prices may change – check with hotel.

BROCKENHURST Hampshire

MAP 2:E2

THE PIG IN THE FOREST

Pigs have foraged in the New Forest since the Norman Conquest, but a different breed arrived in 2011, when Robin Hutson took on a Georgian hunting lodge and reinvented the English country house hotel. The ethos at all the Pigs (see index) is hip but not hooray. Judy Hutson set the shabby-chic style, mixing old and new, rich fabrics and boot-sale finds. Even snug rooms come with designer wallpaper, a large monsoon shower, while comfy-luxe rooms have a shower and freestanding bath. There are hideaway suites in the stable yard, lodges, a forest hut clad in reclaimed timber at the bottom of the garden. Readers tried a wide range of dishes from the seasonal menus, with produce from the kitchen garden or grown and reared close to home, and proclaimed them all 'absolutely delicious'. The menu might include wild garlic tagliatelle, goat's cheese and walnuts, or venison loin with artichokes and smoked yogurt. 'There's so much about the place that we absolutely love,' said our reviewers. 'Every person we dealt with was exceptionally friendly and professional.' There is one rub: the Pigs aren't for pups, who will have to stay at home. (Anna Brewer)

Beaulieu Road
Brockenhurst SO42 7QL

T: 01590 622354
E: info@thepighotel.com
W: thepighotel.com

BEDROOMS: 32. 10 in stable block (100 yds), some on ground floor, 2 lodges and a cabin in the garden, 1 courtyard room suitable for disabled.
OPEN: all year.
FACILITIES: lounge, library, bar, restaurant, in-room TV (Freeview), civil wedding licence, treatment rooms, kitchen garden, 6-acre grounds, EV charging, public rooms wheelchair accessible, adapted toilet.
BACKGROUND MUSIC: in public areas.
LOCATION: 1 mile E of Brockenhurst village.
CHILDREN: all ages welcomed, no charge for extra beds.
DOGS: guide dogs only.
CREDIT CARDS: Amex, MC, Visa.
PRICES: room-only doubles from £195. Breakfast £13.50–£18.50, à la carte £42. 1-night bookings refused at weekends, Christmas, New Year.

Prices may change – check with hotel.

BRUTON Somerset

THE NEWT IN SOMERSET

The buzz caused when Palladian Hadspen manor house opened its doors in 2019 shows no signs of abating; despite high prices, it's hard to get a room without booking months ahead. They come for the gardens created by former owner Penelope Hobhouse, for the cyder bar, apple maze, working farm and interactive experiences in the extensive grounds, and for interiors which mix grand architecture and antiques with designer furniture and witty touches. A dreamy spa has an indoor/outdoor pool. Owners Koos Bekker and Karen Roos have developed The Newt with the same idyllic vision as they brought to Babylonstoren, their hotel on a Dutch Cape wine estate. Some rooms have a four-poster, a huge bathroom with freestanding roll-top bath. Those in converted stables have a more rustic, sometimes playful style, perhaps with heritage stalls and a wood-burner. Some Farmyard rooms, about half a mile away, come with personal steam pods. They have access to an all-day kitchen, or you can borrow a bike to ride over to Hadspen. Here, in the Botanical Rooms, farm-to-fork menus feature estate vegetables, fish from the Dorset coast and cuts from the salt room.

Bruton
Castle Cary BA7 7NG

T: 01963 577777
E: reservations@thenewtinsomerset.com
W: thenewtinsomerset.com

BEDROOMS: 40. 10 in converted outbuildings, 17 in Farmyard, 3 suitable for disabled.
OPEN: all year.
FACILITIES: restaurant, bar, lounge, drawing room, library, lift (main house), bar, snug, kitchen, vitality pool (Farmyard buildings), in-room TV (Sky), spa (hydrotherapy pools, swimming pool), 800-acre estate (parkland, orchards, café, cyder bar, farm shop, museum), EV charging, restaurant and bar wheelchair accessible, adapted toilet.
BACKGROUND MUSIC: in public rooms.
LOCATION: on the A359 between Castle Cary and Bruton.
CHILDREN: all ages welcomed, family rooms.
DOGS: not allowed.
CREDIT CARDS: Amex, MC, Visa.
PRICES: B&B doubles from £495. À la carte £75, tasting menu £95.

Prices may change – check with hotel.

BRUTON Somerset

MAP 2:D1

NUMBER ONE BRUTON

With its bright yellow front door and rhubarb-pink sitting room, this Georgian town house with cottages, forge and low-key Michelin-starred dining is stylish but unstuffy. Aled and Claudia Rees have created 'chic interiors' that 'blend the past beautifully with the present', says a Guide insider: original fireplaces and wooden floors complement the fashion photography and striped furnishings. Main house bedrooms have Georgian-coloured walls, artistic wallpapers and vintage furniture. Overlooking the courtyard garden, Cottage rooms – two with log-burner – and Forge rooms are more rustic, with exposed beams and stonework. All have original art and treats of local Cheddar and crackers, 'just one of the nice details'. Bathrooms are bold, some with hand-painted tiles, others with freestanding baths. Expect 'tasty and unusual dishes' in Merlin Labron-Johnson's Michelin-starred restaurant Osip, which is partnered with the hotel. They might feature smoky duck with beetroots and elderberry, and ewes' milk pudding with rhubarb. Breakfast has just boiled eggs as the cooked option, but it's a fine spread with ham, cheese, rice pudding and home-made brioche.

1 High Street
Bruton BA10 0AB

T: 01749 813030
E: stay@numberonebruton.com
W: numberonebruton.com

BEDROOMS: 12. 4 in forge, 3 in cottages, 1 ground-floor room suitable for wheelchair, bathroom not adapted.
OPEN: all year, restaurant closed Mon–Wed.
FACILITIES: sitting room (honesty bar), restaurant, in-room TV, ¼-acre courtyard garden, free parking in nearby car park, EV charging.
BACKGROUND MUSIC: none.
LOCATION: at one end of the High Street.
CHILDREN: all ages welcomed, extra bed £25, cot free.
DOGS: allowed in cottage rooms (£20 a night, welcome pack), in restaurant at breakfast, not lunch/dinner.
CREDIT CARDS: Amex, MC, Visa.
PRICES: B&B doubles from £150. Taster menu 6-course £85, 9-course £110. Min. 2-night stay preferred at weekends.

Prices may change – check with hotel.

BRYHER Isles of Scilly

MAP 1: inset C1

HELL BAY HOTEL

Sitting above a secluded cove on Bryher's rugged west-facing coast, with 'nothing in between to Canada', this pretty blue-and-white weatherboarded farmhouse-turned-hotel is a '10/10 experience', say smitten guests. 'Very comfortably appointed' rooms are spread between several similarly weatherboarded buildings. All share a light and breezy New England style of ocean blues and sandy hues, Lloyd Loom furniture and floor-to-ceiling windows. Most have sea views, some have balconies, others a patio, all have bold Cornish seascapes. The 'inventive but not fussy' food on the short-choice, daily-changing menu focuses on local and Cornish products and could include gin-cured salmon followed by John Dory with potato, carrot and samphire fricassée. Chef Richard Kearsley's lemon meringue pie is always popular. Or you can eat more casually in the bar – perhaps home-made burger, or bouillabaisse. In the summer, get messy on fresh crab, scallops and mussels in the rustic crab shack. Evenings are for a sundowner on the well-named Sunset Deck. Throughout, staff are 'delightful and efficient and happy'. (David and Katherine Soanes)

Bryher TR23 0PR

T: 01720 422947
E: contactus@hellbay.co.uk
W: hellbay.co.uk

BEDROOMS: 25. In 5 buildings, some on ground floor, 1 suitable for disabled.
OPEN: 10 Mar–27 Oct 2023.
FACILITIES: lounge, games room, bar, dining rooms, in-room TV, gym, treatment shed, yoga studio, grounds (heated pool), public rooms wheelchair accessible, adapted toilet.
BACKGROUND MUSIC: in the bar.
LOCATION: W side of island, boat from St Mary's (reached by boat/plane from mainland).
CHILDREN: all ages welcomed, free cots, under-17s £40, £60 incl. dinner.
DOGS: allowed in ground-floor rooms (max. 2, £15 per night, welcome pack), bar, not in restaurant.
CREDIT CARDS: Amex, MC, Visa.
PRICES: B&B doubles from £210, singles from £136. Set dinner £58. Min. 2-night stay at weekends.

Prices may change – check with hotel.

BUCKLAND MARSH Oxfordshire

MAP 2:C2

THE TROUT AT TADPOLE BRIDGE

The gardens run down to the Thames with free moorings for guests at this gastropub-with-rooms in the Vale of the White Horse, a former toll house for the eponymous 18th-century stone bridge. It is an oasis for walkers on the Thames Path, and a great place to hang your hat. 'We were impressed with the hands-on management, friendly and efficient staff and exceptional food,' wrote Guide insiders. The bedrooms are spruce, with a muted palette, vintage and contemporary furniture, a double or king-size bed, a rain shower or claw-footed bath, cruelty-free bath products. 'We had one of three in a covered garden courtyard' with a 'compact but well-equipped bathroom'. The food is a mix of hearty pub grub and creative dishes such as roasted River Test trout fillet, mussels, white wine and cream chowder, sea beets. 'My starter was the stand-out dish, a deep-fried egg, yellow and runny in the middle, with earthy field mushrooms and cavalo nero. Scrumptious.' 'Portions were just right.' At breakfast there is 'a full range of cooked dishes'. Fly-fishers, bring your tackle and you might catch a trout of your own in one of the local chalk streams.

Buckland Road
Buckland Marsh SN7 8RF

T: 01367 870382
E: info@troutinn.co.uk
W: troutinn.co.uk

BEDROOMS: 6. 3 in courtyard garden.
OPEN: all year, closed for dinner on Sun.
FACILITIES: bar, dining area, breakfast area, private dining room, in-room TV (Freeview), civil wedding licence, 2-acre garden (pagoda, river, moorings), public areas wheelchair accessible, adapted toilet.
BACKGROUND MUSIC: in all public areas.
LOCATION: off the A420, 15 miles SW of Oxford.
CHILDREN: all ages welcomed, free cots, extra bed £15, children's menu.
DOGS: allowed in 4 bedrooms (£15 a night) and public areas.
CREDIT CARDS: MC, Visa.
PRICES: B&B doubles from £130. À la carte £33. 1-night bookings refused Sat.

Prices may change – check with hotel.

BUCKNELL Shropshire

MAP 3:C4

THE BARON AT BUCKNELL `NEW`

Debra and Phil Wright's village pub-with-rooms on the Welsh borders 'puts to shame places that charge twice as much', writes a regular Guide reader. A former Georgian farmhouse with hefty beams, millstones and a cider press, it mixes and matches rusticity with contemporary comforts. Four beamed rooms have 'calm, neutral colours, natural wood and stone', tub chairs, a walk-in or over-bath shower; a superior room has French doors to a balcony, a spa bath and separate shower. Thoughtful extras include 'fresh coffee, home-made shortbread, mini-choc bars'. Four adults-only garden suites have a sofa by a log-effect fire, an espresso machine and minibar, a wet-room shower, a wall of glass on to decking with a hot tub and a natural swimming pond for a morning dip. The menu runs from classics to dishes such as lamb shoulder, pistachio and herb crumb, redcurrant sauce; good plant-based options. 'The jungle curry (veg or chicken) with sticky-rice cakes and crispy salad were nice and spicy, full of fresh veg.' Breakfast brings a full Shropshire with local free-range eggs, or 'an interesting vegetarian choice'. (Jill Cox)

Chapel Lawn Road
Bucknell
Knighton SY7 0AH

T: 01547 530549
E: enquiry@baronatbucknell.co.uk
W: baronatbucknell.co.uk

BEDROOMS: 8. 3 in garden annexe with decking and hot tub, 1 suitable for wheelchair.
OPEN: all year, restaurant closed Sun dinner.
FACILITIES: lounge, restaurant, conservatory, bar, in-room TV (Freeview), beer garden, swimming pond for use of Garden Room guests, public areas wheelchair accessible, ramp to restaurant, adapted toilet.
BACKGROUND MUSIC: 'easy listening'.
LOCATION: 13 miles from Ludlow, 7 mins' walk from Bucknell railway station.
CHILDREN: children welcomed in 2 inn rooms, on Z-beds, not in Garden Rooms, children's menu.
DOGS: allowed in bar, beer garden (water bowls), on a lead, not in bedrooms.
CREDIT CARDS: MC, Visa.
PRICES: B&B doubles from £125, singles from £110. À la carte £32.

Prices may change – check with hotel.

BUDE Cornwall

MAP 1:C3

THE BEACH

The old, pointy-gabled Victorian Summerleaze Court Hotel hardly knows itself these days, with its cool New England style and sunny terrace above a sandy surfers' beach. 'I could not fault the warm and helpful welcome, and the lovely situation,' wrote a reader this year. The bedrooms, though they vary in size and outlook, all have a king- or super-king-size bed, soft-hued decor, limed oak furniture, Lloyd Loom chairs, 'splendid baths and showers'. One is on the ground floor; a lift serves the first and second floors. Rear-facing rooms have walk-in or over-bath showers. Superior sea-facing rooms have a Juliet balcony, while deluxe rooms have a private terrace or are extra-spacious. Be selective when you book. 'Excellent accommodation' but 'my room was great on space but had no view, so could have been anywhere', continues our reader, who found the general vibe 'a little impersonal' and the cooked breakfast disappointing. Things have changed, however, with the bar and restaurant now run by Elements, with people-pleasing, Italian-inspired menus. Bude's 1930s tidal pool offers warm, safe bathing if you're daunted by the mighty Atlantic.

Summerleaze Crescent
Bude EX23 8HJ

T: 01288 389800
E: enquiries@thebeachatbude.co.uk
W: thebeachatbude.co.uk

BEDROOMS: 18. 1 on ground floor, 2 family suites.
OPEN: all year.
FACILITIES: lift, bar, lounge area, restaurant, in-room TV (Freeview), terraces, ground floor wheelchair accessible, adapted toilet.
BACKGROUND MUSIC: all day in public areas.
LOCATION: above Summerleaze beach.
CHILDREN: all ages welcomed, extra bed £30–£50, children's menu.
DOGS: allowed in 2 dog-friendly suites only (£30 a night), not in public areas except the terrace.
CREDIT CARDS: Amex, MC, Visa.
PRICES: B&B doubles from £145, suites for 4 from £175. À la carte £30.

Prices may change – check with hotel.

BURFORD Oxfordshire   MAP 3:D6

THE LAMB INN

In a picturesque Cotswold town, an 18th-century
inn contrived from a row of 15th-century weavers'
cottages has been gently shepherded into the 21st
century. Part of Fuller's Cotswold Inns & Hotels
group – see The Hare and Hounds, Tetbury
(main entry); The Swan, Bibury, and Bay Tree
Hotel, Burford (both in the Shortlist) – it has a
perfect, olde worlde locals bar and comfy lounges
with log fires by which to tuck into a Devonshire
cream tea. A reader enjoyed the 'very pleasant and
relaxing atmosphere'. Bedrooms are a pleasing
mix of original features and contemporary
furnishings and come with nice touches including
an espresso machine and home-made flapjacks.
One classic double has a carved half-tester bed,
while 'Rosie', with its own front door, has a
private garden. For a family, it can be paired with
pretty 'Allium' room above, from which three
steps lead up to a spacious bathroom with a wall-
mounted TV which you can watch while steeping
in the roll-top bath. Eat in the candlelit dining
room or outside, in the flower-filled garden,
choosing from a menu that features 'catch of the
day' alongside dishes such as côte de boeuf with
triple-cooked chips, or aged Parmesan gnocchi.

Sheep Street
Burford OX18 4LR

T: 01993 823155
E: lamb@cotswold-inns-hotels.co.uk
W: cotswold-inns-hotels.co.uk

BEDROOMS: 17. 1 with private garden,
1 on ground floor.
OPEN: all year.
FACILITIES: 3 lounges, bar, restaurant,
in-room TV (Freeview), courtyard,
½-acre walled garden.
BACKGROUND MUSIC: subtle in all public
areas.
LOCATION: 500 yds from High Street.
CHILDREN: all ages welcomed, extra
bed £20.
DOGS: allowed by prior arrangement
in some bedrooms (£20 per night for
one, £10 for each additional dog), bar,
lounges, garden, not in restaurant.
CREDIT CARDS: Amex, MC, Visa.
PRICES: B&B doubles from £175, singles
from £165. À la carte £40.

Prices may change – check with hotel.

SEE ALSO SHORTLIST

BURTON BRADSTOCK Dorset

MAP 1:D6

THE SEASIDE BOARDING HOUSE

A playful mix of Edward Hopper's Cape Cod and Edwardian seaside hotel, this white-painted villa above Chesil Beach has an easy-going stylishness, conducive to fun. 'We arrived at dusk,' writes a reader, 'sat outside to view the spectacular sunset, and were brought pots of tea and blankets. Coming in, we had a jolly time in the bar.' Owners Mary-Lou Sturridge and Tony Mackintosh, who created London's Groucho Club, have filled the cool, stripped-down interiors with marine salvage, seascapes, Peter Blake prints and antique-shop booty. 'Bright, light, seaside-y rooms' all have some view of the coast, a retro dial phone and radio, a walk-in shower or claw-footed bath. 'Ours had a superb large bed, a bathroom on the floor below with a private internal staircase.' In the restaurant and on the terrace, with views over Lyme Bay, short, appealing menus might include John Dory, charred lemon, herb butter or perhaps lamb rack with spiced lentils. What our heroic reader ate after leaving the bar is lost to memory, but it was 'excellent', he recalls. 'Charming staff. We would stay again.' (John Barnes, and others)

Cliff Road
Burton Bradstock DT6 4RB

T: 01308 897205
E: info@theseasideboardinghouse.com
W: theseasideboardinghouse.com

BEDROOMS: 9.
OPEN: all year. Restaurant closed to non-residents Mon and Tues.
FACILITIES: cocktail bar, restaurant, library, function facilities, in-room TV on request, civil wedding licence, terrace, lawn, parking, EV charging, restaurant and bar wheelchair accessible, adapted toilet.
BACKGROUND MUSIC: classical music in bar.
LOCATION: ½ mile from village centre, 3½ miles SE of Bridport.
CHILDREN: all ages welcomed, extra bed £30.
DOGS: allowed in some bedrooms (no charge unless extra cleaning needed), bar, library, terrace, not in restaurant.
CREDIT CARDS: Amex, MC, Visa.
PRICES: B&B doubles from £245, singles from £225. À la carte £45. 1-night bookings refused Sat.

Prices may change – check with hotel.

BUXTON Derbyshire

MAP 4:E3

THE ROSELEIGH

Readers on their annual visit to the Buxton
Festival assure us that all is as good as ever at
Maggi and Gerard Heelan's Victorian B&B. It is
perfectly situated, overlooking the lake in Joseph
(Crystal Place) Paxton's Pavilion Gardens, five
minutes' walk from the Opera House, in this
splendid Peak District spa town. The bedrooms
vary in size but are similar in style, with a
feeling of solid good quality, heavy floral drapes,
patterned blue or red fitted hotel-style carpet,
soft-hued decor, traditional furniture. All have an
en suite bathroom, except one single with separate
private facilities. Dual-aspect Room 4, with lake
view, is a good choice. A crimson-walled guest
lounge overlooking the lake has comfy seating,
exotic ornaments, shelves of travel books (the
Heelans, former adventure tour guides, are a
fount of local knowledge). 'The owners cannot
do enough for you,' say other readers. A 'lovely
breakfast' brings grapefruit segments, pear
halves or prunes, croissants, porridge, cheeses, a
full English or vegetarian, free-range eggs with
smoked salmon. 'We have booked again for next
year.' (Stephen and Pauline Glover, and others)

19 Broad Walk
Buxton SK17 6JR

T: 01298 24904
E: enquiries@roseleighhotel.co.uk
W: roseleighhotel.co.uk

BEDROOMS: 13. 1 on ground floor,
1 single with private bathroom (not
en suite).
OPEN: 27 Jan–1 Dec.
FACILITIES: lounge (computer for
guests' use), breakfast room, in-room
TV (Freeview), parking, unsuitable
for disabled.
BACKGROUND MUSIC: classical baroque
in breakfast room.
LOCATION: central.
CHILDREN: not under 6, no additional
beds.
DOGS: not allowed.
CREDIT CARDS: MC, Visa.
PRICES: B&B doubles from £110, singles
from £75. 1-night bookings usually
refused weekends, bank holidays (call
to check).

Prices may change – check with hotel.

CAMBER Sussex

MAP 2:E5

THE GALLIVANT

The name says it all: a place to skip along Camber Sands, enjoy backgammon in the bar, chill in the garden or relax with yoga – and with no children to disturb the peace. This beachside property has a chic, laid-back vibe with slouchy sofas, stripped-wood floors and designer rugs. Books line walls; there's a fire in the snug; English wines are on the menu at the copper-topped bar. Superb monthly changing dinners reflect the locale: perhaps Rye Bay scallops followed by wood-grilled duck with Kent rhubarb. There are delicious vegetarian dishes, too. Bedrooms are all on the ground floor and most have a terrace and direct access to the garden. Decorated in soothing or nautical shades, with wood panelling, white-painted rafters and jazzy headboards, they have a breezy New England feel. The largest have freestanding baths; all have robes and books. 'All-day' elevenses and drinks at 5 pm are free; the Complete package also includes dinner and wellness classes. Breakfast on dishes such as Turkish poached eggs and sausage with tomato marmalade before heading over the dunes to the empty beach. 'A very welcoming hotel with great staff.'

New Lydd Road
Camber TN31 7RB

T: 01797 225057
E: enquiries@thegallivant.co.uk
W: thegallivant.co.uk

BEDROOMS: 20. All on ground floor, 15 with access to garden.
OPEN: all year.
FACILITIES: bar, sitting room, reading room, restaurant (vegetarian menu), private dining room, in-room TV, civil wedding licence, function facilities, spa treatment room, terrace, 1-acre garden, car park, EV charging, restaurant and bar wheelchair accessible.
BACKGROUND MUSIC: in bar and restaurant.
LOCATION: 3¾ miles SE of Rye.
CHILDREN: not under 16.
DOGS: small to medium-sized allowed in some bedrooms (£25–£35 per stay), sitting room, bar, terrace.
CREDIT CARDS: MC, Visa.
PRICES: B&B doubles (Essentials) from £257, The Complete Gallivant from £389. À la carte £50. Min. 2-night stay usually at weekends.

Prices may change – check with hotel.

CAMBRIDGE Cambridgeshire

MAP 2:B4

DUKE HOUSE

Tucked away in the city centre, within minutes
of its historic colleges, this boutique B&B bolt-
hole has a modern elegance in keeping with the
house's Victorian age, plus a pretty courtyard.
Near Christ's Pieces, one of the city's oldest
green spaces, the house was briefly owned by the
Duke of Gloucester in the 1960s when he was an
architecture student, hence the name. Liz and Rob
Cameron have retained the Victorian features –
fireplaces, ceiling roses – but given rooms a light,
modern touch. The sitting room, where guests
help themselves to tea, coffee and cakes, is large
and light-filled with sofas, fresh flowers and
books. Chic bedrooms are individually styled in
pale colours, perhaps with a feature wallpaper
or original fireplace; one has a balcony, and all
have large bathrooms. Breakfasts, served on
fine china in a room overlooking the courtyard,
are commendably locally sourced with seasonal
fruits in the compote; breads and granola from
an artisan bakery; eggs and tomatoes from the
market, and award-winning sausages from nearby
Ware. For dinner, our readers highly recommend
the nearby Clarendon Arms.

1 Victoria Street
Cambridge CB1 1JP

T: 01223 314773
E: info@dukehousecambridge.co.uk
W: dukehousecambridge.co.uk

BEDROOMS: 5. 1 in adjacent cottage,
plus self-catering apartment.
OPEN: all year except Christmas and
New Year.
FACILITIES: sitting room, breakfast
room with courtyard, balcony, in-
room TV (Freeview), limited parking
(by arrangement), unsuitable for
disabled.
BACKGROUND MUSIC: during breakfast.
LOCATION: city centre.
CHILDREN: babies and over-10s
welcomed, free cot, extra bed from
£20.
DOGS: not allowed.
CREDIT CARDS: MC, Visa.
PRICES: B&B doubles from £150, singles
from £140. 1-night bookings refused
at weekends.

Prices may change – check with hotel.

SEE ALSO SHORTLIST

CAMBRIDGE Cambridgeshire

MAP 2:B4

UNIVERSITY ARMS

Town meets gown at this splendid city hotel, a revamped 19th-century coaching inn, which reopened in 2018 after an £80 million make-over. Behind a grand new portico, interiors are a joyous celebration of Cambridge, 'from corridor carpets striped like the university tie, to Cambridge-blue walls'. A wood-panelled library has works by famous alumni, some of whom lend their names to suites, which have views over Parker's Piece. Bedrooms have 'herringbone carpets, striped fabric headboards and velvet chairs, old-fashioned reading lamps, blackout curtains'. 'The staff, especially the welcome desk, were very helpful,' writes a reader of this 'characterful hotel' although 'one chair only in a bedroom is unacceptable'. In Parker's Tavern, Tristan Welch's signature English menu mixes retro classics such as spaghetti bolognese, fish and chips, steaks and burgers, with more imaginative choices. 'A British sashimi starter is superb.' And mid-afternoon, when it's time for a little something, how about a Winnie-the-Pooh-inspired tea? 'One of the best city hotels we have stayed in,' concludes a Guide insider. (Alice and John Sennett, and others)

Regent Street
Cambridge CB2 1AD

T: 01223 606066
E: enquiries@universityarms.com
W: universityarms.com

BEDROOMS: 192. 10 suitable for disabled.
OPEN: all year.
FACILITIES: library, bar/bistro, ballroom, meeting rooms, fitness centre, in-room TV, civil wedding licence, bicycles, limited guest parking, EV charging, public areas wheelchair accessible, adapted toilet.
BACKGROUND MUSIC: in bar and restaurant.
LOCATION: city centre.
CHILDREN: all ages welcomed, cots free, extra bed £50, children's menu, interconnecting rooms.
DOGS: only assistance dogs allowed.
CREDIT CARDS: Amex, MC, Visa.
PRICES: B&B doubles from £224 (member's rate £191). À la carte £50.

Prices may change – check with hotel.

SEE ALSO SHORTLIST

CAMELFORD Cornwall

PENDRAGON COUNTRY HOUSE

While we await the return of the once and future king, King Arthur is very much a presence at Sharon and Nigel Reed's Victorian former rectory, which they run as a hugely popular B&B. A suit of armour stands sentinel in the hall. There is a sense of space and largesse throughout. Every year, readers sing their praises. 'Nigel and Sharon provide five-star customer service, wonderful breakfasts and evening meals.' Rooms are 'luxurious and comfortable', with 'added touches such as home-made biscuits'. Dual-aspect Lamorak has a four-poster (king-size, naturally), views to Dartmoor and Bodmin Moor, while Kay has a single four-poster for a one-knight stay. Ground-floor, dog-friendly Pelleas has a wet room. Guests gather convivially for drinks before a dinner of local produce in the orangery or dining room. 'When 14 people are served a three-course meal and every plate is returned to the kitchen without a scrap left on it, that tells you all you need to know!' At breakfast there's fresh-baked bread, a full Cornish, locally smoked kipper, free-range eggs, Pendragon rarebit with Davidstow Cheddar. (Jane Knapp, Sally Crowley, Sandra Hart)

Old Vicarage Hill
Davidstow
Camelford PL32 9XR

T: 01840 261131
E: enquiries@
   pendragoncountryhouse.com
W: pendragoncountryhouse.com

BEDROOMS: 7. 1, on ground floor, suitable for disabled.
OPEN: all year except Christmas, restaurant closed Sun eve.
FACILITIES: sitting room, lounge, dining room, games room, in-room TV (Freeview), 1¾-acre grounds, EV charging, some public areas wheelchair accessible, adapted toilet.
BACKGROUND MUSIC: none.
LOCATION: 3½ miles NE of Camelford.
CHILDREN: all ages welcomed, under-2s £20 one-off charge for cot, extra bed 3–15s £25 per night.
DOGS: allowed in ground-floor bedroom (£5 charge), lounge but not restaurant, except guide dogs.
CREDIT CARDS: Amex, MC, Visa.
PRICES: B&B doubles from £110, singles from £80. Set menu £38 (£32 for half board). 2-night min. stay (check for odd 1-night availability)

Prices may change – check with hotel.

CANNINGTON Somerset

MAP 1:B5

BLACKMORE FARM

In springtime, wisteria cascades around the door of this 15th-century red sandstone manor house B&B on the Dyer family's dairy farm. The West Bedroom, with views to the Quantock hills, has an antique oak four-poster, an en suite shower room. The panelled Gallery room has stairs to a bathroom and sitting room. Readers praise hosts Ian and Ann Dyer for 'ensuring a lovely real log fire was lit to keep us warm'. If you are staying a while, rustic open-plan suites in the Wagon House have a kettle, microwave and toaster, while the two-bedroom Cider Press has a fully equipped kitchen, including an Aga, a cruck-beamed sitting and dining room, a patio and small garden. A historic farmhouse breakfast is served at a 20-foot oak table by a cavernous fireplace in the Great Hall, the walls hung with breastplates, pikes and halberds. The café is open from breakfast through to teatime, with barista coffees, home-baked cakes, Sunday roasts, maybe boeuf bourguignon, Brixham fish pie, to eat alfresco or in a 'stable' hut with a heater to keep you snug come rain or shine.

Blackmore Lane
Cannington TA5 2NE

T: 01278 653442
E: dyerfarm@aol.com
W: blackmorefarm.co.uk

BEDROOMS: 14. 10 in annexes, with 6 on ground floor, 1 in shepherd's hut in grounds, 1 suitable for disabled.
OPEN: all year.
FACILITIES: lounge/TV room, Great Hall/breakfast room, in-room TV (Freeview), 4-acre garden (stream, coarse fishing), children's play area, farm shop/café, lounge and dining room wheelchair accessible.
BACKGROUND MUSIC: none.
LOCATION: 3 miles W of Bridgwater.
CHILDREN: all ages welcomed, ages 2–12 £10 to share parents' room.
DOGS: allowed in some bedrooms (£10 per stay), not in public rooms.
CREDIT CARDS: MC, Visa.
PRICES: B&B doubles from £120, singles from £80, shepherd's hut £75 per person. 1-night bookings refused at bank holiday weekends.

Prices may change – check with hotel.

CANTERBURY Kent

MAP 2:D5

THE PIG AT BRIDGE PLACE

A short hop from Canterbury, a Grade I listed Jacobean mansion and former music venue that once hosted rock legends such as The Kinks was the sixth addition to Robin Hutson's Pig collection (see index). Styled by Judy Hutson, it is wildly atmospheric with 'lots of gorgeous snug areas'. A panelled lounge in deep purple has a carved-oak fireplace, gilt-framed portraits, squashy sofas by a wood-burner. Spread over the main house, coach house and converted barn, rooms all have their own quirks and delights. A reader loved their 'luxurious and comfortable suite' and 'fantastic bathroom with a walk-in shower and large roll-top bath'. Another noted that 'even tiny No. 4 manages to fit in an impressive oak four-poster'. Hop-pickers' huts stand on stilts in the water meadow. Menus are created around the bounty of the walled kitchen garden, with produce from the Garden of England and the Kent coast. Imagine Dungeness cod, Northern Light leek and lobster sauce or chargrilled pork chop with garden greens. Pick from 'fabulous locally produced wine, beer, gin and cider' for a tipple to go with the 'most amazing flatbreads' served in the garden.

Bourne Park Road
Bridge
Canterbury CT4 5BH

T: 0345 225 9494
E: reservations@thepighotel.com
W: thepighotel.com

BEDROOMS: 29. 7 in main house, 12 in coach house, 4 on ground floor, 2 suitable for disabled, 2 family-friendly lodges, converted barn, 7 hop-pickers' huts.
OPEN: all year.
FACILITIES: restaurant, bar/lounge, snugs, study, 2 treatment rooms, gardens, terrace, EV charging, wheelchair access to garden, gravel tracks round the property.
BACKGROUND MUSIC: in public areas.
LOCATION: on edge of village, 3 miles S of Canterbury.
CHILDREN: all ages welcomed, no charge for extra beds.
DOGS: not allowed.
CREDIT CARDS: Amex, MC, Visa.
PRICES: room-only doubles from £195, singles/small doubles from £155. Breakfast £13.50–£18.50, à la carte £42. 2-night bookings only at weekends.

Prices may change – check with hotel.

CARTMEL Cumbria

MAP 4: inset C2

AYNSOME MANOR

Step back in time to an age of quiet elegance at this 400-year-old manor house with views over farmland to pretty Cartmel village and its Norman priory church. Indeed, the house was once the home of descendants of the founder of the priory, William Marshal, Earl of Pembroke. Run by the Varley family for over 40 years, the hotel is reassuringly traditional with deep sofas and glowing table lamps in fire-warmed lounges, and a polished sideboard and cut-glass crystal in the panelled Georgian dining room. A daily-changing table d'hôte dinner offers classic dishes with a sophisticated touch such as chicken liver parfait with sherry, and roast Cumbrian sirloin with red onion marmalade and Burgundy wine jus. Diners appreciate the option of two to five courses. Spacious bedrooms are pleasant with patterned wallpapers, modern oak furniture and brightly coloured bedcovers. Second-floor rooms have beams and a sloping ceiling. Breakfast is a fine affair, from poached fruits and creamy porridge to Cartmel Valley smoked haddock and a grill including Cumberland sausage and fried bread – a handsome start for exploring this quiet part of the Lakes.

Aynsome Lane
Cartmel
Grange-over-Sands LA11 6HH

T: 01539 536653
E: aynsomemanor@btconnect.com
W: aynsomemanorhotel.co.uk

BEDROOMS: 12. 2 in cottage across courtyard.
OPEN: all year except 23–27 Dec, 2–26 Jan.
FACILITIES: 2 lounges, bar, dining room, in-room TV (Freeview), ½-acre garden, unsuitable for disabled.
BACKGROUND MUSIC: none.
LOCATION: ¾ mile N of village.
CHILDREN: all ages welcomed, extra bed for under-15s £30, no under-5s in dining room in evening, children's supper available.
DOGS: in bedrooms only and must not be unattended (£7 per night).
CREDIT CARDS: Amex, MC, Visa.
PRICES: B&B doubles from £105. Set dinner £25–£40. 2-night min. usually required but ring to check, race weekends premium prices.

Prices may change – check with hotel.

CASTLE ASHBY Northamptonshire   MAP 2:B3

THE FALCON

Well-being is at the heart of this 'rather lovely boutique hotel', a reinvented 16th-century coaching inn, where guests enjoy nature walks, yoga and the run of Castle Ashby's pleasure grounds. Lord and Lady Northampton ('Spenny and Tracy') have 'lavished attention on it to reflect their core values and interests'. The interiors have earthy, mossy tones designed to connect with the surrounding countryside. Some bedrooms have a balcony, some interconnect for a family, all have an espresso machine and organic toiletries. 'This is a lovely hotel, with excellent staff,' wrote readers this year, though they blenched as the prices mounted. In Eyas, Russell Bateman's ethically sourced tasting menu might feature spring truffles, Orkney scallops, Herdwick lamb. You can eat more casually from a lounge menu, say bavette steak with peppercorn sauce, hand-rolled pasta, a Caesar salad. 'Wild swimming in a lake designed by Capability Brown gives you amazing glimpses of Castle Ashby itself', while the Italian gardens, orangery, arboretum and menagerie await exploration. (John and Elspeth Gibbon, JK)

Castle Ashby
Northampton NN7 1LF

T: 01604 698005
E: reception@thefalcon-castleashby.com
W: thefalcon-castleashby.com

BEDROOMS: 21. 13 in adjacent cottages, 1 suitable for disabled.
OPEN: all year, restaurant closed Mon, Tues.
FACILITIES: reception, lounge, restaurant, cellar bar, yoga studio, juice bar (vegan menu), in-room TV, civil wedding licence, EV charging, private gardens in 10,500-acre Castle Ashby Estate, public areas wheelchair accessible, adapted toilet.
BACKGROUND MUSIC: ambient, in public spaces.
LOCATION: 9 miles E of Northampton.
CHILDREN: all ages welcomed, family suite, baby baths, cots.
DOGS: allowed in some bedrooms (£25 per night), on terraces, not in public rooms.
CREDIT CARDS: Amex, MC, Visa.
PRICES: B&B doubles from £162. Lounge menu (à la carte) £38, tasting menu (Eyas) £75.

Prices may change – check with hotel.

CHADDESLEY CORBETT Worcestershire

MAP 3:C5

BROCKENCOTE HALL

As you drive through landscaped parkland to find this country house hotel overlooking a lake and 17th-century dovecote, you might wonder if you have arrived in the Loire valley. The Victorian mansion, remodelled in château style, is part of the Eden Hotel Collection (see also Mallory Court, Leamington Spa). Public rooms have original maple and pine woodwork and period furniture. Bedrooms range from contemporary classics to stunning feature suites. New this year is the converted Gate Lodge, with three double rooms, private dining and outdoor hot tub. (Friends and families can book it for themselves.) All rooms have home-made biscuits, fruit, savouries, luxury toiletries. 'Really excellent in all respects,' writes a reader. 'Our bedroom was a very good size with a huge, well-laid-out bathroom.' You can dine from a lounge menu or in the restaurant on dishes such as pan-roasted venison loin with cheek brandade, shank croquette, red cabbage and garden beetroot. 'Dinner a delight, with the nice touches of an amuse-bouche and a pre-dessert.' Breakfasts are equally impressive. 'I had bacon, eggs and mushrooms – the best I have eaten in many years.' (Ian Dewey)

Chaddesley Corbett DY10 4PY

T: 01562 777876
E: info@brockencotehall.com
W: brockencotehall.com

BEDROOMS: 24. 3 in The Lodge, some on ground floor, 1 suitable for disabled.
OPEN: all year.
FACILITIES: lift, hall, lounge, conservatory, bar, library, restaurant, function facilities, in-room TV (Freeview), civil wedding licence, 72-acre grounds (fishing, croquet, tennis), helipad, public rooms wheelchair accessible, adapted toilet.
BACKGROUND MUSIC: all day in public areas.
LOCATION: 3 miles SE of Kidderminster.
CHILDREN: all ages welcomed, extra bed for under-13s £25.
DOGS: allowed in some bedrooms (£25 per night), garden and bar.
CREDIT CARDS: Amex, MC, Visa.
PRICES: B&B doubles from £120. À la carte £42.95–£54.95 (2/3 courses), tasting menu (whole table) £79.

Prices may change – check with hotel.

CHETTLE Dorset

MAP 2:E1

CASTLEMAN

In a perfect estate village in the foothills of Cranborne Chase, this hotel and restaurant occupies the dower home of Chettle House, a magnificent baroque building. Owners Niki and Jez Barfoot 'have made a fantastic job of creating a comfortable and welcoming country hotel' while preserving the house's eccentric charm. Fires burn in two 'beautifully furnished' drawing rooms, one with ornate Jacobean carved oak. Each bedroom has its own character. Room 3, with antique four-poster, 'decorated in deep, warm burgundy', was 'spotless, with fresh coffee and a cafetière, a torrential rainfall shower over a deep, claw-footed bath'. Chef Liam Boxall's creative dishes are inspired by home-grown ingredients. Maybe black-garlic-stuffed chicken Kiev with crushed potatoes, broccoli and walnuts; or for vegans, roasted carrots with red lentil dhal, toasted seeds and carrot-top salsa. 'We really enjoyed all three courses, and the home-made rolls with butter, oil and balsamic vinegar.' At breakfast there was 'fresh and beautiful orange juice, a perfect poached egg'. Service is friendly and efficient. 'We have another favourite hotel!' (Jill Cox) NOTE: As the Guide went to press, Castleman announced that it was ceasing to trade as a hotel.

Chettle
Blandford Forum DT11 8DB

T: 01258 830096
E: enquiry@castlemanhotel.co.uk
W: castlemanhotel.co.uk

BEDROOMS: 8. 1 family room.
OPEN: all year, except 25/26 Dec, 31 Dec/1 Jan, lunch on Sun only.
FACILITIES: lounge, snug, bar, restaurant, in-room TV (Freeview), 2-acre grounds (stables for visiting horses), riding, fishing, shooting, cycling nearby, public rooms wheelchair accessible, adapted toilet.
BACKGROUND MUSIC: low-level at dinner, 'matched to the feel of the evening'.
LOCATION: village, 1 mile off A354 Salisbury–Blandford.
CHILDREN: all ages welcomed, cots, extra bed £20.
DOGS: allowed in 3 bedrooms and 1 dining room (£20 a stay).
CREDIT CARDS: Amex, MC, Visa.
PRICES: B&B doubles from £120, singles from £110. À la carte £40, supper Mon–Wed from £20.

Prices may change – check with hotel.

CHILLINGHAM Northumberland

MAP 4:A3

CHILLINGHAM MANOR `NEW`

This light-flooded Georgian manor house, between Northumberland's beaches and hills, feels like a private country retreat – but with fabulous, leisurely breakfasts thrown in. 'A jewel of a place to stay,' says a reader who returned for a second visit. Owners Mhairi and Ed Seymour 'go out of their way to make guests feel at home'; they will even lend you their dogs for walks. Three spacious bedrooms are elegant and pretty, and boast 'super comfortable' beds, armchairs and well-chosen antiques. Spoiling touches include a carafe of whisky and a coffee machine. The large bathrooms have bathrobes and 'capacious' cast iron baths; two have a separate shower. Two sitting rooms, with books, wood-burner and sofas, overlook gardens through floor-to-ceiling windows, while the front garden is a suntrap for evening drinks. The owners are 'a mine of information about places to visit' and where to eat; the village pub is a mile away. 'Delicious' breakfasts at a communal table are relaxed affairs with a 'huge long list' that includes eggs Benedict, pancakes, avocado on sourdough, as well as a full grill. (Lucy Ewing, Philippa Gitlin)

Chillingham
Alnwick NE66 5NP

T: 01668 215614
E: stay@manorhousechillingham.co.uk
W: chillinghammanor.co.uk

BEDROOMS: 3.
OPEN: all year, except Christmas and New Year (open only by request).
FACILITIES: morning room, drawing room, dining room, in-room TV (Freeview), 1-acre garden.
BACKGROUND MUSIC: none.
LOCATION: 1 mile S of Chatton village.
CHILDREN: over-8s, extra bed £25, any age if group booking all 3 rooms.
DOGS: only allowed if group booking all 3 rooms, must sleep in boot room (£15 per stay), allowed in ground-floor rooms and garden, not bedrooms.
CREDIT CARDS: MC, Visa.
PRICES: B&B doubles from £130. Dinner available if group booking of all 3 rooms, 2-course £25, 3-course £35. Min. 2-night stay.

Prices may change – check with hotel.

CHRISTCHURCH Dorset

CAPTAIN'S CLUB HOTEL

You can relax on a terrace beside the River Stour to the sound of lapping waves and popping corks at this streamlined, nautical-themed luxury hotel, spa and popular wedding venue. Launched in 2006 on the site of the old Pontins, it's as family- and dog-friendly as any holiday camp, but bingo has given way to boat trips, sing-songs to sybaritic spa days. 'The position of the hotel is lovely,' writes a reader, who recommends the £1 ferry trip across the water to walk the Stour Valley Way. There are river views through floor-to-ceiling windows, from cosy double and twin rooms, dog-friendly family rooms and luxury two- and three-bedroom self-catering suites. Food is served outdoors and in the restaurant, lounge and, on chilly days, by the fire in the Quay bar. Perhaps potted Dorset crab, fishcakes or Captain's Club ciabatta from the lounge menu; Poole Bay oysters, mushroom linguine or rack of lamb in the restaurant. Breakfast is 'excellent, with plenty of fruit and seeds and delicious yogurts', the full English or veggie, antioxidant juice for the morning after the night before.

Wick Ferry
Christchurch BH23 1HU

T: 01202 475111
E: reservations@captainsclubhotel.com
W: captainsclubhotel.com

BEDROOMS: 29. 2 suitable for disabled.
OPEN: all year.
FACILITIES: lifts, bar/lounge/restaurant, function facilities, in-room TV (Sky, Freeview), civil wedding licence, terrace, spa (hydrotherapy pool for over-16s), parking, EV charging, moorings for guests, public rooms wheelchair accessible, adapted toilet.
BACKGROUND MUSIC: in public areas, live jazz every other Sun lunchtime.
LOCATION: on the river.
CHILDREN: all ages welcomed, family suites, children's menu.
DOGS: allowed in suites and family rooms (£20 per night), on terrace, areas of bar/lounge.
CREDIT CARDS: Amex, MC, Visa.
PRICES: B&B doubles from £269, suites from £360. À la carte £40. 1-night bookings normally refused Sat.

Prices may change – check with hotel.

CLANFIELD Oxfordshire

MAP 3:E6

THE DOUBLE RED DUKE   NEW

The latest addition to Georgie and Sam Pearman's Country Creatures portfolio, this 17th-century Cotswold stone inn is 'one of the best pubs-with-rooms I've ever seen', says our inspector. The bedrooms are 'all special, one with a red bathtub in a red-and-white-tiled nook, others opening on to the garden'. A family room had 'a country-chic feel, old wooden furniture, luxurious fabrics, sisal carpet'. The bathroom was 'enormous, with stand-alone tub and another room with twin walk-in showers'. Many rooms have an emperor bed, hand-blocked wallpaper; all have a cafetière, 100 Acres toiletries. You can have tea by the fire in one of the snugs, dine in the bar, restaurant, garden room, alfresco under a striped parasol, or at the counter of the open kitchen. 'There's the usual pub grub, but meat and fish grilled over charcoal, cherry and apple wood are stars of the show. My son devoured a porterhouse for two and declared it the best steak ever.' Side dishes such as BBQ hispi cabbage and miso butter rack up the bill. A buffet breakfast is included; cooked dishes such as devilled kidneys and smoked haddock omelette are charged extra.

Bourton Road
Clanfield
Bampton OX18 2RB

T: 01367 810222
E: reservations@doublereddduke.com
W: countrycreatures.com

BEDROOMS: 19. 6 in barn annexe.
OPEN: all year.
FACILITIES: bar, restaurant, garden room, snugs, wine room, chef's counter, in-room TV, shepherd's hut treatment room, garden, terraces, some on-site parking, EV charging, dining areas wheelchair accessible, adapted toilet.
BACKGROUND MUSIC: 'background appropriate music in public areas'.
LOCATION: village centre.
CHILDREN: all ages welcomed, 3 family rooms, cots free, extra bed in larger doubles £30, children's menu.
DOGS: allowed in barn bedrooms (£25 a night, beds, bowls), in bar on lead if well-behaved.
CREDIT CARDS: Amex, MC, Visa.
PRICES: B&B doubles from £120 (incl. continental breakfast). À la carte £45. 2-night min. stay Sat, bank holidays.

Prices may change – check with hotel.

CLEARWELL Gloucestershire

MAP 3:D4

TUDOR FARMHOUSE

Where the Forest of Dean meets the Wye valley, rustic Tudor charm meets modern boutique hotel style at Hari and Colin Fell's converted farmhouse, cider house and barn. The setting is bucolic, amid a small farm with sheep, ponies, chickens and runner ducks. Inside, the 'superbly run place' has been 'sensitively converted with tasteful decor'. Four categories of bedrooms (from Hatchling to suites, via Hen and Cockerel) have exposed beams, subtle paint finishes, an espresso machine, a minibar fridge, Bramley bath products. 'Our comfortable room had a roll-top bath and modern shower.' A hen room has bunk beds for kids in an alcove; a cockerel room has a four-poster. 'Such a warm welcome,' reads a typical reader report this year. 'We felt like family. Standards superb, rooms, food, garden, service.' Another reader, who has visited half a dozen times, reports that 'the food is as good as ever, if not better'. Ingredients are sourced close to home for dishes such as aged beef sirloin with braised cheek or potato herb gnocchi with celeriac and truffle. 'Our favourite place for a short break.' (Ann McCormack, Anne Dudley, Andrew Kleissner)

High Street
Clearwell GL16 8JS

T: 01594 833046
E: info@tudorfarmhousehotel.co.uk
W: tudorfarmhousehotel.co.uk

BEDROOMS: 20. 4 on ground floor, 4 in farmhouse, 9 in barn, 7 in cider house.
OPEN: all year.
FACILITIES: lounge, bar, 2 dining rooms, treatment room, in-room TV (Freeview), 14-acre grounds (garden, ancient grassland), restaurant and lounge wheelchair accessible, adapted toilet.
BACKGROUND MUSIC: in restaurant and lounge at lunch and dinner.
LOCATION: 7 miles SE of Monmouth.
CHILDREN: all ages welcomed, extra bed £25, under-6s stay free, children's menu.
DOGS: 1 small dog allowed in 3 bedrooms (£10 a night, bed, bowl, treat).
CREDIT CARDS: Amex, MC, Visa.
PRICES: B&B doubles from £159. À la carte £50. Min. 2-night stay Sat Easter–end Oct.

Prices may change – check with hotel.

CLEY-NEXT-THE-SEA Norfolk

MAP 2:A5

CLEY WINDMILL

'In an idyllic spot', amid 'reed beds on the former quayside on the River Glaven', this five-storey, 19th-century tower mill is home to an unusual B&B. 'There is a certain romance to staying in a windmill,' say our inspectors, who signed a waiver to sleep in the Wheel Room, reached 'via a steep, carpeted ladder', with 'another steep ladder to a shower room, where you can see the old mill machinery in the ceiling'. It was 'characterful, with a small four-poster beneath a timber ceiling' and slightly tired cottage-style decor. 'A wood-effect fire makes it even cosier in winter and there is a mini-honesty bar with fresh milk and cookies', though an extra loo behind a screen, while practical, 'detracts from the romance a bit'. There is less hazardous, more modern accommodation in the old storehouses and boathouses. The restaurant wasn't operating (this may change), but a hamper with wine in the 'cute, curved dining room' brought 'a superb feast, beautifully presented', including 'warmed bread' and salmon from Cley's famous smokehouse. 'Sitting by the window of the windmill as sun set over the marshes was pretty special.'

The Quay
Cley-next-the-Sea
Holt NR25 7RP

T: 01263 740209
E: info@cleywindmill.co.uk
w: cleywindmill.co.uk

BEDROOMS: 10. 1 in Boat House, 1 in Long House, 1 in Cart Shed.
OPEN: all year, usually self-catering only over Christmas.
FACILITIES: bar/lounge, dining room, in-room TV (Freeview), civil wedding licence, ¼-acre garden, ground-floor rooms suitable for more able wheelchair-users.
BACKGROUND MUSIC: in dining room, soft classical and jazz.
LOCATION: in northerly village next to River Glaven, less than a mile from the sea.
CHILDREN: all ages welcomed, extra bed £30.
DOGS: allowed in 1 room (Boat House) and Dovecote (B&B or self-catering cottage).
CREDIT CARDS: MC, Visa.
PRICES: B&B doubles from £179. Hamper for two £65. Min. 2-night stay at weekends.

Prices may change – check with hotel.

CLIPSHAM Rutland

BEECH HOUSE & OLIVE BRANCH

Swing off the A1 down a tree-lined lane to this award-garlanded village gastropub, with rooms in a Georgian house opposite. Host Ben Jones has an impressive CV which includes stints at Gravetye Manor, East Grinstead; Hambleton Hall, Hambleton; and as launch manager at Hart's, Nottingham (see entries). In 1999 he and two friends bought the defunct Olive Branch, refurbished it and revived its fortunes. Chef Luke Holland creates innovative, daily-changing, seasonal menus, but fish and chips is a staple. You can eat indoors by the fire, or in a garden gazebo. 'The food was fab,' writes a reader. 'A steak tartare starter was especially good, bread possibly the best I ever had, guinea hen tender and tasty.' He did, though, crave more of the vegetables grown in the paddock. In Beech House, bedrooms are individually styled, with a Roberts radio and smart TV. Most have a coffee machine. Double Cream has a freestanding roll-top bath and walk-in shower. Accessible, dog-friendly Chocolate has two bedrooms, a lounge, wet room and patio. 'Staff were friendly and efficient.' A great, locally sourced breakfast is served only on days when the pub is open. (Peter Anderson, DW, MM-D)

Main Street
Clipsham LE15 7SH

T: 01780 410355
E: info@theolivebranchpub.com
W: theolivebranchpub.com

BEDROOMS: 6. 2 on ground floor, family room (suitable for disabled) in annexe.
OPEN: all year, closed Sun evening, Mon, Tues, lunch only on 25 Dec, 1 Jan.
FACILITIES: bar, dining room, breakfast room, in-room TV, garden, paddock, public rooms wheelchair accessible, adapted toilet.
BACKGROUND MUSIC: classical/jazz in pub.
LOCATION: in village 7 miles NW of Stamford.
CHILDREN: all ages welcomed, cot £10, extra bed £30.
DOGS: allowed by prior consent in ground-floor bedrooms (£10 per night, with bed, bowl), bar, in paddock on lead.
CREDIT CARDS: MC, Visa.
PRICES: B&B doubles from £205, singles from £120. Set-price dinner £37.50–£45 (2/3 courses), tasting menu (7 courses) £80.

Prices may change – check with hotel.

CONSALL Staffordshire

MAP 3:B5

THE TAWNY

NEW

'Perfect if you want your own space and all the services of a hotel', The Tawny promises bucolic bliss; porters whisk guests by buggy to huts, tree houses, boathouses and retreats in 70 landscaped acres. Our inspectors were impressed by the former colliery site, transformed over 50 years by the late William Podmore, with six lakes and numerous follies. A tree house ('really more a chalet on stilts') was 'the epitome of contemporary chic, with a stand-alone bath by a floor-to-ceiling window so you could wallow with a lovely lakeside view' and a 'generous free minibar'. A deck had 'a shower and a metal bath big enough for four'. In the glass-fronted restaurant, where 'vertical gardens climb the walls', dinner proved a revelation. 'My son couldn't stop raving about the beef brisket in buttermilk with dill popcorn, until his empty plate was replaced by lobster with a Parmesan and bisque croquette.' Equally good were breakfast with a 'range of muffins, creamy yogurts, local cheeses, cooked dishes' and lunch of tapas, flatbreads. 'Every mouthful of every meal was a winner.' 'A beautiful place to enjoy nature with contemporary comforts.'

Consall Gardens Estate
Consall Lane
Consall ST9 0AG

T: 01538 787664
E: relax@thetawny.co.uk
W: thetawny.co.uk

BEDROOMS: 55 across the site (chauffeured buggies). 1 suitable for wheelchair.
OPEN: all year.
FACILITIES: restaurant, games room, 2 lounges, 70-acre estate (woodland, lakes, follies, outdoor heated pool), spa treatments, public areas wheelchair accessible, adapted toilets.
BACKGROUND MUSIC: soft, mainly light jazz.
LOCATION: 8 miles E of Stoke-on-Trent.
CHILDREN: all ages welcomed, family rooms, under-16s £50 per night.
DOGS: allowed in Glade Huts, Boathouses, Feathers lounge, max. one small-to-medium dog (£30 per night).
CREDIT CARDS: Amex, MC, Visa.
PRICES: B&B doubles from £230, family from £520. À la carte £60, tasting menus on certain dates £80. Min. 2-night stay on Sat.

Prices may change – check with hotel.

CORSE LAWN Gloucestershire

MAP 3:D5

CORSE LAWN HOUSE

Ducks glide on a pond and guests take tea in front of this beautifully proportioned Queen Anne-style mansion in a hamlet between the Cotswolds and the Mendip hills. Owned for more than 40 years by Baba Hine, it has 'faded charm, but not in a bad way', writes a reader. Guide insiders on a return visit noted 'lots to like', not least a heated swimming pool, tennis court and croquet lawn. The decor and furnishings may be dated, but are still appealing. Walls are painted in shades of peach. Armchairs propose a fireside snooze. 'Bedrooms are large and opulent, with every extra you need' – fresh milk, ground coffee, leaf tea. 'Our room had a fridge, an ottoman, old brown furniture, a good selection of fresh fruit, lovely home-made shortbread.' The bistro and dining room differ only in ambience. 'Dishes are nicely presented. The food is tasty, and changes. We had fish soup, Waldorf salad, loin of muntjac, and sole. Desserts are excellent.' Breakfast brings 'imaginative touches' such as mango and lime juice, 'a nicely arranged fruit and yogurt plate'. Cooked choices are limited, but 'well done'. (Christine Hodgkin, N and CH)

Corse Lawn GL19 4LZ

T: 01452 780771
E: enquiries@corselawn.com
W: corselawn.com

BEDROOMS: 18. 5 on ground floor.
OPEN: all year, Mon and Tues B&B only, by arrangement.
FACILITIES: 2 drawing rooms, snug bar, restaurant, bistro, private dining/meeting rooms, in-room TV, civil wedding licence, 12-acre grounds (croquet, tennis, indoor heated swimming pool), EV charging, unsuitable for disabled.
BACKGROUND MUSIC: none.
LOCATION: 5 miles SW of Tewkesbury on B4211.
CHILDREN: all ages welcomed, extra bed £10, 3 suites have sofa beds.
DOGS: allowed in bedrooms (max. 2 per room, £10 per dog stay), public rooms, not in eating areas.
CREDIT CARDS: Amex, MC, Visa.
PRICES: B&B doubles from £160, singles from £120. Fixed-price dinner £29.50–£37.50 (2/3 courses), à la carte £38.

Prices may change – check with hotel.

COVERACK Cornwall

MAP 1:E2

THE BAY HOTEL

In 'an excellent position facing the sea and small harbour' this updated Edwardian hotel is 'bright, smart and spotless throughout', while 'its relatively small size gives it an intimacy and friendliness'. Pristine bedrooms are decorated in a muted palette of cool coastal shades. Sea-facing Beachcomber and Bay View bedrooms are snug, with a double bed, a power shower. One suite has a king-size sleigh bed, a balcony, a double-ended bath and separate shower; another, on the ground floor, has a super-king bed, a sofa bed, bath, shower and outdoor seating area. You can dine on 'lovely food' in the restaurant, or with your dog in the lounge or alfresco. New head chef Dan Bowden is a passionate champion of the produce of his native Cornwall. On past form, we expect his modern British menus to include dishes such as scallop, belly pork, wild garlic, seaweed, caviar; Dartmoor beef sirloin, clotted cream, Devon Blue cheese, onion purée, carrot fondant, shimeji mushroom and beef dripping potatoes. Breakfast brings omelette Arnold Bennett, smoked salmon with St Ewe scrambled egg, custard brioche with fruit compote and crème fraîche.

North Corner
Coverack
Helston TR12 6TF

T: 01326 280464
E: reception@thebayhotel.co.uk
W: thebayhotel.co.uk

BEDROOMS: 14. 1, on ground floor, suitable for disabled.
OPEN: mid-Feb–end Dec, closed Sun pm, Mon, Tues Nov–Mar.
FACILITIES: lounge, bar/restaurant, conservatory, in-room TV (Freeview), 2 tiered gardens, wellness room, sun terrace, parking.
BACKGROUND MUSIC: quiet classical music or blues in bar, restaurant.
LOCATION: village centre, 9 miles SE of Helston.
CHILDREN: all ages welcomed ('we are not suitable for babies or very young children'), under-6s free, extra bed for under-16s £45.
DOGS: allowed in bedrooms (£10 a night, treats, towel), on lead in grounds, some public rooms.
CREDIT CARDS: MC, Visa.
PRICES: B&B doubles from £125, singles from £100. À la carte £42. 1-night bookings sometimes refused.

Prices may change – check with hotel.

COWAN BRIDGE Lancashire

MAP 4: inset D2

HIPPING HALL

Between the Yorkshire Dales and the Lake
District – and just ten minutes from the M6 –
Hipping Hall is a surprising foodie find with
understated yet luxurious bedrooms, spacious
gardens and a relaxed atmosphere. Good walks
and covetable views may be close but most guests
are here for the food. Joining in 2021, chef Peter
Howarth previously headed up two-Michelin-star
kitchens and creates dishes that sound simple but
are intricately balanced to bring out flavours. The
eight-course tasting menu might include Cartmel
Valley venison with miso carrot and chanterelles,
hen's egg with wild garlic and asparagus, and
rhubarb with polenta and blood orange. There's
a four-course option, plus vegan and vegetarian
menus. Meals are served in the atmospheric
medieval hall with its beams, grand fireplace
and minstrels' gallery. After dinner, relax in the
drawing room or orangery. Bedrooms have a low-
key luxury and range from country house style
in the 17th-century hall and brightly decorated
cottage rooms across the courtyard to Scandi-style
affairs with terraces in the converted stables. (See
also sister property Forest Side, Grasmere.)

Cowan Bridge
Kirkby Lonsdale LA6 2JJ

т: 01524 271187
е: info@hippinghall.com
w: hippinghall.com

BEDROOMS: 15. 3 in cottage, 5 in stables,
1 suitable for disabled.
OPEN: all year, restaurant closed Mon,
Tues.
FACILITIES: lounge, orangery, bar,
restaurant (vegetarian/vegan menu),
civil wedding licence, in-room TV
(Freeview), 12-acre grounds; orangery,
restaurant and lounge wheelchair
accessible.
BACKGROUND MUSIC: in lounge,
restaurant.
LOCATION: 2 miles SE of Kirkby
Lonsdale, on A65.
CHILDREN: all ages welcomed, extra
bed £25, prefer young children to
dine early.
DOGS: allowed in stable bedrooms
(max. 2, £20 per night), and orangery.
CREDIT CARDS: Amex, MC, Visa.
PRICES: B&B doubles from £239.
8-course tasting menu £90, 4-course £60.

Prices may change – check with hotel.

COWES Isle of Wight

MAP 2:E2

NORTH HOUSE

'The Isle of Wight's chicest boutique hotel,' reports a Guide insider of these Georgian town houses, with a kitchen run by Michelin-starred chef Robert Thompson, set above Cowes harbour. Sara Curran, an island resident and TV executive, took over the hotel in 2022 with her partner Peter, and Robert (the youngest winner of a Michelin star). 'Beautifully styled' public rooms and bedrooms – from the previous interior-designer owners – have remained. 'The decor really is exquisite,' reports our inspector. Bedrooms, with stripped-wood floors, statement wallpapers and armoires, are 'the epitome of elegance, with a dash of country house chic'. You might find a wood-burner, roll-top bath or modern four-poster. All have views of the sea, old town or garden. Some open on to the suntrap terraced garden. The latter is an ideal spot 'to sit with a glass of rosé or a G&T' and consider a dip in the hotel pool. Dine on tapas-style dishes here or the full menu in the buzzy brasserie with its choice of large and small plates, such as 'wafer-thin slices of sea bass' that 'offered a satisfying simplicity and squeaky freshness', and spaghetti of local lobster with 'a velvety finish'.

Sun Hill
Cowes PO31 7HY

T: 01983 209453
E: reception@northhousecowes.co.uk
W: northhousecowes.co.uk

BEDROOMS: 14. 9 across courtyard, 4 on ground floor.
OPEN: all year except 2 weeks in Jan.
FACILITIES: bar, library, restaurant, private dining room, in-room TV (Freeview), civil wedding licence, terrace, garden, outdoor heated swimming pool, public car park (charge) nearby.
BACKGROUND MUSIC: low-level music in public areas.
LOCATION: in centre of Old Town.
CHILDREN: all ages welcomed, extra bed £20.
DOGS: not allowed.
CREDIT CARDS: Amex, MC, Visa.
PRICES: room-only doubles from £295. Breakfast cooked dishes £8–£15, à la carte £60, tasting menu from £79. Min. 2-night stay at weekends.

Prices may change – check with hotel.

COWLEY Gloucestershire

MAP 3:D5

COWLEY MANOR

An Italianate mansion in landscaped gardens and pleasure grounds is today 'a lovely, classic country house hotel with a modern, quirky feel'. It is now part of the Experimental group, which plans to keep things running as they are. The 'extraordinary and beautiful grounds' are thought to have inspired Lewis Carroll's Wonderland. 'Interiors have been sympathetically modernised, with flair,' readers write. There is playfulness here, from papier-mâché hunting trophies to the bold mixing of '60s styling with original features. Rooms range from 'good' to 'best' via various superlatives. 'Marvellous' rooms have a balcony, lounge space, perhaps a modern four-poster. 'Outstanding' rooms in the stables have a balcony or terrace. All have a minibar, a deep bath and rainfall shower, exclusive toiletries inspired by the gardens. Dogs and children are welcome, and dining, in the restaurant or on the terrace, is more fun than fine, with dishes such as spinach and ricotta ravioli; poached chicken supreme, wild garlic mash. 'The food was tasty and interesting, and the staff helpful and friendly.' (Jane and Martin Bailey)

Cowley
Cheltenham GL53 9NL

T: 01242 870900
E: stay@cowleymanor.com
W: cowleymanor.com

BEDROOMS: 31. 15 in converted stables.
OPEN: all year.
FACILITIES: bar, sitting room, billiard room, restaurant, private sitting room, garden room and dining room, in-room TV, 55-acre grounds, civil wedding licence, spa (indoor and outdoor swimming pools).
BACKGROUND MUSIC: in public areas.
LOCATION: 6 miles S of Cheltenham.
CHILDREN: all ages welcomed, extra bed £40 (incl. meals), no under-16s in spa without supervision.
DOGS: allowed in 7 bedrooms (£25 per night), sitting room, terrace, not in restaurant.
CREDIT CARDS: Amex, MC, Visa.
PRICES: B&B doubles from £222 (cooked breakfast extra, full English £10). À la carte £45. 1-night bookings refused Sat, some holidays.

Prices may change – check with hotel.

COXWOLD Yorkshire

THE FAUCONBERG ARMS

With its honey-coloured stonework, tables on the cobbled front terrace and colourful window boxes, you sense this quintessential village inn will have you perched on a bar stool chatting with the locals. You would be right. In the centre of pretty Coxwold, on the edge of the North York Moors, the former coaching inn welcomes dogs, walkers and regulars to relax among the flagged floors, beams, log fires, and shiny copper and brass. Eat in the bar or dining room, the latter with plaid carpet and fresh flowers, from a menu of classic country dishes, perhaps local lamb with wild garlic mash, home-made Aberdeen Angus beefburger, or the catch of the day. A daily-changing specials board adds to the choice, and there's a pleasing range of local ales. Low-ceilinged, cottagey bedrooms differ in shape and size, are furnished with light-oak and antique furniture, floral and striped fabrics, perhaps a wrought iron or sleigh bed – a four-poster in one – and have views over the village or Howardian hills. Some are compact; all have modern bathrooms apart from the log cabin-style Garden Room, with a shower and eco-loo in an adjoining shed.

Thirsk Bank
Coxwold
Thirsk YO61 4AD

T: 01347 868214
E: reservations@fauconbergarms.com
W: fauconbergarms.com

BEDROOMS: 9. 1 log cabin in garden.
OPEN: all year.
FACILITIES: 2 bars, snug, restaurant, private dining room, 1-acre garden with beer garden, pavement terrace, in-room TV, back bar and restaurant wheelchair accessible.
BACKGROUND MUSIC: none.
LOCATION: centre of village, 6 miles N of Easingwold, 7 miles S of Thirsk.
CHILDREN: all ages welcomed, extra bed £15.
DOGS: allowed in bedrooms (£10 a night) and bars.
CREDIT CARDS: Amex, MC, Visa.
PRICES: B&B doubles from £110, singles from £100, garden room from £75, single occupancy £65. À la carte £30.

Prices may change – check with hotel.

CREDITON Devon

MAP 1:C4

PASCHOE HOUSE

Tabitha Amador-Christie spent £1.1 million completing the restoration, begun by her father, of this Tudor-Gothic-style Victorian mansion on a 25-acre estate. The interiors are beautiful, with capricious touches. An alarming array of creatures great and small look out from strawberry-pink walls in the hallway; an ostrich spreads its wings over a fireplace, but only clay pigeons are shot here. Bedrooms have under-floor heating, Designers Guild wallpaper and chic paint finishes. All have an espresso machine, home-made treats, Bamford toiletries. Some bathrooms have a stand-alone roll-top bath and super walk-in shower. Two gorgeous suites can interconnect. There is a casual dining menu in the morning room and library bar, while at night, in the restaurant and on the terrace, James Checkley's menus include dishes such as partridge confit leg with sweetcorn, pearl barley and partridge jus; brill with butternut squash, Cornish mussels and cumin foam. Breakfast buffet items arrive in individual jars and mini-bottles, with dishes cooked to order, and you're encouraged to take a picnic for a day's exploring. Drop in by helicopter if you wish!

Bow
Crediton EX17 6JT

T: 01363 84244
E: theteam@paschoehouse.co.uk
W: paschoehouse.co.uk

BEDROOMS: 10. Plus 1 self-catering suite.
OPEN: all year, except 4–31 Jan, closed from noon Mon to Tues evening.
FACILITIES: lift, lounge, bar, restaurant, in-room TV, civil wedding licence, 25-acre grounds (tennis, croquet), secure parking, EV charging, public rooms wheelchair accessible.
BACKGROUND MUSIC: light jazz in public rooms.
LOCATION: E of Bow, off A3072.
CHILDREN: all ages welcomed, extra bed £50.
DOGS: allowed in 3 bedrooms (£20 per night, bed, treats, toys, towels, day and dinner care), in library bar, morning room and grounds, not in restaurant.
CREDIT CARDS: MC, Visa.
PRICES: B&B doubles from £229, singles from £209. Set-price £75, tasting menu £90, bar menu à la carte £42.

Prices may change – check with hotel.

CROSTHWAITE Cumbria

THE PUNCH BOWL INN

To find a gem in a quiet corner of the visitor-
thronged Lake District is not easy, but this smart
village inn in the lovely Lyth valley is, as one
reader reports, 'always a favourite'. Although
more gastropub than drinkers' pub (with produce
from their village farm, and damsons from
owner Richard Rose's garden), the bar has local
ales as well as champagne by the glass. The six-
strong kitchen brigade produces Modern British
dishes that might include duck with orange and
glazed carrots, or pan-roasted cod with mash,
with cider and mussel sauce. Lemon tart with
local damson sorbet is a favourite. Eat in the
atmospheric beamed bar with its flagged floor
and log-burner, or in the more formal dining
room. On warm days, the terrace, with views
over the neighbouring church, is a lovely spot for
drinks – and for the guests' welcome of tea and
home-made scones. Light-coloured, country-style
bedrooms are pleasingly different – some with
beams, others with valley views – but all offer
king or super-king beds, rich fabrics, and vintage
or solid-oak furniture. Inviting bathrooms have
tongue-and-groove panelling, roll-top baths and
under-floor heating.

Crosthwaite
Kendal LA8 8HR

T: 01539 568237
E: info@the-punchbowl.co.uk
W: the-punchbowl.co.uk

BEDROOMS: 9.
OPEN: all year.
FACILITIES: bar, bar dining area,
restaurant, in-room TV (Freeview),
civil wedding licence, 2 terraces,
EV charging, bar and restaurant
wheelchair accessible, adapted toilet.
BACKGROUND MUSIC: in public areas.
LOCATION: 5 miles W of Kendal, via
A5074.
CHILDREN: all ages welcomed, under-
12s extra bed £25, children's menu.
DOGS: allowed in bar only.
CREDIT CARDS: Amex, MC, Visa.
PRICES: B&B doubles from £175, singles
from £160. À la carte £45.

Prices may change – check with hotel.

CRUDWELL Wiltshire

MAP 3:E5

THE RECTORY HOTEL

Fans of the Beckford group (see The Beckford
Arms, Tisbury) will love the simple sophistication
at this hotel, once home to a Georgian rector who
went forth and multiplied and had 14 children
to house. When music industry exec Alex Payne
bought the place, he consulted his friends the
Tisbury Two, Dan Brod and Charlie Luxton.
Bedrooms are ranked small to biggest, but all
are of a good size, with subtle paint shades,
contemporary and period furniture, seagrass
flooring. Some have a modern four-poster, an in-
room roll-top bath. All have Bramley toiletries, a
Roberts radio. 'Public spaces are stylish enough to
inspire interior lovers but cosy enough for guests
to snuggle up in with a book,' write readers,
who 'ping-ponged' between the Rectory and
sister venture the Potting Shed inn opposite. In
the dining room, a short menu includes dishes
such as crab linguine; rump of beef with truffle
mash; caramelised onion and goat's cheese tart.
More veggie options would be appreciated, but
it's a 'good menu, well presented, especially
sweetbreads and wild venison'. And if you want
great pub grub, you know where to find it. (Stuart
Smith, LG)

Crudwell
Malmesbury SN16 9EP

T: 01666 577194
E: info@therectoryhotel.com
W: therectoryhotel.com

BEDROOMS: 18. 3 in self-catering
cottage in garden.
OPEN: all year.
FACILITIES: living room, drawing
room, dining room, card room, bar,
in-room TV (Freeview, film library),
meeting facilities, civil wedding
licence, 3-acre garden, heated
outdoor swimming pool (10 by 15
metres, May–Oct), restaurant and
bar wheelchair accessible, no adapted
toilet.
BACKGROUND MUSIC: in public areas.
LOCATION: 4 miles N of Malmesbury.
CHILDREN: all ages welcomed, extra
bed £25.
DOGS: allowed in 4 bedrooms (£15 a
night) and public rooms, not in dining
room.
CREDIT CARDS: Amex, MC, Visa.
PRICES: B&B doubles from £150.
À la carte £40. Min. 2-night bookings
at weekends, usually.

Prices may change – check with hotel.

DARLINGTON Co. Durham

MAP 4:C4

HEADLAM HALL

The real charm of this grand country house, with sweeping gardens, terraces, oak panelling and swish spa, lies in its warm and informal atmosphere. Staff 'really looked after us and made us welcome', says one reader. 'A comfortable and homely place to stay,' comments a long-time fan. Run by the Robinsons, a local farming family, the creeper-covered 17th-century hall has flagged and polished-wood floors, panelled walls, an orangery brasserie, and terraces overlooking walled gardens. Yet there's nothing stuffy about the interiors, with their tartan carpets, tweed-covered armchairs, walls with hunting prints and Victorian watercolours. There is plenty of space to relax in, from the elegant drawing room and fire-warmed library bar to the spa and gardens. Spacious bedrooms have a modern country house feel, and range from ones in the main hall, with original features and antiques, to contemporary spa bedrooms and more rustic mews and coach-house rooms. The 'excellent' Modern British menus offer 'variety and value' from roast venison or cod with Thai-spiced prawns to pasta and risotto. 'We will visit again.' (Alwyn and Thelma Ellis, and others)

Gainford
Darlington DL2 3HA

T: 01325 730238
E: reception@headlamhall.co.uk
w: headlamhall.co.uk

BEDROOMS: 38. 9 in coach house, 6 in mews, 7 in spa, 2 suitable for disabled. 1 s/c apartment with hot tub.
OPEN: all year except 24–27 Dec.
FACILITIES: lift, bar-restaurant, brasserie, lounge, drawing room, private dining rooms, in-room TV, civil wedding licence, 4-acre garden, spa, indoor pool, tennis, 9-hole golf course, EV charging, public rooms wheelchair accessible, adapted toilet.
BACKGROUND MUSIC: all day in bar, restaurant.
LOCATION: 8 miles W of Darlington.
CHILDREN: all ages welcomed, under-4s free, extra bed £30, children's high tea, no under-7s in restaurant in evening.
DOGS: allowed in some bedrooms (no charge), not in restaurant.
CREDIT CARDS: Amex, MC, Visa.
PRICES: B&B doubles from £145, singles from £115. À la carte 3 courses £40.

Prices may change – check with hotel.

DARTMOUTH Devon

MAP 1:D4

BAYARDS COVE INN

A stroll from the quay, behind a quaint, jettied, black-and-white facade, a drop-in café, bar and restaurant has excellent, pet-friendly bedrooms, approached via creaky, winding stairs. Each has an en suite shower, a free crab bucket and line and a guide to crabbing hot spots. Drake is set over two floors, with a king-size bed under the eaves, a seating area and bunk beds. Handsome, oak-beamed Mountbatten, above the café, has a super-king bed, a view of the cove, a seating area with a sofa bed. Downstairs there are comfy chairs around a log-burner, a few pavement tables, a counter dispensing cakes, coffees, vegan and gluten-free treats. Lunch and dinner menus include a burger, steak, fish and chips, smoked haddock fishcakes, the catch of the day. Breakfast brings the full Devon, vegetarian or vegan, avocado on sourdough. Enjoy the ambience of the medieval building, much altered over centuries and once known as Agincourt House. Then it's once more unto the beach, dear friends, to Blackpool Sands or Sugary Cove, or to Dittisham by ferry, for a spot of crabbing, with the makings of a picnic in a biodegradable box.

27 Lower Street
Dartmouth TQ6 9AN

T: 01803 839278
E: info@bayardscoveinn.co.uk
w: bayardscoveinn.co.uk

BEDROOMS: 7. 2 family suites.
OPEN: all year except 1 week Jan.
FACILITIES: bar, restaurant, in-room TV (Freeview), bicycle storage, private parking nearby (reservation required, £15 per day), public areas wheelchair accessible, adapted toilet.
BACKGROUND MUSIC: in public areas.
LOCATION: in centre, close to waterfront.
CHILDREN: all ages welcomed, children's menu.
DOGS: allowed throughout (max. 2 per room, £18 per dog per night with prior notice, incl. bed, bowl, treats).
CREDIT CARDS: Amex, MC, Visa.
PRICES: B&B doubles from £135, family room from £165. À la carte £35. Min. 2-night stay Fri and Sat.

Prices may change – check with hotel.

SEE ALSO SHORTLIST

DARTMOUTH Devon

MAP 1:D4

DART MARINA

Watching the changing light and activity on the River Dart from the terrace, restaurant or bedrooms of this stylish and relaxed hotel soothes the soul. 'No matter at what time you visit,' says a regular guest, 'everything ticks over to perfection.' Its 'great location' overlooking the river means every bedroom has a view and often a balcony, balustrade or patio to take in the scene. 'Decorated to a very high standard' in soft shades of grey, with blue and taupe highlights, and in a comfortable but uncluttered style, rooms offer calm spaces and sleek bathrooms. Top rooms have a freestanding bath and binoculars. Tasty food – fresh fish from nearby Brixham market – taken in the panoramic River restaurant could include pan-fried sea bream with saffron potato, local venison with beetroot tarte Tatin, and rib-eye steak. 'All very good, and not too nouvelle!' Breakfast, afternoon tea and cocktails can be enjoyed on the terrace; in summer, a vintage truck in the Waterfront Garden serves coffee, cakes and chilled drinks. With 'friendly and attentive staff' the hotel is 'one of our absolute favourites'. (Peter Anderson, HK, and others)

Sandquay Road
Dartmouth TQ6 9PH

T: 01803 832580
E: reception@dartmarina.com
W: dartmarina.com

BEDROOMS: 49. 4 on ground floor, 1 suitable for disabled. Plus 3 self-catering apartments.
OPEN: all year.
FACILITIES: lounge/bar, restaurant, in-room TV (Freeview), lawn, terrace, pop-up bar, parking, EV charging, lounge and restaurant wheelchair accessible, adapted toilet.
BACKGROUND MUSIC: in restaurant and lounge/bar.
LOCATION: on waterfront.
CHILDREN: all ages welcomed, extra bed £30.
DOGS: allowed in some bedrooms (£10 per night, welcome pack) and lounge, not in restaurant.
CREDIT CARDS: MC, Visa.
PRICES: B&B doubles from £200, singles from £160. À la carte £45. 1-night bookings usually refused at weekends at peak times.

Prices may change – check with hotel.

SEE ALSO SHORTLIST

DEDHAM Essex

MAP 2:C5

DEDHAM HALL

Readers paint an appealing picture of a stay at this characterful timber-frame manor house in deepest Constable country, where residential art courses are a big draw. 'Perfect weekend break. So comfortable and welcoming,' writes one. Another praises the 'casual, relaxed air, which is a big part of the charm', and 'friendly hosts' Wendy and Jim Sarton, who dispensed with check-in formalities in favour of tea and home-made cakes. Four bedrooms are in the hall, with exposed beams and wonky floors. Annexe rooms around the art studio have pleasing rustic style, the occasional quirk (one room was accessed via the kitchen). 'The public rooms are beautiful', with 'lots of comfortable sofas' in the beamed lounge, where you can sit with a drink by the fire as you peruse Wendy's menu. Readers enjoyed the 'delicious food', although one found the duck breast and pork fillet a little overcooked. But the 'other dishes were perfect, particularly the salmon with a Cajun crust'. After 'an excellent breakfast with plenty of fresh fruit as well as cooked dishes', you might visit the Munnings Museum. (Diane Stephens, Mary Hewson, J and AD)

Brook Street
Dedham
Colchester CO7 6AD

T: 01206 323027
E: sarton@dedhamhall.co.uk
W: dedhamhall.co.uk

BEDROOMS: 20. 16 in annexe around art studio, some on ground floor suitable for disabled.
OPEN: all year except Christmas–New Year.
FACILITIES: 2 lounges, bar, dining room, studio, in-room TV (terrestrial), 6-acre grounds (pond, gardens, fields), lounges and dining room wheelchair accessible.
BACKGROUND MUSIC: none.
LOCATION: end of village High Street (set back from road).
CHILDREN: all ages welcomed, extra bed £25.
DOGS: allowed in some bedrooms (no charge), not in public rooms.
CREDIT CARDS: MC, Visa.
PRICES: B&B doubles from £130, singles from £95. À la carte/fixed-price dinner, for residents only (or by prior arrangement), £35.

Prices may change – check with hotel.

DEDHAM Essex

MAP 2:C5

TALBOOTH HOUSE & SPA

The Milsom family's Victorian country house hotel in Dedham Vale, formerly Maison Talbooth, has been subtly rebranded with the addition of a spa by the pool house. Bedrooms, named after poets, have 'flamboyant Essex "chic" that tries perhaps a bit too hard', say our inspectors, or a slightly bland 'muted grey palette, although offset by splashes of colour and artwork'. This, though, is a matter of taste, and all are 'spacious, with large en suite bathrooms', fine toiletries, use of the tennis court, swimming pool and hot tub. You can stroll to sister hotel Milsoms for affordable brasserie-style food, walk or be driven to the venerable Talbooth restaurant in a 'striking Tudor building by the Stour'. It is here that 'the hotel really comes into its own', and though pricy, 'what it takes from your wallet it gives to your palate'. Among dishes enjoyed were 'heavenly, flaky, moist stone bass paired beautifully with white onion sauce; pear Pavlova, aniseed ice cream and white liquorice meringue'. Vegans and veggies have their own menus. Another sister venture, The Pier at Harwich, Harwich (see entry), offers a different experience again.

Stratford Road
Dedham CO7 6HN

T: 01206 322367
E: talboothhouseandspa@
milsomhotels.com
W: milsomhotels.com

BEDROOMS: 12. 5 on ground floor with walk-in shower.
OPEN: all year, restaurant closed Sun pm.
FACILITIES: lounge, Garden Room, courtesy car to restaurant 1 minute away, 5-acre grounds (tennis), outdoor heated pool, in-room TV (Sky, Freeview), spa, civil wedding licence, some public areas wheelchair accessible, adapted toilet.
BACKGROUND MUSIC: none.
LOCATION: ½ mile W of Dedham village.
CHILDREN: all ages welcomed, extra bed £20.
DOGS: allowed in bedrooms (£15 a night), lounge, on terrace and in area of brasserie, not restaurant.
CREDIT CARDS: Amex, MC, Visa.
PRICES: B&B doubles from £300. À la carte £80 (Talbooth), £37 (Milsoms). 1-night bookings refused at weekends.

Prices may change – check with hotel.

DEDHAM Essex   MAP 2:C5

THE SUN INN

'A lovely old building in a nice location', this medieval coaching inn is set amid the pastoral landscape of Dedham Vale. With low beams, comfy sofas around a log-burner, and Suffolk ales on tap, the Sun inspires beams of satisfaction. 'The food was excellent, likewise the beer and wine,' a reader reports. Chef Jack Levine uses day-boat fish from Wivenhoe, humanely reared meat and locally grown organic and biodynamic produce in dishes such as skate, devilled mussel butter sauce, agretti and potato purée. The bedrooms, some with a view of St Mary's church, have period furniture and bags of character. Boudicca has a fireplace and super-king brass bed; bay-windowed Constable has a half-tester. 'Our room, Elsa, was large as described, the bed was comfortable.' When several issues over housekeeping were raised with the owner, Piers Baker, his response was exemplary. Breakfast brings fresh orange juice, local farm eggs and Dingley Dell sausages. Outside, there is a pretty garden and all of Constable country to explore.

High Street
Dedham
Colchester CO7 6DF

T: 01206 323351
E: office@thesuninndedham.com
W: thesuninndedham.com

BEDROOMS: 7. 2 across the terrace, approached by external staircase.
OPEN: all year except 25/26 Dec.
FACILITIES: lounge, bar, dining room, in-room TV (Freeview), 1-acre walled garden (covered terrace, children's play area, garden bar), parking, unsuitable for disabled.
BACKGROUND MUSIC: all day in public areas.
LOCATION: village centre.
CHILDREN: all ages welcomed, roll-out mattress £15.
DOGS: in bar and Oak Room, in guest bedrooms by arrangement (no charge but subject to stringent terms and conditions), not in dining room.
CREDIT CARDS: Amex, MC, Visa.
PRICES: B&B doubles from £175, singles from £105. À la carte £36, weekly set menu £25–£30 (2/3 courses incl. glass of wine).

Prices may change – check with hotel.

DORCHESTER Dorset

MAP 2:E1

THE KING'S ARMS

With its projecting porch, Doric columns and bow windows, this Georgian coaching inn is a commanding presence on the High Street of Thomas Hardy's Casterbridge. It might look traditional with a capital T on the outside, but step inside to see what £5 million and the vision of the Stay Original group has achieved. The 'up-to-date and well-equipped' bedrooms, ranked from 'snug' to 'epic', have subtle decor enlivened here and there by jazzy fabrics. Epic rooms have a super-king bed, vintage furniture, an in-room claw-footed bath. We can't say in which room Robert Louis Stevenson stayed when he visited Hardy at nearby Max Gate, but we think he would have been impressed by the current offering, including an espresso machine, smart TV and Bramley toiletries. At street level there are 'comfortable communal areas, a large bar with sofas and armchairs' where you can eat casually. In the restaurant there is 'a short menu with different ideas', maybe pan-roasted hake, coppa, white wine Puy lentils, charred chicory; good plant-based options. The 'deliciously light chocolate layer cake was worthy of a French patisserie'.

30 High Street
Dorchester DT1 1HF

T: 01305 238238
E: info@thekingsarmsdorchester.com
W: thekingsarmsdorchester.com

BEDROOMS: 27.
OPEN: all year.
FACILITIES: lift, bar, restaurant, lounge, private dining room, 1st-floor function room, terrace, secure car park, public rooms partially accessible for wheelchairs, adapted toilet.
BACKGROUND MUSIC: in public areas.
LOCATION: central.
CHILDREN: all ages welcomed, free cots for under-3s, extra bed for under-13s £20, children's menu.
DOGS: allowed in 1st-floor bedrooms (£15 per stay), bar, lounge and on terrace, subject to some restrictions, not in restaurant.
CREDIT CARDS: MC, Visa.
PRICES: B&B doubles from £105. À la carte £40.

Prices may change – check with hotel.

DUNSTER Somerset

THE LUTTRELL ARMS HOTEL

In a 'lovely little medieval village' overlooked by a red sandstone castle, what was an old guest house for the abbots of Cleeve Abbey is today a 'friendly and relaxed' hotel. A great base for exploring Exmoor national park or for walking the South West Coast Path, it has a good mix of bedrooms, from contemporary-style doubles to eight 'finest' rooms, some with an antique four-poster or perhaps an original fireplace. Dog owners can book rooms with garden access and a private terrace. Eclectically furnished public rooms with mismatched furniture, hunting-themed pictures and plenty of cushions 'give a very casual and cosy feel to the place, which I really enjoyed'. Readers appreciated the 'wonderful snug' with books to read. You can eat in the dining room, with your dog by a log-burner in one of the lounges, or in a gorgeous bar with carved-oak windows overlooking a courtyard. There are also dining pods in the garden, which opens on to National Trust parkland. New chef Allan Woodhall's menus cater to all tastes: rib-eye steak, fish and chips, sun-dried tomato pappardelle, and 24-hour-braised belly pork. (Hilary Nicholson)

Exmoor National Park
Dunster TA24 6SG

T: 01643 821555
E: enquiry@luttrellarms.co.uk
W: luttrellarms.co.uk

BEDROOMS: 28. Some on ground floor, 1 with 'easy access'.
OPEN: all year.
FACILITIES: lounge, 2 bars, snug, restaurant, function rooms, in-room TV (Freeview), civil wedding licence, courtyard, lounge and restaurant wheelchair accessible, no adapted toilet.
BACKGROUND MUSIC: in restaurant.
LOCATION: village centre, 3½ miles SE of Minehead.
CHILDREN: all ages welcomed, some rooms not suitable for under-14s, extra bed (for prices please contact reception), children's menu.
DOGS: allowed in most bedrooms (£10 per night), bar, not in restaurant.
CREDIT CARDS: Amex, MC, Visa.
PRICES: B&B doubles from £120, singles from £107.50. À la carte £35. Min. 2-night stay at weekends.

Prices may change – check with hotel.

EAST CHISENBURY Wiltshire

MAP 2:D2

THE RED LION FREEHOUSE

A 'laid-back, fire-in-the hearth, village pub atmosphere' prevails at this thatched gastropub with riverside guest house on the edge of Salisbury Plain. It is 'a lovely place to stay, in beautiful surroundings'. Chef/proprietors Guy and Brittany Manning make everything possible in-house, from Scotch eggs and sourdough to ice cream and doggie treats. You can dine in the bar/restaurant, or in the garden among the nasturtiums and broad beans. The menu includes dishes such as chargrilled chateaubriand or cod, roast romanesco, cauliflower purée, and brown shrimp. Across the road, stylish guest rooms have decking beside the River Avon from which to watch for otters. One reader had the 'very comfortable' Benjamin, with large rainwater shower, 'terrific views, designer hip bath, all the bells and whistles'. Another regretted that dog-friendly Manser's bathroom was only partially adapted for a wheelchair while commenting that otherwise, the place is 'excellently run with attentive, well-trained staff and out-of-this world food'. Breakfast brings Brittany's pastries, Buck's Fizz or Bloody Mary. 'Bound to return.' (John Chambers, Mark Lowe)

Pewsey
East Chisenbury SN9 6AQ

T: 01980 671124
E: troutbeck@redlionfreehouse.com
W: redlionfreehouse.com

BEDROOMS: 5. On ground floor, 1 partially suitable for disabled.
OPEN: all year except 25/26 Dec, closed all day Sun, Mon, and Tues lunch.
FACILITIES: bar/restaurant, private dining room, in-room TV (Freeview), ½-acre garden, restaurant wheelchair accessible, no adapted toilet.
BACKGROUND MUSIC: in pub/restaurant.
LOCATION: in village, 6 miles S of Pewsey.
CHILDREN: all ages welcomed, travel cot £25, extra bed (aged 3–10) £50.
DOGS: allowed in 1 bedroom by arrangement (£10 per night).
CREDIT CARDS: Amex, MC, Visa.
PRICES: B&B doubles from £195. À la carte £50, 5-course fixed-price menu £55, pre-booked 7-course tasting menu £85.

Prices may change – check with hotel.

EAST GRINSTEAD Sussex

MAP 2:D4

GRAVETYE MANOR

Deep in the Sussex countryside, a romantic Elizabethan manor house, built by an ironmaster for his bride, stands amid 1,000 acres of historically important gardens, pleasure grounds and woodland. Oak-panelled public rooms are filled with antiques. In the dining room, George Blogg's elegant Michelin-starred menus feature produce from orchard and kitchen garden, with foraged ingredients, in dishes such as roe venison, beetroot and red chicory; spring greens, hen of the woods, cèpe and wild garlic; crab apple, caramelised white chocolate and thyme. Beyond glass walls, flowers overspill borders laid out by William Robinson, pioneer of wild and natural gardening, who lived here until his death in 1935. Bedrooms are traditionally furnished, with signature floral fabrics, perhaps dual-aspect windows, a four-poster bed. Praise from readers is unstinted. 'From arrival to departure our stay was magical. Such naturally friendly staff, with such a fantastic kitchen – every meal was perfection.' 'Best hotel we have stayed at in Britain so far.' It is a Relais & Châteaux hotel. (Ralph Wilson, Mrs E Gould)

Vowels Lane
West Hoathly
East Grinstead RH19 4LJ

T: 01342 810567
E: info@gravetyemanor.co.uk
W: gravetyemanor.co.uk

BEDROOMS: 17.
OPEN: all year.
FACILITIES: 2 lounges, bar, restaurant (vegan/vegetarian menus), 2 private dining rooms, in-room TV (Sky), civil wedding licence, 1,000-acre grounds (woodland, ornamental and kitchen gardens, meadow, orchard, lake, croquet lawn, glasshouses), EV charging, restaurant wheelchair accessible, adapted toilet.
BACKGROUND MUSIC: in bar.
LOCATION: 4 miles SW of East Grinstead.
CHILDREN: not under 8, extra bed £40.
DOGS: not allowed.
CREDIT CARDS: Amex, MC, Visa.
PRICES: B&B doubles from £360, single from £193. Fixed-price dinner £105. 1-night bookings sometimes refused at weekends.

Prices may change – check with hotel.

EAST HOATHLY Sussex

MAP 2:E4

OLD WHYLY

'A curling gravel drive lined with mature trees and wild flowers' leads to this 'exceptionally beautiful Georgian manor house' B&B. Our inspectors were greeted by owner Sarah Burgoyne, who served tea 'in pretty china cups' and cake in the garden. The interiors were furnished with 'good antiques, large sofas, Victorian rugs, oil paintings, including a fine full-length portrait of Sarah herself'. Their bedroom was 'spacious, with a big, comfortable bed, good linen, tea, coffee, milk, a few biscuits', and a large private bathroom across the hall, with 'a roll-top bath (no shower)'. The 'sweet-smelling gardens' had a 'small, rather glamorous swimming pool tucked away behind a hedge'. Beyond, 'a wild-flower meadow glowed in the golden evening light'. At night, Sarah cooks a three-course dinner, on request, taken communally. 'The candles were lit, wine was poured, conversation flowed.' If portions were modest, 'breakfast was ample, with freshly squeezed orange juice, first-rate porridge', eggs from Sarah's hens, honey from the hives in the orchard. 'It was a privilege to stay somewhere as unforgettably lovely.' (IW, P and CB, and others)

London Road
East Hoathly BN8 6EL

T: 01825 840216
E: stay@oldwhyly.co.uk
W: oldwhyly.co.uk

BEDROOMS: 4.
OPEN: all year.
FACILITIES: drawing room, dining room, in-room TV (Freeview), 4-acre garden, heated outdoor swimming pool (14 by 7 metres), tennis, unsuitable for disabled.
BACKGROUND MUSIC: none.
LOCATION: 1 mile N of village.
CHILDREN: all ages welcomed, extra bed £35.
DOGS: allowed in bedrooms (£10 charge, not unattended), in drawing room, not in dining room.
CREDIT CARDS: none.
PRICES: B&B doubles from £130. Set dinner £45, hamper £45 per person. No card payments. 1-night bookings may be refused at weekends in summer season.

Prices may change – check with hotel.

EAST PORTLEMOUTH Devon

MAP 1:E4

GARA ROCK

A 'coastal getaway' comes into its own at this chilled-out cliff-top hotel at the end of winding country lanes and poised above a beach accessible only on foot or by boat. No wonder it's popular with families who want to cut loose, dog owners who relish freedom and anyone who wants to just kick back. The 'stylish yet relaxed' hotel 'makes the most if its surroundings'; rooms and apartments offer views of the views or gardens. They are rustic chic with sisal carpets, natural woods and a pale-washed palette; all have robes, coffee machines and luxurious bathrooms, some with freestanding baths. Apartments and the Penthouse are suited to families while the Secret Suite, with a hot tub, is for romantics. Food is 'a highlight', served in the bistro with floor-to-ceiling windows overlooking the sea, or on the terrace. 'Tasty and unpretentious' dishes might include Salcombe crab hotpot and pork belly with burnt apple, as well as steaks, and fish and chips. Enjoy the spa or pool, mess about on the beach, take a walk on the South West Coast Path; if raining, retreat to the cinema. Staff ensure 'we had everything we wanted'.

East Portlemouth
Salcombe TQ8 8FA

T: 01548 845946
E: info@gararock.com
W: gararock.com

BEDROOMS: 33. Accessed externally, 1 suite separate from hotel.
OPEN: all year.
FACILITIES: restaurant, private dining area, lounge bar, spa, cinema room, terrace, indoor and outdoor pool, in-room TV, civil wedding licence, EV charging, public rooms wheelchair accessible, adapted toilet on floor below, reached via lift.
BACKGROUND MUSIC: in public areas.
LOCATION: on cliff-top, 1 mile SE of East Portlemouth.
CHILDREN: all ages welcomed, no charge for extra bed.
DOGS: allowed in some rooms (£40 per stay), grounds, lounge bar and restaurant.
CREDIT CARDS: Amex, MC, Visa.
PRICES: room-only doubles from £325. Breakfast £19.50, à la carte dinner £50. Min. 2-night bookings.

Prices may change – check with hotel.

EASTBOURNE Sussex

MAP 2:E4

BELLE TOUT LIGHTHOUSE

Remote on a cliff-top between the English Channel and the rolling downs, this decommissioned 19th-century lighthouse found new purpose in 2010 as a unique B&B. Only one bedroom, the circular Keeper's Loft, is in the lighthouse proper. It has a fireplace, a view over the red-and-white usurper, Beachy Head Lighthouse, and a ladder to a small double bed. There is more conventional, New England-style accommodation in the adjacent house. The nautical-themed Captain's Cabin has a fireplace, a feature brick wall and an en suite shower room. Old England has countryside views and a shower over a bath. Dual-aspect Shiraz looks towards the famous Seven Sisters chalk cliffs. 'Having looked at nearly all the rooms, we thought Shiraz was the best.' At 5 pm guests are invited to gather for drinks in a comfy sitting room, 'which was great fun'. You can bring a picnic supper, perhaps from the excellent deli in East Dean village, or drive there to dine at the 15th-century Tiger Inn. Afterwards, ascend to the lantern to be dazzled by the night sky. In the morning, breakfast is a feast, with 'good fresh coffee in a cafetière'.

Beachy Head Road
Eastbourne BN20 0AE

T: 01323 423185
E: info@belletout.co.uk
W: belletout.co.uk

BEDROOMS: 6. 5 in house, 1 in lighthouse tower (bunk bed).
OPEN: all year except Christmas/New Year.
FACILITIES: 2 lounges, breakfast room, free Wi-Fi (in some rooms and some public areas), in-room TV (Freeview), terrace, garden, unsuitable for disabled.
BACKGROUND MUSIC: none.
LOCATION: 3 miles W of Eastbourne, 2 miles S of East Dean village (pub, deli).
CHILDREN: not under 16.
DOGS: not allowed.
CREDIT CARDS: MC, Visa.
PRICES: B&B doubles from £175, singles from £136.50. Min. 2-night stay, though 1-night bookings may be accepted (check for availability in the week before proposed stay).

Prices may change – check with hotel.

SEE ALSO SHORTLIST

EASTON GREY Wiltshire   MAP 3:E5

WHATLEY MANOR

Roses ramble over honey stone and wisteria
cascades around stone mullioned casements
at this Cotswolds country house hotel, with
spa, gym, cinema and 'luxury' written all over
it. Owned by Swiss mother and son Alix and
Christian Landolt, it centres on a Georgian
farmhouse, extended over two centuries. Twenty-
six ornamental gardens, many based on a 1920s
plan, have 'wonderful plants and water features'.
Three donkey sculptures are by Edouard-Marcel
Sandoz, Christian's renowned great-grandfather.
Bedrooms range from contemporary classics with
a heated bathroom floor, home-made biscuits and
elderflower cordial, to split-level suites. Try an
elaborate tasting menu from new executive chef
Ricki Weston at the Michelin-starred Dining
Room. In the brasserie and kitchen garden terrace,
there is more casual fare such as confit duck leg
and cassoulet. 'The staff are outstanding,' wrote
a reader, who opted for the brasserie, where 'the
food was good but not outstanding' and 'our
table was tucked behind a display cabinet'. At
breakfast there is honey from the hives, one of
many green initiatives.

Easton Grey SN16 0RB

T: 01666 822888
E: reservations@whatleymanor.com
W: whatleymanor.com

BEDROOMS: 23. Some on ground floor,
1 suitable for disabled.
OPEN: all year, generally Wed–Sun,
Dining Room Thurs–Sun eve.
FACILITIES: 3 lounges, 2 bars, brasserie,
restaurant (vegetarian/vegan menus),
cinema, gym, spa, in-room TV, EV
charging, 12-acre gardens, civil
wedding licence, public areas and
restaurants wheelchair accessible,
adapted toilet.
BACKGROUND MUSIC: in public areas.
LOCATION: 6½ miles from Tetbury.
CHILDREN: not under 12, extra bed £75.
DOGS: in some bedrooms (£30 per
night), garden, not restaurant or bar.
CREDIT CARDS: Amex, MC, Visa.
PRICES: B&B doubles from £279.
Tasting menu £175, à la carte £50
(brasserie). 1-night bookings usually
refused at weekends.

Prices may change – check with hotel.

ECKINGTON Worcestershire

MAP 3:D5

ECKINGTON MANOR

A cavorting Pan with an overflowing cornucopia promises all manner of good things at Judy Gardner's restaurant-with-rooms and cookery school in 60 acres of water-meadow pasture. Bedrooms are spread across the ancient, timber-frame Lower End farmhouse and a beautifully converted cider mill, grain barn and milking parlour. They have character and charm, come with original beams and flagstones, leather chairs, hand-painted silk wallpaper, maybe an in-room feature bath or log-effect gas-burning stove. 'Classic' rooms are on the ground floor. All have apple juice from the orchards, a Fired Earth shower, White Company toiletries. Lunch and dinner are served in a first-floor dining room overlooking the farmhouse. The restaurant combines British and European cuisine to create farm-to-fork dishes such as sirloin of Eckington beef, ox cheek croquette, hay-baked turnip, black garlic. Awake to croissants from the Aga, home-made granola, a full English with Eckington Manor sausages. 'We carried our breakfast to the sunny herb garden one morning.' (TS)

Hammock Road
Eckington WR10 3BJ

T: 01386 751600
E: info@eckingtonmanor.co.uk
W: eckingtonmanor.co.uk

BEDROOMS: 16. In courtyard annexes, some on ground floor.
OPEN: all year except 25/26 Dec, lunch served Thurs–Sun, dinner Wed–Sat.
FACILITIES: lift, 2 sitting rooms (1 with bar), restaurant, function rooms, in-room TV, civil wedding licence, cookery school, 260-acre grounds (herb garden, farm), public areas wheelchair accessible, adapted toilet.
BACKGROUND MUSIC: in bar and restaurant.
LOCATION: 4 miles SW of Pershore.
CHILDREN: not under 8, extra bed £35 in luxury rooms.
DOGS: small/medium dogs allowed in 1 bedroom (£15 per stay), not in public rooms.
CREDIT CARDS: MC, Visa.
PRICES: B&B doubles from £159. Set dinner £49.50, tasting menus (vegetarian option) £75.

Prices may change – check with hotel.

EDENBRIDGE Kent   MAP 2:D4

HEVER CASTLE B&B

If Anne Boleyn could return to her childhood home, she would be astonished to find a 'wonderful B&B for history lovers', housed in a 'Tudor village' in landscaped parkland with Italian garden, Japanese tea house and 35-acre lake. Built for William Waldorf Astor in the early 1900s for the guest overflow from his fairy-tale moated castle, it 'has been done exceptionally well', says an inspector as it enters the main Guide. 'Some bedrooms have elaborate plaster ceilings or beams, perhaps a four-poster.' A twin was 'delightful, with balloon-motif wallpaper and supremely comfy beds'. UHT milk was a minus, an umbrella a thoughtful plus. The Anne Boleyn wing is less grand than the Astor Wing, though the Edward VII suite has 'superb castle views, an enormous bed as well as a sofa bed in the sitting area'. Breakfast, served till a rather early 9.30 in a 'magnificent oak-panelled dining room', included an excellent buffet, 'superb avocado and poached egg on sourdough. I felt like bluff King Hal when I'd finished.' Overnighters not only have use of lounge and billiard room, but the huge bonus of 'out-of-hours access to the gorgeous grounds'.

Hever Castle
Hever
Edenbridge TN8 7NG

T: 01732 861800
E: stay@hevercastle.co.uk
W: hevercastle.co.uk

BEDROOMS: 28. Some on ground floor, some suitable for disabled, 1 adapted for wheelchair. Plus self-catering Medley Court cottage.
OPEN: all year except 25 and 31 Dec.
FACILITIES: lounge, billiard room, in-room TV (Sky, Freeview), civil wedding licence, courtyard garden, tennis court, 625-acre grounds, breakfast rooms, lounges wheelchair accessible, adapted toilet.
BACKGROUND MUSIC: none.
LOCATION: 1½ miles from Hever station.
CHILDREN: all ages welcomed, cot £20, extra bed for under-13s £50, for 2 sharing sofa bed £65.
DOGS: not allowed.
CREDIT CARDS: Amex, MC, Visa.
PRICES: B&B doubles from £175, singles from £110.

Prices may change – check with hotel.

EGTON BRIDGE Yorkshire   MAP 4:C5

BROOM HOUSE
AT EGTON BRIDGE

When you sit in the garden of this farmhouse B&B, with views of fields and moors, it feels very rural yet Egton Bridge is only a ten-minute walk away. Victorian Broom House is 'beautifully situated in a quiet country lane', says a reader. 'Such a restful spot.' The house, run by 'warm and welcoming hosts' Luke and Brianne Cockill, has been stylishly updated with slate floors, light oak doors and Farrow & Ball colours. Bedrooms are 'uncluttered and thoughtfully decorated' with pale-painted or pine furniture, creamy walls – an occasional feature wallpaper – and modern bathrooms. Cosier second-floor rooms have beams; all have garden and moorland views. The garden suite has a patio. Walk from the doorstep – the coast-to-coast path is half a mile away – and return to tea and cake in the fire-warmed sitting room or on the south-facing terrace, or something stronger from the honesty bar. Breakfast, in the French-windowed dining room, has 'a very good fruit cup' and cooked-to-order dishes such as avocado and poached egg, and a full grill. For evenings, village pubs are a stroll along the river, 'a relaxing way to end the day'. (MH)

Broom House Lane
Egton Bridge YO21 1XD

T: 07423 636783
E: info@broom-house.co.uk
W: broom-house.co.uk

BEDROOMS: 7. 1 in cottage annexe.
OPEN: mid-Mar–end of Oct.
FACILITIES: lounge, breakfast room, in-room TV (Freeview), 1-acre garden, unsuitable for disabled.
BACKGROUND MUSIC: in breakfast room.
LOCATION: ½ mile W of village.
CHILDREN: over-12s welcomed.
DOGS: not allowed.
CREDIT CARDS: MC, Visa.
PRICES: B&B doubles from £120. Min. 2-night stay.

Prices may change – check with hotel.

ELLASTONE Staffordshire

MAP 3:B6

THE DUNCOMBE ARMS

A once run-down, boarded-up village boozer
with views over the Dove valley is today a
thriving gastropub-with-rooms in the care of
owners Laura and Johnny Greenall. The bar and
dining rooms have a welcoming ambience, with
flagstones and floorboards, horsy prints, a log
fire, sheepskins, padded banquettes, bare brick
alongside Farrow & Ball. The 'well-equipped-
and-thought-out' bedrooms in Willow House
have lovely wallpaper, carefully curated artwork,
a Roberts radio, an espresso machine, home-made
biscuits, Bamford toiletries. A reader reported that
'one of the nicest hotel rooms I have ever stayed
in' was sadly let down by a restaurant they felt was
'too trendy, too noisy and too expensive'. Guide
insiders, though, commented on the 'excellent
food', which you can eat outside or in the bar from
a choice of pub staples and Jake Boyce's creative
seasonal dishes – maybe glazed baby cauliflower,
radish, kale, walnut or 50-day-aged rib of beef
with wild garlic pesto. The breakfast croissants
and sourdough bread are, like everything else,
fresh from the kitchen. The compleat angler will
want to fish on the River Dove.

Ellastone
Ashbourne DE6 2GZ

T: 01335 324275
E: hello@duncombearms.co.uk
W: duncombearms.co.uk

BEDROOMS: 10. All in Walnut House
annexe, with 2 family rooms,
1 suitable for disabled.
OPEN: all year.
FACILITIES: bar, 2 dining rooms plus
private dining room, in-room TV
(Freeview), no mobile signal, garden
(alfresco dining, fire pit), EV charging,
bar and dining room wheelchair
accessible, adapted toilet.
BACKGROUND MUSIC: in bar and
restaurant.
LOCATION: on B5032, 5 miles SW of
Ashbourne.
CHILDREN: all ages welcomed, under-
12s extra bed £30.
DOGS: allowed in some bedrooms
(£20 per night), bar.
CREDIT CARDS: MC, Visa.
PRICES: B&B doubles from £195.
À la carte £40.

Prices may change – check with hotel.

ERMINGTON Devon

MAP 1:D4

PLANTATION HOUSE

From bread to truffles, they cook as much as possible on site in this little hotel, in the rolling South Hams countryside, between wild Dartmoor and the sandy beaches of Bigbury Bay. But as well as raving over the 'delicious food', readers give the thumbs up to the rooms in the former Georgian rectory. One wrote that he had 'a good bed, though not a huge one', while another was delighted to find that 'the bathroom even had two speakers in the ceiling'. All bedrooms come with much-appreciated extras: home-made cake, ground coffee and a cafetière, biscuits, mineral water, fresh fruit, flowers and luxury toiletries. Meals are the start of the show, with owner Richard Hendey and chef John Raines using home-grown and wild ingredients, plus locally caught fish, to create dishes such as brill with chive potato cake, lime hollandaise, ginger courgettes and asparagus. The choice at breakfast includes 'very tasty home-made bread', locally pressed organic apple juice, nuts, seeds and honey with figs and Hunza apricots, smoked haddock, or four-minute-ten-second boiled egg with asparagus and toast soldiers. (ML, and others)

Totnes Road
Ermington
Plymouth PL21 9NS

T: 01548 831100
E: info@plantationhousehotel.co.uk
W: plantationhousehotel.co.uk

BEDROOMS: 8.
OPEN: all year, restaurant (dinner only) closed some Sun evenings.
FACILITIES: lounge/bar, 2 dining rooms, in-room TV (Freeview), in-room massage, terrace, 1-acre garden, restaurant, bar and lounge wheelchair accessible, no adapted toilet.
BACKGROUND MUSIC: background jazz (sometimes live) in public rooms, classical 'when suitable'.
LOCATION: 10 miles E of Plymouth.
CHILDREN: all ages welcomed, extra bed £15.
DOGS: allowed in 1 bedroom (no charge), not in public rooms.
CREDIT CARDS: Amex, MC, Visa.
PRICES: B&B doubles from £170 (book directly to discuss discounts). Set dinner £45. 1-night bookings sometimes refused at bank holiday weekends.

Prices may change – check with hotel.

EVERSHOT Dorset   MAP 1:C6

THE ACORN INN

Thomas Hardy fans will be in their element at
this local watering hole in Dorset, which was the
model for 'The Sow and Acorn' in Tess of the
d'Urbervilles. While Tess chose not to breakfast
here, today's literary pilgrim should stop in for
a pint of Proper Job and a ploughman's in one
of two bars or the beer garden. Log fires burn
cheerily in public spaces. A reader, dining in the
restaurant, was disappointed with soggy battered
fish, but 'the posher menu was much better. Duck
leg in cherry sauce, ravioli, roast pork and katsu
curry were all excellent.' Bedrooms vary in shape
and size, though the 'characterful old building'
can present challenges. The loft suite, under the
eaves, despite sloping ceilings, has ample space
for a family, with a double and single bedroom,
lounge and large bathroom. A bay-windowed
four-poster room was, however, cramped, more so
the bathroom. 'Nevertheless, we would certainly
visit again.' Staff are 'very friendly and efficient'
and everything runs like a 'well-oiled machine'.
For £15 guests can use the spa at sister hotel
Summer Lodge (next entry). (Peter Anderson,
JT, and others)

28 Fore Street
Evershot DT2 0JW

T: 01935 83228
E: stay@acorn-inn.co.uk
W: acorn-inn.co.uk

BEDROOMS: 10.
OPEN: all year. Closed lunchtime Mon
and Tues.
FACILITIES: 2 bars, restaurant, lounge,
in-room TV (Freeview), skittle
alley, beer garden, access to spa,
gym at sister hotel opposite (£15 per
day), parking, bar and restaurant
wheelchair accessible, toilet not
adapted.
BACKGROUND MUSIC: in bar and
restaurant.
LOCATION: in village, 10 miles S of
Yeovil.
CHILDREN: all ages welcomed, extra
bed £20, childen's menu.
DOGS: allowed by prior arrangement
in bedrooms (£12 a night, towels and
treats), public areas, not restaurant.
CREDIT CARDS: Amex, MC, Visa.
PRICES: B&B doubles from £130.
À la carte £45. Min. 2-night stay at
weekends in peak season.

Prices may change – check with hotel.

EVERSHOT Dorset

MAP 1:C6

SUMMER LODGE

Staying in this Georgian mansion in 'flower-filled and perfectly tended gardens' is 'a pretty faultless experience', with 'every detail properly attended to but the atmosphere still friendly and relaxed', say readers. Tea in a drawing room designed by Thomas Hardy arrived with complimentary 'home-made cookies, the best we'd ever eaten'. Rooms range from a cosy double with fine fabrics and a print of L S Lowry's 'A Cricket Match', to a beautifully presented cottage with an original Matisse. All have fresh fruit and flowers, shortbread and luxury toiletries. One reader's spacious first-floor room had 'a super-king bed, an armchair, a chaise longue, great garden views, some interesting art'. At dinner, Steven Titman's locally sourced menus include dishes such as lamb loin with Jerusalem artichoke and kale; for vegans, maple-roasted pumpkin risotto with curry spice and coconut. 'Dinner was impeccable, with the bonus of a separate menu for vegetarians.' For simpler fare pop out to sister property The Acorn Inn (previous entry). 'Not a cheap stay, but worth every penny.' 'A genuine luxury hotel.' (Ian Bronks, B and ID, JC, and others)

9 Fore Street
Evershot DT2 0JR

T: 01935 482000
E: summerlodge@rchmail.com
W: summerlodgehotel.com

BEDROOMS: 25. 6 in coach house, 4 in courtyard, 5 in cottages, 1 on ground floor suitable for disabled.
OPEN: all year.
FACILITIES: lounge, drawing room, restaurant (vegetarian/vegan menu), conservatory, meeting room, in-room TV (Sky), indoor pool, spa, civil wedding licence, 4-acre grounds (tennis), EV charging, public rooms wheelchair accessible, adapted toilet.
BACKGROUND MUSIC: in bar/whisky lounge.
LOCATION: 10 miles S of Yeovil.
CHILDREN: all ages welcomed, cots £25, extra bed £50, children's menu.
DOGS: allowed in some bedrooms (£20 per night), whisky lounge.
CREDIT CARDS: Amex, MC, Visa.
PRICES: B&B doubles from £265. À la carte £85. 1-night bookings sometimes refused.

Prices may change – check with hotel.

EXETER Devon

SOUTHERNHAY HOUSE

A Roman Doric portico makes a swanky statement about this Grade II listed Georgian house, but within lies a stylish yet relaxed and fun boutique hotel. Owners Deborah Clark and Tony Orchard ran Burgh Island Hotel, Bigbury-on-Sea (see entry) for almost 17 years before selling it, and do things with panache. Bedrooms wittily reference Southernhay's original owner, an officer, diplomat and orientalist, who worked for the East India Company. They range from luxury, with super-king bed, a large bathroom, freestanding bath and walk-in shower, down to 'intimate', with no compromise on quality. 'Sugar' room is adorned with vintage Cuba posters. All rooms have luxury toiletries and a minibar. 'The staff were lovely,' readers relate. 'Food good, beautiful house, lots of interesting furniture.' They were pleased to have taken the train as 'opportunities for parking appeared to be limited'. The kitchen is open all day, and a monthly changing menu of Devon produce includes dishes such as spiced haddock fishcakes with Thai cucumber salad. Eat where you will, in the bar, Club Room, in a glass pavilion or alfresco – just enjoy yourself! (John Saul)

36 Southernhay East
Exeter EX1 1NX

T: 01392 439000
E: home@southernhayhouse.com
W: southernhayhouse.com

BEDROOMS: 12. 1 apartment in separate building.
OPEN: all year.
FACILITIES: bar, Club Room, Green Room (glass pavilion), private dining room, in-room TV (Freeview), 'pocket garden', veranda, terrace, civil wedding licence, public rooms wheelchair accessible.
BACKGROUND MUSIC: in public areas.
LOCATION: central Exeter.
CHILDREN: over-14s welcomed on an adult basis.
DOGS: only in garden and on terrace.
CREDIT CARDS: MC, Visa.
PRICES: B&B doubles from £250. À la carte £40.

Prices may change – check with hotel.

EXMOUTH Devon

MAP 1:D5

LYMPSTONE MANOR

Michelin-starred chef Michael Caines has created a country house hotel for the 21st century (Relais & Châteaux) in a Georgian mansion overlooking the Exe estuary, with an ambience of soft-spoken luxury. Interiors reflect the natural beauty of the landscape, in shades of dove grey, blue, champagne and gold, with oak floors, bespoke wallpaper, and paintings by wildlife artist Rachel Toll of the estuary birds after which bedrooms are named. Even the least expensive rooms have a gin tray, an espresso machine, L'Occitane toiletries and hair straighteners. Some estuary-view suites have a balcony or a terrace with fire pit and marble soak tub. Heron has floor-to-ceiling windows, a marble-tiled bathroom, side-by-side brass bathtubs. Or take one of the shepherd huts for bucolic bliss. They come with kitchenettes, but you'd be crazy not to eat in one of the three beautiful dining rooms. Here, nightly menus might bring butter-poached Brixham turbot, braised leeks, poached scallops, with truffle and chive butter sauce, or barbecued hen of the woods, onion consommé, cauliflower. It's an expensive but memorable experience.

Courtlands Lane
Exmouth EX8 3NZ

T: 01395 202040
E: welcome@lympstonemanor.co.uk
W: lympstonemanor.co.uk

BEDROOMS: 27. 5 on ground floor, 1 suitable for disabled. 6 shepherd huts.
OPEN: all year.
FACILITIES: 3 dining rooms (vegetarian/vegan menus), reception lounge, lounge, bar, in-room TV (Freeview), civil wedding licence, 28-acre grounds, EV charging, public areas wheelchair accessible, adapted toilet.
BACKGROUND MUSIC: all day in public rooms.
LOCATION: in centre, close to waterfront.
CHILDREN: all ages welcomed, extra bed £60, no under-6s in restaurant.
DOGS: in 2 bedrooms and shepherd huts (£30 a night), not in main house.
CREDIT CARDS: Amex, MC, Visa.
PRICES: B&B doubles from £316, singles from £292. Tasting menus £180–£195, à la carte £155.

Prices may change – check with hotel.

FAR SAWREY Cumbria

CUCKOO BROW INN

Upgraded to the main Guide, this jolly country inn, between Lake Windermere and Beatrix Potter's Hill Top home, welcomes walkers, dogs and children with smiles, robust food and toasty log-burners. 'This Lakeland gem is bursting with character and rustic charm,' reports one family. 'From the moment we arrived we were met with warm and friendly owners.' The long bar-dining area, with central log-burner (useful for drying boots), has cheery scrubbed tables and spindle-back chairs, and there's a snug/games room in the adjoining former stables. Meals are 'cooked to perfection and extremely tasty' with 'a good choice of fish, meat and vegetarian dishes' that includes pub classics and more inventive options: venison cheeseburger, perhaps, or king prawn and chorizo linguine. 'Spotlessly clean' bedrooms, in the main pub and an extension above the old stables, have a simple, unfussy style. Family rooms come with bunk beds. Spacious bathrooms, most with baths as well as showers, have 'plenty of hot water with good pressure'. 'Freshly cooked' breakfast will set you up for a day's walking. 'We shall definitely be returning.' (Mark Johnson)

Far Sawrey
Ambleside LA22 0LQ

T: 015394 43425
E: stay@cuckoobrow.co.uk
W: cuckoobrow.co.uk

BEDROOMS: 14. 1 on ground floor.
OPEN: all year.
FACILITIES: lobby lounge, bar/dining room, games room/snug, in-room TV (Freeview), terrace, beer garden, public rooms wheelchair accessible.
BACKGROUND MUSIC: in bar, games room/snug.
LOCATION: centre of hamlet.
CHILDREN: all ages welcomed, extra bed £32.50 incl. breakfast.
DOGS: allowed in bedrooms (£10 per night), public rooms.
CREDIT CARDS: MC, Visa.
PRICES: B&B doubles from £120. 3-course à la carte £33.

Prices may change – check with hotel.

FAVERSHAM Kent

MAP 2:D5

READ'S

You can expect 'really excellent food with an interesting menu and varied wine list' at Rona and David Pitchford's restaurant-with-rooms in a Georgian manor house on the edge of a historic market town. After more than 40 years at the stove, first in the nearby village of Painters Forstal, then in Faversham, including 20 years of Michelin stardom, Mr Pitchford took a step back. Since 2020, Frederick Forster, a former National Chef of the Year and Roux Scholar, has won plaudits here for his dishes, such as Stour valley chicken breast with glazed sweet potato, buttered kale, wild mushroom tempura. There's an added bonus too, in the wine list, 'with lower mark-ups than usual in the UK'. The bedrooms are spacious, the style classic (imagine staying in the country house of a rich aunt), and everything is 'very quiet, even though close to a busy road'. Laurel has an antique four-poster; Lime has pink toile de Jouy wallpaper; dual-aspect Chestnut overlooks the front lawn and eponymous tree. There is tea and coffee in a pantry/honesty bar on the landing. After a delicious breakfast, the fishing town of Whitstable is your oyster. (IGC Farman)

Macknade Manor
Canterbury Road
Faversham ME13 8XE

T: 01795 535344
E: enquiries@reads.com
W: reads.com

BEDROOMS: 6.
OPEN: all year Tues–Sat, except 4 days at Christmas, first 2 weeks Jan, 2 weeks Sept.
FACILITIES: sitting room/bar, 4 dining rooms, in-room TV (Freeview), civil wedding licence, 4-acre garden (terrace, outdoor dining), restaurant wheelchair accessible, adapted toilet.
BACKGROUND MUSIC: none.
LOCATION: ½ mile SE of Faversham.
CHILDREN: all ages welcomed, on sofa bed in one room, £40.
DOGS: guide dogs only.
CREDIT CARDS: MC, Visa.
PRICES: B&B doubles from £230, singles from £170. Set-price lunch £38, tasting menu £48, dinner £65, tasting menu £75.

Prices may change – check with hotel.

FELIXKIRK Yorkshire

MAP 4:C4

THE CARPENTERS ARMS

Overlooking the Vale of York, this deceptively
large village inn blends traditional pub features
with Scandi-style bedrooms, and classy food
with a range of good ales. The whitewashed
exterior, with colourful hanging baskets, leads
to a beamed and flagged bar with copper pans,
wood-burning stove, scrubbed-wood tables and
pea-green walls. Beyond, the light-filled dining
area has sliding glass doors to a heated terrace
and gardens. Choose any of these areas to dine on
food that is strong on local products, including
from the inn's own kitchen garden. Pub classics of
beer-battered fish and chips and home-made pie
are offered alongside smarter dishes such as gin-
cured sea trout, and lamb with tomato, mint and
pea fricassée. Bedrooms in the pub have a cottagey
style with beams, colourful plaid fabrics and
shower-only bathrooms; new-build chalet-style
rooms around the garden are larger and lighter
with space for a sofa, bathrooms with under-floor
heating, a fire for chillier days and glass doors
to a patio. Breakfast includes home-grown fresh
fruit salad, eggs Benedict and a full grill with
vegetarian option – plus those wonderful views.

Felixkirk
Thirsk YO7 2DP

T: 01845 537369
E: enquiries@
    thecarpentersarmsfelixkirk.com
W: thecarpentersarmsfelixkirk.com

BEDROOMS: 10. 8 in single-storey
garden annexe, 1 suitable for disabled.
OPEN: all year.
FACILITIES: bar/sitting area, restaurant,
private dining room, in-room TV
(Freeview), partially covered and
heated terrace, garden, public rooms
on ground floor wheelchair accessible,
adapted toilet.
BACKGROUND MUSIC: at mealtimes in
bar and restaurant.
LOCATION: in village, 3 miles NE of
Thirsk.
CHILDREN: all ages welcomed, extra
bed £35.
DOGS: allowed in garden bedrooms
(£10 a night) and bar.
CREDIT CARDS: Amex, MC, Visa.
PRICES: B&B doubles from £176.
À la carte £36.

Prices may change – check with hotel.

FLEET Dorset

MAP 1:D6

MOONFLEET MANOR

'As a family we have said we need to try to visit
once a year at least,' write readers after a visit to
this child-friendly, dog-friendly hotel occupying
a Georgian manor house above Chesil Beach.
Part of the Luxury Family Hotels group (see
Woolley Grange, Bradford-on-Avon, and Fowey
Hall, Fowey), it 'does what it says on the tin',
providing for all generations, with a crèche, baby-
listening, a Four Bears Den, Sunday breakfast
club, swimming pool and baby pool, and 'Toddle
Waddle' guided walks. A huge indoor play area
has everything from a skittle alley to a climbing
wall. Bedrooms house a mix of contemporary and
period furniture, and even some of the smallest
have a balcony. A two-storey coach house suite
'worked brilliantly for our group' with 'stunning
views over Chesil Beach'. All have Bramley
toiletries, and ongoing improvements should
see any tired decor refreshed. In the restaurant
and on the decked terrace, 'food is a cut above
what you might expect from a family hotel', with
dishes such as Cornish hake with spring vegetable
broth. Child portions extend to breakfast. 'My
grandchildren love the place.' (CL Hodgkin)

Fleet Road
Fleet DT3 4ED

T: 01305 786948
E: info@moonfleetmanorhotel.co.uk
W: moonfleetmanorhotel.co.uk

BEDROOMS: 36. 3 in coach house, 3 in
villa, 3 ground floor.
OPEN: all year.
FACILITIES: 3 lounges, restaurant,
playroom, crèche, cinema, in-room
TV (Freeview), civil wedding licence,
indoor swimming pools, tennis, 5-acre
garden, EV charging, public areas
wheelchair accessible, no adapted
toilet.
BACKGROUND MUSIC: in public areas.
LOCATION: 7 miles W of Weymouth.
CHILDREN: all ages welcomed, no
charge for extra beds, last entrance for
children in dining room 7.30 pm.
DOGS: allowed in bedrooms (£15 a
night), on lead in public rooms, not in
restaurant.
CREDIT CARDS: Amex, MC, Visa.
PRICES: B&B doubles from £120.
À la carte £38. 1- and 2-night bookings
sometimes refused at weekends.

Prices may change – check with hotel.

FOWEY Cornwall

MAP 1:D3

FOWEY HALL

'The friendly, local staff are all smiles' at this fun, stylish hotel occupying a baroque Victorian mansion on a hilltop above the Fowey estuary. Part of the Luxury Family Hotels group (see Woolley Grange, Bradford-on-Avon, and Moonfleet Manor, Fleet), it has something for everyone, not forgetting your dog, with a crèche, cinema, library, den, spa, indoor pool and Wind in the Willows-inspired outdoor play area (Kenneth Grahame wiled away days in Fowey, messing about in boats; Fowey Hall may have been his model for Toad Hall). In public rooms, 'light, modern decor' offsets ornate plasterwork, panelling, pediments and pilasters. Flexible dining includes an all-day menu and a children's high tea. At night, local ingredients appear in dishes such as steaks 'cooked to perfection', roast halibut bouillabaisse, red lentil moussaka. Bedrooms are painted in restful shades with larky touches. Some have an estuary view, extra Z-beds, a glass door to the garden. All have good toiletries. 'Our ground-floor garden-wing room was comfortable and contemporary.' The owners are splurging like Mr Toad on more bedrooms, an outdoor pool and spa terrace.

Hanson Drive
Fowey PL23 1ET

T: 01726 833866
E: info@foweyhallhotel.co.uk
W: foweyhallhotel.co.uk

BEDROOMS: 36. 8 in courtyard, some on ground floor, 1 suitable for disabled.
OPEN: all year.
FACILITIES: drawing room, library, morning room, restaurant, in-room TV (Freeview), crèche, games rooms, civil wedding licence, spa, indoor pool, 5-acre grounds, EV charging, public rooms wheelchair accessible, adapted toilet.
BACKGROUND MUSIC: in bar, lounge, restaurant.
LOCATION: ½ mile from town centre.
CHILDREN: all ages welcomed, no charge for extra beds.
DOGS: allowed in house bedrooms (£15 a night), bar and lounge, not restaurant.
CREDIT CARDS: Amex, MC, Visa.
PRICES: B&B doubles from £185, family from £320. Dinner à la carte £45. 1-night bookings refused at some weekends.

Prices may change – check with hotel.

FOWEY Cornwall

MAP 1:D3

THE OLD QUAY HOUSE

You're never far from watery views at this smart hotel which overlooks Cornwall's Fowey estuary. You can enjoy them as you tuck into lunch or dinner on the sun terrace which projects into the water from the whitewashed Victorian former seamen's billet, or from the restaurant within. They're on show too from some of the bedrooms, perhaps a loft suite with a super-king futon bed and separate lounge, or deluxe rooms with super-king bed, all with slipper bath and walk-in shower. Over three floors, the rooms are all contemporary and stylish, painted a hazy off-white, with stripy fabrics, blues and greys. There are plenty of seafood choices on the menu to reflect the setting. You might tuck into mussels or fish and chips for lunch as the wash from passing boats laps the terrace. For dinner, perhaps roast cod fillet with creamed leeks or smoked ham hock ballotine; then clotted cream parfait, raspberries, oats, champagne granita – if you haven't already lived it large with a cream tea. After breakfast, the independent arts and crafts shops and galleries of this lively little town await discovery.

28 Fore Street
Fowey PL23 1AQ

T: 01726 833302
E: info@theoldquayhouse.com
W: theoldquayhouse.com

BEDROOMS: 13.
OPEN: all year.
FACILITIES: open-plan lounge, bar, restaurant, in-room TV (Freeview), civil wedding licence, terrace, parking permits supplied, bar, lounge and restaurant wheelchair accessible.
BACKGROUND MUSIC: in public areas.
LOCATION: town centre.
CHILDREN: not under 12.
DOGS: not allowed.
CREDIT CARDS: Amex, MC, Visa.
PRICES: B&B doubles from £205.50, singles from £191.50. Set-price dinner £37.50/£45 (2/3 courses).

Prices may change – check with hotel.

GITTISHAM Devon

MAP 1:C5

THE PIG AT COMBE

The Gloriana of Robin Hutson's Pig hotel collection (see index), this Grade I listed Elizabethan beauty stands in 'wonderful grounds in a special location' in the peaceful Otter valley. Judy Hutson has hammed up the decor, with oak-branch chandeliers, lampshades fashioned from old silk saris, Zoffany fabrics, French antiques, oil portraits of bewigged bigwigs. Bedrooms are decorated in restful pastels. The smallest have a monsoon shower; some comfy-luxe rooms have a freestanding bath in the window. Among super-king four-poster rooms, the Laundry, with its own lounge, has a bathroom with circular copper tub. For the ultimate in rustic chic, the Horsebox, with cobbled floor, incorporates the old stable partitions. Whether you eat in the restaurant or outside, there is an 'impressive commitment to local sourcing' with much produce supplied from the three walled kitchen gardens. Dishes might include three-corner leek and ricotta gnocchi with garden kale, or organic lamb leg with lentils. 'The restaurant was busy, but the service was excellent and the food good.' Wood-fired flatbreads are served in and outside the once derelict Folly.

Gittisham
Honiton EX14 3AD

T: 01404 540400
E: reservations@thepighotel.com
W: thepighotel.com

BEDROOMS: 30. 10 in stable yard, 5 in cottages (2 for family), 3 rooms suitable for disabled.
OPEN: all year.
FACILITIES: bar, 2 lounges, restaurant, Folly (communal dining), private dining rooms, in-room TV (Freeview), civil wedding licence, spa treatment rooms, 3,500-acre grounds, EV charging, public rooms wheelchair accessible, adapted toilet.
BACKGROUND MUSIC: in public areas.
LOCATION: on outskirts of village.
CHILDREN: all ages welcomed, no charge for extra beds.
DOGS: not allowed.
CREDIT CARDS: Amex, MC, Visa.
PRICES: room-only doubles from £195, family from £305. Breakfast £13.50–£18.50, à la carte £42. 1-night bookings sometimes refused.

Prices may change – check with hotel.

GRANTHAM Lincolnshire

THE BROWNLOW ARMS

Wing armchairs, table lamps and a Farrow & Ball palette blend with wooden bar stools and high-back settles in the cosy bar of this 19th-century ironstone and limestone village pub-with-rooms. Warmth comes from both the log fire and from much-loved landlady Lorraine Willoughby, who owns and runs the pub with her husband, Paul, and who readers say is the life and soul of the place. The bedrooms are not huge, but are very attractive, with antique furniture, complimentary biscuits and bottled water, and modern bathrooms with drench showers. In the restaurant, the menus are more high end than pub grub, with dishes such as 'excellent cheese soufflé', roast saddle of venison, and good, old-fashioned steak-and-kidney pud. On fine days, eat outside on the terrace and enjoy the rural setting. 'Breakfast was particularly good.' The conservation village, formerly part of the Brownlow estate, sits atop an escarpment with views over the Trent and Belvoir vales. 'Excellent accommodation and wonderful meals in a very interesting setting,' sums up a reader this year. 'Highly recommended.' (Roger Griffiths, Mary and Rodney Milne-Day, and others)

High Road
Hough-on-the-Hill
Grantham NG32 2AZ

т: 01400 250234
е: armsinn@yahoo.co.uk
w: thebrownlowarms.com

BEDROOMS: 5. 1 on ground floor in barn conversion.
OPEN: all year except for all public holidays, incl. 25/26 Dec, Mon all day, Sun eve, Tues–Sat lunch.
FACILITIES: bar, 3 dining rooms, patio, in-room TV (Freeview), unsuitable for disabled.
BACKGROUND MUSIC: in public areas.
LOCATION: rural, in village 7 miles N of Grantham.
CHILDREN: all ages welcomed, extra bed £15, no under-8s in restaurant in the evening.
DOGS: only guide dogs allowed.
CREDIT CARDS: MC, Visa.
PRICES: B&B doubles from £150, singles from £95. À la carte £45.

Prices may change – check with hotel.

GRASMERE Cumbria   MAP 4: inset C2

FOREST SIDE

'This hotel ranks amongst the very best that we
have stayed in,' says a reader about this Victorian
Gothic mansion with its cool, relaxed style, vast
kitchen garden and inspired culinary creations.
Highly praised dishes on chef Paul Leonard's
Michelin-starred menus include 'hand-dived
scallop, smoked bacon and garden alliums' and
'yeast parfait, chocolate and toasted barley'.
'Inspirational' wine choices include 'a good
selection of British' bottles. Vegetarian menus
get equal billing, and much produce comes from
the walled potager. The 'relaxed' dining room
makes the most of the garden views – spot the red
squirrels while enjoying a 'good choice' cooked-
to-order breakfast; other public rooms are in
shades of grey jazzed up with bold wallpapers
and modern art. 'Light and airy' bedrooms are
elegant, with Zoffany fabrics, Herdwick wool
carpets, beds by local company Harrison Spinks,
and Bramley toiletries in the limestone-tiled
bathrooms. There are hikes from the doorstep,
Grasmere is ten minutes across the fields, or just
relax on the terrace with 'the most wonderful
scones' for afternoon tea. (Anthony Bradbury,
David Reid)

Keswick Road
Grasmere LA22 9RN

T: 01539 435250
E: info@theforestside.com
W: theforestside.com

BEDROOMS: 20. 1 suitable for disabled.
OPEN: all year, excl. Mon/Tues Nov–
Mar, restaurant closed Mon/Tues
dinner, Mon–Thurs lunch throughout
year.
FACILITIES: lounge, bar, restaurant
(vegetarian menu), civil wedding
licence, in-room TV (Freeview),
terrace, 43-acre grounds, public rooms
wheelchair accessible, adapted toilet.
BACKGROUND MUSIC: in public areas.
LOCATION: outskirts of village.
CHILDREN: all ages welcomed, extra
bed £50, under-8s not allowed in
dining room in evening.
DOGS: allowed in some bedrooms (not
in public areas except bar 2–6 pm, £25
per night, welcome pack).
CREDIT CARDS: Amex, MC, Visa.
PRICES: B&B doubles from £249.
Tasting menu (residents only) 4-course
£65, 8-course £95.

Prices may change – check with hotel.

GRASMERE Cumbria

MAP 4: inset C2

THE GRASMERE HOTEL

In postcard-pretty Grasmere, this family-run Victorian country house hotel 'ticks all the boxes on accommodation, hospitality, food and reasonable prices'. It is run by the Winslands – Kevin, Nicki and two daughters – and their 'very friendly' staff, who have a 'quiet professionalism, delivered effortlessly and always with a smile'. No wonder so many guests return, as much for the location, with views to iconic Helm Crag and quiet garden overlooking the River Rothay, as the 'delicious food, with varied menus during our two-night stay'. Canapés in one of the fire-warmed lounges are the warm-up to starters such as confit duck leg and damson terrine, perhaps followed by Herdwick lamb with pea purée and basil pesto. The conservatory dining room, elegant with white cloths and napkins, overlooks the garden, 'a great spot to relax' after a day's walking (there are routes from the door). 'Immaculately presented' bedrooms have breezy colours, feature walls and simple furnishings, 'everything we required'. Breakfast is top-notch, with smoked salmon and haddock as well as a full Cumbrian, plus home-made preserves. 'We were spoilt.' (ES, FC)

Broadgate
Grasmere LA22 9TA

T: 01539 435277
E: info@grasmerehotel.co.uk
W: grasmerehotel.co.uk

BEDROOMS: 11. Some on ground floor.
OPEN: all year except 31 Dec–end Jan, restaurant closed Mon eve (lounge menu of soup and sandwiches offered).
FACILITIES: two lounges, restaurant for residents only, in-room TV (Freeview), ½-acre garden, unsuitable for disabled.
BACKGROUND MUSIC: in lounge and restaurant during mealtimes.
LOCATION: in village.
CHILDREN: aged 10 and over welcomed, no extra beds.
DOGS: not allowed.
CREDIT CARDS: MC, Visa.
PRICES: D,B&B doubles from £205 (from £145 on Mon), singles from £110 (from £80 on Mon). Min. 2-night stay normally required (check for 1-night availability).

Prices may change – check with hotel.

GRASMERE Cumbria

MAP 4: inset C2

THE YAN AT BROADRAYNE

Refreshingly different from some more traditional
Lake District offerings, this contemporary hotel,
upgraded from the Shortlist, is in a beautiful
setting overlooking Grasmere. The 'cluster of
old stone buildings almost built into the hillside'
house sleek bedrooms and a popular bistro. A
family affair – owners Dave and Sally Keighley
steer things in the background, daughter Jess
is front-of-house, husband Will is chef – it has
a warm, informal atmosphere that matches the
plentiful use of natural materials: whitewashed
walls, slate-flagged floors, exposed timbers
and upcycled tables. Our inspectors loved the
'unusual take on standard dishes' and the 'very
good food, all home made and reasonably priced'.
Dishes include curried fishcakes with vegetable
chowder, or an Indian-style sharing platter.
'Simple, modern' bedrooms are minimalist affairs
in shades of grey with local wool throws, good
reading lights and bright, shower-only bathrooms
with locally produced Pure Lakes products. All
have fell views. Breakfast brings dishes such as
house-smoked salmon and creamy scrambled eggs
on sourdough; an ideal start for walks from the
door. (HP, and others)

Broadrayne Farm
Grasmere LA22 9RU

T: 015394 35055
E: info@theyan.co.uk
W: theyan.co.uk

BEDROOMS: 7. Plus self-catering
cottages and glamping pods.
OPEN: all year except for Jan.
FACILITIES: lounge, bar/bistro, terrace,
in-room smart TV (Freeview),
drying room, bicycle storage, 10-acre
farmland, EV charging.
BACKGROUND MUSIC: 'chilled' in bistro.
LOCATION: close to A591, 1 mile N of
Grasmere.
CHILDREN: all ages welcomed, extra
bed £50.
DOGS: allowed in 2 rooms (£20 per
stay), on lead in public spaces.
CREDIT CARDS: MC, Visa.
PRICES: room-only doubles from £130.
À la carte breakfast items from £7.
Min. 2-night stay.

Prices may change – check with hotel.

GRASSINGTON Yorkshire

MAP 4:D3

GRASSINGTON HOUSE

In a prime position overlooking Grassington's cobbled village square, this handsome Georgian house, now a restaurant-with-rooms, delights first-time visitors with its chic style. Run by Sue and John Rudden since 2008, it provides a touch of glamour to match John's creative cooking without losing the warmth of a Yorkshire welcome. The bar sports sea-blue velvet seats and lemon-panelled walls while the conservatory dining room has bold lighting, burnished mirrors and shimmery wallpaper. Bedrooms are striking with oversized headboards, designer wallpapers and chandeliers. Decadent touches might include a gold-painted French-style bed or in-room roll-top bath. All rooms have a village view, modern bathroom and home-made biscuits. After a day's walking, have a drink on the buzzy terrace – try their own-label gin – before dining on dishes such as scallops with pancetta and pea purée, and lamb with roast onion and fondant potato. Practically everything is made in-house, including ice cream and cheese biscuits. Generous breakfasts include home-made granola, smoked salmon, and local bacon and sausages in a full Yorkshire grill.

5 The Square
Grassington
Skipton BD23 5AQ

T: 01756 752406
E: bookings@grassingtonhouse.co.uk
W: grassingtonhouse.co.uk

BEDROOMS: 9.
OPEN: all year except 25 Dec (24 Dec, meals only), first 2 weeks Jan, closed Mon (after breakfast)/Tues.
FACILITIES: bar, restaurant, outside dining pod, in-room TV, civil wedding licence, function facilities, terrace, EV charging, public rooms wheelchair accessible.
BACKGROUND MUSIC: in public areas.
LOCATION: in village square, 16 mins' drive from Skipton.
CHILDREN: all ages welcomed, free cot, extra bed £35.
DOGS: allowed in bar and terrace only.
CREDIT CARDS: MC, Visa.
PRICES: B&B doubles from £165, singles from £155. À la carte £46.

Prices may change – check with hotel.

GREAT MASSINGHAM Norfolk

THE DABBLING DUCK

They have all their ducks in a row at this wisteria-decked gastropub-with-rooms overlooking the green in a village where mallards glide on old abbey fishponds. 'It is an excellent pub, serving good food,' our inspectors found. Under the expert management of Mark and Sally Dobby, 'the young staff are absolutely lovely, very well trained'. Rooms above the pub are presented in cottage style with a king-size or double wrought iron bed. Larger rooms in a garden annexe are a shade more contemporary, with a touch of rustic chic, and there are individually styled premium rooms in a refurbished house adjacent to the pub. All have home-made vodka and biscuits and luxury toiletries. A few doors down, three-bedroom Duckling Cottage is now available for self-catering. You can eat in the bar, library, conservatory or, if you fancy wood-fired pizza, in the barn or garden. The menu, with blackboard specials, includes pub classics, game from local estates, fish and shellfish from the Norfolk coast – maybe fish and chips, 'great burger stacks', or smoked buttermilk squash with girolles and chicory. 'We certainly would stay there again.'

11 Abbey Road
Great Massingham PE32 2HN

T: 01485 520827
E: info@thedabblingduck.co.uk
W: thedabblingduck.co.uk

BEDROOMS: 12. 3 on ground floor in garden annexe.
OPEN: all year.
FACILITIES: bar, 3 private dining rooms, hallway/library, in-room TV, barn and garden (pizza oven, alfresco dining).
BACKGROUND MUSIC: jazz and soul throughout the building.
LOCATION: in village 13 miles E of King's Lynn.
CHILDREN: all ages welcomed, extra bed £20, children's menu, play castle.
DOGS: allowed in most bedrooms by arrangement (£10 per night, doggy menu), in bar and 1 dining room.
CREDIT CARDS: Amex, MC, Visa.
PRICES: B&B doubles from £160, singles from £110. À la carte £30.

Prices may change – check with hotel.

GREAT MILTON Oxfordshire

MAP 2:C3

LE MANOIR AUX QUAT'SAISONS

'There is a timeless elegance to Raymond Blanc's gorgeous country house hotel, where English–French relations reach a deliciously stylish entente cordiale,' say Guide insiders. The 15th-century manor house in paradisiacal gardens is a very personal enterprise for M. Blanc, with bedroom styling inspired by his travels. 'Lavande, in shades of purple, overlooked the lavender-fringed pathway, and came with a decanter of Madeira.' Classic French Bluebell, with toile de Jouy wallpaper, has a 'huge, deep, stand-alone bath' (a bit too deep, indeed, for one reader). 'A glass of champagne in the sitting room set the tone for a superb evening.' The restaurant has held two Michelin stars since 1984, and 'although far from cheap, eating here is an experience that always delivers'. Menus are created with produce from the two kitchen gardens. 'I enjoyed a vegetarian tasting menu, while my companion tucked into langoustine and venison. Every course was a triumph, from French onion soup in a teacup, to petits fours with Monbazillac.' At breakfast, le patron was 'much in evidence, greeting guests and taking time to chat'. (JK)

Church Road
Great Milton OX44 7PD

T: 01844 278881
E: lemanoir@belmond.com
W: belmond.com

BEDROOMS: 32. 22 in garden buildings, some on ground floor, 1 suitable for disabled.
OPEN: all year, restaurant closed for lunch Mon–Wed.
FACILITIES: 2 lounges, champagne bar, restaurant (vegetarian/vegan menus), private dining room, in-room TV, cookery school, gardening school, civil wedding licence, 27-acre grounds, EV charging, public rooms wheelchair accessible, adapted toilet.
BACKGROUND MUSIC: in some public areas.
LOCATION: 8 miles SE of Oxford.
CHILDREN: all ages welcomed, extra bed £65.
DOGS: allowed in 3 bedrooms (£20 per night) and public rooms.
CREDIT CARDS: Amex, MC, Visa.
PRICES: B&B doubles from £590. Set menus lunch £190, dinner £220, child £25.

Prices may change – check with hotel.

HALFORD Warwickshire

THE OLD MANOR HOUSE · NEW

With beams, cottage-style bedrooms and 'beautiful gardens' running down to the River Stour, this 16th-century Cotswold manor house is full of charm. So, too, are its owners, Jane and William Pusey, who are 'excellent hosts, bringing afternoon tea on the terrace when we had settled in', reports a reader. After visiting nearby Stratford-upon-Avon or walking in the Cotswolds, the riverside gardens are the perfect place to relax. On cooler days, stay in the 'very comfortable' drawing room with its fire, plump sofas, piles of books, antiques and contemporary art. Plants and family photographs make it feel invitingly homely. 'Lovely and light and airy' bedrooms have views over the garden and river, or a pretty cottage. With their low ceilings, the odd beam, light colours, patterned curtains and cushions, and well-loved antiques, they feel like guest rooms in a friend's charming house, rather than in a B&B. Breakfasts, elegantly served at a polished communal table, are 'generous; we did not have to find anywhere for lunch!' Jane advises on nearby dinner options including The Howard Arms at Ilmington (see entry). (Sara Price)

Halford
Shipston-on-Stour CV36 5BT

T: 01789 740264
E: oldmanorhalford@btinternet.com
W: oldmanor-halford.co.uk

BEDROOMS: 3.
OPEN: 1 Mar–19 Dec.
FACILITIES: hall, dining room, drawing room, in-room TV (Freeview), bicycle storage, 3½-acre grounds (tennis, fishing).
BACKGROUND MUSIC: none.
LOCATION: northern edge of village.
CHILDREN: aged 7 and over welcomed (extra bed from £35, ring to discuss).
DOGS: allowed in bedrooms (confirm when booking, £20 per night, 1 dog max.), in garden, not in dining room.
CREDIT CARDS: MC, Visa.
PRICES: B&B doubles from £120, singles from £95. Min. 2-night bookings (but ring to check 1-night availability).

Prices may change – check with hotel.

HALNAKER Sussex

MAP 2:E3

THE OLD STORE

There is a warm welcome in store for guests at this B&B and former 18th-century bakery in a South Downs hamlet on the edge of the Goodwood Estate. Owners Matt and Amy Marshall love their role as hosts, and invite new arrivals to join them for a drink; in warm weather cake and coffee or a glass of wine can be enjoyed in the sunshine on a decked garden terrace. There is a stripped-back simplicity to the interior, which has a fresh, airy feel, with white walls and varnished wood floors. Bedrooms are also in white, with charcoal carpet and splashes of fabric colour, a painted ladderback chair. Each has an en suite shower room with local bath products. Room 4, a top-floor twin overlooking the garden, has views to Chichester cathedral. Two rooms can sleep a family. A ground-floor room has one step to a bathroom with large shower and grab rails. A locally sourced breakfast includes fresh fruit, muesli, yogurts, Sussex apple juice, American pancakes with crispy bacon and maple syrup, a full English or smashed avocado with poached eggs. Work it off by walking through a magical tunnel of trees to the iconic Halnaker Windmill.

Stane Street
Halnaker
Chichester PO18 0QL

T: 01243 531977
E: info@theoldstoreguesthouse.co.uk
W: theoldstoreguesthouse.com

BEDROOMS: 7. 1 on ground floor with step between bedroom and shower room.
OPEN: all year.
FACILITIES: sitting room, breakfast room, in-room TV (Freeview), parking, ¼-acre garden with seating.
BACKGROUND MUSIC: none.
LOCATION: 4 miles NE of Chichester.
CHILDREN: all ages welcomed, babies and toddlers stay free, extra bed £15 for 3–12s, £25 for over-12s.
DOGS: not allowed.
CREDIT CARDS: Amex, MC, Visa.
PRICES: B&B doubles from £120, singles from £75, family from £135 (higher for Goodwood 'Festival of Speed' and 'Revival' meetings). 1-night bookings refused on some weekends, and some other nights in high season.

Prices may change – chec[

HAM Wiltshire

MAP 2:D2

CROWN & ANCHOR INN

When you've browsed the antique shops of Hungerford, it is a short drive to this pub-with-rooms in a photogenic village. Once an ale house for farm workers, it lived again as the Indigo Palace curry house, and had been closed for three years when two local families took it on. Our inspector found it 'very newly decorated and comfortable without being excitingly original'. There are five in-house bedrooms, named after local farms; three in a rustic cottage a stroll away. Painted lime green, 'Doves' (the organics brand) has pink-striped blinds, a flamingo print from Audubon's Birds of America, a bath and shower. 'Prosperous', overlooking the village green, recalls the farm where Jethro Tull invented the seed drill. Each room is supplied with local botanical bath products – no wardrobe, just hangers. You can eat in the flagstone-floored bar, in either of two dining rooms or on the terrace, pub classics and more exciting dishes. The 'melt-in-the-mouth' home-baked focaccia, 'fried sea bass with crayfish, wild garlic and Jersey royals; lemon curd with burnt meringue and raspberry' are praised. An excellent breakfast and terrific value sealed the deal.

Ham
Hungerford SN8 3RB

T: 01488 503040
E: info@crownandanchorham.co.uk
W: crownandanchorham.co.uk

BEDROOMS: 8. 5 bedrooms in the pub, 2 doubles and 1 twin in cottage 200 yards away.
OPEN: all year, Wed–Sat, Sun lunch (Tues opening is in prospect).
FACILITIES: bar, lower dining room, upper dining room, private dining room (22 covers), function facilities, beer garden, dining terrace, in-room TV, EV charging, parking; upper restaurant wheelchair accessible, adapted toilet.
BACKGROUND MUSIC: 'very soft background, mainly pop/blues/country'.
LOCATION: in centre of village.
CHILDREN: all ages welcomed, extra bed £10 per stay.
DOGS: allowed (£10 per stay, beds, towels, treats provided).
CREDIT CARDS: MC, Visa.
PRICES: B&B doubles from £100, singles from £80. À la carte £40.

Prices may change – check with hotel.

HAMBLETON Rutland

MAP 2:B3

HAMBLETON HALL

'Fay ce que voudras' reads a motto on the porch of Tim and Stefa Hart's Victorian picturesque country house, an invitation to do as you please, and this year, as ever, readers have been pleased by their stay here. It is 'the most wonderful place for relaxation', vouch regular returnees. 'The staff are efficient and pleasant as always, and the decor and furnishings remain a delight.' The style throughout is classic and elegant. Even standard rooms have designer wallpaper, maybe a bath and walk-in shower. Bay-windowed master room Fern overlooks the colourful parterre and shining Rutland Water. Michelin-starred chef Aaron Patterson creates a concise daily menu using produce from the walled kitchen garden. Choices might include poached halibut, cucumber, oyster leaf salad; roast venison, turnips, braised red cabbage. You can spend days by the pool, play croquet or tennis, and when the sun's over the yardarm, as it says on the sundial on the south front of the house, 'Nune Hora Bibendi' – time for a drink! Hambleton Hall is a Relais & Châteaux hotel. (See also Hart's Hotel, Nottingham.) (Anthony Bradbury, and others)

Hambleton
Oakham LE15 8TH

T: 01572 756991
E: hotel@hambletonhall.com
w: hambletonhall.com

BEDROOMS: 17. 2-bedroom suite in cottage.
OPEN: all year.
FACILITIES: lift, hall, drawing room/bar, restaurant (vegetarian menu), 2 private dining rooms, in-room TV (Sky), civil wedding licence, 17-acre grounds (tennis, swimming pool, croquet, vegetable garden), EV charging, public rooms wheelchair accessible, no adapted toilet.
BACKGROUND MUSIC: none.
LOCATION: 3 miles SE of Oakham.
CHILDREN: all ages welcomed, cot £25, extra bed £35, no under-5s in restaurant.
DOGS: allowed in bedrooms (£10 per night, not unattended), hall.
CREDIT CARDS: Amex, MC, Visa.
PRICES: B&B doubles from £310, singles from £220. Set dinner £83. 1-night bookings normally refused at weekends.

Prices may change – check with hotel.

HAROME Yorkshire

MAP 4:D4

THE PHEASANT

The picture-perfect setting of this honey-stone hotel, with its courtyard garden and views over the village pond, has all the ingredients for a restorative stay. 'Informally comfortable' with 'gentle and kind service and lovely food', declares one reader. 'It is all a hotel should be.' Converted from a former blacksmith's and barns, it is stylish yet relaxed with brightly coloured lounges, one with a wood-burning stove. Modern country house bedrooms have designer wallpapers and jazzy headboards, and bathrooms with under-floor heating – some are compact but 'very modern and certainly adequate'. Generous treats include fresh milk, sloe gin and fresh fruit. After a day exploring the North York Moors, relax in the indoor pool before the 'big attraction' of dinner. Sophisticated and 'excellent' dishes could include house-smoked salmon with crumpets and caviar, and charcoal-cooked venison with black trumpet mushrooms and liquorice. There are vegan and vegetarian menus. Breakfast doesn't disappoint, either – guests give it top marks – while owner Jacquie Silk's hands-on presence is 'always a good sign'. (Peter and Anne Davies, PA)

Harome
Helmsley YO62 5JG

T: 01439 771241
E: reservations@thepheasanthotel.com
W: thepheasanthotel.com

BEDROOMS: 16. 3 on ground floor, 4 in courtyard, 1 in hotel suitable for disabled.
OPEN: all year.
FACILITIES: bar, lounge, conservatory, restaurant (vegetarian/vegan menu), in-room TV (Freeview), civil wedding licence, heated indoor swimming pool, terrace, ½-acre garden, public areas wheelchair accessible, no adapted toilet.
BACKGROUND MUSIC: in public areas.
LOCATION: village centre.
CHILDREN: all ages welcomed, extra bed £40.
DOGS: allowed in 2 bedrooms (£30 per night), on terrace and in garden, not in public rooms.
CREDIT CARDS: MC, Visa.
PRICES: B&B doubles from £200, singles from £170. Tasting menu £75, à la carte £55.

Prices may change – check with hotel.

HAROME Yorkshire

MAP 4:D4

THE STAR INN AT HAROME

Devotees of this thatched village pub-with-rooms and Michelin-starred restaurant will be thrilled when it reopens in autumn following 2021's disastrous fire; rooms and breakfast, meanwhile, are unaffected. In quiet Harome, close to the North York Moors, spacious, quirky bedrooms are tucked away from the pub in converted farm buildings and a new-build barn. Characterful and rustic, with beams, low windows and chunky wooden furniture, they're dotted with fun objects: riding boots, board games, a pool table in one, piano in another. Contemporary barn rooms have floor-to-ceiling windows. Cosy up in the lounge, with its hunting lodge feel, log stove and afternoon cake before a drink from the honesty bar and a stroll to the pub for Andrew Pern's 'modern Yorkshire' cooking. Championing local produce – there's a vast kitchen garden – he produces exceptional flavour-dense dishes, perhaps crab stick with seashore vegetables and avocado ice followed by black treacle glazed duck with lovage tortellini. Feast-like breakfasts, with everything from freshly squeezed juice to freshly carved ham, are served at a giant round table. 'Sensational.'

High Street
Harome
nr Helmsley YO62 5JE

T: 01439 770397
E: reservations@thestarinnatharome.co.uk
W: thestaratharome.co.uk

BEDROOMS: 13. All opposite pub in Cross House Lodge with Barn annexe, 6 on ground floor, unsuitable for disabled.
OPEN: all year, restaurant to re-open (following fire in 2021) in autumn 2022, normally closed Mon lunch, last orders Sun 6 pm, ring to check.
FACILITIES: bar, cocktail bar, restaurant (veg/vegan menus), 2-acre garden, lounge, breakfast room, terrace (at building with bedrooms), in-room TV, civil wedding licence, restaurant wheelchair accessible, adapted toilet.
BACKGROUND MUSIC: in lounge, restaurant.
LOCATION: village centre.
CHILDREN: all ages welcomed, extra bed £35.
DOGS: allowed in 3 bedrooms (£30 a night), not in pub.
CREDIT CARDS: MC, Visa.
PRICES: B&B doubles from £150.

Prices may change – check with hotel.

HARWICH Essex

MAP 2:C5

THE PIER AT HARWICH

Cranes, container ships, Holland-bound ferries
… The views from this quayside Victorian hotel
with its striking iron-lace balcony overlooking
the Stour and Orwell estuaries are ocean-going,
stirring, never dull. It is owned by the Milsom
family (see Talbooth House & Spa, Dedham), and
rejoices in its maritime surroundings, from the
industrial-chic ground-floor Navyärd bar, serving
Scandi-inspired small plates, ales and interesting
gins, to the first-floor brasserie with exposed
brick walls, bare bulbs, leather banquettes and an
eye-catching work by Essex's own James Dodds,
'boatbuilding's artist laureate'. An all-day menu
includes burgers (beef or chickpea), Harwich
crab, fish and chips, thyme-roasted celeriac with
crushed butterbeans. The bedrooms, in neutral
shades with splashes of colour, are 'comfortable
enough', and have complimentary snacks and soft
drinks in a minibar fridge. The stand-out is the
spacious Mayflower Suite in the adjacent former
Angel pub, with lots of seating, a telescope in a
huge bay window. Neighbouring Dovercourt –
home to Maplins holiday camp in the sitcom Hi-
de-Hi! – has a sandy Blue Flag beach. Ho-de-Ho!

The Quay
Harwich CO12 3HH

T: 01255 241212
E: pier@milsomhotels.com
W: milsomhotels.com

BEDROOMS: 14. 7 in annexe, 1 on
ground floor suitable for disabled.
OPEN: all year.
FACILITIES: bar, lounge (in annexe),
restaurant, private dining room, small
lift, in-room TV (Sky, BT, Freeview),
civil wedding licence, balcony, small
front terrace, parking, EV charging,
restaurant, bar wheelchair accessible,
adapted toilet.
BACKGROUND MUSIC: in the bar.
LOCATION: on quay, in old town.
CHILDREN: all ages welcomed, extra
bed £20.
DOGS: allowed in bedrooms (no
charge), bar, lounge.
CREDIT CARDS: Amex, MC, Visa.
PRICES: B&B doubles from £140.
À la carte £40.

Prices may change – check with hotel.

HASTINGS Sussex

MAP 2:E5

THE OLD RECTORY

Designer Lionel Copley did not compromise
on comfort when he transformed Georgian All
Saints Rectory on the edge of the Old Town into
a beautiful B&B. The bedrooms have amusing
quirks such as a deep-blue wall hung with
Wedgwood calendar plates, a secret toilet hidden
behind a bookcase, 1970s Sanderson wallpaper. All
are stylish, with a soft-hued palette and individual
touches of luxury – a Carrara marble shower
room, hand-painted wallpaper, a chandelier.
All Saints suite has a super-king/twin room
and additional double room, a bathroom with a
claw-footed bath as well as a wet room. Guests are
welcomed in the lounge with delicious home-
made cake and might enjoy a G&T later in the
landscaped walled garden. Massages and beauty
therapies are available daily in the Treatment
Rooms. The house has a grown-up ethos (no
under-10s), and elegant shared spaces. In the
charming blue-and-white breakfast room, choices
to set you up for the beach include organic apple
juice, home-made bread and jams, a full English
with home-cured bacon, smashed avocado and
halloumi, smoked haddock and caper fishcakes,
or patatas bravas with sautéed chorizo.

Harold Road
Hastings TN35 5ND

T: 01424 422410
E: info@theoldrectoryhastings.co.uk
W: theoldrectoryhastings.co.uk

BEDROOMS: 8. One 2-bed suite.
OPEN: all year except 2 weeks Jan,
exclusive use only at Christmas and
New Year.
FACILITIES: 2 lounges (honesty bar),
breakfast room, treatment rooms,
sauna, in-room TV (Freeview),
civil wedding licence, 1-acre walled
garden, limited on-site parking,
unsuitable for disabled.
BACKGROUND MUSIC: 'easy listening'
in breakfast room, main lounge and
treatment rooms.
LOCATION: edge of Old Town (limited
parking spaces, complimentary
permits).
CHILDREN: not under 10.
DOGS: not allowed.
CREDIT CARDS: Amex, MC, Visa.
PRICES: B&B doubles from £130,
singles from £110. Min. 2-night
bookings weekends, but call to check
availability.

Prices may change – check with hotel.

SEE ALSO SHORTLIST

HAWES Yorkshire

SIMONSTONE HALL

With tall chimneys, multiple gables, vast mullioned windows and sprawling terraces this Yorkshire country house is the real deal, but with a delightfully friendly touch. 'Informal but also luxurious,' concludes one happy guest. Set above Hawes, with staggering views of Wensleydale, the stone-built Georgian mansion has all the 'country house weekend' features – polished-wood floors, wood panelling, leather armchairs, peacocks in the gardens – but mixed with contemporary coloured walls and modern touches. 'The bar is very cosy with open fires.' Bedrooms blend antiques and thick curtains with bold colours, an airy feel and a 'spacious modern bathroom'; some have a roll-top bath. Most have glorious views; the only sound 'the odd nocturnal bird cry'. The excellent menu – at night served in a 'candlelit green-walled dining room; the perfect romantic evening' – gives traditional dishes a contemporary tweak: Yorkshire venison with salt-baked celeriac, perhaps, or mackerel with satay sauce. 'Attentive service' continues at breakfast with 'perfectly cooked scrambled egg'. 'I highly recommend it.' (JF)

Simonstone
Hawes DL8 3LY

T: 01969 667255
E: reception@simonstonehall.com
W: simonstonehall.com

BEDROOMS: 20. 2 on ground floor suitable for disabled.
OPEN: all year, except for short break in Jan.
FACILITIES: bar, restaurant, 2 lounges, meeting/private dining rooms, in-room TV (Freeview), civil wedding licence, 2½-acre grounds (hot tub), EV charging, public rooms wheelchair accessible, adapted toilet.
BACKGROUND MUSIC: 'low key' in public areas.
LOCATION: 1 mile N of Hawes.
CHILDREN: all ages welcomed, extra bed £50–£100.
DOGS: allowed in some bedrooms (£25 per stay, 2 dogs £35, welcome pack), 2 lounges, bar.
CREDIT CARDS: MC, Visa.
PRICES: B&B doubles from £149. Set-price 3-course dinner £55 (£49 for pre-booked residents). 1-night bookings usually refused on public holidays, peak season weekends.
Prices may change – check with hotel.

SEE ALSO SHORTLIST

HEREFORD Herefordshire

CASTLE HOUSE

A 'striking and beautiful' building – two Georgian villas knocked into one by a Victorian owner – is home to a 'well-run, friendly, comfortable hotel', its garden bordered by the moat of the long-gone castle. Bedrooms range from singles to suites, some with a four-poster, some in a town house close by, where two open on to a garden. Readers who booked the main-house Charles II suite 'gasped when we stepped inside'. It had 'six windows, looking towards the cathedral, a huge living area, thick red rugs on parquet flooring, red damask roman blinds'. Each room is individually styled, some contemporary, some more traditional. All have ground coffee, milk in a mini-fridge, a decanter of sherry, fine-quality toiletries. You can drink and dine alfresco or in the 'bright new conservatory', from a 'short, interesting' à la carte or Saturday tasting menu. 'Yummy canapés were brought, but no bread.' A Herefordshire fillet steak with confit potato and oxtail Wellington was 'cooked to perfection'. There were 'good choices' also at breakfast – 'the full Hereford was notably excellent and the service charming'. (Jill Cox)

Castle Street
Hereford HR1 2NW

T: 01432 356321
E: reception@castlehse.co.uk
W: castlehse.co.uk

BEDROOMS: 24. 8 in town house (1-min. walk), some on ground floor, 1 suitable for disabled.
OPEN: all year, restaurant closed Mon/ Tues.
FACILITIES: lift (in main house), lounge, bar/bistro, restaurant, in-room TV (Freeview), civil wedding licence, terraced garden, ground floor wheelchair accessible.
BACKGROUND MUSIC: sometimes in restaurant, bistro, reception.
LOCATION: central.
CHILDREN: all ages welcomed, family suites, cots, extra bed £25.
DOGS: only assistance dogs, others allowed in garden, on a lead.
CREDIT CARDS: Amex, MC, Visa.
PRICES: B&B doubles from £160 (No. 25), £200 (main house), singles from £140. Saturday tasting menu £65, à la carte £42.

Prices may change – check with hotel.

HETTON Yorkshire

THE ANGEL INN

In a quiet corner of the Yorkshire Dales, this long and low 15th-century inn spoils with Michelin-starred food, luxurious yet understated bedrooms and a relaxed vibe. Interiors are pared back in shades of grey with natural woods and Scandi-style furnishings set against beams and log fires. Chef Michael Wignall (ex Gidleigh Park) and his wife, Johanna, have created a series of light but intimate dining spaces that never feel formal and with a service that's 'friendly, efficient and thoughtful'. Michael's 'inventive and creative dishes, beautifully presented', might include scallops with apple and frozen buttermilk followed by Yorkshire venison with salsify, morels and blackcurrant. There are good vegetarian dishes, too. The breakfast 'tasting menu' – small courses including granola, smoked salmon and eggs – was a surprise to some. Bedrooms range from Scandi-style rooms in the inn and cottagey rooms in an adjoining building to rustic-chic affairs in a converted barn across the road. Suites may include a roll-top bath or private patio. Most have glorious fell views. 'We look forward to returning.' (Bill Wood, Tessa Stuart)

Hetton
Skipton BD23 6LT

T: 01756 730263
E: reservations@angelhetton.co.uk
W: angelhetton.co.uk

BEDROOMS: 15. 5 in barn conversion, 4 in cottage, 2 on ground floor suitable for disabled.
OPEN: all year except 24 Dec restaurant only, 25/26 Dec, 2–14 Jan, rooms/restaurant closed Tues, Wed.
FACILITIES: bar, restaurant (vegetarian tasting menu), private dining room, civil wedding licence, terrace, in-room TV (Freeview), some public areas wheelchair accessible, adapted toilet.
BACKGROUND MUSIC: in public areas.
LOCATION: village centre.
CHILDREN: all ages welcomed, extra bed for under-12s £30, children can dine in bar.
DOGS: allowed in 2 bedrooms (£15 per stay), bar.
CREDIT CARDS: Amex, MC, Visa.
PRICES: D,B&B doubles from £430, singles from £330 (no B&B rates). À la carte 3 courses £85, tasting menu £120.

Prices may change – check with hotel.

HEXHAM Northumberland

MAP 4:B3

THE BEAUMONT

The warm, buzzy open-plan bar and restaurant of this attractive town house hotel overlooking the park is one of Hexham's social hot spots. 'It is the place in town for ad hoc meetings, coffee, lunch,' said one impressed guest, 'and clearly has a good local reputation.' Glowing reports have ensured its promotion from the Shortlist this year. The Victorian building, near the 12th-century abbey and market place, has been reinvigorated by restaurateur Roger Davy and his wife, Magda, since taking over in 2016. Bedrooms, some in a modern annexe, are bright with feature wallpapers, colourful armchairs and modern bathrooms. Front rooms overlook the park and abbey; two of the top-floor 'spacious and warm' rear rooms have terraces 'with views over Hexham's rooftops'. Dishes are 'modern British to a high standard', such as wild garlic risotto with goat's curd; a sea trout with samphire and polenta is particularly praised plus a 'perfectly cooked' roast sirloin. Waiter-served breakfasts have a 'good choice from full English to a range of egg dishes'. 'The food and service represents excellent value for money.' (Donald Reid, Rosalind Gunning)

Beaumont Street
Hexham NE46 3LT

T: 01434 602331
E: reservations@
  thebeaumonthexham.co.uk
W: thebeaumonthexham.co.uk

BEDROOMS: 33. 1 suitable for disabled.
OPEN: all year.
FACILITIES: open-plan bar/lounge/restaurant, in-room TV (Freeview), function facilities, EV charging, parking, restaurant and bar wheelchair accessible, adapted toilet.
BACKGROUND MUSIC: in bar, restaurant.
LOCATION: in town centre.
CHILDREN: all ages welcomed, extra bed £22.50, children's menu.
DOGS: not in bedrooms, only designated public areas.
CREDIT CARDS: Amex, MC, Visa.
PRICES: B&B doubles from £145. À la carte £35.

Prices may change – check with hotel.

SEE ALSO SHORTLIST

HINTON ST GEORGE Somerset   MAP 1:C6

THE LORD POULETT ARMS

'Gardez le Foi' reads the Poulett family motto
over the door of this thatched, ham-stone village
pub, and the trio behind the Beckford group
(see The Beckford Arms, Tisbury) have kept
absolute faith with their winning concept here.
The ambience is friendly and relaxed. You can
drink and dine in the real-ale locals bar, which is
furnished with mix-and-match wooden tables,
its walls hung with portraits of Earls Poulett,
benevolent feudal overlords until well into the
last century. Food is served, also, in the pretty
oasis garden. The staff are young, enthusiastic
and valued. A short menu offers pub classics
along with dishes such as venison and wild boar
meatloaf or Lyme Bay fish curry (Lyme Regis is
just 35 minutes away). Breakfast gets a thumbs up
from readers too, with home-made granola and
pastries as well as a full English. The eminently
affordable bedrooms are stylish and uncluttered,
supplied with Welsh blankets, comfy seating,
home-made treats and Bramley toiletries. One
has its own private entrance and an in-room
slipper bath. A family room has bunks for the
kids. They don't 'do' wardrobes: use a hanger
or the 'floordrobe'.

High Street
Hinton St George TA17 8SE

т: 01460 73149
е: reservations@lordpoulettarms.com
w: lordpoulettarms.com

BEDROOMS: 6. 4 with en suite, 2 with
private bathroom, 1 for family.
OPEN: all year except 25 Dec, closed
Mon, Tues.
FACILITIES: bar, restaurant, private
dining room, in-room TV (Freeview),
1-acre grounds, unsuitable for
disabled.
BACKGROUND MUSIC: throughout pub.
LOCATION: in village, 4 miles NW of
Crewkerne.
CHILDREN: all ages welcomed, travel
cot £10, bunk beds £25 per child,
Room 6.
DOGS: in bedrooms (small charge for
extra housekeeping), all public areas.
CREDIT CARDS: MC, Visa.
PRICES: B&B doubles from £95.
À la carte £35.

Prices may change – check with hotel.

HOLT Norfolk

MAP 2:A5

MORSTON HALL

Birdwatchers and bon vivants beat a path to Tracy and Galton Blackiston's Michelin-starred restaurant-with-rooms in a flint farmhouse with Blakeney nature reserve on the doorstep. You can walk through the big, flat, beautiful, faintly melancholic salt-marsh moonscape to Morston Quay, take a boat trip to see seals and return for afternoon tea in the sun lounge. It might be Michelin starred, but it is a 'friendly, comfortable place'. House bedrooms, named after Norfolk stately homes, have a contemporary country house look. Felbrigg has a balcony, windows overlooking the front and the herb garden at the side. Spacious garden pavilion suites have a lounge area and patio, a bath and shower. Almost all rooms are pet-friendly. At night, canapés are served in the lounge or in the lavender-scented garden, before a seven-course tasting menu of home-grown and locally sourced produce – maybe butternut squash velouté, King's Lynn brown shrimps or Middle White sucking pig. At breakfast there is locally smoked fish, smashed avocado on sourdough, a full English with boudin noir and kidneys. 'The attention to detail was sublime.' (JC)

Morston
Holt NR25 7AA

T: 01263 741041
E: reception@morstonhall.com
W: morstonhall.com

BEDROOMS: 13. 6 on ground floor, 100 yds from house, in garden pavilion, 1 (in main house) suitable for disabled.
OPEN: all year except 24–26 Dec, Jan, restaurant closed Mon.
FACILITIES: reading lounge, sun lounge, conservatory, restaurant, in-room TV (Freeview), civil wedding licence, 3-acre garden (pond, croquet), restaurant wheelchair accessible, adapted toilet.
BACKGROUND MUSIC: none.
LOCATION: 2 miles W of Blakeney.
CHILDREN: all ages welcomed, over-3s £50 a night.
DOGS: allowed in bedrooms (£10 a night), some public rooms, not in restaurant.
CREDIT CARDS: Amex, MC, Visa.
PRICES: per person D,B&B doubles from £210, singles from £280. Tasting menu £115.

Prices may change – check with hotel.

HOPE Derbyshire

UNDERLEIGH HOUSE

With walks from the doorstep, views of Peak District hills, a peaceful garden, breakfast feasts and restful bedrooms, it's no surprise that Underleigh wins so much praise. 'An absolute gem!' enthuses a reader who has been returning for five years. 'The location is stunning.' Vivienne Taylor's handsome stone longhouse, with its colourful garden – 'a bonus on warm days when you can enjoy the fresh air and scenery' – is comfortable with beams, glowing table lamps, and deep sofas in the fire-warmed lounge. Bedrooms, 'with amazing views', are elegant with pretty wallpaper, pale-painted furniture, an occasional antique. Three are suites with large sofas; one opens to the garden. Thoughtful touches include bathrobes and fresh milk. Breakfast, served at a large table in the beamed and flagged dining room, offers a 'wonderful array', from home-made bread and compotes to Aga-cooked porridge, eggs Benedict, and a full grill. 'They kept us fuelled for the day.' Vivienne can advise on walks and nearby places, including Chatsworth. She is 'the perfect host' who 'ensures guests are really well catered for'. (Jonathan Evans, Sarah Dennis)

Lose Hill Lane
Hope S33 6AF

T: 01433 621372
E: underleigh.house@btconnect.com
W: underleighhouse.co.uk

BEDROOMS: 4. 3 suites, each with a private lounge.
OPEN: all year except mid-Dec to mid-Feb.
FACILITIES: lounge, breakfast room, in-room TV (Freeview), ¼-acre garden, EV charging, unsuitable for disabled.
BACKGROUND MUSIC: none.
LOCATION: 1 mile N of Hope.
CHILDREN: not under 12, extra bed £20.
DOGS: allowed in 1 suite by prior arrangement (no charge), not in public rooms.
CREDIT CARDS: Amex, MC, Visa.
PRICES: B&B doubles from £115, singles from £95. 1-night bookings normally refused Fri/Sat, bank holidays.

Prices may change – check with hotel.

HORNINGSHAM Wiltshire

MAP 2:D1

THE BATH ARMS

You could be in rural France as you take a forest drive to this creeper-covered stone inn 'scenically situated in rolling fields in the Longleat estate', with tables and umbrellas under pollarded limes. A fourth venture for the Beckford group (see The Beckford Arms, Tisbury), this dining pub-with-rooms with 'well-kept gardens' has a buzzy, relaxed vibe, flagstone and wood floors, assorted brown furniture, walls hung with vintage maps and Vanity Fair caricatures. A maze of corridors leads to 'nicely decorated' bedrooms in the signature style – pastel walls, seagrass flooring, no wardrobe, an 'excellent bathroom' with roll-top bath and/or walk-in shower, posh toiletries. 'Avoid attic rooms 6 and 7' if you're built like LeBron James, our inspectors advise. There are further rooms in the stable block. Food, served by 'friendly, chatty staff' in the dining room or snug, or under canvas on the terrace, is sourced from local farmers and producers. Menus include dishes such as Thai marinated flank steak, garlic-fried pak choi and fries, along with pub classics. 'Loved the tomato and avocado purée, olive tapenade, salsa verde and pistachios.'

Longleat Estate
Horningsham BA12 7LY

T: 01985 844308
E: info@batharmsinn.com
W: batharmsinn.com

BEDROOMS: 17. 6 in stables, 1 suitable for disabled.
OPEN: all year, except 25 Dec.
FACILITIES: bar, restaurant, snug, covered terrace, second terrace, landscaped gardens (sandpit), in-room TV (Freeview), not wheelchair accessible.
BACKGROUND MUSIC: 'very quiet' in bar and restaurant.
LOCATION: between Frome and Warminster.
CHILDREN: all ages welcomed, cot £10, foam bed £25.
DOGS: allowed in some bedrooms (small charge for cleaning), all public areas.
CREDIT CARDS: MC, Visa.
PRICES: B&B doubles from £120. À la carte £32. 1-night bookings refused Fri.

Prices may change – check with hotel.

HOVE Sussex

THE GINGER PIG   `NEW`

Across the road from Hove's shingle beach,
Ben and Pamela Mckellar's Edwardian mock-
timbered gastropub is 'loved by locals for its
foodie reputation'. Part of a small local restaurant
group, it was gingered up in 2017 with the
addition of guest bedrooms. Beyond a grey
facade, our inspector found 'lots of endearing
qualities, such as elegant revolving Art Deco
doors into the modern dining room and bar'.
The rooms are 'far more than an afterthought',
with 'minimalist decor, dark grey walls, Dan
Hillier modern art'. Extras include a minibar
with 'a pre-made Negroni and Old Fashioned
for two, a beach towel in a Ginger Pig tote bag',
air conditioning, an espresso machine. 'Uplifting,
roomy bathrooms' have 'striking tiled floors, a
freestanding bath, a walk-in shower, Cowshed
toiletries'. In the bar and buzzy restaurant, the
menu brings dishes such as roast cod fillet with
crispy cheeks, carrot and cumin purée, dhal,
confit tomato and saffron velouté, with good
meaty and vegan choices, though 'I would have
liked to taste more punchy flavours'. Interesting
breakfast options include baked eggs with
muhammara and toast'.

3 Hove Street
Hove
Brighton BN3 2TR

T: 01273 206577
E: rooms@gingermangroup.com
W: thegingerpigpub.com

BEDROOMS: 11.
OPEN: all year.
FACILITIES: restaurant, bar, private
dining/meeting room, in-room TV,
civil wedding licence, public car park
nearby.
BACKGROUND MUSIC: 'soft mood music'.
LOCATION: 2 mins from Hove beach.
CHILDREN: all ages welcomed.
DOGS: allowed in 2 bedrooms (£35
per night, bowl, bed), in bar but not
restaurant.
CREDIT CARDS: MC, Visa.
PRICES: room-only doubles from £120.
Breakfast from £8.50, full English £11,
à la carte £40. 2-night stays preferred
at weekends.

Prices may change – check with hotel.

HUMSHAUGH Northumberland

MAP 4:B3

WALWICK HALL HOTEL

In a tranquil spot, with far-reaching views over the Tyne valley, this small yet glamorous country house hotel offers a restful base for exploring Hadrian Wall country. The modest entrance of the 'handsome Georgian building' belies spacious interiors of 'bold country-print wallpapers' and designer sofas. Public rooms have large sash and bay windows overlooking the terrace, 'beautiful gardens' and valley. Afternoon tea in the elegant, fire-warmed drawing room or on the terrace makes the most of 'those gorgeous views' – if you're feeling active, a swim in the 'swish glass-walled pavilion' allows you to enjoy the views, too. Bedrooms are cosseting, with Aubusson carpets, country-print wallpapers, plaid wool rugs and thick curtains; many have a freestanding bath in the marble bathrooms. Wedgwood china cups and saucers, and home-made biscuits add to the 'sense of refinement'. Evening meals, in the classy bar or the main dining room, have a creative edge, such as turbot with Thai green curry sauce. 'We recommend the ham hock, the scallops, the wild mushroom risotto with truffle,' writes a reader. 'The petits fours were outstanding.' (DG, and others)

Humshaugh
Hexham NE46 4BJ

T: 01434 620156
E: hello@walwickhall.com
W: walwickhall.com

BEDROOMS: 10.
OPEN: all year.
FACILITIES: lift, lounge, bar, snug, restaurant, private dining room, terrace, in-room TV (Freeview), 1-acre garden, indoor pool (10 metre), spa (incl. treatment rooms and gym), public areas wheelchair accessible, adapted toilet.
BACKGROUND MUSIC: in public areas and dining room.
LOCATION: 6 miles N of Hexham.
CHILDREN: all ages welcomed, 1 family room, cots £10, for under-13s extra beds £35, small outdoor playground.
DOGS: allowed on terrace only, unless guide dogs.
CREDIT CARDS: Amex, MC, Visa.
PRICES: B&B doubles from £270, singles from £255. À la carte £42.

Prices may change – check with hotel.

HUNSTANTON Norfolk

NO. 33

In the only west-facing resort on England's east coast, Jeanne Whittome's B&B appeals to those seeking space and freedom, without cosseting, live-in hosts. A concierge service can arrange bike hire, birdwatching tours and beauty treatments, but you're left to your own devices to enjoy the Victorian seaside town or to explore the wilder shores of the north Norfolk coast. Interiors are stylish, with a palette of soft greys and white. Bedrooms have a bath and walk-in shower. Bay-windowed Room 2 has a wall of Zoffany's 'Verdure' wallpaper, back-to-back original fireplaces in bedroom and bathroom. There are distant sea views from the balcony of rear-facing Room 3, with white, barley-sugar-twist four-poster. A ground-floor room opens on to a small courtyard. More suites can be found at nearby sister property Thornham Deli, source of a continental breakfast that includes pods for espresso machines. Guests receive a 10% discount for meals taken there or taken out. The lounge has a DVD library, the dining room a log-burner. The Coast Path runs from 'Hunny' to Cromer, or you can cheat and take the CoastHopper bus.

33 Northgate
Hunstanton PE36 6AP

T: 01485 524352
E: reception@33hunstanton.co.uk
W: 33hunstanton.co.uk

BEDROOMS: 5. 1 on ground floor, wheelchair accessible, unadapted shower room.
OPEN: all year.
FACILITIES: small sitting room, breakfast room, in-room TV (Freeview), small garden, lawn with tables and chairs.
BACKGROUND MUSIC: none.
LOCATION: town centre.
CHILDREN: well-behaved children welcomed, cot £10, extra bed for child under 14 (max. 1 per room) £30.
DOGS: allowed in bedrooms (max. 1 per room, £10 per night, bowl, bed, biscuits), not in dining room, must stay with owners at all times.
CREDIT CARDS: MC, Visa.
PRICES: B&B doubles from £105 (suites at Thornham Deli from £150), single occupancy discount £10 a night.

Prices may change – check with hotel.

HUNTINGDON Cambridgeshire

MAP 2:B4

THE OLD BRIDGE

In the fine tradition of a town-centre hostelry, this ivy-smothered inn hums with energy, as people drop in for drinks and snacks in the buzzy lounge, bar or patio garden. Some come for tastings in the wine shop run by proprietor John Hoskins, a Master of Wine. Bedrooms are chic, with smart wallpaper and fabrics, and there is a good mix of singles, twins and doubles, including four-poster rooms, all styled by John's wife, Julia. Some overlook the street, some have views over the garden and river or riverside park. Guide stalwarts who live nearby treated themselves to a stay in one of two Riverside Rooms, 'which are off the restaurant, with the great advantage of being on the flat, no stairs'. It was 'of generous size', though the bathroom was 'a bit compact'. Another Guide regular had a super-king room, 'very comfortable, quiet, overlooking the car park'. In the restaurant, a varied menu of 'wonderful, amazing produce' caters to all tastes. 'Excellent meal – halibut on a bed of squid-ink risotto. Excellent service for such a busy place. Nothing wrong at all, no issues, wonderful.' (John and Elspeth Gibbon, Bill Wood, Kim Evans)

1 High Street
Huntingdon PE29 3TQ

T: 01480 424300
E: oldbridge@huntsbridge.co.uk
W: huntsbridge.com

BEDROOMS: 24. 2 on ground floor.
OPEN: all year.
FACILITIES: lounge, bar, restaurant, private dining room, wine shop, business centre, in-room TV (Freeview), civil wedding licence, 1-acre grounds (riverside patio for private events), parking, unsuitable for disabled.
BACKGROUND MUSIC: none.
LOCATION: 500 yds from town centre, station 10 mins' walk.
CHILDREN: all ages welcomed, no extra beds.
DOGS: allowed in 2 bedrooms (no charge), lounge and bar, by arrangement, not in restaurant.
CREDIT CARDS: MC, Visa.
PRICES: B&B doubles from £149, singles from £109. À la carte £44.

Prices may change – check with hotel.

ILMINGTON Warwickshire   MAP 3:D6

THE HOWARD ARMS

It was nearly Howard's end in 2015 before two
local families stepped in to restore the fortunes
of this 'delightful gem of a pub-with-rooms', in a
village on the northern fringes of the Cotswolds.
A creative make-over has preserved the character
of the beamed, flagstone-floored bar, a social
hub with creaky leather armchairs by a log fire.
The walls are hung with fun artwork and old
photographs. 'We did enjoy our night's stay. We
had a wonderful room,' report readers, who spent
the night after a theatre visit in Stratford. 'It is
excellent value for money.' Individually styled
bedrooms have bags of character. Most have a bath
and shower, and all are supplied with percolator
coffee and gingerbread. The dual-aspect Village
Room has a half-tester bed, a view of the green
complete with spreading chestnut tree. Study
Room, under the eaves, can sleep a family.
The imaginative menu includes dishes such as
Cotswold lamb, braised gem, wild garlic pesto
and aubergine purée. Service is slick and tables
hold vases of fresh flowers. 'Breakfast had a huge
choice, with the option of a very full English.'
(Chris and Erika Savory)

Lower Green
Ilmington
Stratford-upon-Avon CV36 4LT

T: 01608 682226
E: info@howardarms.com
W: howardarms.com

BEDROOMS: 8. 4 in extension, 1 on
ground floor.
OPEN: all year.
FACILITIES: snug, bar, restaurant,
in-room TV (Freeview), terrace,
garden (alfresco dining), parking,
bar wheelchair accessible, toilet not
adapted.
BACKGROUND MUSIC: all day in public
areas.
LOCATION: 8 miles S of Stratford-
upon-Avon, 6 miles NE of Chipping
Campden.
CHILDREN: all ages welcomed, under-
3s/cots free, extra bed £25, children's
menu.
DOGS: allowed in bar and on patio
only.
CREDIT CARDS: Amex, MC, Visa.
PRICES: B&B doubles from £135, singles
from £110. À la carte £45. 1-night
bookings sometimes refused.

Prices may change – check with hotel.

KENTISBURY Devon

MAP 1:B4

KENTISBURY GRANGE HOTEL

A gravel drive sweeps up to this Victorian cotton merchant's house in leafy landscaped grounds with spring-fed ponds on the edge of Exmoor national park. The bedrooms have had a designer make-over, with muted decor, rich fabrics, good bathrooms, some with roll-top bath and walk-in shower. There are five dog-friendly, stand-alone suites in the grounds, as well as self-catering lodges with decking and a hot tub for longer stays. Since all meals are served in the coach house, 'there is little for staff to do in terms of offering service country house-lounging style'. However, 'we felt the ambience, food and service were excellent'. An imaginative dinner menu includes dishes such as wild mushroom arancini, pickled mushrooms, herb emulsion, Parmesan, or crab and langoustine cannelloni which 'tasted delicious', followed by a 'rich intense chocolate mousse' or an 'excellent banana soufflé with toffee ice cream'. Afternoon tea is a treat too, while a varied breakfast menu brings 'perfect eggs Florentine', a full English or full veggie with bubble-and-squeak, smoked salmon, avocado on home-baked sourdough toast. (CJ)

Kentisbury
Barnstable EX31 4NL

T: 01271 545008
E: reception@kentisburygrange.com
W: kentisburygrange.com

BEDROOMS: 15. 5 stand-alone cottage suites, some suitable for disabled.
OPEN: all year.
FACILITIES: restaurant and bar in coach house, drawing room in main house, in-room TV (Freeview), civil wedding licence, 7-acre grounds, 3 lakes, ground-floor public areas wheelchair accessible, adapted toilet in restaurant.
BACKGROUND MUSIC: Spotify in restaurant, Classic FM in drawing room.
LOCATION: 10 miles NE of Barnstaple on A39.
CHILDREN: all ages welcomed, extra bed £30.
DOGS: allowed in cottage suites (£25 per stay), not in main house.
CREDIT CARDS: Amex, MC, Visa.
PRICES: B&B doubles from £155. À la carte £48.

Prices may change – check with hotel.

KING'S LYNN Norfolk

MAP 2:A4

CONGHAM HALL

Thirty acres of parkland surround this Georgian merchant's manor house in the Norfolk countryside, renowned for its fragrant garden of 400 herb varieties. Public rooms are 'furnished with suitable reproductions (and occasionally antiques), garnished with drapes, paintings, objets d'art', a reader relates. Bedrooms have a coffee machine, fresh milk, home-made cookies, complimentary use of the spa. Dog-friendly rooms around the spa garden have a private terrace. Five new cabins overlooking the orchard are in apple-pie order, with comfy seating and a wall of windows to a terrace with freestanding bath. 'The place felt to be in good shape,' wrote Guide regulars (although one felt let down by his evening meal). 'Our bedroom was incredibly comfortable and peaceful.' In the 'airy conservatory restaurant', menus inspired by home-grown produce might feature wild garlic and pea soup, hake with salsa verde, rhubarb crumble tart with verbena ice cream. Children under seven are served high tea with due ceremony, 'silver cutlery and folded napkin'. Breakfast brings free-range eggs, grilled kipper with mustard butter, the full omnivore and herbivore. (Anna and Bill Brewer, and others)

Lynn Road
Grimston
King's Lynn PE32 1AH

T: 01485 600250
E: info@conghamhallhotel.co.uk
W: conghamhallhotel.co.uk

BEDROOMS: 31. 6 garden rooms, 5 orchard cabins, 1 suitable for disabled.
OPEN: all year.
FACILITIES: bar, sitting room, library, restaurant, in-room TV, civil wedding licence, conference facilities, terrace, spa, 12-metre indoor pool, 30-acre grounds, EV charging, public areas wheelchair accessible, adapted toilet.
BACKGROUND MUSIC: in bar, restaurant.
LOCATION: 6 miles E of King's Lynn.
CHILDREN: all ages welcomed, free cots and extra beds for under-12s.
DOGS: allowed in some bedrooms (£10 per night, bowl, blankets), some public rooms.
CREDIT CARDS: MC, Visa.
PRICES: D,B&B doubles from £265, room only from £165 (Mon–Thurs, breakfast £8–£15). À la carte £40. 1-night bookings sometimes refused Sat.

Prices may change – check with hotel.

SEE ALSO SHORTLIST

KIRKBY LONSDALE Cumbria

MAP 4: inset C2

THE SUN INN

This 'splendid old inn', in a market town between the Lake District and the Yorkshire Dales, deftly mixes historic charm – beams, crackling fires and exposed stonework – with an updated, modern touch. Step into a 'welcoming low-beamed, long bar' with local ales, light colours and a wood-burning stove; beyond is a smart dining area with claret-red walls. Food is imaginative and tasty with dishes such as beetroot-cured trout, and pork belly with chorizo and Cajun potatoes; portions are on the hearty side. Bedrooms, which have kept their original features, have been stylishly refurbished with handmade wooden furniture, local artwork and country colours that make the most of sometimes small spaces. One reader praised the 'comfy chairs and large beds' while the view 'over the beautiful churchyard is a good-for-the-soul treat'. Bright, white bathrooms, most with bath as well as shower, are stocked with sweet-smelling soaps from the local producer, Bath House. A generous buffet at breakfast is followed by well-prepared hot dishes, while staff are unfailingly 'welcoming and helpful'. (Andrew Warren, and others)

6 Market Street
Kirkby Lonsdale LA6 2AU

T: 01524 271965
E: admin@sun-inn.info
W: sun-inn.info

BEDROOMS: 11.
OPEN: all year, restaurant closed Mon lunch.
FACILITIES: bar, restaurant, in-room TV (Freeview), bar and restaurant wheelchair accessible, adapted toilet.
BACKGROUND MUSIC: in bar.
LOCATION: town centre.
CHILDREN: all ages welcomed, cots free, extra bed £20.
DOGS: allowed in bedrooms (1 dog £20 per night, 2 dogs £30, welcome pack), public rooms (separate dog-friendly area in restaurant).
CREDIT CARDS: MC, Visa.
PRICES: B&B doubles from £105, singles from £95. À la carte £34. 1-night bookings usually refused Sat (but ring to check).

Prices may change – check with hotel.

KIRKBY STEPHEN Cumbria

MAP 4:C3

AUGILL CASTLE

With its towers and battlements this Victorian-folly castle, in 15 acres of grounds, looks imposing yet is 'a wonderful place to relax, kick back and take it easy'. Owners Simon and Wendy Bennett have furnished the huge rooms – wood panelling, ornate ceilings – in a grandly shabby, homely style. Family photographs and cushion-heaped window seats complement the antiques. 'It is quirky but very welcoming' and 'family-friendly', report readers. 'Our girls had a blast around the gardens.' Bedrooms in the castle and separate buildings range from big to vast. Eccentrically furnished with saleroom finds, bold wallpapers and 'sumptuous bedding, towels and robes', they might have a four-poster or Victorian chaise longue. Bathrooms are huge, some with a roll-top bath. Evening meals in the former Music Room might include spiced venison haunch with celeriac purée, and local lamb with parsnip mash. An 'amazing breakfast' includes freshly squeezed orange juice, smoked salmon and scrambled egg, and field mushroom and poached egg Florentine. 'A fantastic experience and cannot wait to rebook.' (Guillaume Post, Mark Vincent, and others)

Leacett Lane
South Stainmore
Kirkby Stephen CA17 4DE

T: 01768 341937
E: enquiries@stayinacastle.com
W: stayinacastle.com

BEDROOMS: 13. 8 in main castle, 5 in stables and orangery, 2 on ground floor, 1 suitable for disabled.
OPEN: all year, restaurant closed Mon/Tues.
FACILITIES: hall, sitting room, 2 dining rooms, bar, conservatory, private dining room, in-room TV (Freeview), civil wedding licence, 15-acre grounds (tennis), EV charging, public rooms wheelchair accessible, adapted toilet.
BACKGROUND MUSIC: light jazz/piano in dining room.
LOCATION: 3 miles NE of Kirkby Stephen.
CHILDREN: all ages welcomed (family rooms, or extra bed £25).
DOGS: allowed in 4 bedrooms (£10 per night, by arrangement, welcome pack), not public rooms.
CREDIT CARDS: Amex, MC, Visa.
PRICES: B&B doubles from £220. 2-course meal £38, 3-courses £45. 1-night bookings often refused at weekends.

Prices may change – check with hotel.

LANGAR Nottinghamshire

MAP 2:A3

LANGAR HALL

Everything is peachy at this apricot-hued Georgian country house in the Vale of Belvoir, at the end of a long avenue of lime trees, transformed from a family home into a delightful, idiosyncratic and much-loved hotel. It is run by Lila Arora, whose grandmother, the late chatelaine extraordinaire Imogen Skirving, inherited the house in 1983 and – inspired by a dream – welcomed paying guests there as friends. Bedrooms have antiques, paintings, clocks, books, cameos, curios and a story. Cartland was a favourite of the 'Pink Lady of Romance' (though it is no longer pink). Ground-floor Barristers, with panelled walls and porcelain plates around the picture rail, was where a QC pal of Imogen's hung out his suit. A cosy wooden pod and chalet can be booked in the grounds. Public rooms are similarly beguiling. In the flagstone-floored dining room, Gary Booth's short menus of 'outstanding food' include locally sourced dishes such as fillet of Blackberry Farm beef, ox cheek and salsa verde, or salt-baked beetroot, herb falafel and chickpea dressing. 'Dishes arrived promptly, with delicious amuse-bouche. Service is alert and courteous.' (RG)

Church Lane
Langar NG13 9HG

T: 01949 860559
E: info@langarhall.co.uk
W: langarhall.com

BEDROOMS: 13. 1 on ground floor, 3 in annexe, 1 in garden chalet, 1 in pod.
OPEN: all year Thurs–Sun.
FACILITIES: bar, study, garden room, main dining room, Indian room, sitting room, in-room TV (Freeview), civil wedding licence, 30-acre grounds, restaurant wheelchair accessible, adapted toilet.
BACKGROUND MUSIC: at lunch and dinner.
LOCATION: 12 miles SE of Nottingham.
CHILDREN: all ages welcomed, extra bed £30.
DOGS: in some bedrooms (£20 per stay), sitting room and bar, not in restaurant.
CREDIT CARDS: MC, Visa.
PRICES: B&B doubles from £135, singles from £120. Fixed-price dinner £59.50.

Prices may change – check with hotel.

LANGHAM Norfolk

MAP 2:A5

THE HARPER

You don't have to blow a fortune to stay at this 'relaxed yet refined' hotel in converted barns, former home of Langham Glass, with many fun nods to its heritage. Created by Sam Cutmore-Scott, 'the style is artfully mismatched, with old car seats and upcycled pipework'. In Ivy's lounge (after Sam's granny), 'an enormous stained-glass window features Norfolk birds, plus a couple of canaries' to honour Norwich City FC. 'Decadent sofas cry out to be slouched in with something from the wine-vending machine.' The restaurant, Stanley's (Sam's granddad), is 'full of character, with exposed brick, beams, wood floor, copper tables'. You can dine here on wood-fired steak, maybe tandoori monkfish. There is an all-day bar menu: eat indoors or in a courtyard with fire pit and water features (the lobster and samphire mac 'n' cheese is recommended). Bedrooms have a heated oak floor, complimentary cocktails, fresh milk and goodies in a fridge, an espresso machine, Irene Forte products. 'They are very rustic chic, many with a modern four-poster; some with a bath as well as a shower.' It is residents only, so 'never felt crowded'. (JK)

North Street
Langham
Holt NR25 7DH

T: 01328 805000
E: stay@theharper.co.uk
W: theharper.co.uk

BEDROOMS: 32. Some on ground floor, 2 suitable for disabled.
OPEN: all year.
FACILITIES: lift, hall, bar, lounge, dining room, games room, in-room smart TV, spa (12 by 5 metre pool), courtyard, bicycles, EV charging, public rooms wheelchair accessible.
BACKGROUND MUSIC: in public areas.
LOCATION: 2 miles S of Blakeney, within the Norfolk Coast Area of Outstanding Natural Beauty.
CHILDREN: all ages welcomed, interconnecting rooms, no under-16s in hot tub, steam room, sauna.
DOGS: allowed in ground-floor bedrooms (£25 per night, wash facilities, towels), bar, yard, not in dining rooms.
CREDIT CARDS: MC, Visa.
PRICES: B&B doubles from £205. À la carte £50. Min. 2-night stay Fri, Sat.

Prices may change – check with hotel.

LASTINGHAM Yorkshire

MAP 4:C4

LASTINGHAM GRANGE

The comforting, unchanging nature of this country hotel in a quiet village on the edge of the North York Moors is the big attraction for guests. 'It was delightful to find the same warm and welcoming hospitality, the same high levels of comfort,' report readers returning after a 15-year gap. Run by the Wood family for more than 60 years, the wisteria-covered former 17th-century farmhouse with its 'beautiful garden' looks across fields to the moors. 'It is deeply peaceful.' Interiors are as perennial as the views, with patterned carpets, floral fabrics, open fires and linen tablecloths. Guests are welcomed with home-made scones and tea; walkers will find wet clothes whisked to the drying room. Bedrooms are 'comfortable' rather than stylish but pin-neat with 'wonderful beds', fresh milk and coffee machines. Food is 'a real highlight', the five-course dinner perhaps starting with hot smoked salmon salad – 'so good I had it again for lunch' – followed by braised venison and 'strawberry pavlova with exquisite fairy castle meringues'. The Woods take 'great care to help you feel at home'. (Jo Adams, Alison Forrester, Helen Boaden)

High Street
Lastingham YO62 6TH

T: 01751 417345
E: reservations@lastinghamgrange.com
W: lastinghamgrange.com

BEDROOMS: 11. Plus self-catering cottage in village.
OPEN: all year except mid-Nov–early Mar.
FACILITIES: hall, lounge, dining room, in-room TV (Freeview), 10-acre grounds (terrace, garden, orchard, croquet, boules), restaurant and garden wheelchair accessible.
BACKGROUND MUSIC: none.
LOCATION: 5 miles NE of Kirkbymoorside.
CHILDREN: all ages welcomed, under-12s free, 12s and over ring to check, high teas, adventure playground.
DOGS: allowed in bedrooms with prior consent (£15 per stay), lounge, in garden (on lead), but not in dining room.
CREDIT CARDS: Amex, MC, Visa.
PRICES: B&B doubles from £240, singles from £180. À la carte £45.

Prices may change – check with hotel.

LAVENHAM Suffolk   MAP 2:C5

THE GREAT HOUSE

Creature comforts are assured at this Franglais-style hotel and restaurant in a Georgian-fronted medieval house on the market square of a charming old wool town. Owned by Nice-born Dominique Tropeano, MD and saviour of Colchester Zoo, it has a range of bedrooms, from bijou Bohème, which may be small in size but is big on character beneath the eaves, to Versailles, with a Jacobean four-poster. Montmartre, with sloping, beamed ceilings, has 'a particularly good view from the bathroom, of the charming marketplace', readers found. Pleasing touches include 'coffee, fruit and sherry (the latter an odd choice)'. Chef Swann Auffray cooks a three-course, fixed-price lunch, and a five-course dinner of dishes such as steamed wild sea bass with broccoli purée and anchovy and rocket pesto, and grilled beef fillet, with Roscoff onion petals and beef jus. 'Dinner was excellent.' A continental breakfast brings freshly squeezed orange juice or Suffolk apple juice and great croissants. There are also free-range egg dishes to order at extra cost, and while there is no full English, an oeuf is as good as a feast. (J and EG)

Market Place
Lavenham CO10 9QZ

T: 01787 247431
E: info@greathouse.co.uk
W: greathouse.co.uk

BEDROOMS: 5.
OPEN: all year except Jan, restaurant closed Sun eve, Mon, Tues.
FACILITIES: restaurant/bar, in-room TV (BT, Freeview), patio dining area, street parking, unsuitable for disabled.
BACKGROUND MUSIC: in restaurant.
LOCATION: town centre (free public car park).
CHILDREN: all ages welcomed, extra bed from £24, cot, high chair, children's portions.
DOGS: only assistance dogs allowed.
CREDIT CARDS: Amex, MC, Visa.
PRICES: B&B doubles from £120 when restaurant closed, from £261 with tasting menu on other nights. Continental breakfast incl., cooked dishes charged extra. 5-course dinner £62. 1-night bookings sometimes refused Sat.

Prices may change – check with hotel.

LAVENHAM Suffolk

MAP 2:C5

THE SWAN HOTEL & SPA

When you've walked a crooked mile around delightful medieval Lavenham, admiring the wonky timber-frame buildings, return to the Swan, which is 'packed with historical features, oak beams, uneven floors'. Occupying three 15th-century buildings, it is 'a friendly hotel with superb customer service', promoted this year from the Shortlist. 'There are plenty of communal spaces to sit and relax in, and we loved the courtyard hot tub.' 'Although there are 45 bedrooms and suites, it still feels cosy.' You can opt for anything from the Cygnet Rooms with a double bed to Constable Suites with a king-size bed, a separate lounge, garden views and many original features. Bathrooms are 'stylish and well equipped'. In the atmospheric brasserie at lunch and dinner, the menu runs from simple dishes such as tempura cod to beef short rib. At night in the lofty, cruck-beamed Gallery, a menu of either/or small/main plates includes, for example, hogget with wild garlic and morels or stone bass, kohlrabi with pak choi. The Swan is part of the Hotel Folk group. (Susan Court)

High Street
Lavenham CO10 9QA

T: 01787 247477
E: info@theswanatlavenham.co.uk
W: theswanatlavenham.co.uk

BEDROOMS: 45. 1 suitable for disabled.
OPEN: all year.
FACILITIES: 3 lounges, bar, brasserie, restaurant, in-room TV (Freeview), civil wedding licence, private dining/function facilities, spa (treatment rooms, sauna, steam room, outdoor hydrotherapy pool), terrace, garden, some public areas wheelchair accessible, adapted toilet.
BACKGROUND MUSIC: occasionally in public areas.
LOCATION: in village.
CHILDREN: all ages welcomed, extra bed for 1–4s free, £10 for those 5–17.
DOGS: in some bedrooms (£10 a night), bar, lounge, garden, not in restaurants.
CREDIT CARDS: Amex, MC, Visa.
PRICES: B&B doubles from £150. À la carte £40 (Gallery dinner menu), £37 (brasserie menu).

Prices may change – check with hotel.

LEAMINGTON SPA Warwickshire

MAP 2:B2

MALLORY COURT

A romantic Elizabethan-style Edwardian mansion, built for a Manchester cotton bleacher and set in landscaped gardens, is the epitome of a well-run country house hotel. Part of the Eden group (see also Brockencote Hall, Chaddesley Corbett), with Relais & Châteaux cred, it is 'at once sumptuous and relaxing ... The lovely staff made us feel welcome from the second we arrived.' First-floor doubles in the Knight's Suite are most affordable, but main-house rooms with modern comforts and period charm, an espresso machine and fine toiletries, have more ambience. 'Our room was spacious and practical, elegantly furnished, with a wonderful view across the gardens and south Warwickshire.' There are further lovely rooms in Orchard House, above the spa. You can eat informally from a lounge menu, while in the dining room produce from the kitchen garden features on a nightly tasting menu. Perhaps Mallory garden salad, goat's curd and black olives; bavette of Wagyu beef with crown pumpkin, morel and Madeira sauce. 'Food and drink are of very high quality,' say readers, with special praise for 'the impressive sommelier'. (Stephen and Pauline Glover, AB, IW)

Harbury Lane
Bishop's Tachbrook
Leamington Spa CV33 9QB

T: 01926 330214
E: reception@mallory.co.uk
W: mallory.co.uk

BEDROOMS: 43. 11 in Knight's Suite, 12 in Orchard House, 2 suitable for disabled.
OPEN: all year, restaurant for dinner only.
FACILITIES: 2 lounges, restaurant, lift, in-room TV, civil wedding licence, spa (hydrotherapy pool, outdoor vitality pool), 10-acre gardens, EV charging, public rooms wheelchair accessible, adapted toilet.
BACKGROUND MUSIC: in public rooms.
LOCATION: 3 miles S of Leamington Spa.
CHILDREN: all ages welcomed, cot £15, extra bed £35.
DOGS: in some bedrooms (£25 per dog per night, cushion, bowl, treats), gardens, not public rooms.
CREDIT CARDS: Amex, MC, Visa.
PRICES: B&B doubles from £211.50, singles from £198. À la carte £38, 5-course tasting menu £74.50.

Prices may change – check with hotel.

LETCOMBE REGIS Oxfordshire

MAP 2:C2

THE GREYHOUND INN

This is a proper village inn with locals enjoying pints in the bar, scrubbed tables, robust food, and light, creaky-floored bedrooms. In the Vale of the White Horse, close to both Oxford's charms and excellent walks, the red brick Georgian inn has been turned into a popular pub by owners Martyn Reed and Catriona Galbraith. 'The welcome was friendly,' say readers who have returned several times. 'We were all highly impressed.' There are local ales and pub quizzes in the beamed bar with a wood-burner in the inglenook fireplace. Eat here or in the red-walled dining area on mouth-watering dishes – sure to continue under new chef Martin Sherriff – such as guineafowl and truffle ballotine, and pan-roasted ling with sweet potato gnocchi, as well as pub classics. 'Beautifully decorated' bedrooms, on the first and second floors, are in soft country colours with a mix of vintage and painted furniture, fresh milk and home-made biscuits; most with bath and shower. Some have exposed beams and timbers, such as the family suite in the eaves. 'Excellent breakfasts' include home-made granola, eggs cooked to order and veggie options. (Rob and Shirley Lyne)

Main Street
Letcombe Regis
Wantage OX12 9JL

T: 01235 771969
E: info@thegreyhoundletcombe.co.uk
W: thegreyhoundletcombe.co.uk

BEDROOMS: 8.
OPEN: all year except 24/25 Dec, 1 week in Jan.
FACILITIES: bar with snug, 3 dining rooms (1 available for private dining/meetings), function room, in-room TV (Freeview), garden, EV charging, ground floor and garden wheelchair accessible, adapted toilet.
BACKGROUND MUSIC: occasionally in public rooms.
LOCATION: in village, 2 miles SW of Wantage.
CHILDREN: all ages welcomed, under-3s free, extra bed for ages 3–12 £20.
DOGS: allowed in 3 bedrooms (£15 per night, welcome pack), bar, garden, not dining rooms.
CREDIT CARDS: MC, Visa.
PRICES: B&B doubles from £95.
À la carte £40, 2-course Midweek Fix dinner (Wed) £20.

Prices may change – check with hotel.

LEWDOWN Devon

LEWTRENCHARD MANOR

A 'stunning Jacobean building' is, astonishingly, largely the creation of Victorian squire, parson and prolific author the Revd Sabine Baring-Gould. Salvaged Tuscan columns, Renaissance woodwork, rococo plasterwork, a Jacobean ceiling from a demolished house in Exeter, with antiques and Gould ancestral portraits, add to a rich ambience. A four-poster in Melton bedroom, overlooking the sunken garden and fountain, once belonged to Charles I's wife, Henrietta Maria. Sadly, the view from a 'huge, comfortable' annexe room was over a courtyard where the laundry van delivered. In the dining room, David Brown's menus use produce from the kitchen garden in dishes such as venison loin and braised leek with blue cheese and pear. 'The food is superb,' says a very happy reader and 'the service was exceptional.' Others report lapses, while a 'delicious, succulent pork fillet' had 'too many fussy extras' and, in unseasonably cold weather, how much nicer if the fires had been lit. For all that, this is a special place where a 'forgotten' Edwardian woodland garden, with waterfall and grotto, awaits discovery. (Lara Osgood)

Lewdown
Okehampton EX20 4PN

T: 01566 783222
E: info@lewtrenchard.co.uk
W: lewtrenchard.co.uk

BEDROOMS: 14. 1 in folly, 4 with separate entrance, 1 suitable for disabled.
OPEN: all year, currently closed Mon, Tues, but check.
FACILITIES: lounge, bar, library, restaurant, function rooms, in-room TV, civil wedding licence, 12-acre gardens, public rooms wheelchair accessible, adapted toilet.
BACKGROUND MUSIC: none.
LOCATION: rural, 10 miles N of Tavistock.
CHILDREN: all ages welcomed, extra bed £25, no under-8s in restaurant (eve).
DOGS: allowed in bedrooms (£15 per stay), in public rooms, not in restaurant.
CREDIT CARDS: Amex, MC, Visa.
PRICES: B&B doubles from £180, singles from £145. Set-price dinner £57.50, tasting menu £74. 1-night bookings sometimes refused Sat.

Prices may change – check with hotel.

LINCOLN Lincolnshire

MAP 4:E5

BRIDLEWAY BED & BREAKFAST

Tucked away down a farm track just three miles from the city centre, this rustic-chic B&B was a shoo-in this year for promotion from the Shortlist. 'Nothing is too much trouble' for artist Jane Haigh, who welcomes new arrivals with a home-made cream tea. Bedrooms are in former outbuildings, converted with wit and imagination. The Garden Room, with super-king bed, has a bath and wet-room shower, and a furnished patio under a pergola 'overlooking a pretty garden'. Harris Room has Harris tweed fabrics, a king-size bed and a large wet room. All rooms have under-floor heating, an espresso machine, mini-fridge, milk, flowers, original artwork, and posh toiletries. In the morning, a hamper, delivered to the door, contains a cooked breakfast, fruit salad, yogurt, croissants, pain au chocolat and free-range eggs from the resident hens. Two stables and a paddock are available by arrangement if you want to bring your own horse. Advice on and lifts to local restaurants are freely given. 'A great way to combine staying in the country with visiting Lincoln.' 'We were sad to leave.' (Roger Griffiths, Chris Powell, and others)

Riseholme Gorse
Hall Lane
Lincoln LN2 2LY

T: 01522 545693
E: bridlewaybandb@gmail.com
W: bridlewaybandb.co.uk

BEDROOMS: 4. All on ground floor in converted outbuildings.
OPEN: early/mid-Jan–12 Dec.
FACILITIES: conservatory, in-room TV (Freeview), ½-acre grounds, 2 stables, manège, paddock for guests' horses.
BACKGROUND MUSIC: none.
LOCATION: 3½ miles N of Lincoln.
CHILDREN: not under 16.
DOGS: only assistance dogs allowed.
CREDIT CARDS: Amex, MC, Visa.
PRICES: B&B doubles from £90, singles from £79. 2-night bookings preferred.

Prices may change – check with hotel.

LITTLE ECCLESTON Lancashire

THE CARTFORD INN

You can sit on the balcony of a studio cabin and gaze across the River Wyre to the Bowland fells, at this singular gastropub-with-rooms, art gallery and deli. Created by Patrick and Julie Beaumé, it rates a full entry on the strength of glowing reports. 'We were in the beautifully planned and luxurious Ziggy's Cabin, all done up with David Bowie memorabilia,' say friends of this Guide, who loved watching the swans with their cygnets. Like its robin-themed neighbour, it has an in-room egg-shaped bath. All rooms have emphatic style, maybe bare brick, beams, hand-blocked wallpaper, a '60s hammock chair, fun artwork. In the restaurant all the young dudes are 'pleased to see you and chatty'. Chef Chris Bury sources prime Lancashire produce for dishes such as 'whole plaice, simply cooked and served with linguine and spinach, but delicious'; bean, apricot and almond tagine, with polenta and chickpea fritter, zhoug and coriander slaw. Readers dined in one of the individual greenhouses. 'It was so much fun, putting our own music on and looking at the night sky.' (Jackie and Hugh Tunstall-Pedoe, Susannah Roberts, Jane Oldroyd)

Cartford Lane
Little Eccleston PR3 0YP

T: 01995 670166
E: info@thecartfordinn.co.uk
W: thecartfordinn.co.uk

BEDROOMS: 16. Some in riverside annexe, 1 suitable for disabled, 2 cabins in grounds.
OPEN: all year except 24–28 Dec, restaurant closed Mon lunch except on bank holidays.
FACILITIES: bar, restaurant, vegan/vegetarian menu, in-room TV (Freeview), function facilities, deli/coffee shop, riverside terrace, garden.
BACKGROUND MUSIC: in public areas.
LOCATION: 8 miles E of Blackpool, easily reached from M6 and M55.
CHILDREN: all ages welcomed (some time restrictions in bar, restaurant).
DOGS: not allowed.
CREDIT CARDS: Amex, MC, Visa.
PRICES: B&B doubles from £160, singles from £85. À la carte £38, plant-based £35. Min. 2-night stay in some rooms.

Prices may change – check with hotel.

LIVERPOOL Merseyside

MAP 4:E2

2 BLACKBURNE TERRACE

Everything is on song at this boutique B&B on a cobbled drive behind a row of lime trees, in the city's Georgian quarter, minutes from the Royal Philharmonic. It is run in a spirit of generosity by hosts Sarah and Glenn Whitter, who imbue beautiful, art-filled interiors with the ambience of home. Each of the four bedrooms is special. First-floor Room 3 has triple floor-to-ceiling windows, a balcony of iron lace, a king-size bed, a palette of deep blue and white, silk drapes, a French sofa, a marble bathroom with freestanding bath. Cosier Room 2, in shades of gold, has a ceiling-high headboard with integral lighting, a wingback chair and ottoman, a red maple secretaire, works by Korean artist Eun Sook Choi, a slipper bath in the marble en suite. All rooms have fresh flowers, Tappers Darkside gin, fine bath oils and toiletries. Guests will find books to read in the elegant drawing room, have use of the pretty walled garden and can ask to be shown a private in-house gallery. Breakfast, served communally, includes rare-breed meats, smoked salmon, grilled kipper, Baltic Bakehouse breads, vegetarian options.

2 Blackburne Terrace
Liverpool L87 PJ

T: 0151 708 5474
E: info@2bbt.co.uk
W: 2blackburneterrace.com

BEDROOMS: 4.
OPEN: all year except 24 Dec–1 Jan.
FACILITIES: drawing room, dining room, in-room smart TV (Freeview), walled garden, parking space, unsuitable for disabled.
BACKGROUND MUSIC: none.
LOCATION: city centre.
CHILDREN: not under 12.
DOGS: not allowed.
CREDIT CARDS: MC, Visa.
PRICES: B&B doubles from £190. 1-night bookings refused Fri/Sat.

Prices may change – check with hotel.

SEE ALSO SHORTLIST

LODSWORTH Sussex   MAP 2:E3

THE HALFWAY BRIDGE

At the heart of the South Downs national park, this village pub-with-rooms is the rural sister of the seaside Crab & Lobster, Sidlesham (see entry), country but no bumpkin. Our inspectors gave it the thumbs up for both its 'delicious food' and rooms. The latter are in a single-storey stable block 'across a little lane behind the pub', which meant 'there was no road noise' although the gravel lane was 'tricky if you wear heels'. Their room was 'comfortable and easy' with a super-king bed, a 'fridge with bottled water and milk (civilised)'. The decor is a mix of rusticity and contemporary comfort. A room with a sleigh bed has a wall of timber planks, an antique chest of drawers, leather tub chair and small settle. Food is served in 'lots of interesting little spaces', and under parasols in a 'large, grassy garden'. It is largely pub grub done well, with good ingredients; 'the self-proclaimed burger expert said it was top quality'. The pan-fried sea bream was also enjoyed. Breakfast ticked all the boxes, with freshly squeezed orange juice, smashed avocado, a full English and barista-style coffee. 'One could imagine enjoying a few nights here.'

Lodsworth
Petworth GU28 9BP

T: 01798 861281
E: enquiries@halfwaybridge.co.uk
w: halfwaybridge.co.uk

BEDROOMS: 8. In Cowdray Barns, 165 yds from main building. 1 shepherd's hut.
OPEN: all year.
FACILITIES: bar, 2 restaurant areas, private party facilities (16 covers), in-room TV (Freeview), bar terrace, small beer garden, unsuitable for disabled.
BACKGROUND MUSIC: 'quiet' in bar and restaurant.
LOCATION: 3 miles W of Petworth, on A272.
CHILDREN: all ages welcomed, extra bed £40, children's menu.
DOGS: allowed in some bedrooms (£30 per stay), bar area and garden.
CREDIT CARDS: Amex, MC, Visa.
PRICES: B&B doubles from £150, singles from £100. Set lunch menu (Mon–Sat) £22–£26, à la carte £35. 1-night bookings refused Fri and Sat, when single occupancy is charged at full double rate.

Prices may change – check with hotel.

LONG SUTTON Somerset

MAP 1:C6

THE DEVONSHIRE ARMS

Behind a handsome 18th-century blue-lias-stone facade, a former village inn overlooking the green is these days a contemporary drop-in bar and restaurant-with-rooms. Long Sutton saw fierce fighting in the Civil War and was described as 'extremely wanting in provisions'. No one seeking food or drink could say that today, with ales on tap and meals served in the restaurant and walled garden. Menus are a mix of pub classics (sausages and mash, chargrilled steak) and more imaginative dishes, maybe wild mushroom risotto, or hake with mussels and ratatouille. Although the exterior looks traditional, interiors are surprisingly contemporary. You can expect padded banquettes and floral wallpaper as well as walls of deep blue, aubergine and charcoal, hung with lithograph caricatures and portraits of Tudor and Stuart monarchs. Bedrooms have a dreamy, soft-focus palette, and up-to-date styling. One has a modern four-poster. There are two ground-floor doubles in an annexe cottage behind the main building. If you liked the village-produced Harry's Cider in the bar, you can visit a cider shop for an orchard tour and tastings.

Long Sutton
Langport TA10 9LP

T: 01458 241271
E: mail@thedevonshirearms.com
W: thedevonshirearms.com

BEDROOMS: 9. 2, on ground floor, in annexe behind main building.
OPEN: all year except 25/26 Dec.
FACILITIES: open-plan bar and restaurant, private dining room, in-room TV (Freeview), courtyard, garden (croquet lawn, vegetable garden), parking, public areas wheelchair accessible, no adapted toilet.
BACKGROUND MUSIC: in bar.
LOCATION: by the village green.
CHILDREN: all ages welcomed, free travel cot, extra bed £20, children's menus.
DOGS: allowed in bar only.
CREDIT CARDS: MC, Visa.
PRICES: B&B doubles from £120, singles from £95, Sun–Thurs, subject to availability. À la carte £45. 1-night bookings sometimes refused at weekends.

Prices may change – check with hotel.

LONGHORSLEY Northumberland   MAP 4:B3

THISTLEYHAUGH FARM   NEW

This 'excellent, traditional farmhouse B&B',
with huge bedrooms, generous hospitality and
breakfasts to fuel the day, is now in the capable
hands of the family's second generation of hosts.
The Nellesses' organic farm, reached by country
lanes, feels remote yet is only two miles from
the main road. In autumn, the 'picture-book
perfect' Georgian farmhouse's Virginia creeper-
covered walls 'glow like a scarlet beacon in the
quiet Northumbrian countryside'. Downstairs
rooms are understatedly elegant with polished
antiques and well-upholstered sofas while 'very
comfortable' bedrooms have huge mahogany
wardrobes, 'proper towel rails and dressing tables',
and broderie anglaise bedcovers. 'Well-stocked'
trolleys include fresh milk and home-made
biscuits; there are roll-top baths in the bathrooms.
'Breakfast was excellent with fresh orange juice'
and a range of cooked items. 'Extremely good'
light suppers of sandwiches, 'a delicious dessert
and excellent cheeseboard' are served in the fire-
warmed sitting room. Zoe and Janice continue
the famed Nelless hospitality; 'the welcome
is unchanged and is as warm as ever'. (Mary
Hewson, and others)

Longhorsley
Morpeth NE65 8RG

T: 01665 570629
E: thistleyhaugh@hotmail.com
W: thistleyhaugh.co.uk

BEDROOMS: 2.
OPEN: all year except 10 Dec–8 Jan.
FACILITIES: lounge, garden/breakfast
room, hall, in-room TV (Freeview),
¼-acre garden (summer house),
fishing, shooting, golf, riding nearby.
BACKGROUND MUSIC: none.
LOCATION: 10 miles N of Morpeth,
W of A697.
CHILDREN: all ages welcomed, free cot.
DOGS: not allowed (kennels nearby).
CREDIT CARDS: MC, Visa.
PRICES: B&B doubles from £125,
singles from £100. Light supper (book
ahead) £15.

Prices may change – check with hotel.

LORTON Cumbria

MAP 4: inset C2

NEW HOUSE FARM

Away from the Lake District's hot spots, in quiet Lorton Vale north of Buttermere, this whitewashed farmhouse B&B mixes rustic authenticity with modern comforts. Dating from the 17th century, and enlarged in Georgian times, it retains original features of slate-flagged floors, open beams, sturdy oak doors and big fireplaces. With its backdrop of fields and fells, lawned garden and atmospheric spaces – including a hayloft, cart shed and milking parlour – it's a popular wedding venue. (B&B and tea room availability fit around these bookings.) Ever-cheery owner Hazel Thompson greets guests with a cream tea to take in the fire-warmed sitting room or on the lawn. Spacious bedrooms are rich with character – exposed-stone walls, oak beams – luxuriously updated with thick curtains, brass beds and four-posters, and country antiques. Bathrooms are huge, with perhaps a roll-top bath. With those views, you won't mind the lack of TVs. Two rooms are separate from the farmhouse, with private entrances. Breakfast is a homely affair in the cosy dining room while supper options include the local pub or Kirkstile Inn, three miles away.

Lorton
Cockermouth CA13 9UU

T: 07841 159818
E: hazel@newhouse-farm.co.uk
W: newhouse-farm.com

BEDROOMS: 5. 2 on ground floor in adjacent barn.
OPEN: all year except 23 Dec–2 Jan, and weekends and some weekdays (for weddings), tea room open Apr–Nov, subject to wedding bookings.
FACILITIES: entrance hall, 2 lounges, dining room, civil wedding licence, 17-acre grounds (garden, fire pit, streams, woods, field, lake and river, safe bathing 2 miles), unsuitable for disabled.
BACKGROUND MUSIC: none.
LOCATION: on B5289, 2 miles S of Lorton.
CHILDREN: all ages welcomed.
DOGS: 'clean and dry' dogs with own bed allowed in bedrooms (£10 per night), not in public rooms.
CREDIT CARDS: MC, Visa.
PRICES: B&B doubles from £190, singles from £90. Min. 2-night stay usually.

Prices may change – check with hotel.

LOWER BOCKHAMPTON Dorset

MAP 1:D6

YALBURY COTTAGE

Deep in Thomas Hardy country, this picture-perfect thatched cottage is a popular restaurant-with-rooms run with great charm by Ariane Jones and her husband, Jamie. They extend guests a 'very warm welcome' while staff are 'friendly and efficient'. One reader's country-style bedroom in a modern extension was 'on the small side but quiet and comfortable, overlooking fields' with a 'good shower' in the 'compact bathroom'. Lounge and dining room are cosy with low beams, exposed brickwork and a wood-burning stove. Take drinks in the former before moving on to what many regard as the highlight of a stay. 'The real attraction here is the food,' says a regular who praises Jamie's short menu of dishes such as braised beef and dauphinoise potatoes. 'The lemon roast chicken breast with tabbouleh salad was one of my best meals this year.' Another reader was delighted to have a 'gluten-free menu with the same level of choice as the main menu'. Breakfast is a feast of omelettes, smoked haddock, the full grill, and croissants baked to order: 'delicious and meant we did not need lunches'. (Peter Anderson, Steve Hur, SP)

Lower Bockhampton
Dorchester DT2 8PZ

T: 01305 262382
E: enquiries@yalburycottage.com
W: yalburycottage.com

BEDROOMS: 8. 6 on ground floor.
OPEN: all year except 23 Dec–20 Jan, closed Sun pm, Mon.
FACILITIES: lounge, restaurant, in-room TV (Freeview), garden with outdoor seating, EV charging, restaurant wheelchair accessible, no adapted toilet.
BACKGROUND MUSIC: 'easy listening' in lounge in evening.
LOCATION: 2 miles E of Dorchester.
CHILDREN: all ages welcomed, extra bed for under-12s free, 12s and over £25, no under-12s in restaurant after 8 pm.
DOGS: allowed in bedrooms (£8.50 per night), in lounge, not in restaurant.
CREDIT CARDS: MC, Visa.
PRICES: B&B doubles from £130, singles from £95. À la carte £47.50.

Prices may change – check with hotel.

LUDLOW Shropshire

MAP 3:C4

OLD DOWNTON LODGE

Amid rolling hills, where Shropshire nudges Herefordshire, Pippa and Willem Vlok's restaurant-with-rooms is a picturesque set piece of medieval and Georgian farm buildings. It lies on the historic Downton Estate (not that Downton!), and caters to shooting parties, but you are as welcome to take tea outdoors and just shoot the breeze. Bedrooms occupy former stables and barns, some with lofty, beamed ceilings, perhaps an oak four-poster. 'Our room was stunning, with a beautiful bathroom with romantic lighting,' a reader writes. 'We enjoyed a bottle of wine on the garden chairs overlooking the colourful garden.' Others take a drink by the log-burner in a sitting room fashioned from a milking parlour. In a baronial-style dining room, Nick Bennett's cooking is 'five star'. Although another reader staying for several nights would have liked more variety, 'ham hock with pineapple chutney and pistachio, and duck breast with beetroot, kohlrabi and cherry were highlights'. 'Willem, Pippa and their team are knowledgeable, professional and make you feel so special, it's a hard place to leave!' (Amanda Bateman, Frances M Thomas, and others)

Downton on the Rock
Ludlow SY8 2HU

T: 01568 771826
E: bookings@olddowntonlodge.com
W: olddowntonlodge.com

BEDROOMS: 9. In buildings round courtyard.
OPEN: all year, except Christmas.
FACILITIES: sitting room, dining room, 'museum' (function room), in-room TV (Freeview), civil wedding licence, 1-acre courtyard, EV charging, unsuitable for disabled.
BACKGROUND MUSIC: soft classical in sitting and dining room.
LOCATION: 6 miles W of Ludlow.
CHILDREN: over-13s only.
DOGS: allowed in 4 bedrooms by prior arrangement (£15 per dog, max. 2 per room), only assistance dogs in sitting room and dining room.
CREDIT CARDS: Amex, MC, Visa.
PRICES: B&B doubles from £185. Fixed-price dinner (24 hours' notice) £50–£60 (2/3 courses), tasting menu £75.

Prices may change – check with hotel.

SEE ALSO SHORTLIST

LYME REGIS Dorset

MAP 1:C6

DORSET HOUSE

Dorset House describes itself as 'breakfast with rooms', which is a clue that the morning feast in this eco-friendly, cream-washed Georgian house is a bit out of the ordinary. It is cooked by Lyn Martin, co-owner with husband Jason, and who in a former life travelled the world experiencing indifferent hotel meals and determined to do better. Expect 'delicious' home-made granola, perhaps followed by avocado and mint on home-baked sourdough, honey-baked figs with rose-scented ricotta or the full Dorset. Sourcing is local and organic, and there are vegan options. If warm, you can eat on the veranda. Bedrooms are town house smart and uncluttered, with waxed floorboards, large sash windows and mid-century and antique furniture. Designer bathrooms are shower-only. Thoughtful touches include books, locally baked treats and chilled water. Most rooms have coastal views or a glimpse of the sea (the house is up a hill). There's a snug with honesty bar where you can dine on a takeaway or the Martins will recommend restaurants. 'They could not have been more helpful,' say guests. 'They have created a remarkable oasis of calm.' (H and AB)

Pound Road
Lyme Regis DT7 3HX

T: 01297 442055
E: info@dorsethouselyme.com
W: dorsethouselyme.com

BEDROOMS: 5.
OPEN: all year except Christmas.
FACILITIES: snug, breakfast room, reception, in-room TV (Freeview), veranda, paid parking or free on street nearby.
BACKGROUND MUSIC: 'subtle' in breakfast room.
LOCATION: 300 yds from town centre.
CHILDREN: all ages welcomed, extra bed £30, babies free.
DOGS: not allowed.
CREDIT CARDS: Amex, MC, Visa.
PRICES: B&B doubles from £125, singles from £115. 1-night bookings usually refused.

Prices may change – check with hotel.

LYMINGTON Hampshire

MAP 2:E2

BRITANNIA HOUSE

Uber-friendly host Tobias Feilke welcomes guests to his idiosyncratic B&B in a yachting town and ancient seaport on the edge of the New Forest. You step inside the Victorian red brick corner house to find a suit of armour and a fine display of hats (pith helmet, trilbies, naval caps . . .). The ethos is one of unstinting generosity. Attention has been lavished on affordable bedrooms, such as first-floor Britannia Suite, styled in imperial gold and black, with bath and shower. The hand-painted ground-floor Courtyard Suite overlooks the courtyard and evergreen garden, the walls hung with an eccentric mix of artwork. The dual-aspect lounge has a marble fireplace, plush sofas, opulent drapes, views across the quay. Rhineland-born Tobias's career in hospitality began with a spell as a bellhop in Munich. He moved on up via the swanky Brenners Park-Hotel in Baden-Baden, and our own Chewton Glen, New Milton (see entry). He launched his B&B in 2000, and remains in sole charge, rustling up a range-cooked breakfast for guests, served at the kitchen table, before they head off for a puffin cruise or to catch a ferry to the Isle of Wight.

Station Street
Lymington SO41 3BA

T: 01590 672091
E: enquiries@britannia-house.com
W: britannia-house.com

BEDROOMS: 5. 2 on ground floor, one 2-storey apartment.
OPEN: all year except mid-Dec–mid-Jan.
FACILITIES: lounge, kitchen/breakfast room, in-room TV (Freeview), courtyard garden, parking, unsuitable for disabled.
BACKGROUND MUSIC: none.
LOCATION: 2 mins' walk from High Street/quayside, close to station.
CHILDREN: not under 8.
DOGS: not allowed.
CREDIT CARDS: MC, Visa.
PRICES: B&B doubles from £99, singles from £89. 2-night bookings preferred, but check availability.

Prices may change – check with hotel.

LYNDHURST Hampshire

LIME WOOD

A New Forest bolt-hole, this country house hotel
has an easy glamour, romantic and family-friendly
rooms, heart-warming Italian food and top-notch
spa. 'Laid-back luxury at its very best,' says our
Guide insider. Public rooms in the Georgian main
house mix panelled walls and checkerboard-
tiled floors with leather chairs and modern art.
Particularly atmospheric is the glass-ceilinged
courtyard bar. Bedrooms in a chic country house
style radiate comfort, and range from main-
house rooms with woodland views and a bath by
the window to rustic cottages and cabins in the
grounds, perhaps with an open fire. The Lake
Cabin is the ultimate in privacy with a wrap-
around balcony over the water. After a walk in
the grounds or New Forest (there are trails from
the door), relax in the Herb House Spa with its
choice of pools, rooftop garden and Raw & Cured
café offering nutritious dishes such as home-cured
salmon, and borlotti bean salad. Come evening,
Angela Hartnett and Luke Holder serve 'the best
of Italian and British food' in Hartnett Holder &
Co. The short menu could include confit cod with
white onion risotto or venison with spiced pear.

Beaulieu Road
Lyndhurst SO43 7FZ

T: 02380 287177
E: info@limewood.co.uk
w: limewoodhotel.co.uk

BEDROOMS: 33. 5 on ground floor,
2 suitable for disabled, 16 in pavilions,
cottages in the grounds.
OPEN: all year.
FACILITIES: lifts, 2 bars, 3 lounges,
2 restaurants, private dining rooms,
in-room TV, civil wedding licence,
spa (indoor pool), 14-acre gardens,
cookery school, public rooms
wheelchair accessible, adapted toilet.
BACKGROUND MUSIC: all day in public
areas.
LOCATION: in New Forest, 12 miles
SW of Southampton.
CHILDREN: all ages welcomed, no
charge for extra bed.
DOGS: allowed in outside bedrooms
(£30 per stay), grounds, not main
house.
CREDIT CARDS: MC, Visa.
PRICES: room only from £435.
Continental breakfast £18.50, full
breakfast (incl. cont.) £25, à la carte
£65. 1-night bookings refused at most
weekends.

Prices may change – check with hotel.

MADEHURST Sussex

THE PIG IN THE SOUTH DOWNS

NEW

'The perfect restaurant-with-rooms for lovers of British bubbles', this latest addition to Robin Hutson's Pig litter is surrounded by some of Britain's best wine-making country and offers 'plenty of fizz with your food'. It is also the first to have its own vineyard; you dine in a conservatory with 'glorious views over the vines'. Centred on a handsome Georgian mansion which is perhaps 'smaller and less grand than its siblings', most of its rooms are scattered across converted stable-yard buildings and wagons as well. 'The signature shabby-chic style has a floral feel,' a Guide insider reports; Judy Hutson modelled it on a fictitious 1940s housewife called Mary. Dual-aspect Room 2 has a huge avocado freestanding bath, 'now looking oddly fashionable'. Best is the Chicken Shack, with lights in old chicken feeders and a bath next to a chaise longue at the end of a long, beamed room. The menus are created with produce from the kitchen garden and orchard, Sussex coast and countryside. 'The lamb shoulder melts in the mouth.' 'At breakfast, I was glad of the beetroot juice to help my liver cope with the excesses of the night before.' (JK)

Madehurst
Arundel BN18 0NL

T: 01243 974500
E: info@thepiginthesouthdowns.com
W: thepighotel.com

BEDROOMS: 28. Most in stable-yard buildings, field and garden wagons, 2 on ground floor suitable for disabled, gravel tracks around property.
OPEN: all year.
FACILITIES: bar/lounge, restaurant, snug, treatment rooms, gardens, pasture, orchard, vineyard, walled kitchen garden, EV charging.
BACKGROUND MUSIC: in public areas at all times.
LOCATION: Arundel and Amberley stations a 10-min. drive.
CHILDREN: all ages welcomed, no charge for extra beds.
DOGS: not allowed.
CREDIT CARDS: MC, Visa.
PRICES: Room-only doubles from £155. Breakfast £13.50–£18.50, à la carte £42.

Prices may change – check with hotel.

MAIDEN BRADLEY Wiltshire

MAP 2:D1

THE BRADLEY HARE

NEW

'It's a good thing it's not my local or I'd be there all the time,' said our inspector of this 'practically perfect pub-with-rooms' four miles from the Arcadian landscape of Stourhead. Co-owner James Thurstan Waterworth (formerly of hip Soho House) has created 'a highly styled version of ye olde village inn within a handsome Victorian building', mixing bare floorboards and flagstones with 'rugs and kilims, Farrow & Ball colours, striped armchairs by a wood-burner, striking modern art'. Bedrooms have individual quirks and flourishes. 'Ours came with a stripy fabric headboard and jute carpet, a compact, sleek, sexy bathroom with aubergine and black tiles and powerful shower.' Annexe rooms are generally larger. In the dining room, with candles from Charles Farris, the Queen's chandler, the food didn't quite measure up. 'The roasted tomato and chilli soup was fine, but some bread would have been nice.' A halibut dish was overcooked, and why the lack of vegetables when they make much of the fresh and seasonal produce they take from community gardens and allotments? Still, 'the air was relaxed and welcoming' and 'I did say it was "practically" perfect'.

Church Street
Maiden Bradley
Warminster BA12 7HW

T: 01985 801018
E: reception@thebradleyhare.co.uk
W: thebradleyhare.co.uk

BEDROOMS: 12. 5 in coach house.
OPEN: all year, closed Sun pm, Mon, 25/26 Dec.
FACILITIES: bar, library/snug, dining room, function room, skittle alley, in-room TV, garden, main restaurant, bar wheelchair accessible.
BACKGROUND MUSIC: ambient, in pub, dining room.
LOCATION: on B3092, between Bruton and Warminster.
CHILDREN: all ages welcomed, under-16s must be accompanied by adult, free cots, small charge for extra bed.
DOGS: allowed in annexe rooms by arrangement (bowls, treats, possible small charge for cleaning), pub, garden, not in dining room.
CREDIT CARDS: Amex, MC, Visa.
PRICES: room-only doubles from £135 (incl. continental breakfast). Cooked breakfast from £12. 1-night bookings usually refused at weekends, but check for availability.

Prices may change – check with hotel.

MARKET DRAYTON Shropshire   MAP 3:B5

GOLDSTONE HALL

Everything in the garden is lovely at John and Sue Cushing's red brick Georgian manor house hotel in dairy-farming country five miles outside Market Drayton. Double-tiered herbaceous borders, a rose-lined walkway, laburnum arch, and one of the UK's largest hotel kitchen gardens are perennial delights. When you sit down to dine, the kale with your sirloin of beef might be Uncle Bert's Purple, the tomato with your chalk stream trout Darby Striped – just two of the heritage varieties grown here. 'The roses were magnificent,' writes a reader, 'the garden a joy to explore.' Bedrooms are supplied with fresh milk in a fridge and home-made cookies. One deluxe room has an antique four-poster. The chambers have a hand-built bed, a large bath and wet-room shower. A reader there for a single night 'wished we could have stayed longer'. Another reader thought the willing junior staff were 'in need of more training' but, on the plus side, found 'the food was of a consistently high standard, with plenty of fruit on offer at the breakfast buffet', while 'poached egg on smashed avocado on sourdough toast was a welcome change'. (Christine Hughes, John Saul, and others)

Goldstone Road
Market Drayton TF9 2NA

T: 01630 661202
E: enquiries@goldstonehall.com
W: goldstonehall.com

BEDROOMS: 12. 2 on ground floor.
OPEN: all year.
FACILITIES: bar, lounge, drawing room, dining room, orangery, in-room TV (Sky, Freeview), function facilities, civil wedding licence, 5 acres of grounds (walled garden, kitchen garden, Great Lawn), EV charging, public rooms and garden wheelchair accessible, adapted toilets.
BACKGROUND MUSIC: bar and dining room.
LOCATION: 5 miles S of Market Drayton.
CHILDREN: all ages welcomed, extra bed £11.50–£28.
DOGS: not allowed.
CREDIT CARDS: Amex, MC, Visa.
PRICES: B&B doubles from £160, singles from £100. À la carte (garden menu) £32, 7-course tasting menu £40.

Prices may change – check with hotel.

MARTINHOE Devon

THE OLD RECTORY HOTEL

In an isolated hamlet on the edge of Exmoor national park, where hog-backed cliffs tower above the Bristol Channel, this hotel in a 16th-century-cum-Georgian rectory 'goes from strength to strength'. 'The hotel interiors are very tasteful', while the 'dining experience is special'. Bedrooms, in the main house and coach house, mix contemporary and period style. Dual-aspect Watersmeet Suite has an open-plan seating area, a freestanding bath and walk-in power shower. A new, two-bedroom duplex suite in the former coachman's house has a sitting room with log-burner, luxury bathroom and shower room. All have luxury toiletries and spring water on tap. 'The orangery is a delightful spot to sit and relax in view of the pleasant garden.' Hosts Huw Rees and Sam Prosser invite guests to join them for aperitifs and canapés as they order from a nightly changing menu of locally sourced dishes such as breast of Creedy Carver duck with a blackberry reduction or cauliflower, cashew, coconut and spinach curry. 'We enjoy the luxury and very personal attention so much that this is our fourth visit and we are booked for next year.' (Mary Coles)

Berry's Ground Lane
Martinhoe EX31 4QT

T: 01598 763368
E: reception@oldrectoryhotel.co.uk
W: oldrectoryhotel.co.uk

BEDROOMS: 12. 2 on ground floor, 3 in coach house, 1 in cottage annexe.
OPEN: Mar–early Nov.
FACILITIES: 2 lounges, orangery, dining room, in-room TV (Freeview), 3-acre grounds, EV charging, public rooms including restaurant wheelchair accessible, toilet not adapted.
BACKGROUND MUSIC: 'very quiet', in dining room only.
LOCATION: 4 miles W of Lynton.
CHILDREN: not under 14.
DOGS: not allowed.
CREDIT CARDS: Amex, MC, Visa.
PRICES: B&B doubles from £210, singles from £195. À la carte £35. 1-night bookings refused at present (but check).

Prices may change – check with hotel.

MAWGAN PORTH Cornwall

MAP 1:D2

BEDRUTHAN HOTEL AND SPA

Seen through walls of windows, the sea is a huge presence at this family-run hotel 'in a fabulous location' on the cliffs above a surfers' beach. Built in 1959 in the California Modern style, it has breezy, Scandi-inspired decor. The bedrooms have been recently refurbished. Some overlook countryside, but most have Atlantic views. Doubles have a bath and walk-in shower or double monsoon shower, an Italian espresso machine. 'Apartments' have a king-size bed, a separate bunk room, living area and patio or Juliet balcony. Activities include everything from painting classes to open-air theatre. The spa, bar, lounge, shop, art gallery and two restaurants are at your disposal. Outside, there is a sun terrace, play area, pods, hammocks, a hot tub. You can eat in the Wild Café, a bakery breakfast (cooked items extra), salads and sandwiches (roasts on Sunday); dinner à la carte – maybe smoked haddock and mussel chowder, coconut cauliflower curry, rack of lamb. In The Herring, short carnivore and vegan menus start with small plates for sharing – because it's a sharing sort of place. (See also sister hotel The Scarlet, next entry.)

Trenance
Mawgan Porth TR8 4BU

T: 01637 860860
E: stay@bedruthan.com
W: bedruthan.com

BEDROOMS: 101. 1 suitable for disabled, apartment suites in separate block.
OPEN: all year.
FACILITIES: lift, bar, terrace, 2 restaurants (vegan menu), lounge, in-room TV (Freeview), spa (indoor pool), shop, art gallery, civil wedding licence, 5-acre grounds (3 heated pools, tennis), EV charging, several areas wheelchair accessible, adapted toilet.
BACKGROUND MUSIC: in restaurant, café and bar.
LOCATION: 4 miles NE of Newquay.
CHILDREN: all ages welcomed, family rooms but no extra beds.
DOGS: allowed in some bedrooms (£15 per night), some public areas.
CREDIT CARDS: MC, Visa.
PRICES: B&B doubles from £165, singles from £95. Set-price dinner £50 (Herring), à la carte £35 (Wild Café).

Prices may change – check with hotel.

MAWGAN PORTH Cornwall   MAP 1:D2

THE SCARLET

Eco values as well as enjoyment are fundamental
to this cliff-top hotel, with sea thrift-covered roof,
sweeping curves, reed-filtered pool and walls of
windows to soak up the light and the seascape.
A sister to Bedruthan (see previous entry), it
makes the most of its commanding position
above the beach at Mawgan Porth. The view is
on show everywhere you go, from the restaurant
with outdoor terrace and 'exceptional food' to
the sublime spa. Outdoor hot tubs are perfectly
positioned to watch the sun set and a meadow
garden with private pods runs down to the South
West Coast Path. The Scandi-styled bedrooms,
with stripped-wood floors and floor-to-ceiling
windows, all have outside space – a balcony,
terrace or rooftop viewing 'pod'. Readers praise
the serenity in this adults-only bolt-hole as well
as the 'wonderful, relaxed service'. Public spaces
have bespoke furniture, works by Cornish artists.
At dinner, the menu might include 'delicious
rabbit loin' or perhaps hake with seaweed beurre
blanc and smoked cod's roe. The wine list is
'interesting, with good choices'. 'All in all would
highly recommend.' (Anthony Pithers, Tessa Stuart)

Tredragon Road
Mawgan Porth TR8 4DQ

T: 01637 861800
E: stay@scarlethotel.co.uk
W: scarlethotel.co.uk

BEDROOMS: 37. 2 suitable for disabled.
OPEN: open all year.
FACILITIES: lift, 2 lounges, bar, library,
restaurant (vegetarian/vegan menus),
in-room TV (Freeview), civil wedding
licence, spa, indoor pool, outdoor
reed pool, terrace, meadow garden,
EV charging, public areas wheelchair
accessible, adapted toilet.
BACKGROUND MUSIC: all day in bar and
restaurant.
LOCATION: 4 miles NE of Newquay.
CHILDREN: not allowed.
DOGS: allowed in 5 selected bedrooms
(£15 per night), some public areas.
CREDIT CARDS: MC, Visa.
PRICES: B&B doubles from £255, singles
from £225. Fixed-price dinner £60,
vegan £52, tasting menu £70. 1-night
bookings refused Fri/Sat.

Prices may change – check with hotel.

MAWNAN SMITH Cornwall

BUDOCK VEAN

With golf, tennis, kayaking and powerboating, indoor pool and outdoor hot tub, this spa hotel is a holiday resort in its own right. Amid 65 acres of gardens and woodland on the Helford river, the Barlow family's former manor house sails back into the main Guide on a wash of approval, as it undergoes extensive refurbishment. 'Upgrades done with careful thought, and the decor has a modern, soft, relaxing feel,' writes one reader, whose bedroom was 'furnished to a high standard, with an excellent bed, good lighting, attention to detail'. Choices include dog-friendly standard rooms, more contemporary signature rooms, and suites with sitting room, a bath and walk-in shower. Christian Jordan has stepped up to head chef and is praised for his dishes, which might include pan-fried wild turbot with saffron potatoes and nage; roast loin of venison with port and thyme jus; and African peanut and sweet potato stew. 'Fish dishes particularly enjoyed.' At breakfast there are locally made sausages, locally smoked salmon and haddock. 'How good it was to see items cooked to order!' 'The grounds are fabulous.' (Ian Dewey, Tony and Shirley Hall)

nr Helford Passage
Mawnan Smith
Falmouth TR11 5LG

T: 01326 252100
E: relax@budockvean.co.uk
W: budockvean.co.uk

BEDROOMS: 49. 1 suitable for disabled. Plus 4 self-catering cottages.
OPEN: all year except 2 weeks early Jan.
FACILITIES: lift, 2 lounges, cocktail bar, conservatory, golf bar, restaurant (vegan/vegetarian menus), in-room TV (Freeview), civil wedding licence, 65-acre grounds, spa, 15-metre indoor pool. EV charging, bar, lounges wheelchair accessible, adapted toilet.
BACKGROUND MUSIC: 'gentle' live piano or guitar at dinner.
LOCATION: 6 miles SW of Falmouth.
CHILDREN: all ages welcomed, children's menu.
DOGS: allowed in some bedrooms (£10 a night), lobby, conservatory, terrace.
CREDIT CARDS: MC, Visa.
PRICES: per person B&B from £76. Set-price dinner £30 (£49 for non-residents).

Prices may change – check with hotel.

SEE ALSO SHORTLIST

MELLS Somerset

THE TALBOT INN

This 15th-century coaching inn with its old arched carriageway has been beautifully made over in casual-chic style as a pub-with-rooms. It was a second venture for Dan Brod and Charlie Luxton, with Matt Greenlees (see also The Lord Poulett Arms, Hinton St George, and The Bath Arms, Horningsham). There is nothing precious here. Drop in for a pint and you find flagstones and bare floorboards, scuffed leather-upholstered chairs, rough plasterwork, blazing log fires, vintage maps and clocks, a record player to spin the vinyl … In the various dining spaces, and on the cobbled courtyard, locally sourced menus major on pub classics done well – perhaps a ploughman's with home-baked bread or cider-battered fish and chips. More inventive dishes might include supreme of guineafowl with haggis croquette. A beamed coach house serves as a grill room. Bedrooms have Bramley bath products, Egyptian cotton sheets, seagrass flooring, but nothing so brown as a wardrobe. One has a modern emperor-size four-poster, a sitting room, an in-room roll-top bath and shower room. Breakfast brings thyme-roasted mushrooms on toast, smoked salmon and scrambled eggs, the full Monty.

Selwood Street
Mells
Frome BA11 3PN

T: 01373 812254
E: info@talbotinn.com
W: talbotinn.com

BEDROOMS: 8. 1 on ground floor.
OPEN: all year except 25 Dec.
FACILITIES: sitting room, bar, restaurant, coach house grill room, in-room smart TV (including Freeview), cobbled courtyard, small garden, parking.
BACKGROUND MUSIC: in public areas.
LOCATION: in village.
CHILDREN: all ages welcomed, cots £10, extra bed £25.
DOGS: allowed in 1 bedroom (£10 one-off charge), and in all public areas.
CREDIT CARDS: MC, Visa.
PRICES: B&B doubles from £120. À la carte £35. 1-night bookings refused at weekends.

Prices may change – check with hotel.

MILTON ABBOT Devon

MAP 1:D3

HOTEL ENDSLEIGH

'An enchanting destination' is how readers describe Olga Polizzi's Regency hunting lodge, which stands by the River Tamar in an Elysian landscape designed by Humphry Repton. Built for the 6th Duke of Bedford and his Duchess, Georgiana, it has eight miles of riverbank on which to fish for salmon and sea trout. Readers arrived in winter to find 'the fires roaring' and the members of a shooting party departing. Bedrooms have a restrained elegance, with hand-painted wallpaper, fresh flowers, vintage bathroom fittings, Mitchell and Peach toiletries. You can take afternoon tea in the panelled library, dine on dishes such as haunch of venison, ragout, piccolo parsnip, garlic cavolo nero. 'We had venison, duck, lamb en croûte, perfectly cooked,' another reader reports. At breakfast there is 'good fruit salad, excellent porridge', kippers, local sausages. 'The croissants were a bit small but freshly baked and the waiter brought me three to make sure I wouldn't go hungry!' 'We left with a warm glow of a brilliant two days away.' See also sister hotels Tresanton, St Mawes, and The Star, Alfriston. (Peter Anderson, C and ES)

Milton Abbot
Tavistock PL19 0PQ

T: 01822 870000
E: hotelendsleigh@
   thepolizzicollection.com
W: hotelendsleigh.com

BEDROOMS: 19. 1 on ground floor, 3 in stables, 1 in lodge (1 mile from house), 1 suite suitable for disabled.
OPEN: all year.
FACILITIES: drawing room, library, card room, bar, 2 dining rooms, in-room TV, civil wedding licence, 108-acre estate (fishing, ghillie), EV charging, public rooms wheelchair accessible, adapted toilet.
BACKGROUND MUSIC: none.
LOCATION: 7 miles NW of Tavistock.
CHILDREN: all ages welcomed, cots free, extra bed £40.
DOGS: allowed in bedrooms (£25 a night), lounges, not in restaurant (but allowed in library at tea time).
CREDIT CARDS: MC, Visa.
PRICES: B&B doubles from £240. Set-price dinner £62.50. 1-night bookings refused Fri, Sat, but ring to check.

Prices may change – check with hotel.

MOUSEHOLE Cornwall

MAP 1:E1

THE OLD COASTGUARD

'My favourite hotel anywhere in the world,' writes a reader, of this welcoming pub-with-rooms in an enchanting fishing village. The third venture for the Inkin brothers (see The Felin Fach Griffin, Felin Fach, Wales, and The Gurnard's Head, Zennor), it has their signature relaxed, child-friendly, dog-friendly ambience and understated chic. 'The rooms are perfect (and the views).' Some bedrooms have a balcony; all have ground coffee, books, Bramley toiletries, a Roberts radio, no TV. Other readers had a top-floor double with adjoining twin room. 'Both were spacious, as was the bathroom, which boasted a walk-in shower (very powerful) as well as a bath. Decor was very tasteful, the bed very comfortable.' Eat at an oak table by the fire, on the sun deck overlooking the sub-tropical garden, or on the sea-facing terrace. There was praise this year for 'chicken liver parfait with just the right amount of toast and onion marmalade, perfectly cooked pork loin with rösti, hispi cabbage, toffee-apple purée and cider sauce'. At breakfast, there is muesli, soda bread, apple juice, smoked salmon, the full Cornish, and 'the marmalade is a highlight'. (Mick Eldridge, John Charnley, and others)

The Parade
Mousehole
Penzance TR19 6PR

T: 01736 731222
E: enquiries@oldcoastguardhotel.
co.uk
W: oldcoastguardhotel.co.uk

BEDROOMS: 14.
OPEN: all year except 24–26 Dec.
FACILITIES: bar, sun lounge, restaurant, sea-facing garden with path to beach, no in-room TV, parking, restaurant and bar wheelchair accessible, no adapted toilet.
BACKGROUND MUSIC: Radio 4 at breakfast, selected music at other mealtimes.
LOCATION: 2-min. walk from village, 3 miles S of Newlyn.
CHILDREN: all ages welcomed, no charge for under-5s, extra bed for 5s and over £25, children's menu.
DOGS: allowed in bedrooms (no charge, treats, towels, bowls), in bar and on sun deck, not in dining room.
CREDIT CARDS: MC, Visa.
PRICES: B&B doubles from £172.50, singles from £135. Set-price dinner £42. 1-night bookings only rarely refused.

Prices may change – check with hotel.

MULLION Cornwall

MAP 1:E2

POLURRIAN ON THE LIZARD

While some of us bring home a fridge magnet
or a Cornishware teapot, businessman Andrew
Long has gone one better and bought a hotel.
After spending blissful family holidays over the
past 30 years at this iconic white cliff-top edifice in
12-acre grounds, in January 2022 he acquired it.
There are plans for some necessary upgrading, but
the 'lovely staff' will be staying and, with Nigel
Chapman at the helm, this happy ship sails into
the main Guide this year. As founder of Luxury
Family Hotels (see Fowey Hall, Fowey), Mr
Chapman brings a flexible approach to hospitality,
with a wide choice of bedrooms in simple,
contemporary style, a sea or countryside view and
baby-listening. An all-day menu offers people-
pleasing dishes, from wood-fired pizzas, beef or
falafel burgers and fish and chips, to chargrilled
steak, herb-crusted fish of the day, and lobster. A
free-and-easy ambience includes alfresco dining,
cocktails and cream teas, spa treatments, a health
club, swimming pools, a gym, hot tub and tennis
court. The hotel's own cove is a ten-minute walk
away, and the South West Coast Path runs right by.

Polurrian Road
Mullion TR12 7EN

T: 01326 240421
E: info@polurrianhotel.com
W: polurrianhotel.com

BEDROOMS: 41. Some on ground floor,
2 suitable for disabled. Plus four 3-bed
self-catering villas.
OPEN: all year.
FACILITIES: lift, bar, lounge, snug,
restaurant, in-room TV, civil wedding
licence, function facilities, cinema,
games room (table football, table
tennis), spa, indoor pool, 9-metre
outdoor pool (Apr–Sept), gym,
12-acre grounds, terrace, tennis court,
climbing frame. Restaurant, bar,
Vista lounge (via lift), part of gardens
wheelchair accessible, adapted toilet.
BACKGROUND MUSIC: in public areas.
LOCATION: in village.
CHILDREN: all ages welcomed, high
chairs, baby-listening.
DOGS: allowed in some bedrooms
(£15 per night), not in restaurant.
CREDIT CARDS: Amex, MC, Visa.
PRICES: B&B doubles from £118, family
from £139.

Prices may change – check with hotel.

MULLION COVE Cornwall

MAP 1:E2

MULLION COVE HOTEL

Where better for a sun salutation than on the cliff-top of the Lizard peninsula at this iconic white, late-Victorian hotel, where yoga classes are a regular feature. Owned by the Grose family, it is a dog-friendly, family-friendly relaxing holiday destination with spectacular views. You can take in the Cornish coastal vista through a wall of glass in the spa, which also has an outdoor pool and hot tub. There are sea views, too, from many bedrooms, which have muted decor and a mix of period and contemporary furniture. Partial sea-view rooms look variously over the harbour, cove and National Trust headland. A garden sea-view suite has a patio door leading from a lounge to the garden. You can lunch informally in the Glenbervie bar on sandwiches, steak, fish and chips, a beef or falafel burger. In the Atlantic View restaurant, the menu of locally sourced produce includes dishes such as slow-roasted pork belly, crackling, mustard mash, braised hispi cabbage. Give 24 hours' notice if you want the seafood platter or a vegan menu. A full Cornish or one of the varied breakfast offerings the next day sets you up to walk the Cornish Coast Path.

Mullion Cove
Helston TR12 7EP

T: 01326 240328
E: enquiries@mullion-cove.co.uk
W: mullion-cove.co.uk

BEDROOMS: 30. Some on ground floor.
OPEN: all year.
FACILITIES: lift, 3 lounges, bar, restaurant (vegan menu, 24 hours' notice), in-room TV (Freeview), 1-acre garden, 10-metre heated outdoor swimming pool, EV charging, public areas wheelchair accessible, adapted toilet.
BACKGROUND MUSIC: in restaurant and bar.
LOCATION: on edge of village.
CHILDREN: all ages welcomed, extra bed £35.
DOGS: allowed in some bedrooms (£9 a night) and in 1 lounge.
CREDIT CARDS: Amex, MC, Visa.
PRICES: B&B doubles from £120, singles from £115. Set-price dinner £40, à la carte (Glenbervie bar) £32. 1-night bookings sometimes refused bank holiday Sat.

Prices may change – check with hotel.

NEAR SAWREY Cumbria

MAP 4: inset C2

EES WYKE COUNTRY HOUSE

With views over Esthwaite Water, a friendly welcome and high-quality home-cooked food, this Georgian house ticks all the boxes for 'a warm, comfortable, traditional, country house hotel'. Chef and owner Richard Lee ensures the handsome, whitewashed building with traditionally furnished rooms – floral-print sofas, lamps on side tables, dado panelling, open fires – has the feel of an inviting family home. Bedrooms have soft colours, pretty wallpapers, a sprinkling of antiques and decanters of sherry. Even the cosier, beamed rooms on the second floor have space for armchairs to enjoy 'quite stunning views of Esthwaite Water and the fells beyond'. Bathrooms, mainly shower only, have luxurious amenities. Richard's cooking is 'of a very high standard' and produces a daily-changing short-choice menu which could include roast duckling breast with thyme, ginger and honey followed by spiced pear poached in red wine. Vegan and vegetarian dishes upon request. 'Hugely enjoyable' breakfasts offer fresh juices, home-made bread and marmalade, haddock and a Lakeland grill. 'Wonderfully helpful and friendly staff.' (John Southern, TH)

Near Sawrey
Ambleside LA22 0JZ

T: 01539 436393
E: mail@eeswyke.co.uk
W: eeswyke.co.uk

BEDROOMS: 9. 1 on ground floor, 7 en suite, 2 with separate private bathroom.
OPEN: all year except 23–29 Dec.
FACILITIES: 2 lounges, restaurant, in-room TV (Freeview), veranda, ½-acre garden, EV charging, unsuitable for disabled.
BACKGROUND MUSIC: none.
LOCATION: edge of village 2½ miles SE of Hawkshead on B5285.
CHILDREN: not under 12.
DOGS: not allowed.
CREDIT CARDS: Amex, MC, Visa.
PRICES: B&B doubles from £137, singles from £109. Set dinner £45. Min. 2-night bookings usually at weekends, bank holidays.

Prices may change – check with hotel.

NETHER WESTCOTE Oxfordshire

THE FEATHERED NEST

Guests have a bird's-eye view over the Evenlode valley from Adam Taylor's gastropub-with-rooms in a hilltop Cotswold village. You can drink real ales by a log fire or on a saddle stool at the bar, dine in the restaurant, enjoying panoramic vistas, or on the terrace, under a canopy. Chef Matt Weedon arrived in 2019 with feathers in his cap and Michelin accolades under his belt, to cook a short, modern menu of dishes such as Aberdeen Angus burger; halibut with soft-shell crab; pumpkin and coconut soup with chickpea crackers; chargrilled hispi cabbage heart, mushroom, leeks, celeriac, grapes, verjus, truffle. There are Sunday roasts, wood-fired pizzas, and a tasting menu for whole tables. Overnight guests will find a fresh fruit plate, home-baked biscuits, handmade chocolates, an espresso machine and Bramley toiletries in their rooms. The spacious Cuckoo's Den (a new one on David Attenborough!) has a king-size bed, roll-top bath and walk-in drench shower. The smallest room, the Cockerel's Roost, has a shower only. All rooms are airy and stylish, without shouting 'designer'. Be up with the lark for an award-winning breakfast.

Nether Westcote
Chipping Norton OX7 6SD

T: 01993 833030
E: info@thefeatherednestinn.co.uk
W: thefeatherednestinn.co.uk

BEDROOMS: 5. 1 in self-catering cottage.
OPEN: closed Tues/Wed (except special trading days), open on Christmas Day.
FACILITIES: 2 bars, small lounge, dining room (vegan menu), in-room TV (Freeview), civil wedding licence, 2-acre garden, restaurant and bar wheelchair accessible, adapted toilet.
BACKGROUND MUSIC: all day in bar, restaurant and on terrace, occasionally live.
LOCATION: in hamlet, 5 miles S of Stow-on-the-Wold.
CHILDREN: all ages welcomed, no extra beds, children's menu.
DOGS: allowed in bar only.
CREDIT CARDS: Amex, MC, Visa.
PRICES: B&B doubles from £195.
À la carte £55, 4-course vegan menu £40, 6-course tasting menu (whole table) £80.

Prices may change – check with hotel.

NEW MILTON Hampshire

MAP 2:E2

CHEWTON GLEN

This quintessential English country house with spa, pools, kids' club, elegant bedrooms and fun treehouses hits all the right luxurious notes for a romantic or family stay. 'I have been to Chewton Glen many times and it never disappoints,' confirms a regular. Tennis, golf, croquet, gardens and woodland – plus a path to the beach – mean that there's no need to leave this five-star cocoon. Relax in one of the lounges with their old-school elegance or around the pool in the light-flooded spa or refresh in the outdoor pool. Main house bedrooms are lightly traditional – soft colours, marble bathrooms – with parkland views, many with balcony or terrace. Suites are more contemporary while the treehouses are sharply modern, with hot tubs and log-burners: 'out of this world, with every possible detail considered to make it as comfortable and luxurious as possible'. 'Wonderful food' is served in the glass-roofed Dining Room for traditional fine dining such as Dover sole and venison (vegetarian, too), and the breezier Kitchen for gourmet burgers and pizzas. 'Very attentive' staff were 'helpful throughout our stay'. (Victoria Sterman, and others)

Christchurch Road
New Milton BH25 6QS

T: 01425 275341
E: reservations@chewtonglen.com
W: chewtonglen.com

BEDROOMS: 72. 14 on ground floor, 14 treehouse suites in grounds, 1 suitable for disabled.
OPEN: all year.
FACILITIES: lounges, bar, 2 restaurants, in-room TV, civil wedding licence, cookery school, spa, indoor pool, 130-acre grounds (heated pool, tennis, golf), EV charging, public rooms (not spa) wheelchair accessible.
BACKGROUND MUSIC: 'subtle' in public areas.
LOCATION: on S edge of New Forest.
CHILDREN: all ages welcomed, no charge for extra bed.
DOGS: allowed in treehouse suites (£35 per night, welcome pack), on Kitchen terrace.
CREDIT CARDS: Amex, MC, Visa.
PRICES: B&B doubles from £435. À la carte £70 (Dining Room), £48 (Kitchen). 1-night stays sometimes refused Sat.

Prices may change – check with hotel.

NEWCASTLE UPON TYNE Tyne and Wear   MAP 4:B4

JESMOND DENE HOUSE

With its flamboyant architecture, gardens and views over a wooded valley, this Arts and Crafts mansion has the trappings of a country house hotel, yet is only a ten-minute drive from Newcastle centre. It was designed for entertaining – grand rooms, inglenook fireplaces – and continues to impress: 'The interior was splendid, with imposing design features,' reports a reader who found the public rooms, 'especially the bar, very congenial'. Bold colours, contemporary furniture and modern art keep the atmosphere relaxed. Bedrooms have an understated elegance with muted colours, feature wallpapers and modern, clean-lined furniture. Metro-tiled bathrooms have under-floor heating. Dinner from MasterChef: The Professionals finalist Danny Parker offers Modern British dishes such as halibut with brown shrimps and samphire, and braised feather blade of beef, plus good vegetarian options. 'Our evening meal was excellent.' There's a simpler bar menu and a 'wide choice of appetising dishes' at breakfast, best taken in the conservatory with 'pretty views of the garden'. (Mary Hewson, John and Elspeth Gibbon)

Jesmond Dene Road
Newcastle upon Tyne NE2 2EY

T: 0191 212 3000
E: info@jesmonddenehouse.co.uk
W: jesmonddenehouse.co.uk

BEDROOMS: 40. 8 in adjacent New House, some ground floor, 2 suitable for disabled.
OPEN: all year, Sun eve, Mon and Tues limited House Menu and for hotel guests only.
FACILITIES: lift, lounge, cocktail bar, restaurant, conference/function facilities, terrace, in-room TV (Sky), civil wedding licence, ¼-acre garden, parking, public areas wheelchair accessible, adapted toilet.
BACKGROUND MUSIC: in public areas and restaurant.
LOCATION: 2 miles from city centre.
CHILDREN: all ages welcomed (extra bed £20).
DOGS: allowed on restaurant terrace only.
CREDIT CARDS: Amex, MC, Visa.
PRICES: B&B doubles/singles from £150. À la carte £52.

Prices may change – check with hotel.

NEWTON ABBOT Devon

MAP 1:D4

THE ROCK INN

'Our favourite place to go for a meal,' wrote loyal Guide readers who live near this traditional family-run inn in a rural Dartmoor hamlet. Dating from 1820, it was built to feed and water labourers who worked the granite quarries on Haytor Down. Reached from the A38 by narrow back roads, it is both 'difficult to find and to leave', says another reader. The bedrooms are old-fashioned and characterful, with views over the garden and moorlands. One has an antique four-poster, another a balcony. All are accessed via steep stairs and come with a 'colour television' as the inn makes known. The pub interior is cosy, with log fires lit on chilly days. In a bar area and dining room, an imaginative menu at lunch and dinner brings dishes such as hake with mussels and curry velouté or slow-cooked lamb, lamb croquette, and pea and mint ketchup. 'The food is delicious, service efficient, friendly, unobtrusive.' Despite being so tucked away it is popular with diners; at busy times do call to book, don't just rock up. 'The location, near Haytor Rock and its glorious views, is lovely' with walks on Dartmoor straight from the door. (GM, and others)

Haytor Vale
Newton Abbot TQ13 9XP

T: 01364 661305
E: info@rock-inn.co.uk
W: rock-inn.co.uk

BEDROOMS: 9.
OPEN: all year except 25/26 Dec, Sun dinner, Mon, Tues.
FACILITIES: bar, restaurant, snug bar, conservatory, in-room TV (Freeview), ½-acre garden, bar and restaurant wheelchair accessible, no adapted toilet.
BACKGROUND MUSIC: in bar, restaurant.
LOCATION: 3 miles W of Bovey Tracey.
CHILDREN: all ages welcomed, extra beds £20, no under-14s in main bar area, children's menu.
DOGS: allowed in 2 country-view bedrooms (£10 a night), bar, 1 dining room.
CREDIT CARDS: MC, Visa.
PRICES: B&B doubles from £125. Fixed-price menu £30, à la carte £50. Sat night bookings must include dinner, 1-night bookings sometimes refused.

Prices may change – check with hotel.

NORTH WALSHAM Norfolk   MAP 2:A6

BEECHWOOD HOTEL

Agatha Christie memorabilia, murder mystery weekends and Art Deco touches set the tone at this creeper-clad hotel, former home of doctor friends of Christie, in a bustling market town. Rooms range from a modest single to garden pods with roll-top bath, walk-in shower and a deck with hot tub/sauna. A main-house bedroom was 'splendid – very roomy, comfortable four-poster bed, two armchairs, fridge, good-sized TV, lots of storage space'. The enthusiasm of the owner proved a little Tiggerish for one trusted reader who had arrived very tired, while, for another, the host's 'charm and attention' were 'very much a plus'. In the restaurant and converted summer house, 'interesting and varied' menus include dishes such as treacle-cured Norfolk venison with port jus. 'The dining experience was exceptional.' 'Halibut, sea trout, venison and chicken were all fine. Decent-sized portions and plenty of vegetables.' Service was 'efficient and friendly'. Golf packages, South African and Fawlty Towers nights are among the attractions. 'A superb hotel for touring this area of Norfolk', and there is a bar if you could murder a pint for the money. 'We will certainly return.' (Mary Coles, Peter Anderson, PA, and others)

20 Cromer Road
North Walsham NR28 0HD

T: 01692 403231
E: info@beechwood-hotel.co.uk
W: beechwood-hotel.co.uk

BEDROOMS: 20. 4 on ground floor suitable for disabled, 2 garden spa rooms with deck, hot tub and sauna.
OPEN: all year.
FACILITIES: bar, 2 lounges, restaurant (vegetarian/vegan menus, pre-ordered), in-room TV (Freeview), EV charging, 100-metre landscaped garden (croquet), public areas wheelchair accessible, adapted toilet.
BACKGROUND MUSIC: all day in public rooms.
LOCATION: near town centre.
CHILDREN: all ages welcomed, extra bed £25 (under-12s).
DOGS: allowed in bedrooms by prior arrangement (£15 per night), public rooms, not in restaurant.
CREDIT CARDS: Amex, MC, Visa.
PRICES: B&B doubles from £110, single room £70. À la carte £45, (vegetarian/vegan) £31.50, tasting menu £70. 1-night bookings refused Fri, Sat, May–Oct.

Prices may change – check with hotel.

NORWICH Norfolk

MAP 2:B5

THE ASSEMBLY HOUSE

A Grade I Georgian House of Assemblies, where
Fanny Kemble played Shakespeare, Liszt played
piano, and people danced for joy in the ballroom
at the end of the Crimean War, is still the place
to have a ball. An events venue, hotel, restaurant
and cookery school, it has 15 spacious bedrooms in
the East and West Wing buildings, six with their
own garden, six with a lounge. They have been
styled by Annabel Grey with tremendous pizzazz
and a sense of fun. A reader's room had 'all mod
cons (espresso machine, DeLonghi kettle, stylish
TV on oval glass stand), a super-king-size bed,
a three-seater sofa, appealing prints of Norfolk
countryside and' – a whimsical touch – 'a variety
of beautifully polished brass cooking moulds'. You
can raise a glass of fizz under chandeliers in the
Grand Hall, take afternoon tea or a pre-theatre
supper in the dining room – maybe beetroot,
new potato, red onion and artichoke tarte Tatin,
or confit duck leg, white bean cassoulet, parsley
salad. Breakfast brings free-range eggs, herby
baked beans, a full vegan, eggs Benedict, Norfolk
rarebit – with Colman's mustard, of course.

Theatre Street
Norwich NR2 1RQ

T: 01603 626402
E: admin@assemblyhousenorwich.
co.uk
W: assemblyhousenorwich.co.uk

BEDROOMS: 15. All in St Mary's House
extension, 6 with private garden,
2 suitable for disabled.
OPEN: all year.
FACILITIES: grand entrance hall,
restaurant, 6 event rooms, civil
wedding licence, in-room TV (Sky,
Freeview), 1-acre courtyard garden,
parking, public rooms wheelchair
accessible, adapted toilet.
BACKGROUND MUSIC: classic
instrumental.
LOCATION: central, car park permits
for pay-and-display.
CHILDREN: all ages welcomed, extra
bed £25, daytime children's menu.
DOGS: not allowed.
CREDIT CARDS: Amex, MC, Visa.
PRICES: B&B doubles from £170,
singles from £140. Fixed-price early
supper £21–£28 (2/3 courses, steak
£3 supplement, side dishes £3–£3.50).

Prices may change – check with hotel.

NOTTINGHAM Nottinghamshire   MAP 2:A3

HART'S HOTEL

A sleek, modern hotel on the ramparts of what remains of medieval Nottingham Castle, Hart's is where your home is when you want to escape the bustling city. Built in 2003 to award-winning designs with the emphasis on sustainability, it owes its urban-chic interiors to Stefa Hart, who, with husband Tim, owns Hambleton Hall, Hambleton (see entry). Rooms range from classic doubles with a king- or super-king-size bed, to suites with a sitting room. Dog-friendly garden rooms have French doors to a furnished patio. All are painted in soft, neutral colours, with modern art prints. Generous extras include fresh milk, a minibar, spoiling toiletries, 24-hour room service. You can drink a 'Hart of a Lion' cocktail in the bar, dine in Hart's Kitchen or alfresco on dishes such as pan-fried sea bass, hen of the woods, pea and leek purée; trio of salt-baked celeriac with goat's curd, or artichoke salad with pine nuts, olive oil and truffle mayonnaise. At breakfast there is freshly squeezed orange juice, a fruit smoothie, the full English or veggie, with Windy Ridge Farm eggs and bread from the Hambleton Bakery.

Standard Hill
Park Row
Nottingham NG1 6GN

T: 0115 988 1900
E: reception@hartshotel.co.uk
W: hartsnottingham.co.uk

BEDROOMS: 32. 2 suitable for disabled.
OPEN: all year, restaurant closed 1 Jan.
FACILITIES: lift, bar, restaurant, in-room TV (Sky, Freeview), exercise room, meeting room, courtyard, garden, car park (£9.95), restaurant wheelchair accessible, adapted toilet.
BACKGROUND MUSIC: in bar and restaurant.
LOCATION: city centre.
CHILDREN: all ages welcomed, cot £19, extra bed £29, children's menu.
DOGS: max. 2 in garden rooms (£10 per night, no large/aggressive breeds), not in restaurant or bar.
CREDIT CARDS: Amex, MC, Visa.
PRICES: room-only doubles from £139. Breakfast £10 (cooked dishes from £5), à la carte £38, vegetarian/vegan £32.

Prices may change – check with hotel.

NUN MONKTON Yorkshire

MAP 4:D4

THE ALICE HAWTHORN

Off the beaten track, yet only five miles from the A1(M), this smart 18th-century village inn with a reputation for inspired pub food and Scandi-cool rooms impressed our inspectors, who upgraded it to the main Guide. Overlooking Nun Monkton's idyllic green, the red brick Alice Hawthorn (named after a famous racehorse) is as much a 'local' as a dining destination, with 'warm, friendly, helpful staff'. Beams, flagged floors, scrubbed tables and green-velvet seating are in the bar and restaurant; artwork by the village primary school on the walls. Chef/patron John Topham produces upmarket, Yorkshire-influenced pub food such as venison with roasted beetroot and celeriac terrine. A sea bass ceviche impressed 'with its burst of flavourful combinations', as did 'exquisite steak'. With calm colours and natural woods, bedrooms, with fresh milk, biscuits and organic toiletries, are above the pub and in fir-clad chalet-style buildings around the garden. The latter were 'spacious' with a 'contemporary, clean look', but no USB ports. 'Faultless' breakfasts include fresh juices, porridge with honey, pancakes as well as the full Yorkshire.

The Green
Nun Monkton
York YO26 8EW

T: 01423 330303
E: enquiries@thealicehawthorn.com
W: thealicehawthorn.com

BEDROOMS: 12. 8 in garden, 1 suitable for disabled.
OPEN: all year, restaurant closed Mon/ Tues, no accommodation Sun, Mon, Tues.
FACILITIES: bar, 3 dining areas (incl. private dining room), in-room TV, beer garden, ground floor wheelchair accessible, adapted toilet.
BACKGROUND MUSIC: all day in public areas.
LOCATION: in village, 11 miles NW of York.
CHILDREN: all ages welcomed, extra bed £25 per night.
DOGS: allowed in 2 bedrooms (£20 per stay) and bar.
CREDIT CARDS: MC, Visa.
PRICES: B&B doubles from £120, singles from £100. À la carte £45.

Prices may change – check with hotel.

OLD HUNSTANTON Norfolk   MAP 2:A5

THE NEPTUNE

It is 16 years since Jacki and Kevin Mangeolles opened their restaurant-with-rooms, inspired by the little places you happen on in France, run with passion by a husband-and-wife team. A former coaching inn, it stands on the A149, ten minutes' walk from the beach. Rooms are definitely not an afterthought to the Michelin-starred food; the decor is stylish, with lots of white and soft greys. 'Bedroom 1 was of a higher standard than is typical of a restaurant-with-rooms. It was light and bright and larger than "snug", with a 6-foot bed and two chairs, a good coffee machine, home-made biscuits.' The 'well-appointed' bathroom had a bath with a rather half-hearted shower over it. With no garden or hotel facilities, the Neptune is 'more suitable for an overnight treat than a longer stay' – but what a treat! Kevin's locally sourced menus include dishes such as scallop mousse with Brancaster mussel sauce, beef sirloin, and blueberry parfait with cinnamon ice cream. 'The main aspect was the food, which was excellent, and – one of my benchmarks – there was home-made jam and marmalade for breakfast.' (John and Elspeth Gibbon, Christine Hughes)

85 Old Hunstanton Road
Old Hunstanton PE36 6HZ

T: 01485 532122
E: reservations@theneptune.co.uk
W: theneptune.co.uk

BEDROOMS: 4.
OPEN: all year, except Sun, Mon, 26 Dec, 3 weeks Jan, 2 weeks May, 1 week Nov.
FACILITIES: bar area, restaurant, in-room TV (Freeview), parking, unsuitable for disabled.
BACKGROUND MUSIC: in restaurant in evening.
LOCATION: village centre, on A149.
CHILDREN: not under 10.
DOGS: not allowed.
CREDIT CARDS: Amex, MC, Visa.
PRICES: D,B&B doubles from £305 (with tasting menu £345), single occupancy rates on request. Set-price dinner £75, tasting menu £95 (to be taken by whole table). 1-night bookings sometimes refused in high season.

Prices may change – check with hotel.

OLDSTEAD Yorkshire

MAP 4:D4

THE BLACK SWAN AT OLDSTEAD

The somewhat elusive location of this North York Moors Michelin-starred restaurant-with-rooms is a suitably tantalising teaser for the unexpected creations on the menus. It's the unique setting – the terroir – of the old drovers' inn, on a sleepy country lane overlooking rich farmland, that inspires chef/director Tommy Banks. It's a family affair, too: the Bankses have farmed here for generations; brother James is front-of-house. Using ingredients grown or foraged locally, including kitchen-garden produce, the food is about 'tradition and culture cut through with earthy exuberance'. Start the evening in the fire-warmed snug of a bar with a nasturtium martini before moving upstairs to the Scandi-light dining room for dishes such as smoked eel with apple and caviar, chicken with wild garlic and morel, and sea buckthorn with chocolate and hazelnut. Bedrooms, in converted stables behind the inn or across the road in a Georgian village house, have a fresh country style with soft colours, solid wood furnishings, plaid wool fabrics and cottagey bathrooms. Breakfast includes omelettes and home-made granola with fruit and fresh brioche.

Oldstead
York YO61 4BL

T: 01347 868387
E: enquiries@blackswanoldstead.
co.uk
W: blackswanoldstead.co.uk

BEDROOMS: 9. 4 on ground floor in annexe wing, 5 in village house, 50 yds away.
OPEN: all year except 24 Dec–2 Jan, closed Mon/Tues in 2022, closed Sun/Mon in 2023.
FACILITIES: bar, restaurant (vegetarian menu), private dining room, in-room TV (Freeview), 2 small gardens, 2-acre kitchen garden and orchard.
BACKGROUND MUSIC: in restaurant.
LOCATION: in village 7 miles E of Thirsk.
CHILDREN: no under-18s overnight, over-10s only in restaurant.
DOGS: not allowed.
CREDIT CARDS: MC, Visa.
PRICES: D,B&B doubles £660 (Attic Room), £700 (all others). Tasting menu £170 (dinner and Sat lunch).

Prices may change – check with hotel.

OSWESTRY Shropshire
MAP 3:B4

PEN-Y-DYFFRYN

'As close to the Welsh border as you can get' this 'charming, family-run hotel' in a Georgian rectory has 'tremendous views from the beautiful garden'. Miles and Audrey Hunter, with son and daughter Tommy and Charlotte, are natural hosts (see The Castle Hotel, Bishop's Castle, for brother Henry's venture). The personal attention impresses. 'I was chuffed that they had a gluten-free scone for me with a cream tea on arrival,' writes a returning guest. Bedrooms, some in the coach house, have the look of a smart private home. Several have a spa bath, a private patio, 'magnificent views of the Welsh hills'. 'We had a large room with giant bed … a bath with spa system and a fancy shower, which worked very well.' A nightly changing menu caters to all, with 'very generous portions' of 'well-cooked, tasty dishes' such as pea and lemon risotto; haunch steak of venison, venison and apricot sausage, blueberry and cassis jus. 'The cooked breakfast menu is extensive.' 'Excellent sautéed potatoes with the eggs and bacon.' A morning newsletter with suggested activities adds to the hotel's charm. (John G P Barnes, Steven Hur, and others)

Rhydycroesau
Oswestry SY10 7JD

T: 01691 653700
E: stay@peny.co.uk
W: peny.co.uk

BEDROOMS: 14. 4, each with patio, in coach house, 2 garden suites with patio, 1 on ground floor.
OPEN: all year except Christmas.
FACILITIES: 2 lounges, bar, restaurant, in-room TV (Freeview), 5-acre grounds (summer house, dog-walking area, fly-fishing pool).
BACKGROUND MUSIC: in evening, in bar and restaurant.
LOCATION: 3 miles W of Oswestry.
CHILDREN: not under 3 except by special arrangement, extra bed £50.
DOGS: allowed in some bedrooms (no charge), max. 1 except by arrangement, not in public rooms after 6.30 pm.
CREDIT CARDS: MC, Visa.
PRICES: B&B doubles from £170, singles from £130. Set-price dinner £53. 1-night bookings occasionally refused Sat.

Prices may change – check with hotel.

OXFORD Oxfordshire

MAP 2:C3

OLD BANK HOTEL

Jeremy Mogford's conversion of the old Barclays Bank gets credit from a Guide insider for its 'brilliant location, right in the city centre'. It occupies two Georgian buildings and a former Tudor apothecary. Food is served all day in 'busy, bistro-like' Quod in the old banking hall, hung with art from Mr Mogford's collection, and on the Italian-style terrace. An all-day menu mixes staples such as burgers, steaks and pizzas with imaginative dishes including sea bass, brown shrimp and seaweed sauce. 'The vibe in the hotel is calmer and more sophisticated' with art 'adding to the character of the place' with its 'slight corporate feel'. 'There are amazing views of the dreaming spires from some of the light-filled rooms.' Those at the rear overlook Merton College. Each has contemporary furniture, a bespoke writing desk, treats and milk in a minibar, a marble bathroom with under-floor heating, Noble Isle toiletries. The height of luxury, a penthouse suite atop the Tudor building has glass doors to a rooftop terrace garden. Take one of the complimentary Oxford bikes and explore the city. (See also next entry.)

92–94 High Street
Oxford OX1 4BJ

T: 01865 799599
E: reservations@oldbankhotel.co.uk
W: oldbankhotel.co.uk

BEDROOMS: 43. 1 suitable for disabled.
OPEN: all year.
FACILITIES: lift, residents' library/bar, restaurant/bar, dining terrace, 2 meeting/private dining rooms, in-room TV (Freeview), in-room spa treatments, civil wedding licence, small garden, use of bicycles, parking, EV charging, restaurant, bar wheelchair accessible, adapted toilet.
BACKGROUND MUSIC: in restaurant and reception area.
LOCATION: central, car park.
CHILDREN: all ages welcomed, free extra bed, children's menu.
DOGS: allowed on terrace only.
CREDIT CARDS: Amex, MC, Visa.
PRICES: B&B doubles from £320. À la carte £38 (plus 12½% discretionary service charge). 1-night bookings refused at weekends in peak season.

Prices may change – check with hotel.

OXFORD Oxfordshire

OLD PARSONAGE HOTEL

'A stone's throw from everything Oxford has to offer', Jeremy Mogford's second hotel (see also preceding entry) impressed our inspectors with its 'peaceful, classy vibe'. Occupying a wisteria-draped 17th-century stone manor house, it has 'sophisticated, intimate and stylish interiors' with 'striking art lining every wall'. Bedrooms, some with Juliet balcony or private terrace, are 'immaculately kept', with fabrics in the signature deep red, purple and grey. The two new Churchill suites are 'something special', filled with photographs and memorabilia. All have a handmade bed, a minibar with milk and treats, a marble-clad bathroom with under-floor heating, Noble Isle toiletries. 'Nice touches include a hand-written welcome note and a beautifully presented collection of stories by the shortlisted entrants to the annual Mogford Prize.' Guests have use of bikes and the library. In the 'cosy and intimate' restaurant, a 'sophisticated menu' includes dishes such as a 'very good' crispy potato terrine; lamb rump with wild garlic sauce. 'Staff are very professional, welcoming and friendly.' 'Complimentary parking is a real bonus in Oxford.'

1 Banbury Road
Oxford OX2 6NN

T: 01865 310210
E: reservations@oldparsonage-hotel.
co.uk
W: oldparsonagehotel.co.uk

BEDROOMS: 35. 10 on ground floor, 2 suitable for disabled.
OPEN: all year.
FACILITIES: lounge, library, bar/restaurant, in-room TV (Freeview), civil wedding licence, terrace, rear garden with summerhouse, parking, EV charging, restaurant wheelchair accessible, adapted toilet.
BACKGROUND MUSIC: 'very light' in restaurant and bar.
LOCATION: NE end of St Giles, small car park.
CHILDREN: all ages welcomed, under-3s free, extra bed £65, all-day children's menu.
DOGS: allowed in bar area of restaurant, on terrace.
CREDIT CARDS: Amex, MC, Visa.
PRICES: B&B doubles from £300. À la carte £45 (plus 12½% discretionary service charge). 1-night bookings sometimes refused at peak weekends.

Prices may change – check with hotel.

PADSTOW Cornwall

MAP 1:D2

PADSTOW TOWNHOUSE

Hidden in a back street of Padstow's old town, these sybaritic B&B suites, created by chef Paul Ainsworth and his wife, are an ideal retreat for foodies. Three of Paul's ventures – including the Michelin-starred Paul Ainsworth at No.6 – are in Padstow and nearby Rock. The spacious suites dazzle with rich fabrics and furniture as well as witty foodie hints – perhaps a candy-striped wallpaper or bedside tables made out of flour bins. Indulgent touches include a gold-and-white double-ended bath in one, and white French-style bed in another. A kitchen pantry, with bar and home-made treats, is run on an honesty basis and breakfast arrives in a hamper. For evening dining you can try one of the sister companies: The Mariners pub in Rock offers British classics while Caffè Rojano in Padstow has a casual menu of favourites such as pizza, pasta and grilled mackerel on sourdough (also the best choice for vegans). No.6 is the creative option with a limited-choice four-course menu of dishes such as morel with roast chicken and manzanilla sherry, and beef with seaweed savarin. Borrow a pair of the B&B's wellingtons to work up an appetite.

16–18 High Street
Padstow PL28 8BB

T: 01841 550950
E: info@paul-ainsworth.co.uk
W: paul-ainsworth.co.uk

BEDROOMS: 6. 2 on ground floor.
OPEN: all year except 24–26 Dec, 2 weeks Jan, open at New Year.
FACILITIES: honesty pantry, in-room smart TV, in-room spa treatments, EV charging, parking, electric shuttle car for guest transport.
BACKGROUND MUSIC: in reception and kitchen pantry area.
LOCATION: in old town, 5 mins' walk from harbour.
CHILDREN: over-4s welcomed, extra bed £40.
DOGS: allowed in 2 ground-floor bedrooms (max. 2, £25 per dog per night).
CREDIT CARDS: MC, Visa.
PRICES: B&B doubles from £245. Set menu (Paul Ainsworth at No.6) £120, à la carte (Caffè Rojano) £35.

Prices may change – check with hotel.

PADSTOW Cornwall

THE PIG AT HARLYN BAY

Frilly waves lap the sands of Harlyn Bay, a
short stroll from Robin Hutson's seventh Pig
(see index), but it is the seaside of JMW Turner
that is conjured here. Behind a Georgian facade,
medieval and Jacobean interiors are dramatic
and brooding. 'The love Judy Hutson lavished
on this property is evident in every element,'
writes an inspector. 'Everywhere feels relaxed
and atmospheric.' House bedrooms are reached
via 'an impressive staircase' under a cupola, 'with
enormous stormy seascape'. All have a monsoon
shower, some a freestanding bath. 'The tiniest
has a sea view, with the loo and shower tucked
behind the bed.' Welcome extras include fresh
milk in a fridge and beach mats. Ground-floor
rooms in the Stonehouse annexe have a private
terrace. 'Seriously chic' garden wagons have a
wood-burner, bathroom and outdoor shower. In
the restaurant, kitchen-garden produce shines
in dishes such as wood-roast Cylindra beetroot,
crispy gnocchi and herb risotto, or chargrilled
line-caught mackerel with celeriac and pickled
apple. On warm days, eat outside at the Lobster
Shed. 'The classic lobster grill and the Thermidor
were both superb.'

Harlyn Bay
Padstow PL28 8SQ

T: 01841 550240
E: reservations@thepighotel.com
W: thepighotel.com

BEDROOMS: 30. 15 in courtyard
building, 4 in garden wagons.
OPEN: all year.
FACILITIES: bar, Map Room, 3 dining
rooms, snug, civil wedding licence,
Potting Shed treatment room, Lobster
Shed (alfresco dining), kitchen garden,
orchard, 8-acre grounds, EV charging,
public rooms wheelchair accessible,
adapted toilet.
BACKGROUND MUSIC: all day in public
areas.
LOCATION: 10-min. drive from
Padstow.
CHILDREN: all ages welcomed, no
charge for extra beds.
DOGS: not allowed.
CREDIT CARDS: Amex, MC, Visa.
PRICES: room-only doubles from £155.
Breakfast £13.50–£18.50, à la carte £42.

Prices may change – check with hotel.

PADSTOW Cornwall

MAP 1:D2

THE SEAFOOD RESTAURANT

If you can't get enough of the freshest of seafood at this restaurant-with-rooms, you can learn to prepare your own lobster for grilling and the perfect hollandaise sauce at Rick Stein's cookery school across the road. It is some 48 years since the newly married Rick and his first wife, Jill, launched a harbourside bistro that would spawn a mini-empire and earn this buzzy town the nickname Padstein. Bedrooms, designed by Jill with a mix of panache and practicality, range from 'cosy and comfy', with a power shower, to master rooms with a roof terrace and sublime views of the Camel estuary. Some have a modern four-poster; all have fresh milk, good coffee, Stein's biscuits, Jill Stein Porthdune toiletries. In the restaurant, with its zinc-topped seafood bar and floor-to-ceiling windows, fillet steak finds its way on to the menu alongside dishes such as fish and chips, monkfish Goan curry and Singapore chilli crab. On sunny days, you can also dine on the terrace. At breakfast, fish plays a starring role again, with dishes including kedgeree and scrambled eggs with smoked salmon, plus a complimentary sausage for your dog.

Riverside
Padstow PL28 8BY

T: 01841 532700
E: reservations@rickstein.com
W: rickstein.com

BEDROOMS: 16.
OPEN: all year except 24–26 Dec.
FACILITIES: lift (to bedrooms), restaurant (vegan menu), in-room TV (Freeview), EV-charging, some parking, restaurant and toilet wheelchair accessible.
BACKGROUND MUSIC: in restaurant.
LOCATION: town centre.
CHILDREN: all ages welcomed, extra bed £30, no under-3s in restaurant.
DOGS: allowed in all but 4 bedrooms (£30 first night, £5 additional nights), in conservatory at breakfast.
CREDIT CARDS: Amex, MC, Visa.
PRICES: B&B doubles/singles from £170. À la carte £60. 1-night bookings refused Sat.

Prices may change – check with hotel.

PENRITH Cumbria

MAP 4: inset C2

ASKHAM HALL

With a Michelin-starred restaurant, Grade II
listed garden, 17th-century pele tower and French
drawing room, Askham Hall sounds as if it might
be very formal; not a bit of it. The ancestral home
of the Lowthers, now a restaurant-with-rooms, is
relaxed and unpretentious with dogs and children
mingling among family heirlooms, books and
modern art. One drawing room has doors to a
classic English country house garden. 'A lovely
place in a lovely setting.' Main house bedrooms
– some with leaded windows and fireplace – mix
antiques with modern pieces, while those in the
courtyard have a rustic style. Quirky shapes can
mean unconventional layouts, and a walk-in
shower in the bedroom surprised one couple –
though some other bathrooms have a roll-top
bath. The tasting menu's 'utterly delicious food',
with produce from the kitchen garden, might
include salt-baked duck with lingonberry sauce,
and barbecued pork with rosehip and pickled
pear. Book dinner ahead, advises one reader. A
'very good breakfast' delighted one guest with
'an excellent kipper!' Guests on their fourth visit
described the whole experience as 'first-rate'.

Askham
Penrith CA10 2PF

T: 01931 712350
E: enquiries@askhamhall.co.uk
W: askhamhall.co.uk

BEDROOMS: 19. 2 suitable for disabled.
OPEN: all year excl. Christmas,
restaurant closed Sun/Mon.
FACILITIES: 2 drawing rooms, snug,
2 dining rooms (vegetarian menu),
in-room TV, civil wedding licence,
12-acre grounds, outdoor swimming
pool, hot tub, function facilities,
EV charging, restaurant wheelchair
accessible, adapted toilet.
BACKGROUND MUSIC: in reception
rooms in evening.
LOCATION: 10 mins from Penrith and
Jct 40 on M6.
CHILDREN: all ages welcomed, free
cots, extra bed £35, no under-10s in
restaurant in evening.
DOGS: allowed (£15 per night, welcome
pack), not in restaurant, on lead in
grounds.
CREDIT CARDS: Amex, MC, Visa.
PRICES: B&B doubles from £180, singles
from £168. Tasting menu £95.

Prices may change – check with hotel.

PENRITH Cumbria

MAP 4: inset C2

THE HOUSE AT TEMPLE SOWERBY

Between the Lake District and Yorkshire Dales national parks, in the quiet Eden valley, this country house B&B offers an elegant retreat against a background of fell views. Well placed for exploring both areas – the energetic can climb Cross Fell, the highest point on the Pennine Way – or for a north–south stop-over (the M6 is ten minutes away), the Georgian-fronted house has a traditional style yet a relaxed atmosphere. Owners Andi and Alison Sambrook ensure guests, and their dogs, feel at home, as does the beautiful walled garden. Readers say the service is excellent. 'Well-appointed and comfortable' bedrooms are smart but unfussy, with soft colours, pretty fabrics, elegant furniture and a contemporary bathroom. Coach-house rooms are cosy with beams; bigger bedrooms in the main house have a spa bath or hydrotherapy shower. Breakfast, taken in the red-panelled dining room or morning room, includes own-grown smoothies, home-made smoky beans and hash browns, and a full English with vegetarian option. For evening meals, local pubs include the Black Swan at Culgaith, two miles away.

Temple Sowerby
Penrith CA10 1RZ

T: 01768 361578
E: stay@templesowerby.com
W: templesowerby.com

BEDROOMS: 11. 2 on ground floor, 4 in coach house. Plus 3-bed self-catering cottage.
OPEN: all year, except Mon and Tues.
FACILITIES: 2 lounges, bar, coffee shop (Fri–Sun), conference/function facilities, in-room TV (Freeview), 1½-acre walled garden, EV charging, public rooms wheelchair accessible, adapted toilet.
BACKGROUND MUSIC: none.
LOCATION: village centre, 8 miles from Penrith.
CHILDREN: all ages welcomed, no extra beds.
DOGS: allowed in coach house rooms (£10 per night, not unattended), all areas of main house, coffee shop, garden.
CREDIT CARDS: MC, Visa.
PRICES: B&B doubles from £100, singles from £90.

Prices may change – check with hotel.

PENRITH Cumbria

MAP 4: inset C2

WESTMORLAND HOTEL

Speed past this hotel on your M6 journey through
the Lake District and you're missing a treat:
quiet rooms with fell views, tasty Cumbrian food,
excellent value and an overall feeling of 'peace
and well-being'. Part of Tebay Services, the site,
which includes a farm shop, was created by the
resourceful Dunning family after the M6 carved
up their hill farm. The chalet-style building
has 'spacious and quiet' modern bedrooms
with countryside views, 'large and comfortable
beds' and bathrooms with under-floor heating.
Home-made biscuits and locally produced
Sedbergh Soap toiletries are part of their local
sourcing ethos which continues on the menus.
'Well-presented and delicious' unfussy food could
include home-made burgers, and duck with white
bean cassoulet. Beef and lamb come from the
family farm; ice creams are home made. Eat in
the fire-warmed lounge or the restaurant with its
panoramic windows. 'After a good night's sleep,
so quiet', more farm produce features at breakfast
in the grill and egg dishes, with locally produced
granola and preserves, too. 'Cheerful and friendly'
staff add to the 'thoroughly relaxing atmosphere'.
(S and MT, RB)

Orton
Penrith CA10 3SB

T: 01539 624351
E: reservations@westmorlandhotel.
com
W: westmorlandhotel.com

BEDROOMS: 51. 1 suitable for disabled.
OPEN: all year except 24/25 Dec.
FACILITIES: lounge/bar with log fire,
mezzanine, restaurant, in-room TV
(Freeview), function/conference
facilities, farm shop, restaurant, bar
and lounge wheelchair accessible,
adapted toilet.
BACKGROUND MUSIC: none.
LOCATION: 2½ miles SW of Orton.
CHILDREN: all ages welcomed, family
rooms with bunk beds (£15 per child).
DOGS: allowed in some bedrooms
(£15 per night), one area of lounge.
CREDIT CARDS: Amex, MC, Visa.
PRICES: B&B doubles from £116, singles
from £87. À la carte £35.

Prices may change – check with hotel.

PENSFORD Somerset

MAP 2:D1

THE PIG NEAR BATH

The setting is pure hog heaven at Robin Hutson's third Pig hotel, surrounded by a deer park in a fold in the Mendips. The part-Georgian building comes in the group's signature shabby-chic style. 'The chic outweighs the shabby, though I'd welcome a splash of colour,' writes a reader, whose room was 'huge, with two proper armchairs and a table at the end of the bed' and had an 'excellent bathroom'. The smallest bedrooms have a walk-in monsoon shower; the largest have a four-poster, freestanding bath and walk-in shower. The Hide, in the kitchen garden, has a four-poster bed and log-burner. In the restaurant and conservatory, and under canvas, 25-mile menus are built around produce from the huge kitchen garden, with dishes such as thyme-roasted romanesco, mountain mint and pickled raisin or chalk-stream trout, rainbow chard and Fowey mussels. Our reader found the portions a tad large, but loved the home-grown vegetables and 'excellent triple-cooked chips'. Flatbreads are dispensed from a wood-fired oven. Breakfast brings 'big jugs of freshly squeezed juices, huge loaves of fresh bread, croissants, pastries', the works.

Hunstrete House
Pensford BS39 4NS

T: 01761 490490
E: reservations@thepighotel.com
W: thepighotel.com

BEDROOMS: 29. 5 in gardens, some on ground floor, 1 with wheelchair access and wet room.
OPEN: all year.
FACILITIES: 2 lounges, bar, restaurant, snug, private dining room, in-room TV (Freeview), civil wedding licence, treatment room, kitchen garden, wild flower meadow, deer park, EV charging, ground floor/garden areas wheelchair accessible.
BACKGROUND MUSIC: all day in public areas.
LOCATION: 7 miles SW of Bath.
CHILDREN: all ages welcomed, no charge for extra beds.
DOGS: only guide dogs.
CREDIT CARDS: Amex, MC, Visa.
PRICES: room-only doubles from £195. Breakfast £13.50–£18.50, à la carte £42. 1-night bookings refused at weekends, Christmas/New Year.

Prices may change – check with hotel.

PENTON Cumbria

MAP 4:B2

PENTONBRIDGE INN

The humble setting of this former coaching inn, half a mile from the Scottish border, belies its chic bedrooms and creative cooking. Owners Gerald and Margo Smith, of nearby Netherby Hall, have created a stylish interior – soft colours, tweedy fabrics, modern art – while retaining a traditional pub character of exposed stone walls and wood-burning stove. In the kitchen, Chris Archer has gained a Michelin plate and three AA rosettes for his skilful treatment of seasonal produce, much from the Hall's walled garden. The tasting menu offers dishes such as wild garlic with morel vinaigrette, Herdwick lamb with stuffed cabbage and sweetbreads, and lemon meringue with pistachio and green tea. Bedrooms – some in the adjoining converted barn with high ceilings and exposed beams, others up a swanky glass-banister staircase – have tartan throws and headboards, rustic wooden cladding and designer bathrooms. All enjoy views across Cumbria or into Scotland, fresh flowers from the Hall and home-made shortbread. Breakfast in the conservatory – with more views – includes freshly squeezed juice, omelettes, and avocado and poached eggs.

Penton CA6 5QB

T: 01228 586636
E: info@pentonbridgeinn.co.uk
W: pentonbridgeinn.co.uk

BEDROOMS: 9. 3 in converted barn, covered walkway from reception, 3 on ground floor.
OPEN: all year, except 25 Dec (bar only) to 12 Jan, closed Sun (apart from bar), Mon, Tues.
FACILITIES: bar, restaurant, conservatory, in-room TV (Freeview), beer garden, EV charging, bar and conservatory wheelchair accessible, adapted toilet.
BACKGROUND MUSIC: in bar and restaurant.
LOCATION: rural, 10 mins from Longtown.
CHILDREN: all ages welcomed, free cot, no extra bed.
DOGS: allowed in 3 bedrooms (£15 per stay, welcome pack), bar and conservatory, not in restaurant.
CREDIT CARDS: Amex, MC, Visa.
PRICES: B&B doubles from £120, D,B&B doubles from £325. 8-course tasting menu £95.

Prices may change – check with hotel.

PENZANCE Cornwall

MAP 1:E1

CHAPEL HOUSE

There is a friendly, open-house ambience at Susan Stuart's beautiful B&B with views over the harbour and Mount's Bay: drop into the kitchen at any time for coffee, cake and a chat. The interiors are gorgeous, with a sea-inspired palette of soft, pearly greys. A double drawing room, its walls hung with paintings by students from Newlyn School of Art, is home to a grand piano, while throughout you find antique and retro furniture, artwork and sculpture. Every bedroom has a sea view, a handmade oak bed, perhaps a deep, in-room bath, a powerful rainforest shower. There are three bedrooms on the top floor, with an open-plan landing and retractable glass roof for bathing under the stars. Two self-catering suites in an adjoining building would suit a family. On Fridays and Saturdays you can sit down to a communal kitchen supper of local ingredients, maybe after drinks in the sub-tropical garden. Breakfast includes freshly baked breads, smoothies, sizzled cod's roe, smoked bacon, samphire and poached egg, pastries, vegan options. 'Susan got five stars from me.' (ME)

Chapel Street
Penzance TR18 4AQ

T: 01736 362024
E: hello@chapelhousepz.co.uk
W: chapelhousepz.co.uk

BEDROOMS: 6. Plus 2 self-catering suites in annexe.
OPEN: all year except 24–29 Dec, kitchen supper served Fri and Sat.
FACILITIES: double drawing room, open-plan kitchen/dining area, in-room TV, function facilities, holistic treatments, terrace, garden, free street parking, unsuitable for disabled.
BACKGROUND MUSIC: none.
LOCATION: town centre.
CHILDREN: all ages welcomed, under-5s/cots free, extra bed £20 per night.
DOGS: allowed in bedrooms (no charge) and public areas with consent of other guests, not at brunch or supper.
CREDIT CARDS: MC, Visa.
PRICES: B&B doubles from £195, singles from £160. Set dinner £30. 1-night bookings refused at bank holiday weekends.

Prices may change – check with hotel.

SEE ALSO SHORTLIST

PETWORTH Sussex

MAP 2:E3

THE OLD RAILWAY STATION

Readers report transports of delight this year
after staying at this B&B, occupying surely
Britain's prettiest disused station, a former stop
on the Mid-Sussex line in the South Downs
national park. 'We had such an amazing stay.
The whole experience was so special.' There
are two bedrooms in the station building, one at
ground level, one reached via a spiral staircase.
Both have a super-king/twin bed and en suite
shower room. More romantic are the bedrooms
in the 'cosy and quirky' Pullman carriages, proud
survivors from the golden age of rail travel, with
splendid mahogany fittings, a bath with shower
over. 'The room was beautiful. Everything you
could possibly want and so peaceful (though we
did enjoy hearing an owl nearby!)' A champagne
cream tea can be taken by the fire in the waiting
room, or in the sunshine, on the platform. Owners
Jennie Hudson and Blair Humphry have rescued
another carriage, Princess Ena, which will enjoy
a new lease of life as a buffet car. Sleepers wake
to a continental breakfast in bed, or get up for the
'generous' and 'sumptuous' full English. (Rachael
Greenyer, Geoffrey Bignell)

Station Road
Petworth GU28 0JF

T: 01798 342346
E: info@old-station.co.uk
W: old-station.co.uk

BEDROOMS: 10. 8 in Pullman carriages,
1 room suitable for guests with slightly
restricted mobility.
OPEN: all year except 20–27 Dec.
FACILITIES: lounge/bar/breakfast room,
in-room TV (Freeview), platform/
terrace, 2-acre garden, public areas
wheelchair accessible.
BACKGROUND MUSIC: 'soft '20s, '30s, '40s
music' at breakfast and all day in the
Waiting Room.
LOCATION: 1½ miles S of Petworth.
CHILDREN: not under 10.
DOGS: not allowed.
CREDIT CARDS: MC, Visa.
PRICES: B&B doubles from £150,
reduced rates for single occupancy
'sometimes offered'.

Prices may change – check with hotel.

PICKERING Yorkshire

MAP 4:D4

THE WHITE SWAN

The Buchanan family's 16th-century coaching inn offers a warm Yorkshire mix of traditional pub, smart food and modern bedrooms with character. Overlooking the market square, it's a popular locals' spot both for the ales in the fire-warmed bar and snug and the accomplished cooking. With most items, including bread and ice cream, made from scratch, chef Darren Clemmit delivers classic dishes with creativity but without pretension: perhaps a starter of gin-and-lime-cured sea trout followed by roast Yorkshire lamb with charred carrots and caper sauce. There are pub standards, too. Meals are taken in the atmospheric dining room with candlesticks, polished tables and a fire. The extensive wine list, with its collection of St-Émilions, impressed one reader. Bedrooms in the main building have feature wallpapers, colourful fabrics and the occasional antique; one has a grand four-poster. More spacious and modern rooms with slate floors are in converted stables at the back. All have fresh milk and bathrobes. Breakfast is a feast including home-made granola, smoked haddock, mushrooms on brioche, plus a full Yorkshire.

Market Place
Pickering YO18 7AA

T: 01751 472288
E: welcome@white-swan.co.uk
W: white-swan.co.uk

BEDROOMS: 21. 9 in annexe, 8 on ground floor.
OPEN: all year.
FACILITIES: bar, snug, lounge, restaurant, private dining room, bothy bar/lounge, event room, in-room TV, small courtyard (alfresco meals), EV charging, bike storage, restaurant, bar and snug wheelchair accessible, adapted toilet only in bothy/residents' lounge.
BACKGROUND MUSIC: in bar occasionally.
LOCATION: central.
CHILDREN: all ages welcomed, under-5s free, extra bed £20.
DOGS: allowed in some bedrooms (£12.50 a night, welcome pack), bar and snug, not in restaurant (owners may dine with dogs in snug).
CREDIT CARDS: Amex, MC, Visa.
PRICES: B&B doubles from £179, singles from £159. À la carte £38.

Prices may change – check with hotel.

PORLOCK WEIR Somerset

MAP 1:B4

LOCANDA ON THE WEIR

In a tiny coastal village, with the sea in front and Exmoor behind, this eclectic restaurant-with-rooms oozes personality, style and Italian foodie flair. 'A little gem that takes you on a cultural voyage,' say readers. Co-owner and chef Pio Catemario di Quadri conjures memorable and 'outstanding' meals from foraging, the kitchen garden and local produce: perhaps burrata with aged tomatoes followed by smoked lamb cutlets with fennel, and lemon tart with a pine-nut crust. Breakfast is 'equally delicious'. The dining room, as elsewhere, is crammed with art, the style throughout – courtesy of co-owner Cindy Siu – a 'classy' mix of Italian and English antiques and contemporary finds. Books, a fire in the sitting room, plants and fresh flowers keep things homely with 'something to look at everywhere and nothing that feels out of place'. Bedrooms, up a tapestry-hung staircase, have sea views, and are more calmly furnished in country house or breezy seaside style. All but one is shower-only, sometimes quite small. The owners 'are always on hand', 'still happily chatting to guests in the dining room after dinner'. (Mr and Mrs Sachak-Patwa)

Porlock Weir
Exmoor National Park TA24 8PB

T: 01643 863300
E: czs@locandaontheweir.com
W: locandaontheweir.co.uk

BEDROOMS: 4 (5 if whole house booking), not suitable for disabled.
OPEN: all year except Jan.
FACILITIES: bar/lounge, restaurant, in-room TV (Freeview), gift boutique, civil wedding licence, garden, public rooms wheelchair accessible.
BACKGROUND MUSIC: low music in public areas.
LOCATION: within Exmoor national park, in a coastal hamlet on the South West Coast Path.
CHILDREN: not under 12, unless whole house booking.
DOGS: allowed in 3 bedrooms (£10 per night), in lounge, restaurant if well behaved.
CREDIT CARDS: MC, Visa.
PRICES: B&B doubles from £225, singles from £215. Set menu £55. Min. 2-night stay, but 1-night stays sometimes available by phone booking.

Prices may change – check with hotel.

PORTSCATHO Cornwall

DRIFTWOOD HOTEL

'A very nice hotel with its own private beach, secluded and quiet,' writes a reader of this cliff-top retreat in gardens overlooking Gerrans Bay. 'As close to flawless as you can get,' writes another. Superb location overlooking beautiful gardens and Gerrans Bay.' Throughout, the look is coastal chic, with occasional driftwood lamps and artwork. Bedrooms vary in size, most with a sea view, though one overlooks the countryside. Superior sea-view rooms have French windows to a private patio or a Juliet balcony. Head chef Olly Pierrepont cooks an imaginative nightly three-course menu, with a separate no-choice menu for vegetarians. Typical dishes include roast Cornish skate wing, Fowey mussels, cauliflower, golden raisins, pomegranate, almond, curry oil. 'The food was excellent,' one reader continues, although he felt that, as he had given the hotel advance notice, more account might have been taken of his wife's allergies. Still, 'to keep it in perspective, it's a beautiful hotel, well situated, well appointed', while at breakfast, 'a wide choice includes very good pancakes and kedgeree'. (Peter Anderson, J and KP)

Rosevine
Porthscatho TR2 5EW

T: 01872 580644
E: info@driftwoodhotel.co.uk
W: driftwoodhotel.co.uk

BEDROOMS: 15. 4 accessed via courtyard, plus 2-bedroom cabin.
OPEN: all year except Jan.
FACILITIES: bar, restaurant (vegetarian menu), drawing room, snug, children's games room, in-room TV (Freeview), 7-acre grounds (terraced gardens, private beach, safe bathing), EV charging, unsuitable for disabled.
BACKGROUND MUSIC: all day in restaurant and bar.
LOCATION: 1½ miles N of Portscatho.
CHILDREN: all ages welcomed, extra bed £15–£20, children's early supper (under-10s 'not encouraged' at dinner).
DOGS: not allowed.
CREDIT CARDS: MC, Visa.
PRICES: B&B doubles from £215, singles £174. Fixed-price dinner £60/£70 (2/3 courses), tasting menu £90. 1-night bookings refused at weekends.

Prices may change – check with hotel.

RADNAGE Buckinghamshire

THE MASH INN

Nick Mash wants guests to step back in time and reconnect with nature at his restaurant-with-rooms on a leafy back road in a scattered Chilterns village. Duck into the low-lit, atmospheric beamed bar of the former 18th-century Three Horseshoes, and you leave the high-tech modern world behind. Everything is authentic, from a wood-fired range forged by local ironmongers in the open kitchen of the dining extension, to bespoke oak furniture. There are four bedrooms above the restaurant, with contemporary comforts such as a king-size bed, organic L:A Bruket toiletries, a hip bath or monsoon shower. Two larger annexe rooms have French doors on to a private terrace, a monsoon shower. Former sous-chef Tomas Topolar is now head chef. His days are spent foraging, pickling, fermenting, curing, harvesting produce from the kitchen garden, while the no-choice menu is devised around the finest ingredients on the night. Typically, it might include wild garlic vichyssoise, lobster, flame-grilled Aberdeen Angus rib of beef with confit duck fat chips. Breakfast in the restaurant includes home-baked pastries, house yogurt, home-made jams.

Horseshoe Road
Bennett End
Radnage HP14 4EB

T: 01494 482440
E: reservations@themashinn.com
W: themashinn.com

BEDROOMS: 6.
OPEN: all year, Wed–Sat for dinner and Sat lunch.
FACILITIES: snug bar and dining area, semi-open-plan kitchen/dining room, 5-acre garden and grounds, EV charging, restaurant wheelchair accessible, adapted toilet.
BACKGROUND MUSIC: in public areas.
LOCATION: in hamlet 7 miles NW of High Wycombe.
CHILDREN: not under 16.
DOGS: not allowed.
CREDIT CARDS: MC, Visa.
PRICES: D,B&B doubles from £320. Set menu £95.

Prices may change – check with hotel.

RAVENSTONEDALE Cumbria

THE BLACK SWAN

Holding court in the centre of Ravenstonedale, 'twixt the Lakes and the Dales, The Black Swan has the hallmarks of a much-loved village inn: home-cooked food, cheery atmosphere and comforting bedrooms. The Victorian building, run with warm efficiency by Louise Dinnes for 17 years – 'staff couldn't have been more helpful' – has a reputation for its food. Classic dishes are given a creative twist in delicious dinners such as baked scallops with chorizo followed by lamb saddle with salsa verde. You can eat either in the dining room with sage-green dado panelling and bold bird-and-floral wallpaper, or in the jolly bar with exposed-stone walls, tartan carpet and copper jugs. 'Very comfortable' bedrooms are 'charming, lovely' with homely furnishings – including the odd antique – and 'nice armchairs for reading when the rain kept us in!' Some are more compact or there are dog-friendly annexe rooms plus glamping tents, the latter in the riverside beer garden. A snug lounge with panelling and fire beckons for a late-night tot, while cooked-to-order breakfasts – 'scrambled eggs were to die for!' – set you up for the day. (Caroline Thomson)

Ravenstonedale
Kirkby Stephen CA17 4NG

T: 01539 623204
E: enquiries@blackswanhotel.com
W: blackswanhotel.com

BEDROOMS: 16. 6 in annexe, 4 on ground floor, 1 suitable for disabled, 3 glamping tents.
OPEN: all year except first full 2 weeks of Jan and of Oct, kitchen closed Tues, Wed (continental breakfast only) but ring to check.
FACILITIES: 2 bars, lounge, 2 dining rooms, in-room TV, beer garden in wooded grounds, tennis/golf in village, public rooms wheelchair accessible.
BACKGROUND MUSIC: in public areas all day, but optional.
LOCATION: in village 5 miles SW of Kirkby Stephen.
CHILDREN: all ages welcomed, extra bed £30.
DOGS: in 4 ground-floor annexe rooms (£15 per night, welcome package), not in restaurant.
CREDIT CARDS: MC, Visa.
PRICES: B&B doubles/singles from £125. À la carte £45.

Prices may change – check with hotel.

REEPHAM Norfolk

THE DIAL HOUSE

Highly idiosyncratic and seriously fun, Hannah Springham and Andrew Jones's hotel features bedrooms themed on the Georgian Grand Tour and Victorian global gallivanting. The interiors are 'a joy – quirky, and constantly brought a smile to my face'. A reader sampled China room, in blue and white, with bamboo wallpaper, as well as Africa, with animal prints, tribal artefacts, and a roll-top bath at the foot of the bed. 'Both were beautifully decorated and furnished, and very comfortable, with splendid marble bathrooms.' In the retail wing, you can browse antiques and vintage fashions, kit yourself out in Prada or a puffball skirt before repairing to the cocktail bar for a Porn Star Martini. In the restaurant, Mr Jones's 'extremely good dinners' favour top-quality produce, with ingredients sourced from local farmers, and fish from Brancaster. 'The food was consistently good.' Evolving menus include dishes such as cod, seaweed, saffron and mussels. 'The staff were all young, cheerful and busy.' Free-range eggs at breakfast are sourced from the allotment at Reepham High School. (Mary Hewson, Julie Smith, and others)

Market Place
Reepham
Norwich NR10 4JJ

T: 01603 879900
E: info@thedialhouse.org.uk
W: thedialhouse.org.uk

BEDROOMS: 8.
OPEN: all year, restaurant closed Sun night, Mon, Tues.
FACILITIES: lounge, 3 restaurant areas, private dining rooms, sun terrace, in-room TV (Sky), terrace, civil wedding licence, hairdresser's, vintage clothing shop, public rooms wheelchair accessible, no adapted toilet.
BACKGROUND MUSIC: 'retro classics' in public areas.
LOCATION: on main square.
CHILDREN: all ages welcomed, extra bed £40, children's menu.
DOGS: allowed in 2 bedrooms (£20 a night), some public rooms and in part of restaurant.
CREDIT CARDS: Amex, MC, Visa.
PRICES: B&B doubles from £140, singles from £130. À la carte £45.

Prices may change – check with hotel.

REETH Yorkshire

CAMBRIDGE HOUSE

You may find it hard to leave this large stone villa with sweeping views south over Swaledale, spacious rooms, home-made cake, triumphant breakfasts and walks from the doorstep. Sheila and Robert Mitchell give a 'fantastic welcome' with tea and cake, and offer 'excellent knowledge of the local area'. The large, light-filled rooms are 'beautifully furnished' with Arts and Crafts touches; there are sofas, books and a wood-burning stove in the lounge, and views over the pretty cottage garden and beyond from the conservatory. 'Extremely comfortable bedrooms', with exposed-stone walls, pine or brass bedsteads, pretty fabrics and plaid throws, share those 'superb, far-reaching' views. All have bathrobes, and baths as well as showers; edible treats, too. Delicious breakfasts are highly praised for their extensive choice, including pancakes, smoked haddock, local eggs, croissants from the village bakery, and Sheila's award-winning marmalade. The Mitchells advise on dining options (some walkable), can provide picnics and packed lunches, and suggest walks. 'They were truly a fount of information.' (Caroline Kaye, Stella Mannion)

Arkengarthdale Road
Reeth DL11 6QX

T: 01748 884633
E: info@cambridgehousereeth.co.uk
W: cambridgehousereeth.co.uk

BEDROOMS: 4.
OPEN: closed 19 Dec–9 Feb.
FACILITIES: lounge, dining room, conservatory, in-room TV (Freeview), small garden, terrace, bicycle storage.
BACKGROUND MUSIC: none.
LOCATION: 500 yards from centre of Reeth.
CHILDREN: not allowed.
DOGS: 1 dog allowed, by arrangement (£5 per night, welcome pack), not allowed in dining room.
CREDIT CARDS: MC, Visa.
PRICES: B&B doubles from £95. Limited availability of 1-night bookings Apr–Sept.

Prices may change – check with hotel.

RICHMOND Yorkshire   MAP 4:C3

THE COACH HOUSE
AT MIDDLETON LODGE

The good life just gets better at this tranquil
retreat in 200 acres of Georgian parkland,
with rooms in the coach house and beautifully
styled hideaways. James and Rebecca Allison
are creating an evolving arcadia around their
Palladian mansion. 'It's a very special place,' says
a devotee. Sensitively restored outbuildings are
the acme of rustic chic. The Doghouse, in the
orchard, overlooking a wild-flower meadow, has
French doors to a patio. The Head Gardener's
Cottage, with timber-panelled walls, super-king
bed and wood-burning stove, opens on to the
vast, prolific kitchen garden. Dairy hot-tub rooms
have a private garden, a bath and walk-in shower,
Roberts radio and espresso machine. In the
restaurant and outside, an estate-to-plate menu
features dishes from land, sea and garden, with
inventive plant-based options. Our reader enjoyed
'delicious bramble mocktails; a beautiful crab
starter, full of intense flavours, helped along by
a bowl of fries; gorgeous chocolate mousse'. The
Forest Spa is being restored, a gourmet tasting-
menu restaurant is due to open, and Middleton
Lodge is available for private hire. (P and PT)

Kneeton Lane
Middleton Tyas
Richmond DL10 6NJ

T: 01325 377977
E: stay@middletonlodge.co.uk
W: middletonlodge.co.uk

BEDROOMS: 52. In coach house and
other buildings, including 16 rooms
in main house for exclusive hire only,
several on ground floor, 1 suitable for
disabled.
OPEN: all year.
FACILITIES: lounge, bar, snug,
2 restaurants, in-room TV (Sky),
function rooms, civil wedding licence,
treatment rooms, EV charging,
courtyard, 200-acre gardens and
grounds, public rooms wheelchair
accessible, adapted toilet.
BACKGROUND MUSIC: in public areas.
LOCATION: 1 mile N of village.
CHILDREN: all ages welcomed, under-
5s free, extra bed £30.
DOGS: allowed in 1 bedroom (£30 per
night), and courtyard.
CREDIT CARDS: Amex, MC, Visa.
PRICES: B&B doubles from £200, singles
from £175. À la carte £37.

Prices may change – check with hotel.

RICHMOND Yorkshire

MAP 4:C3

THE FRENCHGATE RESTAURANT & HOTEL

A warm Yorkshire welcome and accomplished cooking are the hallmarks of this Georgian town house on a characterful cobbled street near the centre of a handsome market town. Run for almost 20 years by David Todd, it has an intimate feel. Public rooms are traditionally but elegantly furnished, with modern art adding eye-catching touches; there's a wood-burning stove in the lounge and a cosy, atmospheric bar. The highlight of most guests' stay is dinner, served in the Georgian dining room aglow with candlelight and polished oak tables. An amuse-bouche could be followed by Whitby crab with tempura samphire, and local venison with wild mushrooms. A delicate pre-dessert fills the gap before the dessert proper: perhaps Yorkshire parkin with poached rhubarb and cream. Bedrooms have a mix of modern and antique furniture, large custom-made beds and views over the garden or River Swale. The hi-tech bathroom might have a roll-top bath or Swedish shower. Breakfast is a feast that includes freshly squeezed juice, home-made bread, poached haddock, buttermilk pancakes and a full grill.

59–61 Frenchgate
Richmond DL10 7AE

T: 01748 822087
E: info@thefrenchgate.co.uk
W: thefrenchgate.co.uk

BEDROOMS: 9. 1 on ground floor with 2 steps to en suite.
OPEN: all year.
FACILITIES: dining room, bar, lounge, terrace, in-room TV (Freeview), civil wedding licence, small garden, parking, public rooms wheelchair accessible, adapted toilet.
BACKGROUND MUSIC: soft jazz in public rooms.
LOCATION: 200 yds NE of town square.
CHILDREN: all ages welcomed (16 and under, extra bed £30).
DOGS: not allowed.
CREDIT CARDS: Amex, MC, Visa.
PRICES: B&B doubles from £148, singles from £98. À la carte set-price menu £39.

Prices may change – check with hotel.

RICHMOND-UPON-THAMES Surrey   MAP 2:D3

BINGHAM RIVERHOUSE

You can paddleboard on the river, stroll to see the
deer in Richmond Park, and feel a world away
from central London at this smart, multifaceted
Thames-side hotel. Owned by mother and
daughter Ruth and Samantha Trinder, the
Georgian house is home to a members' club and
fine-dining restaurants. Designer bedrooms
with contemporary furnishings are named after
poems and verse dramas by Michael Field, nom
de plume of two Victorian poets, Katherine
Bradley and Edith Cooper, who lived here until
1914. All have climate control, and the best, such
as river-view Sappho and Baudelaire, have an
in-room copper bathtub. Dinner is served in the
library, which is lined with Penguin classics, in
the parlour, the members' lounge/bar, in a garden
'pod' or on terraces. Flexible tasting menus by
Steven Edwards allow you to mix and match
such dishes as beetroot tartare, horseradish ice
cream and coriander; lamb rump with salsify and
braised celery; John Dory with salt-baked celeriac
and lovage. The staff are 'friendly, relaxed and
thoughtful'. Cooked breakfast items include 'eggs
Florentine cooked to perfection'.

61–63 Petersham Road
Richmond-upon-Thames TW10 6UT

T: 020 8940 0902
E: be@binghamriverhouse.com
W: binghamriverhouse.com

BEDROOMS: 15.
OPEN: all year, restaurant closed Sun
evening.
FACILITIES: parlour and library dining
rooms (vegan menus), lounge/bar,
function room, in-room TV, civil
wedding licence, terrace, ½-acre
garden, parking, nearby wellness
centre, public rooms wheelchair
accessible, adapted toilet.
BACKGROUND MUSIC: 'easy listening'
in bar and dining rooms.
LOCATION: ½ mile S of centre.
CHILDREN: all ages welcomed, no
charge for extra bed.
DOGS: allowed with prior permission
in some bedrooms (charges apply,
welcome pack) and public areas.
CREDIT CARDS: Amex, MC, Visa.
PRICES: B&B (continental) doubles
from £165. Cooked breakfast from
£14, tasting menu £40–£85, Fri, Sat
£85 only.

Prices may change – check with hotel.

ROBERTSBRIDGE Sussex

THE GEORGE INN

Do you remember an inn, Miranda? Hilaire
Belloc certainly remembered this Georgian
coaching inn, from which he described setting out
in The Four Men. In 'a historic village of lovely
little medieval houses', it is 'an excellent place
for locals and for a good meal out'. Bedrooms
are named after people with historical links to
the pub. Hilaire, the cheapest, has a rich, earthy
palette – no tedding and spreading of straw for
bedding, but a Hypnos king-size and antiques.
Pooke, overlooking a 1921 war memorial clock
tower, recalls the first landlord to run an inn on
this site. All rooms have a monsoon shower and
are 'in good decorative nick'. Downstairs, food
and drinks are served in a single, open-plan,
dog-friendly space. There is also 'a little paved
courtyard with tables and chairs, lit with fairy
lights'. 'Carefully sourced and well-cooked food'
includes Romney Marsh lamb, chargrilled beef
or lentil burger, fish and 'really good, big chips'
– proper pub fare at proper pub prices. 'The
rhubarb was delicious.' Breakfast brings 'the
usual, with vegetarian options, light and fluffy
scrambled free-range eggs'. (MH, and others)

High Street
Robertsbridge TN32 5AW

T: 01580 880315
E: rooms@thegeorgerobertsbridge.
co.uk
W: thegeorgerobertsbridge.co.uk

BEDROOMS: 4.
OPEN: all year, except Sun pm, Mon,
25/26 Dec, New Year's Day.
FACILITIES: bar/dining area, dining
nook, in-room TV, courtyard garden
(covered, heated area for alfresco
dining), parking, public areas
wheelchair accessible, adapted toilet.
BACKGROUND MUSIC: soft background
music.
LOCATION: in village, 11 miles N of
Hastings.
CHILDREN: all ages welcomed, extra
bed £30–£45 a night, depending on
age.
DOGS: allowed in bar, dining room,
courtyard, not in bedrooms.
CREDIT CARDS: MC, Visa.
PRICES: B&B doubles from £120, singles
from £110. À la carte £30.

Prices may change – check with hotel.

ROMALDKIRK Co. Durham

MAP 4:C3

THE ROSE & CROWN

This inn, next to a Grade I listed village church and overlooking the green, is in the heart of Teesdale's walking country and strikes a happy balance between old-world charm and modern comforts. 'There is something reassuring and cosy about a traditional English country inn on a winter's night,' says a reader about the bar's flagged floors, cheering fire and panelled dining room. Thomas Robinson, co-owner with wife Cheryl, comes from a local farming family, and the inn has a good reputation for food: a mix of pub classics and smarter options – venison bourguignon, and cod with lemon velouté, for example, as well as hog-roast sausages and mash. Guests eat in the candlelit restaurant or buzzier bar. Rooms are divided between more characterful ones in the main building (with window seats and exposed stone) – one couple enjoyed their room 'facing the village green, well appointed and spotless' – and more contemporary, dog-friendly mews cottages with patio. Staff are 'uniformly friendly and efficient' and can advise on local walks. 'Very good value for money. We will certainly return.' (Karen and Jeremy Bonnett, PA, and others)

Romaldkirk
Barnard Castle DL12 9EB

T: 01833 650213
E: info@rose-and-crown.co.uk
W: rose-and-crown.co.uk

BEDROOMS: 14. 2 in Monk's Cottage, 5 in rear courtyard, some on ground floor, 1 suitable for disabled.
OPEN: all year except 23–28 Dec.
FACILITIES: lounge, bar, restaurant, front terrace, in-room TV (Freeview), boot room, EV charging, public rooms wheelchair accessible, no adapted toilet.
BACKGROUND MUSIC: in restaurant.
LOCATION: village centre, 6 miles W of Barnard Castle.
CHILDREN: all ages welcomed, extra bed £25, no under-8s in restaurant after 8 pm.
DOGS: allowed in most bedrooms (no charge) plus public rooms, except restaurant.
CREDIT CARDS: Amex, MC, Visa.
PRICES: B&B doubles from £140, singles from £125. À la carte £35.

Prices may change – check with hotel.

ROWSLEY Derbyshire

MAP 3:A6

THE PEACOCK AT ROWSLEY

'Really excellent' food is at the very heart of this lovely Peak District hotel in a 17th-century manor house, surrounded by good walking country, and known for its fly-fishing. Owned by Lord and Lady Manners, it was built for the steward of their stately home, Haddon Hall, and is full of tradition, with paintings of aristocrats on the walls, a beamed bar, four-posters in some of the country style bedrooms. Along with antiques, these all have air conditioning. Some readers report minor niggles – 'the bathroom was modern but on the small side and the shower lacked power' – but these are more than made up for by the 'high standard of cooking', with meals served by 'well-trained, efficient staff'. Regular visitors were 'slightly disappointed' to find that 'the food has got rather pretentious. It was still good but who needs blackberry and chocolate sauce with their beautifully sourced venison?' In the atmospheric bar, a less-expensive menu impresses, with 'extremely tender shoulder of lamb, smoked tomato risotto, salmon, sublime lemon tart'. After breakfast, visit Haddon Hall and Chatsworth House. (PA, P and AD, and others)

Bakewell Road
Rowsley DE4 2EB

T: 01629 733518
E: reception@thepeacockatrowsley. com
W: thepeacockatrowsley.co.uk

BEDROOMS: 15.
OPEN: all year except dinner 24 Dec, 25/26 Dec, 2 weeks in Jan, closed Mon (but check).
FACILITIES: lounge, bar, 2 dining rooms, private dining room, in-room TV (Freeview, Apple), ½-acre garden on river, fishing rights, public areas wheelchair accessible.
BACKGROUND MUSIC: in public rooms.
LOCATION: village centre.
CHILDREN: not under 10 at weekends.
DOGS: allowed in bedrooms only (£30 per dog per night, food, bowls supplied).
CREDIT CARDS: Amex, MC, Visa.
PRICES: B&B doubles from £235, singles from £165. À la carte in bar £34, restaurant (Tues–Sat) £75, tasting menu (Fri and Sat) £90. 1-night bookings sometimes refused.

Prices may change – check with hotel.

RYE Sussex

MAP 2:E5

JEAKE'S HOUSE

Swathed with creepers and bedecked with flowers, this wildly atmospheric B&B stands on a cobbled street in a medieval citadel with views over Romney Marsh. Combining a wool store built in 1689 by merchant, minister and alchemist Samuel Jeake, and a Quaker meeting house-turned chapel, it was once home to American novelist Conrad Aiken. Steep stairs lead to bedrooms named after writers, artists and reformers who visited the property. The four-poster suite Malcolm Lowry has drapes of English toile, a roll-top bath and walk-in shower. In the parlour you will find a warming fire in winter, board games and a piano. A well-supplied honesty bar is furnished with pews from the galleried chapel, now the dining room, where the breakfast menu includes everything from devilled kidneys and smoked haddock to Rye rarebit on walnut bread, a full English, vegetarian or vegan, and French toast with warm spiced fruit and crème fraîche. 'Very helpful hosts, delightful room and delicious breakfast,' reads one of this year's endorsements. Parking is a real bonus at peak tourist times. (Tim Halstead, JG and others)

Mermaid Street
Rye TN31 7ET

T: 01797 222828
E: stay@jeakeshouse.com
W: jeakeshouse.com

BEDROOMS: 11.
OPEN: all year.
FACILITIES: parlour, bar/library, breakfast room, in-room TV (Freeview), parking permit, unsuitable for disabled.
BACKGROUND MUSIC: chamber music in breakfast room.
LOCATION: central, private car park 6 mins' walk away (charge for parking permit, advance booking).
CHILDREN: not under 8.
DOGS: allowed in bedrooms by pre-arrangement (£5 a night), public rooms on leads and 'always supervised', not in breakfast room.
CREDIT CARDS: MC, Visa.
PRICES: B&B doubles from £100 (private bathroom), £130 en suite, triple from £160, 4 guests £225. 1-night bookings sometimes refused Fri/Sat.

Prices may change – check with hotel.

ST IVES Cornwall

MAP 1:D1

BLUE HAYES

After a day browsing the galleries of this buzzy, arty town, you can escape the crowds to sit serenely sipping cocktails in the sub-tropical gardens at Michael Herring's small hotel. With no drop-ins or children under ten, this is a peaceful and exclusive bolt-hole. Interiors are light and airy, in coastal colours. A gate leads to the South West Coast Path and down to Porthminster Beach. There is plenty of comfy seating, and the bar opens on to a terrace, where you might take a cream tea, enjoying views across the bay and to Godrevy Lighthouse. A single room has garden views, a bath with shower over. The spacious sea-facing master suite has a four-poster and balcony, a spacious bathroom with bath and walk-in shower. The garden suite has French doors to a patio. If you can't tear yourself away, you can order ahead a supper of, say, Trelawny cheese and asparagus tart, Coronation chicken, oak-smoked salmon steak or seafood platter. Breakfast brings a wide choice, including Cornish gammon steak with eggs as you wish, smoked salmon, grilled mackerel and kippers, croissants and vegetarian options.

Trelyon Avenue
St Ives TR26 2AD

T: 01736 797129
E: bluehayes@btconnect.com
W: bluehayes.co.uk

BEDROOMS: 6.
OPEN: Mar–Oct.
FACILITIES: 2 lounges, bar, dining room, in-room TV (Freeview), small function facilities, room service, terrace, garden, parking.
BACKGROUND MUSIC: in bar and dining room only, at breakfast and supper.
LOCATION: ½ mile from centre of St Ives.
CHILDREN: no under-10s, extra bed for ages 10–15 40% of room rate per night.
DOGS: not allowed.
CREDIT CARDS: Amex, MC, Visa.
PRICES: B&B doubles from £235, singles from £160. Supper from £18. Min. 2-night stay, but check availability.

Prices may change – check with hotel.

SEE ALSO SHORTLIST

ST IVES Cornwall

MAP 1:D1

BOSKERRIS HOTEL

Welcome to cloud nine, an adults-only hotel floating above Carbis Bay, where you can sit over a cream tea on a decked terrace, away from the bustle of hip, arty St Ives. Built in 1931, it is decorated in coastal-chic colours and infused with Mediterranean cool. Bedrooms have an espresso machine, a Grohe rainfall or over-bath shower, 100 Acres toiletries. They are 'not large, but the bed was extremely comfortable'. Superior rooms have a super-king bed, a roll-top bath and walk-in shower. A 'Celebration' room has an in-room bath for two and wet-room shower. Short, appealing menus include dishes such as fish and chips, steak with Café de Paris butter, wild mushroom orzo, Cornish crab, mussels, lobster. 'We had a fabulous three-course meal on the terrace,' write readers after 'a really lovely stay'. Very reasonably priced snack boards of Cornish cheeses and charcuterie are available at lunch and dinner every day. At breakfast there is home-made granola, fresh-baked croissants. 'We benefited from being close to the station – three minutes to central St Ives, a town not to be visited by car!' (Donna Ockenden, AW)

Boskerris Road
Carbis Bay
St Ives TR26 2NQ

T: 01736 795295
E: reservations@boskerrishotel.co.uk
W: boskerrishotel.co.uk

BEDROOMS: 15. 2 on ground floor, 1 suitable for disabled.
OPEN: mid-Mar–end Oct, restaurant closed Mon, Tues.
FACILITIES: lounge, bar, breakfast room, supper room, in-room TV (Freeview), decked terrace, massage and reflexology treatment room, 1½-acre garden, parking, EV charging, public rooms wheelchair accessible.
BACKGROUND MUSIC: 'chilled', in public rooms.
LOCATION: 1½ miles from centre (20 mins' walk), close to station.
CHILDREN: not allowed.
DOGS: not allowed.
CREDIT CARDS: Amex, MC, Visa.
PRICES: B&B doubles from £250. À la carte £30. 1-night bookings usually refused in high season.

Prices may change – check with hotel.

SEE ALSO SHORTLIST

ST MARY'S Isles of Scilly

MAP 1: inset C1

STAR CASTLE

You can sit on the ramparts and watch for puffins, seals and invading armadas over a cream tea at this Elizabethan artillery castle and family-run hotel within star-shaped walls. 'The location, setting and history are exceptional.' Some castle rooms are very snug, though smart. Superior sea-view rooms are less cramped, with a four-poster or half-tester bed. Cottage-style annexe rooms and suites have a bath and shower, some with a veranda or private lawn. They are 'where children and dogs are welcome and take a bit more wear and tear', wrote a trusted reader on a return visit. Sadly, wear and tear were among issues for others, who said the rooms were 'more like a Butlin's chalet than a country cottage', with thin walls. Still, all agree about the quality of the cooking, in the dining room, and in the conservatory under a vine. 'The food is totally amazing, and so well balanced that the diner is never outfaced.' Typical dishes might feature venison with black truffle, or lobster and crab caught from the hotel's own boat, with produce from the kitchen garden. The Dungeon bar is indeed in a dungeon, though painted a soothing blue.

The Garrison
St Mary's TR21 0JA

T: 01720 422317
E: info@star-castle.co.uk
W: star-castle.co.uk

BEDROOMS: 38. 27 in 2 garden wings.
OPEN: all year, B&B only Nov–early Mar, closed Christmas and New Year.
FACILITIES: lounge, bar, 2 restaurants, in-room TV (Freeview), civil wedding licence, sun deck, 2-acre gardens, covered swimming pool (12 by 4 metres), tennis, EV charging, unsuitable for disabled.
BACKGROUND MUSIC: none.
LOCATION: ¼ mile from town centre.
CHILDREN: all ages welcomed, extra bed £20, early supper for under-5s.
DOGS: allowed in garden bedrooms (£15 a night), lounge, bar, not in restaurants.
CREDIT CARDS: Amex, MC, Visa.
PRICES: B&B doubles from £189, singles from £112. Set-price menu £39.50–£49.50. 1-night bookings usually refused (but call to check).

Prices may change – check with hotel.

ST MAWES Cornwall

THE IDLE ROCKS

A cream tea (jam first, the Cornish way) on the waterside terrace of this Edwardian hotel in a fishing village on the Fal estuary is a perfect way to enjoy fine weather. On cold days you can relax with a book by a log fire in the lounge; there is even a cinema with reclining leather chairs, a bar, ice creams and popcorn. A Relais & Châteaux member, the hotel is owned by David Richards and his wife, Karen, who designed the coolly stylish interiors, with hand-picked artwork and sculpture. The bedrooms are a dream in coastal white and blues, here and there perhaps vivid coral. Some have a sea view, French doors to a patio or Juliet balcony, a shower and freestanding roll-top bath. Country-view doubles overlooking fields have a bath with hand-held shower. Extra touches include a Roberts radio, an espresso machine, minibar and Aromatherapy Associates products. Dorian Janmaat, a former chef at Raymond Blanc's Manoir aux Quat'Saisons, Great Milton (see entry), creates short, refined menus of dishes such as roasted Newlyn cod, spiced yellow pea, cauliflower, lemon, yogurt, and guests can eat at the bistro belonging to sister St Mawes Hotel.

Harbourside
St Mawes TR2 5AN

T: 01326 270270
E: reservations@idlerocks.com
W: idlerocks.com

BEDROOMS: 18. 4 in adjacent cottage, 1 suitable for disabled.
OPEN: all year.
FACILITIES: lounge, restaurant, kids' room, boot room, in-room TV (Sky), terrace, civil wedding licence, parking, EV charging, public areas wheelchair accessible, adapted toilet.
BACKGROUND MUSIC: all day in public areas, except lounge.
LOCATION: central, on the harbour.
CHILDREN: all ages welcomed, family rooms, under-12s not encouraged in restaurant after 8 pm.
DOGS: allowed in 2 cottage bedrooms (£30 per stay), not in hotel.
CREDIT CARDS: Amex, MC, Visa.
PRICES: B&B doubles from £340. Set-price dinner £85, tasting menu £105. Min. 2-night stay weekends, 3 nights in high season, 1 on D,B&B.

Prices may change – check with hotel.

ST MAWES Cornwall

MAP 1:E2

TRESANTON

'You feel as though you're on the French Riviera' at Olga Polizzi's seaside hotel 'in one of the most idyllic locations you could hope to come across'. Once home to a yacht club, it is spread across a cluster of houses on the hillside with views to St Anthony's lighthouse. Inside it is 'charmingly decorated', effortlessly stylish yet unstuffy. 'It seemed like a place where people were happy to bring families and felt right at home,' our inspector reports. There is a great holiday vibe, with summer Sunday barbecues, a skippered 1930s yacht, a beach club with café/bar and private terraces. Each bedroom has its own style, from bright and breezy to country chic. Most have a sea view; four are dog-friendly. The mosaic-floored restaurant, its terrace a riot of pelargonium, is 'nothing short of spectacular', with a 'short menu showcasing local fare with an emphasis on seafood' – maybe cod, asparagus, hollandaise, mash. 'The food is beautiful and portions just the right size.' Breakfast is imaginative, as you would expect. If you're not nimble on your feet request valet parking; it is 132 steps up to the car park.

27 Lower Castle Road
St Mawes TR2 5DR

T: 01326 270055
E: hoteltresanton@
   thepolizzicollection.com
W: tresanton.com

BEDROOMS: 30. In 5 houses.
OPEN: all year.
FACILITIES: lounge, lounge/bar, restaurant, cinema, playroom, conference facilities, in-room TV (Freeview), civil wedding licence, terrace, ¼-acre garden, beach club (May–Sept), 48-foot yacht, EV charging, restaurant wheelchair accessible, adapted toilet.
BACKGROUND MUSIC: none.
LOCATION: on seafront, valet parking (car park up hill).
CHILDREN: all ages welcomed, extra bed £40, family rooms.
DOGS: allowed in some bedrooms (£25 a night, welcome pack) and in dogs' bar.
CREDIT CARDS: MC, Visa.
PRICES: B&B doubles from £270. À la carte £48. Min. 2-night bookings at weekends, 3-night bookings on bank holidays.

Prices may change – check with hotel.

SALCOMBE Devon

MAP 1:E4

SOAR MILL COVE HOTEL

A single-storey hotel enfolded in a gorse-clad valley, a stroll through National Trust land to the eponymous cove, has been in the Makepeace family for three generations. With flexible family suites and high tea for tinies, it happily accommodates children. Book a cove-facing room for 'a wonderful view down to the cove with the sea beyond'. Readers have differing opinions on the contemporary, unfussy rooms, which have full-height glass doors to a patio. 'We had a spacious family room,' one tells us. 'The beds were very comfortable, with good-quality sheets.' Another praises a 'good-sized room with comfortable chairs', a 'well-designed bathroom with the best shower in a bath I have ever seen'. A third reader, though, decreed his country-facing room was 'simple' rather than 'stylish', while another complained of a 'dated, windowless bathroom'. Opinions on the food are less divided. 'Food was first class. Wonderful soufflé, pan-roasted salmon, hand-picked Salcombe crab.' Awake to a full Devon breakfast and take a packed lunch to the beach. 'The night sky was a deep navy with stars aplenty.' (Richard Bright, SR, and others)

Soar Mill Cove
Salcombe TQ7 3DS

T: 01548 561566
E: info@soarmillcove.co.uk
W: soarmillcove.co.uk

BEDROOMS: 22. 21 on ground floor.
OPEN: all year.
FACILITIES: lounge, bar, restaurant, coffee shop, in-room TV (Freeview), indoor swimming pool, spa, gym, civil wedding licence, 10-acre grounds, EV charging, public rooms wheelchair accessible, adapted toilet.
BACKGROUND MUSIC: in restaurant and bar.
LOCATION: 3 miles SW of Salcombe.
CHILDREN: all ages welcomed, no under-7s in restaurant after 8.45 pm.
DOGS: allowed in bedrooms (£15 per night), bar, coffee shop.
CREDIT CARDS: Amex, MC, Visa.
PRICES: B&B doubles from £249, singles 25% discount, family from £319. À la carte £39. 1-night bookings refused Fri, Sat and holiday weekends.

Prices may change – check with hotel.

SALCOMBE Devon
MAP 1:E4

SOUTH SANDS

Families and four-legged friends feel wonderfully welcome at this smart contemporary hotel, with steps leading from the terrace to a sheltered cove. 'We were a three-generation group, aged four to 73, and loved it!' wrote a reader, buoying it up from the shortlist. The atmosphere is relaxed and informal yet professional. Bedrooms, in five categories, are decorated in a fresh marine palette, and have a sea or valley view. The largest sea-view room has a Caesar-size bed, two slipper baths in a bay window, a full balcony and two Juliet balconies. A valley-facing room proved unexpectedly 'spacious, with a large bathroom' and 'fresh milk in the fridge'. You can eat in the restaurant or alfresco, enjoying views across the estuary with a Devon crab sandwich or cream tea. At lunch and dinner the menu has something for everyone – maybe chilli crab linguine, soy and ginger roasted chicken, or sumac-roasted cauliflower steak. 'The tapas selection was excellent.' Breakfast brings 'a good range of either cold or freshly cooked dishes'. 'The sea tractor linking South Sands to Salcombe is an added attraction.' (Chrissie Davis)

Bolt Head
Salcombe TQ8 8LL

T: 01548 845900
E: enquiries@southsands.com
W: southsands.com

BEDROOMS: 22. Some on ground floor, 1 suitable for disabled, plus 5 self-catering suites.
OPEN: all year.
FACILITIES: bar, restaurant, in-room TV (Freeview), EV charging, terrace, bar and restaurant wheelchair accessible, adapted toilet.
BACKGROUND MUSIC: in public areas.
LOCATION: on South Sands beach, 1½ miles from Salcombe town centre.
CHILDREN: all ages welcomed, extra bed £35 with breakfast, cots £12.50, children's menu.
DOGS: allowed in some bedrooms (£19.50 per night), bar, half the restaurant.
CREDIT CARDS: MC, Visa.
PRICES: B&B doubles from £265, singles from £250. À la carte £45. 2-night min. stay at weekends.

Prices may change – check with hotel.

SEAHAM Co. Durham   MAP 4:B4

SEAHAM HALL

Garden suites with hot tubs, a state-of-the-art
spa, brightly coloured sofas under gleaming
chandeliers … this country house hotel offers
luxury with a contemporary edge. Ten minutes'
walk from the cliffs of County Durham, the
white Georgian hall – where Lord Byron married
– is a mix of classical features and modern design.
With its Asian-themed spa, lounges and terrace,
the emphasis is on switching off. 'A wonderfully
relaxing experience,' reports a reader, 'nothing
was too much trouble.' The team have a 'can-do
attitude'. Bedrooms are huge affairs – 'magnificent,
a real suite with a separate adjoining room' –
with a contemporary country house style of bold
feature wallpapers and zinging colours. High-
quality bathrooms have 'excellent fittings'. Rooms
in the hall have sea views, those in the newer wing
overlook gardens; some have a hot tub. Eat in the
'very comfortable dining room' on 'high-standard
food' that could include turbot with mussels, and
lamb with barbecued aubergine, or more casually
in the spa's Asian-themed restaurant, Ozone. 'We
have already booked another stay.' (Stephen and
Pauline Glover, Ian Larrington, and others)

Lord Byron's Walk
Seaham SR7 7AG

T: 0191 516 1400
E: hotel@seaham-hall.com
W: seaham-hall.com

BEDROOMS: 23. 2 bungalow 2-bedroom
suites, 1 suitable for disabled.
OPEN: all year.
FACILITIES: lift, lounge, lounge/bar,
2 restaurants, private dining room,
conference facilities, in-room TV
(Sky, BT), civil wedding licence,
spa (treatment rooms, outdoor hot
tubs, terrace, gym, small outdoor
pool, 20-metre indoor pool), 37-acre
grounds (terraces, putting green),
public areas wheelchair accessible,
adapted toilet.
BACKGROUND MUSIC: all day in public
areas.
LOCATION: 5 miles S of Sunderland.
CHILDREN: all ages welcomed, extra
bed £50.
DOGS: guide dogs only.
CREDIT CARDS: Amex, MC, Visa.
PRICES: B&B doubles from £315.
À la carte (in restaurant) £55,
(in Ozone in spa) £31.

Prices may change – check with hotel.

SEAHOUSES Northumberland

MAP 4:A4

ST AIDAN HOTEL

This small, friendly, modern seaside B&B is a front-runner for having some of the finest coastal views in Northumberland. On the edge of jolly Seahouses, with the beach across the road, it has an uninterrupted panorama that sweeps from Bamburgh Castle and out to sea, to the Farne Islands and the fishing village's harbour. Most bedrooms, done out in breezy seaside colours with a simple neat style, enjoy these views. Some are on the cosy side, but all have nice touches such as local artwork, blanket throws and binoculars to scan the horizon. Two ground-floor annexe rooms have private entrances; dog owners find this ideal. Owners Rob and Tegan Tait create 'a friendly, welcoming and informal atmosphere'. Rob grew up in the area and has 'plenty of suggestions for walks and day-trips'. Breakfast sets you up for exploring: home-made compote, local jams and marmalades, treats such as freshly baked banana bread, as well as eggs Benedict and the full Northumbrian. Return to a drink from the honesty bar – on the front terrace, if warm – before taking Rob and Tegan's advice on dinner, perhaps at Beadnell Towers in nearby Beadnell (see entry).

1 St Aidan's
Seahouses NE68 7SR

T: 01665 720355
E: info@staidanhotel.co.uk
W: staidanhotel.co.uk

BEDROOMS: 9. 3 on ground floor, 2 in annexe.
OPEN: Feb–end Oct.
FACILITIES: breakfast room, bar area (honesty bar), in-room TV (Freeview), front lawn (picnic tables), parking, unsuitable for disabled.
BACKGROUND MUSIC: chilled acoustic in public rooms.
LOCATION: 300 yds from harbour, on north side of village, with views towards Bamburgh.
CHILDREN: not under 12.
DOGS: allowed in annexe rooms (no charge), 1 area of breakfast room.
CREDIT CARDS: MC, Visa.
PRICES: B&B doubles from £125. Min. 2-night stay usually required.

Prices may change – check with hotel.

SEDBERGH Cumbria   MAP 4:C3

THE BLACK BULL

This 17th-century coaching inn has sleek, elegant bedrooms and highly creative food, but retains its warm, pubby credentials. It joins our main entries this year. Sitting on Sedbergh's main street, and with views to the Howgill fells (you can climb the hills direct from the pub), it's a place where dogs, drinkers and diners mingle happily. Dales-born James Ratcliffe and chef/partner Nina Matsunaga are keen to showcase local producers. There are local wool carpets, handwoven blanket throws and striking photographs of the surrounding landscape in the 'very comfortable' bedrooms with fuss-free furnishings. Bathrooms are ultra-modern, some with a deep freestanding bath. Saly, some ensuites have transparent glass doors. Nina's innovative Japanese-inspired cooking transforms local produce, 'each course a surprise in its presentation and flavour': perhaps scallop with lotus root and shiso followed by Herdwick lamb with sesame and Korean chilli. The wine list is pricey but also 'unusual' and carefully chosen. Breakfast wins equal praise for its variety including mushrooms on toast, Welsh rarebit and a full grill. (Bill Wood)

44 Main Street
Sedbergh LA10 5BL

T: 015396 20264
E: bookings@theblackbullsedbergh.
   co.uk
W: theblackbullsedbergh.co.uk

BEDROOMS: 18.
OPEN: every day May–Oct, Wed–Sun Nov–Apr, restaurant open Wed–Sun year round, closed 25 Dec.
FACILITIES: bar, restaurant, in-room TV (Freeview), 1-acre garden (outdoor bar, beer garden), parking, bar and restaurant wheelchair accessible, adapted toilet.
BACKGROUND MUSIC: in public rooms.
LOCATION: in town centre, close to M6 (Jct 37).
CHILDREN: all ages welcomed, extra bed £22.
DOGS: allowed in several bedrooms (£25 per stay, welcome pack), bar, garden area, not in restaurant.
CREDIT CARDS: Amex, MC, Visa.
PRICES: B&B doubles from £139.
À la carte £37. Min. 2-night stay at weekends.

Prices may change – check with hotel.

SHAFTESBURY Dorset

MAP 2:D1

LA FLEUR DE LYS

It is more than 30 years since David and Mary
Griffin-Shepherd and Marc Preston opened
a restaurant-with-rooms in this market town
overlooking Blackmore Vale in Hardy country.
The trio met at Lewtrenchard Manor, Lewdown
(see entry), and, as their first venture prospered,
20 years ago they relaunched it at the 19th-century
former Sundridge Hotel. It's as good today as it's
always been, to quote Ridley Scott's iconic 1970s
Hovis ad, shot on cobbled Gold Hill. In fact,
it is in every way as it has always been, a little
dated now, but welcoming and run with pride by
Mary front-of-house and David and Marc in the
kitchen. Bedrooms are spotless and comfortable,
with a mini-fridge, fresh milk, ground coffee and
home-baked biscuits. A family room has a draped
four-poster. Typical dishes include pan-fried
noisettes of Dorset lamb with couscous, sun-
blushed tomatoes, broad beans, spring onions and
creamy thyme sauce; for vegetarians, asparagus
with mushroom, herb and garlic cream cheese
pancakes, spinach with pine nuts, and wild
mushrooms in garlic sauce. Don't expect textures
of cauliflower, foams, spumes, smoke or fairy dust
– just good, tasty food.

Bleke Street
Shaftesbury SP7 8AW

T: 01747 853717
E: info@lafleurdelys.co.uk
W: lafleurdelys.co.uk

BEDROOMS: 8. 1, on ground floor,
suitable for disabled.
OPEN: all year, restaurant closed Sun.
FACILITIES: lounge, bar, dining
room, conference room, in-room
TV (Freeview), courtyard garden,
parking, bar and restaurant
wheelchair accessible, adapted toilet.
BACKGROUND MUSIC: none, but some
live music events.
LOCATION: N edge of historic town
centre.
CHILDREN: all ages welcomed.
DOGS: not allowed.
CREDIT CARDS: Amex, MC, Visa.
PRICES: B&B doubles from £115, singles
from £95, triples from £185. À la carte
£38/£45 (2/3 courses), tasting menu
£58. 1-night bookings sometimes
refused at weekends in summer.

Prices may change – check with hotel.

SEE ALSO SHORTLIST

SHEFFIELD Yorkshire

BROCCO ON THE PARK

Behind the solid exterior of an Edwardian park-side villa lies a Scandi-chic boutique hotel and popular drop-in restaurant. Picasso is said to have stayed here in 1950, a visit celebrated in top-floor Dove room, with grey-blue palette, a balcony affording views across the treetops towards Derbyshire. It has a freestanding copper bath, monsoon shower, espresso machine, fridge, smart TV, Roberts radio. Other rooms have a modern four-poster, and an egg-shaped bath for two. Ground-floor Nightjar's Nest, with wet room, can accommodate an extra bed. A reader was impressed with the 'great attention to detail', and 'complimentary lime and coconut cake, a glass of fizz at 5.30 pm'. Food is served in the restaurant and on the terrace, from breakfast through brunch and afternoon tea, to a dinner of small plates – hasselback Jerusalem artichoke with hen of the woods and truffle; lamb rump with rosemary and garlic butter and braised shallot. 'We had an excellent meal and the advice from staff was most helpful.' Service went awry at breakfast – ordered à la carte, with tempting choices – for one reader, but it may have been a one-off.

92 Brocco Bank
Sheffield S11 8RS

T: 0114 266 1233
E: hello@brocco.co.uk
W: brocco.co.uk

BEDROOMS: 8. 1, on ground floor, suitable for disabled.
OPEN: all year, restaurant closed Mon/Tues, Sun from 6 pm and Christmas Day.
FACILITIES: reception with sofas, restaurant/bar, terrace (alfresco dining), in-room TV, parking, restaurant wheelchair accessible, adapted toilet.
BACKGROUND MUSIC: in restaurant, Sunday jazz afternoons.
LOCATION: 1½ miles W of city centre.
CHILDREN: all ages welcomed, under-3s free, extra bed for under-13s £35, children's menu (breakfast/brunch).
DOGS: allowed only on terrace.
CREDIT CARDS: Amex, MC, Visa.
PRICES: room-only doubles from £130. Breakfast and brunch à la carte, full English £13, vegan £12, dinner small plates from £10.

Prices may change – check with hotel.

SHREWSBURY Shropshire

MAP 3:B4

DARWIN'S TOWNHOUSE

Named in honour of Shrewsbury's famous son, the Grade II* listed Sandford House, moments from the Severn towpath, has evolved into a contemporary B&B. It is promoted to a full entry after Guide inspectors visited, in a spirit of scientific inquiry, and were impressed by the ambience, 'as if walking into a friend's home. The decoration is fun and characterful, with animal and plant wallpapers, maps, natural history objets and antiques.' An octagonal drawing room has 'a splendid decorative ceiling' depicting signs of the Zodiac. The snug has a well-stocked honesty bar. Muted bedroom decor offsets 'Darwinian-appropriate patterning on curtains and cushions'. Two ground-floor bedrooms have garden access. Two superior rooms have a super-king bed, a bath and shower. There is a 'terrific lawned garden', a 'light-filled conservatory', where a locally sourced breakfast brings artisan jams, free-range eggs from Hollowdene's happy hens. Guests can claim a 10% discount at two sister restaurants (not inspected). Book one of the 'more functional, smaller' rooms in the garden annexe if you want to bring the beagle.

37 St Julian's Friars
Shrewsbury SY1 1XL

T: 01743 343829
E: info@darwinstownhouse.com
W: darwinstownhouse.com

BEDROOMS: 19. 5 on ground floor, 8 in garden annexe, 1 suitable for disabled.
OPEN: all year, continental breakfast only on 25 Dec.
FACILITIES: lounge, snug (honesty bar), conservatory breakfast room, in-room TV, garden, bicycle storage, public car park nearby.
BACKGROUND MUSIC: in lounge, snug.
LOCATION: in town centre.
CHILDREN: all ages welcomed.
DOGS: allowed in garden bedrooms, not in breakfast room.
CREDIT CARDS: Amex, MC, Visa.
PRICES: B&B doubles from £135, singles from £90. À la carte (at sister restaurants) £28, residents' discount cards supplied.

Prices may change – check with hotel.

SEE ALSO SHORTLIST

SIDLESHAM Sussex   MAP 2:E3

THE CRAB & LOBSTER

Overlooking the reed beds and salt marsh of
Pagham Harbour Nature Reserve, this 'lovely
little pub' is not a local boozer but a very good
restaurant-with-rooms, a sister venture to The
Halfway Bridge, Lodsworth (see entry). Oak-
beamed bedrooms have a subtle palette of pale
blue, sage and taupe, with some overlooking
open farmland. A reader's deluxe room had
a perpendicular beam at the centre – a sort of
17th-century jack post, more curiosity than
hazard. 'The bed was comfy, though a bigger
duvet would have prevented some tugs of war.'
There are rooms in adjacent Crab Cottage, which
has a comfy sitting room and a kitchen with an
espresso machine, should you want to self-cater,
but a full English awaits next door. The restaurant
is stylish, but also comes with a log-burner in an
inglenook. Specials are chalked up on a fish-
shaped blackboard, while the à la carte brings
dishes such as baked Selsey crab gratin, fennel
marmalade, salsa verde; fish and chips; steaks. A
separate vegan menu might include sweet potato
gnocchi, Moroccan spiced chickpea tagine. 'The
staff are young, efficient and friendly. We will
return.' (PA)

Mill Lane
Sidlesham PO20 7NB

T: 01243 641233
E: enquiries@crab-lobster.co.uk
W: crab-lobster.co.uk

BEDROOMS: 4. 2 in adjacent Crab
Cottage.
OPEN: all year.
FACILITIES: bar/dining room/snug
(vegetarian/vegan menu), in-room
TV (Freeview), terrace, small beer
garden, parking, bar and restaurant
wheelchair accessible, adapted toilet.
BACKGROUND MUSIC: 'quiet' music in
restaurant and bar.
LOCATION: 6 miles S of Chichester.
CHILDREN: all ages welcomed, under-
9s on extra bed £40.
DOGS: allowed in garden area.
CREDIT CARDS: Amex, MC, Visa.
PRICES: B&B doubles from £220, singles
from £145 (full rates apply Fri–Sun).
À la carte £45. Min. 2-night stay at
weekends.

Prices may change – check with hotel.

SIDMOUTH Devon

MAP 1:C5

HOTEL RIVIERA

For more than 40 years the Wharton family have welcomed guests to their bow-fronted, stuccoed, seafront hotel – and if little has changed over time, that's fine with devotees. New carpets have been laid and the bedrooms refurbished, but they retain their quilted headboards, swags and pelmets, 'sheets, blankets, no duvet nonsense'. 'Lovely sea views from our room on the third floor,' readers relate this year. 'Well equipped and comfortable. Good public rooms with first-rate service.' You don't come here to be trendy, but to enjoy a Devonshire cream tea among the potted palms on the terrace, to be served by attentive, uniformed staff, to relax on the beach, to walk the South West Coast Path, and to listen to the brass band in Connaught Gardens on a summer Sunday evening. In the restaurant there is a sense of occasion, as diners tuck into chicken liver parfait, grilled Dover sole, or roast rack of lamb with thyme jus and ratatouille. The breakfast menu brings fresh orange or grapefruit juice, prunes, gammon, Loch Fyne smoked fish, along with the usual full English. (Tony and Shirley Hall, P and AD, IM, and others)

The Esplanade
Sidmouth EX10 8AY

T: 01395 515201
E: enquiries@hotelriviera.co.uk
W: hotelriviera.co.uk

BEDROOMS: 26. None on ground floor.
OPEN: all year.
FACILITIES: small lift, foyer, lounge, bar, restaurant, function rooms, in-room TV (Freeview), terrace, parking (£8 a day), public rooms wheelchair accessible.
BACKGROUND MUSIC: in bar and restaurant, occasional pianist in bar.
LOCATION: central, on the esplanade.
CHILDREN: all ages welcomed, under-3s free, extra bed 25%–75% of per-person adult rate.
DOGS: small dogs allowed in some bedrooms (£17.50 a night, by arrangement), not in public rooms.
CREDIT CARDS: Amex, MC, Visa.
PRICES: B&B doubles from £260, singles from £130. Set-price dinner £45–£49 (3/5 courses), à la carte £60.

Prices may change – check with hotel.

SNETTISHAM Norfolk

MAP 2:A4

THE ROSE & CROWN

As ringed plovers and pink-footed geese flock to Snettisham's shingle beaches, lagoons, tidal mudflats and cattle-grazed salt marsh, so happy families and their dogs flock to Jeannette and Anthony Goodrich's friendly pub. They are constantly upgrading, and have created a new residents' lounge for guests seeking a quiet corner. 'Redecorated, and new menu since I last stayed two years ago, not that either needed doing,' writes a reader. Bedrooms are light and airy, in seaside colours of white and blues, coral and sand. Bathrooms have a walk-in shower, luxury toiletries. 'The room was well laid out and very clean, the bed was extremely comfortable,' another reader reports. 'The food was brilliant – lots of choice and delicious.' The locally sourced menu changes every six to eight weeks, with three or four daily specials. Pub classics such as fish and chips sit alongside Brancaster mussels, Moroccan spiced lamb tagine, a superfood salad. You can eat in the garden, where a new beach hut dispenses 'street food' and children swarm over the Merry Rose climbing ship. 'I cannot speak more highly of the staff.' (Helen Lewis, Rupert Baker, TS)

Old Church Road
Snettisham PE31 7LX

T: 01485 541382
E: info@roseandcrownsnettisham.
co.uk
W: roseandcrownsnettisham.co.uk

BEDROOMS: 16. 2 on ground floor, 1 suitable for disabled.
OPEN: all year except lunch on 25 Dec.
FACILITIES: 3 bar areas, 2 restaurant rooms, in-room TV (Freeview), large walled garden (children's play area, climbing ship), EV charging, Garden Room restaurant wheelchair accessible, adapted toilet.
BACKGROUND MUSIC: low-key, mainly soft jazz in dining areas.
LOCATION: in village centre, 5 miles S of Hunstanton.
CHILDREN: all ages welcomed, cots £10, extra bed £20, children's menu.
DOGS: well-behaved dogs allowed in bedrooms (max. 2, £15 per night), bars and garden room, not in dining areas.
CREDIT CARDS: Amex, MC, Visa.
PRICES: B&B doubles from £140, singles from £110. À la carte £38.

Prices may change – check with hotel.

SOMERTON Somerset

MAP 1:C6

THE LYNCH COUNTRY HOUSE

Tucked away on the edge of a little market town 40 minutes' drive from the Jurassic coast, this late Georgian mansion, topped by a belvedere with viewing deck, is an unusual and special B&B. It is owned by veteran jazz saxophonist Roy Copeland, who, in his varied career, once modelled Bonsoir pyjamas. When it's time to say 'bonsoir', head up to a bedroom furnished in period style – perhaps Goldington, with a carved oak four-poster, or Somerton, with a super-king/twin bed and a folding bed for an extra guest. Two cosy rooms are tucked away under the eaves. No one-man band, Mr Copeland is aided by welcoming manager Lynne Vincent. Breakfast, served until 10 am in the beautiful orangery, is thoughtfully sourced, with freshly squeezed orange juice, French yogurts, dry-cured Wiltshire bacon, Clonakilty black and white pudding, Loch Fyne smoked salmon, creamy scrambled eggs on a toasted muffin, all cooked to order. The gardens are a particular delight, with topiary, specimen trees and a rill. A black swan event here is entirely good news, involving a visit from the curious Cygnus atratus that glide on the lake.

4 Behind Berry
Somerton TA11 7PD

T: 01458 272316
E: enquiries@thelynchcountryhouse.co.uk
W: thelynchcountryhouse.co.uk

BEDROOMS: 5. 2-bedroom self-catering annexe in coach house.
OPEN: all year, only coach house rooms at Christmas and New Year, no breakfast 25/26 Dec, 1 Jan.
FACILITIES: breakfast room, small sitting area, in-room TV (Freeview), ¾-acre grounds (lake), unsuitable for disabled.
BACKGROUND MUSIC: none.
LOCATION: edge of town.
CHILDREN: all ages welcomed, extra bed £20–£35.
DOGS: not allowed.
CREDIT CARDS: Amex, MC, Visa.
PRICES: B&B doubles from £80, singles from £70.

Prices may change – check with hotel.

SEE ALSO SHORTLIST

SOUTH DALTON Yorkshire

MAP 4:D5

THE PIPE AND GLASS INN

In an enchantingly lovely village, this classic coaching inn continues to impress guests with Michelin-starred food, traditional pub features and indulgent bedrooms. 'We have visited every year for the last eight years and it remains excellent,' enthuses a fan. Co-owner James Mackenzie's cooking puts a creative spin on classic British dishes such as parkin-crusted venison with Yorkshire rhubarb pickle, wild halibut with roast salsify and cockles, and 'meltingly tender duck'. Portions are 'very generous' while dining areas include a conservatory overlooking the charming garden, which has quirky sculpture, hidden arbours and supplies herbs and other goodies for the kitchen. Bedrooms are equally indulgent with statement wallpapers, bold colours, velvet fabrics and sleigh or four-poster beds. Five open to the garden while the four largest are in outbuildings. All have private patios plus 'spectacular' bathrooms, most with bath and shower. Return from a country walk to a hand-pulled ale in the bar with its exposed brick, beams and gleaming copper, and a cheery welcome from 'friendly, attentive and very efficient' staff. (Peter Anderson)

West End
South Dalton HU17 7PN

т: 01430 810246
E: email@pipeandglass.co.uk
w: pipeandglass.co.uk

BEDROOMS: 9. 5 in main building, 4, in converted buildings, all on ground floor, 1 suitable for disabled.
OPEN: all year except 2 weeks in Jan, closed Sun eve, all Mon.
FACILITIES: lounge, conservatory, bar, restaurant (vegetarian/vegan menus), in-room TV (Freeview), patio (alfresco dining), garden, EV charging, public rooms wheelchair accessible, adapted toilet.
BACKGROUND MUSIC: in bar and restaurant.
LOCATION: 7 miles NW of Beverley.
CHILDREN: all ages welcomed, under-3s free, extra bed for under-16s £30.
DOGS: not allowed.
CREDIT CARDS: Amex, MC, Visa.
PRICES: B&B doubles from £210, singles from £180. À la carte £55. Dinner usually required as part of booking.

Prices may change – check with hotel.

SOUTH LEIGH Oxfordshire

MAP 3:E6

ARTIST RESIDENCE OXFORDSHIRE

With funky artwork in the bar and attractive salvaged furniture, this is not your conventional thatched village inn, but it brims with a quirky charm and a warm, open-to-everyone welcome. The former 16th-century farmhouse has the expected features of beams, flagged floors, exposed stone and wood-burning stoves but mixed with modern art, retro features, striking photography and bold floral wallpapers. Part of Justin and Charlotte Salisbury's small collection of Artist Residences (see index), its bohemian style is a playful take on a country pub. Rustic-chic bedrooms have rugs on bare floorboards, colourful cushions and bedheads, vintage armchairs and upcycled tables, along with an espresso machine, minibar and organic toiletries. Most have a roll-top bath while several (one with additional bunk beds) are in outbuildings with their own entrance; some with a log-burner and private terrace. Tucked at the end of the garden, the shepherd's hut is for romantics. Dine on interesting pub grub – double beef burger and Monterey Jack, perhaps, or Balinese curry – in the bar or garden; Prosecco and eggs Benedict for breakfast.

Station Road
South Leigh OX29 6XN

T: 01993 656220
E: oxford@artistresidence.co.uk
W: artistresidence.co.uk/our-hotels/oxford

BEDROOMS: 11. Some on ground floor, 5 rooms in outbuildings including a 2-bedroom suite, shepherd's hut in garden.
OPEN: all year.
FACILITIES: bar, restaurant (2 dining areas, closed Sun eve), in-room TV, large beer garden, kitchen garden, EV charging, unsuitable for disabled.
BACKGROUND MUSIC: in pub and restaurant.
LOCATION: countryside, 10 miles from Oxford, 3 miles from Witney centre.
CHILDREN: all ages welcomed, free cots, extra bed £30.
DOGS: allowed in some bedrooms (£15 per night, welcome pack), and public rooms.
CREDIT CARDS: Amex, MC, Visa.
PRICES: room-only doubles from £165. Breakfast items from £4, full English £12.50. Min. 2-night stay at weekends.

Prices may change – check with hotel.

SOUTHAMPTON Hampshire

MAP 2:E2

THE PIG IN THE WALL

This little piggy, the babe in the litter of Robin Hutson's Pig hotels, is set in a crenellated Georgian house and former pub built into the city's medieval wall. Inside, you find the group's signature shabby-chic style, with scuffed bare floorboards, herbs in flowerpots, the odd stuffed owl. The granny's attic aesthetic is deceptive: every piece has been chosen with an unerring eye by Robin's wife Judy. There are only a dozen bedrooms, from the smallest in the eaves, with beamed and slanted ceiling, to a spacious room with a roll-top bath under the window, a barley-sugar-twist white four-poster and separate shower room. Unlike its siblings, this Pig doesn't ham it up with huts and hideaways. It has neither restaurant nor vegetable garden; the deli uses produce grown at the mother Pig in Brockenhurst (see entry), a half-hour drive away. You eat in the lounge by the log-burner, choosing from dishes such as quiche, cured meats, curried red lentil stew and whole baked Shakespeare (a variety of red onion, as you like it, with chutney and sourdough). At breakfast there are continental options or a cooked 'Piggy Pan'.

8 Western Esplanade
Southampton SO14 2AZ

T: 02380 636900
E: reception@thepiginthewall.com
W: thepighotel.com

BEDROOMS: 12. 2 on ground floor, 1 with wet room and wheelchair access via side door from car park (not suitable for wider wheelchairs).
OPEN: all year.
FACILITIES: open-plan lounge/bar/ deli counter, in-room TV (Freeview), car park (free if you're dining, £10 overnight), EV charging, public rooms wheelchair accessible, adapted toilet.
BACKGROUND MUSIC: in public areas.
LOCATION: close to city centre.
CHILDREN: all ages welcomed, cots free, small charge for extra bed.
DOGS: not allowed.
CREDIT CARDS: Amex, MC, Visa.
PRICES: room-only doubles from £170. Continental breakfast £12, cooked £16.

Prices may change – check with hotel.

SOUTHROP Gloucestershire

MAP 2:C2

THYME

With the feel of a charmed Cotswolds village, this collection of honeyed buildings house chic rooms surrounded by pretty gardens, as well as a spa, pub and cookery school. The manor house estate and farm were restored by Caryn Hibbert with fastidious attention to detail: sheepskin rugs on Scandi-style chairs, 'country-chic interiors' and everything 'beautifully done out and cleverly themed on the farm', with a Baa bar and an enormous Ox Barn restaurant. It is here where Caryn's son, Charlie, creates his short menu of modern dishes including sirloin with pickled walnut and horseradish or baked chickpeas with pumpkin and goat's curd; 'delicious breakfasts', too. The grounds are home to a 'rather lovely outdoor pool with natural spring water'. Bedrooms, spread between the main house and different cottages, are 'designed impeccably' with soft colours, feature wallpapers, antique and modern furniture. They vary from beamed, under-eaves rooms to suites with 'a massive bathroom built for a princess, with chandelier, dusk-pink walls and a working fireplace'. 'Friendly' staff 'are never intrusive, but they spot what needs attending to'.

Southrop Manor Estate
Southrop GL7 3NX

T: 01367 850174
E: reception@thyme.co.uk
W: thyme.co.uk

BEDROOMS: 32. 8 in main building, others in a lodge, outbuildings and cottages.
OPEN: all year except Christmas Day.
FACILITIES: drawing room, cocktail bar, restaurant, pub, in-room TV (Freeview), civil wedding licence, event space, 150-acre estate (farm, gardens, swimming pool, spa), EV charging, unsuitable for disabled.
BACKGROUND MUSIC: in public spaces.
LOCATION: on large Cotswold estate N of Lechlade.
CHILDREN: not under 12, except in 1 cottage, Ox Barn at lunchtime and The Swan pub.
DOGS: only in 1 cottage (no charge) and pub.
CREDIT CARDS: Amex, MC, Visa.
PRICES: B&B doubles from £360. À la carte (3 courses) £50. Min. 2-night stays, ring to check 1-night availability.

Prices may change – check with hotel.

STAMFORD Lincolnshire

MAP 2:B3

THE GEORGE OF STAMFORD

'Over five decades the dear old George has never missed a beat, and our stay was as perfect as ever in this beautiful, old but supremely comfortable hotel in a lovely town.' A reader praises this historic coaching inn on the Great North Road, owned by Lawrence Hoskins for half a century. Some bedrooms have contemporary decor, and all have individually controlled air conditioning but, from antique four-posters to silver-domed carvery trolleys in the panelled Oak Room restaurant, which serves 'perfect Dover sole and succulent roast beef', this is a classic hotel of its kind. You can eat less formally in the Garden Room, where every taste is catered for, from pasta, fish and chips and burgers to steak-and-kidney pudding, lobster Benedict, 'the best sea bass I can recall'. 'Tea in the courtyard with a pianist playing songs from the 1930s has been a delight,' another reader related, although wincing at prices 'that seem well over the top'. Service at its best is 'perfect', though yet another reader found it haphazard. Still, 'lovely to stay in a famous hotel of such character'. (Ralph Wilson, Geoffrey Bignell, and others)

71 St Martins
Stamford PE9 2LB

T: 01780 750750
E: reservations@
　georgehotelofstamford.com
W: georgehotelofstamford.com

BEDROOMS: 45.
OPEN: all year.
FACILITIES: 2 lounges, 2 bars, 2 restaurants (vegetarian/vegan menu), 3 private dining rooms, business centre, in-room TV (Sky, Freeview), civil wedding licence, 2-acre grounds, parking, public rooms wheelchair accessible, adapted toilet.
BACKGROUND MUSIC: quiet, in summer in garden covered area, pianist with afternoon tea at weekends.
LOCATION: ¼ mile from centre.
CHILDREN: all ages welcomed, extra bed £60.
DOGS: small dogs allowed with prior notice, not unattended in bedrooms (£25 per night), not in restaurants.
CREDIT CARDS: Amex, MC, Visa.
PRICES: B&B doubles from £270, singles from £150. À la carte £75 (Oak Room), £55 (Garden Room).

Prices may change – check with hotel.

STANTON HARCOURT Oxfordshire

MAP 2:C2

THE HARCOURT ARMS

Although it has been taken over by the Barkby group, this 17th-century gastropub-with-rooms in a rural village between the rivers Thames and Windrush 'still feels individual', say readers. A cosy, beamed bar has leather armchairs by a log-burner, rugs on flagstone floors. Bedrooms, most in a new extension, blend modern comforts with vintage pieces, and have boldly patterned headboards, an espresso machine, posh toiletries. The impressive Blenheim Suite, with exposed rafters, has a four-poster, a stand-alone copper bath, heated bathroom floor and rainfall shower. 'Aston, a deluxe double, was light and pleasant, of adequate size. The bathroom was quite large, with a window, a wet shower area.' In the atmospheric dining room, its dark-green walls hung with gilt-framed paintings, menus mix pub classics with locally sourced dishes such as garden herb gnocchi or tasting of mutton lamb with honeyed squash and cabbage dauphinoise. At breakfast there is 'a wide choice of bread and croissants, fruit, cheese, cold meats', with cooked dishes charged extra. 'We liked this hotel.' (John and Elspeth Gibbon)

Main Road
Stanton Harcourt
Witney OX29 5RJ

T: 01865 416516
E: theharcourtarms@barkbygroup.
com
W: www.theharcourtarms.com

BEDROOMS: 10. 1 garden room across small rear courtyard suitable for disabled.
OPEN: all year.
FACILITIES: snug bar, dining bar, dining room, ½-acre garden, in-room TV (Freeview), all ground floor wheelchair accessible, adapted toilet.
BACKGROUND MUSIC: in all public areas.
LOCATION: 6 miles SE of Witney, 4 miles SW of Eynsham.
CHILDREN: all ages welcomed, family rooms.
DOGS: allowed in all areas (£20 a stay).
CREDIT CARDS: Amex, MC, Visa.
PRICES: B&B (continental breakfast) doubles from £121, singles from £105, family from £145. Cooked breakfast charged per item, full English/vegetarian £14, à la carte £40. 1-night stays refused at weekends in high season.

Prices may change – check with hotel.

STANTON WICK Somerset

MAP 1:B6

THE CARPENTERS ARMS

Rambling roses and 'an amazing display of hanging baskets and planters' adorn 'the Carps', a friendly local pub-with-rooms in a hamlet 25 minutes from Bath. Part of the small Buccaneer Holdings pub group, it has been run with considerable polish since 1999 by manager Simon Pledge. Created from a row of miners' cottages, it has picnic tables at the front and a terrace at the side. Bedrooms are contemporary in style, with a comfy chair or two, and an eclectic selection of artworks. Like the rest of the place, they sit comfortably between the no-frills and too-frilly sector of the market, say readers. A change in the kitchen has seen the return of Chris Dando, head chef here from 2003 to 2017. The menu, served in bar, dining rooms and garden, is a mix of pub classics and more inventive dishes, with day-boat fresh fish from Brixham, local beef, lamb, game in season. They do Sunday roasts, of course, which guests report come with copious amounts of vegetables and potatoes. Or you can just swing by for a pint of Butcombe and oodles of atmosphere in the stone-walled, beamed bar, by the fire or the log-burner.

Wick Lane
Stanton Wick
Pensford BS39 4BX

T: 01761 490202
E: carpenters@buccaneer.co.uk
W: the-carpenters-arms.co.uk

BEDROOMS: 13.
OPEN: all year except evenings 25/26 Dec, 1 Jan.
FACILITIES: bar, snug, lounge, 2 restaurants, function room, in-room TV (Freeview), patio, secure parking, public areas wheelchair accessible, adapted toilet.
BACKGROUND MUSIC: in some areas.
LOCATION: 8 miles S of Bristol, 8 miles W of Bath.
CHILDREN: all ages welcomed, under-12s stay free, children's menu, high chairs, changing facilities.
DOGS: allowed in bar, snug and outside areas.
CREDIT CARDS: Amex, MC, Visa.
PRICES: B&B doubles from £160, singles from £90. À la carte £38.

Prices may change – check with hotel.

STUDLAND Dorset

MAP 2:E2

THE PIG ON THE BEACH

There is a fairy-tale aspect with more than a hint of Hogwarts to this 1820s marine villa with a sandy beach at the bottom of the garden in a village that inspired Noddy's Toy Town. Hospitality wizard Robin Hutson had long coveted the property, with its jumble of towers and gables, which joined his Pig collection (see index) in 2014. Interiors were created by Judy Hutson for an imaginary great-aunt, an eccentric artist. Bedrooms, with a breezy marine palette, range from snug, with a countryside view, to spacious, with a sea view, super-king bed, monsoon shower and freestanding bath. A thatched 'dovecote' in the kitchen garden has a four-poster and (coo!) its own beach hut. 'My first pig!' writes a reader, who liked 'such pleasing touches as a powerful shower and milk in a fridge'. Produce from the prolific kitchen garden appears in dishes such as rolled porchetta, garden greens and pickled rhubarb or Poole Bay ray wing with caper and parsley brown butter. On the terrace, sourdough pizza comes hot from a wood-fired oven. 'I was blessed with brilliant weather and made full use of the chairs on the lawn and the beach.' (David Sefton)

Manor House
Manor Road
Studland BH19 3AU

T: 01929 450288
E: info@thepighotel.com
W: thepighotel.com

BEDROOMS: 28. Some on ground floor, 2 dovecote hideaways, Harry's Hut and Pig Hut in grounds, 1 suitable for disabled.
OPEN: all year.
FACILITIES: bar, lounge, snug, restaurant, private dining room, in-room TV (Freeview), civil wedding licence, 2 treatment cabins, garden, EV charging, ground-floor public rooms and part of gardens wheelchair accessible, adapted toilet.
BACKGROUND MUSIC: all day in public areas.
LOCATION: above Studland beach.
CHILDREN: all ages welcomed, no charge for extra beds.
DOGS: not allowed.
CREDIT CARDS: Amex, MC, Visa.
PRICES: room-only doubles from £155. Breakfast £13.50–£18.50, à la carte £42. 1-night bookings refused at weekends, Christmas, New Year.

Prices may change – check with hotel.

STURMINSTER NEWTON Dorset

MAP 2:E1

PLUMBER MANOR

For more than 40 years the Prideaux-Brune family have welcomed guests to their ancestral Jacobean manor house in an English country garden with the Divelish stream skipping through. An upgrading programme is now complete, with old bathrooms rooted out and decor refreshed, but the interiors retain their traditional feel, with antiques and blazing fires, and a grand piano in the gallery hung with ancestral portraits. The ambience is of a much-loved home. As well as main-house bedrooms, some with window seats where you can look out over the garden and stream, there are ten spacious rooms in a restored stone barn surrounding a topiary courtyard. Four are dog-friendly; the Prideaux-Brunes' black Labradors make canine visitors feel at home. Richard curates the wine list, while his brother Brian, with head chef Louis Haskell, cooks a varied menu of dishes such as brill with dill and Pernod, carré of lamb with redcurrant jelly; sweet potato, beetroot and spinach Wellington. Relax in a deckchair on the lawn, or bring your gun and join a shooting party. 'A charming oasis in the midst of a hectic world.'

Sturminster Newton DT10 2AF

T: 01258 472507
E: book@plumbermanor.co.uk
W: plumbermanor.co.uk

BEDROOMS: 16. 10 on ground floor in courtyard, 2 suitable for disabled.
OPEN: all year except Feb.
FACILITIES: snug, bar/lounge, dining room, gallery, in-room TV (Freeview), civil wedding licence, 14-acre grounds (3-acre garden, tennis, croquet, stream), EV charging, restaurant, lounge wheelchair accessible, adapted toilet.
BACKGROUND MUSIC: none.
LOCATION: 2½ miles SW of Sturminster Newton.
CHILDREN: all ages welcomed, cots free, extra bed for under-13s £30.
DOGS: allowed in 4 courtyard bedrooms (no charge), not in main house bedrooms or public rooms.
CREDIT CARDS: MC, Visa.
PRICES: B&B doubles from £180, singles from £140. Fixed-price dinner £38–£45 (2/3 courses).

Prices may change – check with hotel.

SWAFFHAM Norfolk

MAP 2:B5

STRATTONS

There is 'an air of a chic curiosity shop' about this singular hotel with café/deli, centred on a Palladian-style villa, up a narrow lane, where resident cats sun themselves on the front lawn. 'The whole place is head-to-toe eccentric, with a whacky interior that somehow works really well,' say our inspectors, who were warmly greeted by name on arrival. Boudoir bedroom was 'suitably luxurious, with a mural of cherubs, a fridge with milk and water, well-stocked minibar, a teapot' but no robe or slippers. A 'more industrial-themed bathroom' had 'a roll-top bath, a separate shower, organic lavender toiletries in glass bottles'. Other rooms have perhaps a woodland mural on the walls, a cinema screen, even a Jacobean four-poster on a plinth. Across the drive, the restaurant, with 'yellow banquettes, modern lighting, wooden tables and open kitchen' features a menu of locally sourced sharing boards and platters. A 'delicious crab starter' was followed by well-composed but poorly executed paella. Breakfast was 'very tasty', with good choices including 'smoked salmon, freshly laid eggs, a full English very nicely done'. NOTE: As the Guide went to press, Strattons announced it was being sold.

4 Ash Close
Swaffham PE37 7NH

T: 01760 723845
E: enquiries@strattonshotel.com
W: strattonshotel.com

BEDROOMS: 14. 6 in annexes, 1 on ground floor (entrance steps), 2 with self-catering facilities.
OPEN: all year except 1 week Christmas.
FACILITIES: drawing room, reading room, restaurant (vegan menu), in-room TV, terrace, café/deli, 1-acre garden, some guest parking, EV charging, café/restaurant wheelchair accessible, adapted toilet.
BACKGROUND MUSIC: all day in public areas.
LOCATION: central, parking.
CHILDREN: all ages welcomed, cot £10, extra bed £25.
DOGS: allowed in some bedrooms (£10 per night), public rooms.
CREDIT CARDS: Amex, MC, Visa.
PRICES: B&B doubles from £119, singles from £92. À la carte £32 (2 courses). Min. 2-night stays at weekends, 3-night bank holidays.

Prices may change – check with hotel.

SWALLOWCLIFFE Wiltshire

MAP 2:D1

THE ROYAL OAK

This 'welcoming hideaway inn' lies off the beaten track in a pretty village amid the Vale of Wardour. The 18th-century part-thatched former tannery and ale house had been standing empty for years when three villagers bought it, spending more than a few tanners on a 'careful renovation'. In October 2020 it relaunched, with Top Gear's James May owning a half-share. Inside, 'the decor has a stylish contemporary rustic simplicity' throughout, with work from local artists on the walls. Unfussy bedrooms are 'really spacious, with oak furniture and a Lloyd loom chair'. Two interconnect for a family, one is dog-friendly, all have fresh coffee with guests given 'milk in a flask'. In the dining room, 'the menu seems limited but changes frequently', with pub classics and more complex dishes such as roast lamb rack, black olive and goat's cheese panisses. Locals come for quiz nights and tasting menu evenings. A 'good breakfast, with all the usual choices' is served in a modern oak-beamed barn with glass panels, 'a successful addition to the rear of the original building' and overlooking a 'large, pleasant, leafy rear garden'.

Common Lane
Swallowcliffe
Salisbury SP3 5PA

T: 01747 870211
E: hello@royaloakswallowcliffe.com
W: royaloakswallowcliffe.com

BEDROOMS: 6. 1 suitable for disabled.
OPEN: all year, but no accommodation 25 Dec evening.
FACILITIES: lift, bar, dining room, Oak Room, in-room TV (Freeview), garden with outdoor seating, public rooms wheelchair accessible, adapted toilet.
BACKGROUND MUSIC: none.
LOCATION: 2 miles SE of Tisbury.
CHILDREN: all ages welcomed, extra bed £15.
DOGS: 'friendly, well-behaved' dogs allowed in 1 bedroom (£15 a night, treats, towels provided), public rooms except Oak Room.
CREDIT CARDS: Amex, MC, Visa.
PRICES: B&B doubles from £100. À la carte £33.

Prices may change – check with hotel.

TALLAND-BY-LOOE Cornwall

TALLAND BAY HOTEL

In 'one of the most idyllic spots ever', this dog-friendly hotel 'near the end of an extremely narrow lane' overlooks pretty cliff-top gardens filled with larky sculpture and Wonderland whimsy. The playfulness extends to zany public spaces inside, where wall sculpture might include a full-size pair of legs or part of a table and chair. Bedrooms have colourful wallpapers and fabrics, perhaps with a nautical or woodland theme. 'Room 20, overlooking the gardens to the sea, had a terrace, a hot tub and plenty of space.' The food gets a big thumbs up, although readers who stayed for a week thought 'it would have been nice if they changed the menu a bit more often'. On Sundays the lunchtime roast appears again at dinner. Typical dishes might include Looe plaice Grenobloise, loin of venison or, if you will, haddock and chips. There is praise for the 'enthusiastic staff' and the easy way they accommodated dietary restrictions. A breakfast of smoked haddock, St Ewe eggs or a full Cornish supplies the ballast for a hike on the South West Coast Path, while later in the day, you can try the hotel's own-label gin on the terrace. (M and EL)

Porthallow
Talland-by-Looe PL13 2JB

T: 01503 272667
E: info@tallandbayhotel.com
W: tallandbayhotel.co.uk

BEDROOMS: 20. 3 in cottages, 6 on ground floor, 2 suitable for disabled. Plus 2-bed self-catering bungalow.
OPEN: all year, except Jan.
FACILITIES: lounge, bar, restaurant, brasserie/conservatory, in-room TV (Freeview), civil wedding licence, terrace, outside seating, 2-acre garden, public rooms wheelchair accessible.
BACKGROUND MUSIC: in bar and restaurant.
LOCATION: 2½ miles SW of Looe.
CHILDREN: all ages welcomed, extra bed £45.
DOGS: in bedrooms (£15 per night) and brasserie, not in restaurant.
CREDIT CARDS: Amex, MC, Visa.
PRICES: B&B doubles from £240, singles from £230. À la carte £52, fixed-price dinner menu £75. 1-night bookings refused at weekends in peak season.

Prices may change – check with hotel.

TAPLOW Berkshire

MAP 2:D3

CLIVEDEN HOUSE

History, opulence and a tantalising whiff of
scandal enrich a stay at this palatial Italianate
mansion in National Trust gardens and parkland.
Designed by Charles Barry for the Duke of
Sutherland, and forever associated with the
'Profumo affair', it is 'a pile with a past'. From
club rooms with a queen-size bed, to hot-tub
rooms and lavish suites, all are furnished with
antiques. Readers' deluxe double 'looked on
to the bin area' but 'our marble bathroom was
luxurious'. The dining room, 'with magnificent
views over the parterre to the Thames, is a
stunning location'. Christopher Hannon's
fine-dining menus include dishes such as estate
venison with chestnut, tamarind and carob; sole
with sorrel, baby turnip and white berries; confit
artichoke with vanilla and preserved lemon. In
the old stables, the Astor Grill is more informal
and affordable, with a menu that includes beer-
battered fish and chips, burgers, gnocchi and rib-
eye steak. 'The pools, indoor and out, and the
spa area are an oasis of calm; we enjoyed them.'
Like its country cousin, Chewton Glen, New
Milton (see entry), this is a Relais & Châteaux
hotel. (Tessa Stuart)

Taplow SL6 0JF

T: 01628 668561
E: reservations@clivedenhouse.co.uk
W: clivedenhouse.co.uk

BEDROOMS: 47. Some on ground floor,
1 suitable for disabled.
OPEN: all year.
FACILITIES: Great Hall, bar/lounge,
library, 2 restaurants (vegetarian/
vegan menus), private dining rooms,
in-room TV (Sky), civil wedding
licence, spa, swimming pools, 376-acre
estate, EV charging, public areas
wheelchair accessible, adapted toilet.
BACKGROUND MUSIC: all day in public
areas.
LOCATION: 20 mins from Heathrow,
40 mins central London.
CHILDREN: all ages, extra bed free in
school holidays.
DOGS: allowed in bedrooms (£35 per
night), most public areas.
CREDIT CARDS: Amex, MC, Visa.
PRICES: B&B doubles from £505.
Tasting menu £95, à la carte £75
(dining room). 1-night bookings
sometimes refused.

Prices may change – check with hotel.

TAVISTOCK Devon

MAP 1:D4

THE HORN OF PLENTY

Gazing over a glorious expanse of the Tamar valley, The Horn of Plenty has garnered praise for gastronomic excellence since it opened as a restaurant in 1967. A hotel since 1985, it outgrew the original Victorian house, to occupy the coach house, then a new 'coach house' annexe. Dual-aspect house room 3 is a favourite, with a balcony, roll-top bath and walk-in shower. Coach house rooms have more contemporary styling. Sought-after room 11 has bifold doors to a west-facing terrace overlooking the walled garden. One reader whose room had 'a sideways view over a sloping field' noted without rancour that 'most others probably had a better view over a lovely valley, best seen from the restaurant'. There, Ashley Lewis's menus feature dishes such as pan-roasted sea bass, mussels and sea vegetables. 'Food and service were good', with 'friendly and welcoming staff'. A dog's dinner awaits your four-legged friend on arrival, while you might treat yourself to a Devonshire cream tea. New owner Jeremy Vincent says he plans to keep everything much the same, but with ongoing refurbishment. (Tony and Shirley Hall, Anthony Bradbury, and others)

Gulworthy
Tavistock PL19 8JD

T: 01822 832528
E: enquiries@thehornofplenty.co.uk
W: thehornofplenty.co.uk

BEDROOMS: 16. 12 in old and new coach houses (1–2 mins' walk), 7 on ground floor, 1 suitable for disabled.
OPEN: all year.
FACILITIES: lounge/bar, library, drawing room, restaurant, in-room TV (Freeview), civil wedding licence, 5-acre grounds, EV charging, ground-floor public areas wheelchair accessible, no adapted toilet.
BACKGROUND MUSIC: occasionally in restaurant, 'when it's quiet'.
LOCATION: 3 miles SW of Tavistock.
CHILDREN: all ages welcomed, extra bed £25.
DOGS: allowed in 12 bedrooms (£15 per night), library, not restaurant or drawing room.
CREDIT CARDS: MC, Visa.
PRICES: B&B doubles from £175. Set-price dinner £60, tasting menu £80.

Prices may change – check with hotel.

TEFFONT EVIAS Wiltshire

HOWARD'S HOUSE

A loyal following of guests returns time and again to this 17th-century house, with stone-mullioned windows in 'a lovely quiet location, with nice gardens'. 'I am delighted to say that all is as good as ever,' reports one, raving about the 'great staff and superb food'. Bedrooms, with a restrained country house feel, are rated 'cosy' and 'superior'; one has a four-poster. One reader, returning after 26 years, found their room 'a wee bit plain' but loved the dishes created by chef Andy Britton, who has worked under Albert Roux and Michael Caines. Starters of 'a fab gazpacho and gorgeous smoked trout were both so good that we repeated them the next evening'. There was 'beautifully cooked salmon on garden peas and lettuce in a delicate cream sauce' and 'although we don't often eat puddings we couldn't resist sharing a crème brûlée'. On cold days a fire burns in an ancient fireplace. Flowers are cut from the garden, where you can take afternoon tea and play croquet. Guests go walking, shooting, stalking, or fish in the River Nadder. 'Staff lovely, coping with timings of our shooting party.' (IGC Farman, Joanna Gibbon, Simon Orlik)

Teffont Evias
Salisbury SP3 5RJ

T: 01722 716392
E: enq@howardshousehotel.co.uk
W: howardshousehotel.co.uk

BEDROOMS: 9.
OPEN: all year except 23–27 Dec.
FACILITIES: lounge, snug, restaurant, function facilities (coach house, adapted toilet), in-room TV (Freeview), 2-acre grounds, public rooms wheelchair accessible.
BACKGROUND MUSIC: in dining room.
LOCATION: 10 miles W of Salisbury.
CHILDREN: all ages welcomed, children's menu, free cot, high chair, extra bed £35.
DOGS: allowed in bedrooms (£15 a night), in public rooms except restaurant.
CREDIT CARDS: MC, Visa.
PRICES: B&B doubles from £155, singles from £100. Tasting menu £80, à la carte £38–£49 (2/3 courses), seasonal menu £28.50–£35.

Prices may change – check with hotel.

TENBURY WELLS Herefordshire

MAP 3:C5

PENSONS

NEW

With just two rooms, Pensons is 'possibly Britain's smallest Michelin-starred restaurant-with-rooms'. Added to the successful restaurant in 2021, they are 'certainly no afterthought', says our inspector. 'As much care has been lavished on them as on the food.' Styled in azurites and sea greens, they are 'compact', with a super-comfy bed and 'a walk-through bathroom behind a statement headboard, fresh milk in the minibar, home-made cookies'. Guests can roam on the Netherwood Estate; there is a deep sense of place here. 'Fabrics are made on the estate's mill, local artists' works hang on bedroom walls, where furniture is made by the estate joiner.' In a double-height beamed barn, walls display 'items unearthed on the estate, including Jacobean smoking pipes and a mammoth set of bellows from the farm forge'. Chris Simpson's estate-to-plate tasting menu was 'exquisite, starting with individual loaves and yeast butter. John Dory with crab butter sauce was particularly good, and a starter of mushroom, hazelnut truffle, artichoke and sourdough was memorable.' In the morning, 'young, smiling staff' serve a 'perfectly cooked' breakfast.

Pensons at The Netherwood Estate
Tenbury Wells WR15 8RT

T: 01885 01885 410333
E: bookings@pensons.co.uk
W: pensons.co.uk

BEDROOMS: 2. In separate building across courtyard.
OPEN: all year, Wed dinner–Sun lunch, closed Christmas.
FACILITIES: restaurant (vegetarian/pescatarian menus), snug, in-room TV, kitchen garden, courtyard, access to 1,200-acre estate, restaurant fully wheelchair accessible, adapted toilet.
BACKGROUND MUSIC: soft jazz in restaurant.
LOCATION: on B4124 halfway between Bromyard and Tenbury Wells.
CHILDREN: all ages welcomed in restaurant, not under 16 in bedrooms.
DOGS: not allowed.
CREDIT CARDS: Amex, MC, Visa.
PRICES: D,B&B doubles £440, single occupancy £345. À la carte lunch £48, nightly tasting menu £95.

Prices may change – check with hotel.

TETBURY Gloucestershire

CALCOT & SPA

Amid 240 acres of native woodland, rewilded organic meadow and grassland, this 16th-century stone manor house offers a real escape to the country. Flagship of the Calcot Collection (see also The Lord Crewe Arms, Blanchland), it is supremely child-friendly, with family suites, a supervised play barn, a pirate ship, mini-football, heated pool, kids' tea, babysitting by arrangement. The rooms range from cosy doubles to family suites. All are decorated in soft, hazy colours, with contemporary furniture and artwork, an espresso machine, fresh fruit and shortbread, a pantry, mini-fridge and Aromatherapy Associates toiletries. It's not cheap, and one reader found their annexe room sunless, but most are light-filled, some even with a private garden. You can eat in the Gumstool Inn and alfresco, or more formally in the Conservatory. Menus are a mix of pub classics and more ambitious dishes, such as Shetland mussels with lemongrass, coconut and chilli; rigatoni with Brecon venison ragout, sweet potato and bean curry. At breakfast there is home-baked bread, and any day now there could be honey from the hives.

Tetbury GL8 8YJ

T: 01666 890391
E: reservations@calcot.co
W: calcot.co

BEDROOMS: 35. 10 (for families) in cottage, 13 around courtyard on ground floor, some suitable for disabled.
OPEN: all year.
FACILITIES: lounge, 2 bars, 2 restaurants, crèche, in-room TV (Sky, Freeview), civil wedding licence, 240-acre grounds (tennis, heated swimming pool), spa (with pool), EV charging, public areas wheelchair accessible, adapted toilet.
BACKGROUND MUSIC: in restaurants.
LOCATION: 3 miles W of Tetbury.
CHILDREN: all ages welcomed, extra bed £40, children's menu (Gumstool).
DOGS: allowed in courtyard bedrooms (no charge), not in public rooms.
CREDIT CARDS: Amex, MC, Visa.
PRICES: B&B doubles from £309.
À la carte (Conservatory) £45, (Gumstool Inn) £35.

Prices may change – check with hotel.

TETBURY Gloucestershire

MAP 3:E5

THE HARE AND HOUNDS

Perfectly placed next to Westonbirt National Arboretum, this Victorian Cotswold stone hotel offers a relaxed family- and dog-friendly break. Built by the arboretum's founder, Robert Stayner Holford, and set in its own lovely gardens and woodland, it is now part of Fuller's Cotswold Inns & Hotels group. There's plenty of character and charm alongside pleasing original features. It is an easy-going place, where you can wander the gardens, play board games in the drawing room, curl up with a book in the library, enjoy a drink and a snack by the log-burner in Jack Hare's bar. 'The staff are excellent and very helpful, the food is very good,' reports a reader, whose extended family had a 'memorable three nights' there. Another reader found the service rather impersonal. In the Beaufort restaurant, a varied menu includes dishes such as sole à la Grenobloise and seaweed potatoes, or torched leek risotto with roasted celeriac and sherry jus. Bedroom choices include singles, large doubles, a suite with an outdoor hot tub. Some of the more contemporary-style rooms in the Silkwood Court annexe have their own garden terrace. (Alice Sennett)

Bath Road
Westonbirt
Tetbury GL8 8QL

T: 01666 881000
E: hareandhounds@
   cotswold-inns-hotels.co.uk
W: cotswold-inns-hotels.co.uk

BEDROOMS: 42. 2 suitable for disabled, 3 in coach house, 5 in garden cottage, 12 in Silkwood Court, 1 in Game Keeper's Cottage.
OPEN: all year.
FACILITIES: drawing room, lounges, library, bar, restaurant, in-room TV (Freeview), function room, business centre, civil wedding licence, gardens, ground-floor public areas wheelchair accessible, adapted toilet.
BACKGROUND MUSIC: in lounge and bar.
LOCATION: 3 miles SW of Tetbury.
CHILDREN: all ages welcomed, extra bed £20.
DOGS: allowed by arrangement in some bedrooms (£20 per night, £10 per extra dog), bar, garden, not in restaurant.
CREDIT CARDS: Amex, MC, Visa.
PRICES: B&B doubles from £150, singles from £140. À la carte £40.

Prices may change – check with hotel.

TETBURY Gloucestershire

MAP 3:E5

THE ROYAL OAK

With quiz nights, a jukebox, a well-patronised bar and a choice of dining spaces, the 18th-century Royal Oak has a lively community feel where both locals and visitors feel welcome. Bedrooms, quietly tucked away across the courtyard in a converted outbuilding, have a modern rustic look of stripped-wood floors, neat wooden furniture and breezy blues and greys. Some are on the cosy side, three are dog-friendly, two have seating areas, one of which is a striking affair with open rafters, mezzanine and in-room bath. Sample one of the local real ales or maybe a signature cocktail before dining, either in the courtyard, the convivial bar with its upcycled furniture or in the upstairs restaurant below the rafters. (Dogs are welcome in the bar and outside.) Modern European dishes with an American flavour include harissa pulled lamb, fried halloumi with chilli jam, and one-pot stews, plus a strong selection of vegan dishes such as the popular superfood burger. In summer, world street food is dispensed from a silver Airstream trailer. Breakfast includes bread from a nearby artisan bakery and eggs Benedict.

1 Cirencester Road
Tetbury GL8 8EY

T: 01666 500021
E: stay@theroyaloaktetbury.co.uk
W: theroyaloaktetbury.co.uk

BEDROOMS: 6. In annexe, 3 on ground floor, 1 suitable for disabled.
OPEN: all year except 1 week Jan, kitchen closed Mon/Tues, Sun eve.
FACILITIES: bar, restaurant, private dining/meeting room, in-room TV, courtyard, garden, parking, bar and garden wheelchair accessible, adapted toilet.
BACKGROUND MUSIC: in bar and restaurant, free jukebox, monthly live music sessions.
LOCATION: a few mins' walk up the hill from the town centre.
CHILDREN: all ages welcomed, extra bed £30, children's menu.
DOGS: allowed in ground-floor bedrooms (no charge), bar and courtyard.
CREDIT CARDS: Amex, MC, Visa.
PRICES: B&B doubles from £95. À la carte £32. 1-night bookings usually refused Fri and Sat.

Prices may change – check with hotel.

THORNBURY Gloucestershire

MAP 3:E5

THORNBURY CASTLE

Playing Kings and Queens is more than a fantasy at this Tudor castle 'where you can feel the history in the thick walls', along with turrets, oriel windows, spiral staircase and grand fireplaces. Henry VIII, Anne Boleyn and Mary Tudor have all bedded down here – and you too can sleep in the portly king's tower suite with four-poster, ornate ceiling plus loo in the original garderobe. 'It's all very regal.' Even modest bedrooms might have a four-poster bed as well as lavish curtains. The castle has been beautifully brought up to date with 'a touch of contemporary style among the olde-worlde splendour'. Chandeliers, modern frescoes and tartan-patterned chairs now rub shoulders with brocade in the palatial public rooms. Power showers sit alongside arrow-slit windows in bathrooms; all rooms have sloe gin and fresh milk. Take a turn in the walled garden before drinks in the fire-warmed drawing room and dinner, 'served with some ceremony' in the panelled dining room; perhaps Loch Duart salmon followed by pork with celeriac and apple. 'Most impressive is the friendly, welcoming attitude of the staff.' Member of Relais & Châteaux.

Castle Street
Thornbury BS35 1HH

T: 01454 281182
E: info@thornburycastle.co.uk
W: thornburycastle.co.uk

BEDROOMS: 27. Some across courtyard, 2 on ground floor suitable for disabled.
OPEN: all year.
FACILITIES: lounge, library, dining rooms (vegetarian menu), in-room TV, treatment room, civil wedding licence, 15-acre grounds (walled garden, meadow), partially wheelchair accessible, adapted toilets.
BACKGROUND MUSIC: classical in public rooms.
LOCATION: 15 miles N of Bristol.
CHILDREN: aged 8 and over welcomed, no charge for extra bed.
DOGS: allowed in some bedrooms (£15 per night), public areas, not dining rooms.
CREDIT CARDS: Amex, MC, Visa.
PRICES: B&B doubles from £279, singles from £249. À la carte £78, tasting menus £72 and £82. 1-night stays sometimes refused at peak times.

Prices may change – check with hotel.

THORPE MARKET Norfolk

THE GUNTON ARMS

'A fun take on a gallery crossed with an old boozer, and a good-value one at that', a former steward's house in a 1,000-acre deer park is now an 'anything-but-traditional' pub-with-rooms, say inspectors. It is owned by art dealer Ivor Braka, with provocative works by the likes of Emin and Hirst on casual display. A room in a rustic annexe was 'the height of granny chic, with standard lamp, Roberts radio, patterned curtains, a colourful rug on sisal flooring, an enormous roll-top bath and large walk-in shower'. You can eat and drink in 'a series of beguiling rooms with flagstones or floorboards'. In the Elk Room, huge prehistoric antlers hang above a blazing fire, where estate venison and local beef are flame-grilled every day but Sundays. A menu strong on seafood brought 'rich but delicate wild garlic and potato soup, delicious cod with fish fingers, beef sirloin – a Sunday roast as it should be'. A slightly sparse breakfast buffet was amply compensated for by 'a generous portion of smoked salmon with scrambled eggs and sourdough toast' and the 'friendly, helpful staff'. Sadly, 'guests can't ramble on the estate'.

Cromer Road
Thorpe Market NR11 8TZ

T: 01263 832010
E: office@theguntonarms.co.uk
W: theguntonarms.co.uk

BEDROOMS: 16. 4 in coach house, 1 suitable for disabled, 4 suites in barn.
OPEN: all year except 25 Dec, dinner on 1 Jan.
FACILITIES: 3 restaurants, 3 lounges, bar, TVs in bar and lounges, set in privately owned 1,000-acre deer park, public rooms wheelchair accessible, adapted toilet.
BACKGROUND MUSIC: in bar area.
LOCATION: 5 miles from Cromer, 4 miles from North Walsham.
CHILDREN: all ages welcomed, extra beds and cots £15, plus 2 family rooms.
DOGS: allowed in some bedrooms (£10), public rooms, not in Elk Room.
CREDIT CARDS: Amex, MC, Visa.
PRICES: B&B doubles from £99, singles from £89. À la carte £32–£40. Min. 2-night stays on Sat.

Prices may change – check with hotel.

TISBURY Wiltshire

MAP 2:D1

THE BECKFORD ARMS

The bar was 'buzzing with convivial chatter' when readers arrived at this Georgian dining pub-with-rooms on the edge of rolling parkland on the Fonthill Estate. It was here that Dan Brod and Charlie Luxton set the template for a handful of similarly fun, laid-back, brilliant boozers (see The Talbot Inn, Mells; The Lord Poulett Arms, Hinton St George; and The Bath Arms, Horningsham). These are very 'people' places, with valued, motivated staff. 'James, the manager, is seemingly everywhere, sorting problems calmly and effortlessly.' Bedrooms have a stripped-back stylishness, home-made treats, Bramley toiletries, a restful palette. Some have an in-room freestanding bath. Attic rooms will sleep a family while self-catering lodges are a walk away, on the estate. The food is a mix of pub classics (a ploughman's perhaps, or cider-battered fish and chips), and dishes such as roasted venison loin, black pudding croquette, celeriac purée, cavolo nero, blackberries. Wash it down with a glass of their own Beckford Phoenix. In winter, log fires burn, in summer there are alfresco pizzas and barbecues. A 'relaxed breakfast' brings eggs from very happy hens. (Tessa Stuart)

Fonthill Gifford
Tisbury SP3 6PX

T: 01747 870385
E: info@beckfordarms.com
W: beckfordarms.com

BEDROOMS: 10. 2 in lodges on the Fonthill Estate.
OPEN: all year except 25 Dec.
FACILITIES: sitting room (sometimes Sunday classic-movie nights), bar, restaurant, private dining room, in-room TV (Freeview), function facilities, 1-acre garden, parking.
BACKGROUND MUSIC: in public areas all day.
LOCATION: in village, 1 mile N of Tisbury.
CHILDREN: all ages welcomed, travel cot £10, over-3s £25, family room, no children under 8 in lodges.
DOGS: allowed in 1 bedroom by arrangement (£10) and public areas.
CREDIT CARDS: MC, Visa.
PRICES: B&B doubles from £105, family room from £135 (lodges £195). À la carte £40. 1-night bookings usually refused at weekends (but check).

Prices may change – check with hotel.

SEE ALSO SHORTLIST

TITCHWELL Norfolk

MAP 2:A5

TITCHWELL MANOR

With views over meadows and marshes to the sea, this hotel with award-winning dining bedazzles with its vibrant interiors within the walls of a Victorian farmhouse. Behind the scenes, bedrooms have more of a Hamptons-style coastal cool. Dog-friendly ground-floor rooms in the herb garden have a hot tub while two shepherds' huts have a log-burner, a shower, a terrace with sunken spa bath. 'Our room was warm and cosy, with an arched window overlooking a wall with grapes dangling,' readers report. Dine casually in the eating rooms, or more formally in the 'beautifully decorated' conservatory. Chef/proprietor Eric Snaith's parents bought the hotel back in 1988, so he had plenty of time to hone his cooking skills. Having enjoyed a meal at his chippie down the road in Thornham, our readers were disappointed with the hotel fish and chips, but they were replaced without question with a duck dish that was 'absolutely wonderful, cooked perfectly, with a layered potato, sprout tops and delicious jus'. Breakfast, served by 'really cheery staff', was 'the best we have enjoyed in a hotel for a good few years'. (Kevin and Victoria Seymour, SP)

Titchwell
Brancaster PE31 8BB

T: 01485 210221
E: info@titchwellmanor.com
W: titchwellmanor.com

BEDROOMS: 28. 12 in herb garden, 3 in stables, 1 in Potting Shed, 2 in shepherds' huts, 18 on ground floor, 2 suitable for disabled.
OPEN: all year.
FACILITIES: lounge, bar, conservatory, restaurant, in-room TV, civil wedding licence, in-room treatments, ¼-acre walled garden, public rooms wheelchair accessible, adapted toilet.
BACKGROUND MUSIC: in restaurant and bar.
LOCATION: off A149 between Burnham Market and Hunstanton.
CHILDREN: all ages welcomed, extra bed £25.
DOGS: allowed in some rooms (£15 per night), bar, not lounge or restaurant.
CREDIT CARDS: Amex, MC, Visa.
PRICES: B&B doubles from £146, singles £131. À la carte £45. 1-night bookings occasionally refused.

Prices may change – check with hotel.

TITLEY Herefordshire

MAP 3:C4

THE STAGG INN

A former local boozer in a rural village where two drovers' roads meet, The Stagg made history in 2001 when it became the first repurposed village pub to gain a Michelin star. Now Steve and Nicola Reynolds, who put the place on the map, have handed over to an enthusiastic new owner, Sri Lankan-born Muralidhar Shanmugam ('Shan'), while long-serving chef Matthew Handley remains in the kitchen. Along with pub classics (not on offer on Friday and Saturday nights), his menus feature dishes such as duck breast and spiced poached rhubarb or perhaps roast cauliflower, spiced cauliflower purée and cauliflower couscous. Occasional 'Taste of Sri Lanka' evenings showcase Shan's native cuisine. There are four simple, cottage-style beamed bedrooms above the pub, three with a bath, one with a walk-in shower. All have tea- and coffee-making facilities, and if you want a beer in the afternoon when the pub is closed, there will be someone to pull you a pint. The inn was once known as The Balance when farmers came here to weigh their wool. Having weighed the evidence in the balance, the Guide believes it will continue on good gastronomic form.

Titley
Kington HR5 3RL

T: 01544 230221
E: reservations@thestagg.co.uk
W: thestagg.co.uk

BEDROOMS: 4.
OPEN: all year, Wed–Sat, Sun lunch, except 24–26 Dec, 1 Jan, 1 week Jan/Feb, 1 week June, 2 weeks Nov.
FACILITIES: bar, dining room, small outside seating area, in-room TV (Freeview), wheelchair access to bar and lower dining area via fire exits, no accessible toilet.
BACKGROUND MUSIC: in bar.
LOCATION: on B4355 between Kington and Presteigne.
CHILDREN: all ages welcomed, extra bed £15.
DOGS: allowed in bedrooms (£10 per dog), public rooms.
CREDIT CARDS: Amex, MC, Visa.
PRICES: B&B doubles from £100. À la carte £37. 1-night bookings occasionally refused at bank holiday weekends.

Prices may change – check with hotel.

TORQUAY Devon

MAP 1:D5

THE 25 BOUTIQUE B&B

This delightfully eccentric boutique B&B, a stroll from Torquay's seafront, has won numerous awards for its singular style and luxurious standards. Run with great warmth by Andy and Julian Banner-Price, it is known for its funky features, state-of-the-art touches and fastidious attention to detail. Bedrooms and suites are strikingly decorated: perhaps a zebra head above an Art Deco-style bedhead, an oversized silver headboard against a sparkly purple wall, or a giant orange gerbera mural and tangerine-accented furniture. All have smart room controls, bathrobes, coffee machines and daily home-made treats, while bathrooms, with power showers – two also with baths – are sleek in grey and white. Relax with a drink from the honesty bar in the Edwardian-style drawing room or on the terrace with its palms and chic furniture. Breakfast is a feast, with home-made granola and smoothies, eggs scrambled with butter and cream, sausage muffins, and the full English with vegan and vegetarian options. Order a tapas-style 'grazing box' (48 hours' notice required) for evenings in or picnics, or Andy and Julian will advise on local restaurants.

25 Avenue Road
Torquay TQ2 5LB

T: 01803 297517
E: stay@the25.uk
W: the25.uk

BEDROOMS: 5.
OPEN: April–end Oct.
FACILITIES: drawing room, dining room, in-room smart TV, patio, EV charging, parking.
BACKGROUND MUSIC: at breakfast.
LOCATION: 5 mins' walk from the sea, 20 mins' walk from town.
CHILDREN: not under 17.
DOGS: not allowed.
CREDIT CARDS: Amex, MC, Visa.
PRICES: B&B doubles from £169. Min. 2-night stay, 3 nights in high season, but check availability.

Prices may change – check with hotel.

SEE ALSO SHORTLIST

TUDDENHAM Suffolk

MAP 2:B5

TUDDENHAM MILL

The setting is pure Nellie Dean, with an old watermill by a stream in 12 acres of meadow. Run by chef/patron Lee Bye, it offers 'top-notch cooking' in a 'beautiful hotel' and a whole menu of accommodation. In the mill building are rustic-chic rooms and Scandi-cool suites, with double-ended stone bath, walk-in shower and whizzy sound system. Distinctly Nordic Meadow Nooks, two with cedar hot tubs, have French doors on to decking. One reader had a 'good-sized room overlooking the water meadows with an outside patio area' with a 'comfortable bed', but felt that the 'big bathroom was poorly lit'. The spirit is generous, though, with king-size bed, fresh coffee and orange juice, and designer robes as standard. Take a culinary glossary to dine in the oak-beamed restaurant, among the mill mechanisms, on dishes such as stone bass, guanciale, wild leeks, agretti. If you want more choice, you can eat under canvas at Tipi on the Stream, warmed by a fire pit. Maybe Brancaster Staithe mussels, white wine, garlic; Baron Bigod bun, field mushroom, truffle, pit-roasted beets, fries. 'Breakfast was great, with a very generous fruit salad.'

High Street
Tuddenham
Newmarket IP28 6SQ

T: 01638 713552
E: info@tuddenhammill.co.uk
W: tuddenhammill.co.uk

BEDROOMS: 21. 18 in 2 separate buildings, 8 on ground floor, 6 in pods in meadow, 2 with hot tub, 1 suitable for disabled.
OPEN: all year.
FACILITIES: bar/snug, restaurant (vegetarian menu), tipi dining area, function rooms, in-room TV (Freeview), civil wedding licence, 12-acre meadow, bar area wheelchair accessible, adapted toilet.
BACKGROUND MUSIC: in bar, reception and restaurant.
LOCATION: in village, 8 miles NE of Newmarket.
CHILDREN: all ages welcomed, extra bed £25, children's menu.
DOGS: allowed in some bedrooms (£25 a night), bar.
CREDIT CARDS: MC, Visa.
PRICES: B&B doubles from £165. À la carte £45 (Tipi £30), 5-course tasting menu £65, vegetarian £59. Min. 2-night stay at weekends.

Prices may change – check with hotel.

ULLSWATER Cumbria

MAP 4: inset C2

HOWTOWN HOTEL

If you want a hotel with hi-tech wizardry and hot tubs, this place is not for you, but 'if you are happy with traditional hospitality' and 'like to be cosseted, Howtown Hotel will do nicely'. On the shores of Ullswater, the creeper-covered former farmhouse, owned by the Baldry family for more than 120 years, is renowned for its old-fashioned customs (luggage taken care of, early-morning tea room service) balanced with a 'personal touch' – Mrs Baldry is much in evidence. Comfortable bedrooms (no TVs or door locks), with 'lovely views over the gardens', have blankets not duvets and Imperial Leather in the bathrooms; no shampoo but plenty of hot water for a soak after a day's walking. There are hikes from the door as well as lakeside strolls. Return to one of the fire-warmed lounges, with 'welcoming armchairs', copper pans and country antiques, or a drink in the oak-panelled and red-velvet bar. A gong announces a four-course dinner of classic dishes such as Stilton soufflé and 'duckling breast with a splendidly sharp apple sauce'. The duck-egg-blue dining room is a treat of silver cutlery and polished-wood tables. 'I loved it.' (Mary Hewson)

Ullswater
Penrith CA10 2ND

T: 01768 486514
W: howtown-hotel.com

BEDROOMS: 15. 2 in annexe, plus 4 self-catering cottages.
OPEN: end Mar–early Nov.
FACILITIES: 3 lounges, TV room, 2 bars, dining room, tea room, Wi-Fi (bedrooms, 1 lounge, cottages and tea room), 2-acre grounds, 200 yds from lake (private foreshore, fishing), restaurant wheelchair accessible, toilet not adapted.
BACKGROUND MUSIC: none.
LOCATION: 4 miles S of Pooley Bridge, bus from Penrith station 9 miles.
CHILDREN: all ages welcomed, call for prices.
DOGS: allowed in some bedrooms (£7 per night), not in public rooms.
CREDIT CARDS: MC, Visa.
PRICES: D,B&B doubles from £300 (reduced for 4- and 7-night stays), B&B prices on request. 4-course dinner £45 (Sun 'cold table' £28).

Prices may change – check with hotel.

UPPER SLAUGHTER Gloucestershire

MAP 3:D6

LORDS OF THE MANOR

A luxury afternoon tea in gardens on the River Eye and fine dining in the evening are among the sybaritic pleasures to be enjoyed at this Cotswold-stone former rectory. Past incumbents, the Witts, rectors-turned-squires and prodigious diarists, did not stint themselves; why should you? Bedrooms are chic, with soft-hued decor, good fabrics, some well-judged antiques. Those in the main house, including the big, bay-windowed Lords rooms, overlook the grounds, while those in the stables and granary have views of the village or courtyard. There is a bar menu for light lunches, while in the dining room à la carte menus for omnivores and vegans include dishes such as pea and spring onion risotto; lamb rump, champ, Wye valley asparagus, artichoke. Head chef Charles Smith's creative tasting menus are available in the more formal Atrium. In summer the meadow is spangled with wild flowers; bees buzz in the lavender. By autumn, in the walled garden, espaliered fruit trees are heavy with apples and pears. Non-residents can book a guided tour; residents are free to roam. 'What a beautiful hotel and grounds; an absolute delight.' (Ralph Wilson)

Upper Slaughter GL54 2JD

T: 01451 820243
E: reservations@lordsofthemanor.com
W: lordsofthemanor.com

BEDROOMS: 25. 15 in granary and stables.
OPEN: all year.
FACILITIES: lounges, bar, 2 restaurants (vegan menu), library, games room, in-room TV (Freeview), civil wedding licence, 8-acre grounds, EV charging, some public rooms wheelchair accessible, no adapted toilet.
BACKGROUND MUSIC: in lounge bar and restaurant.
LOCATION: in village, 2 miles N of Bourton-on-the-Water.
CHILDREN: all ages welcomed, cot £10, for under-13s extra bed £50.
DOGS: allowed in some bedrooms (£30 charge), public rooms, not restaurant.
CREDIT CARDS: Amex, MC, Visa.
PRICES: B&B doubles from £155. À la carte £45, vegan £35, tasting menu £105. 1-night bookings refused mid-summer Sat.

Prices may change – check with hotel.

UPPINGHAM Rutland   MAP 2:B3

LAKE ISLE

Tucked away in the oldest part of Uppingham,
this 18th-century whitewashed former shop
is a welcoming restaurant-with-rooms with
large dining-room windows overlooking the
High Street. The name? A previous restaurant
owner named it after the WB Yeats poem. Run
by Richard and Janine Burton, it continues to
build on its culinary reputation. 'The menu was
imaginative and the locally sourced food was
excellently cooked,' reports a reader. Dishes could
include a starter of beetroot and juniper-cured
salmon with horseradish sorbet and main courses
such as grilled sea bass with samphire pakora and
mussels, or guineafowl with salt-baked celeriac.
There's an impressive wine list, too. Breakfast
doesn't disappoint, with a 'wide and appealing
choice' that runs to salmon and smoked haddock
fishcakes, cheese omelette and the full English.
Bedrooms are bright with feature wallpapers
and pale-washed furniture; they are 'really
comfortable', though most are on the cosy side.
Larger rooms have a spa bath, while two cottages
in the courtyard are suitable for families. 'The
staff were all friendly and helpful, and the town
is lovely.' (Sara Price)

16 High Street East
Uppingham LE15 9PZ

T: 01572 822951
E: info@lakeisle.co.uk
W: lakeisle.co.uk

BEDROOMS: 11. 2 in cottages, 1 sleeps
3/4.
OPEN: all year, except 26–30 Dec, Sun
night and all day Mon, incl. bank
holidays.
FACILITIES: bar, restaurant, courtyard
(alfresco dining), in-room TV
(Freeview), small car park, unsuitable
for disabled.
BACKGROUND MUSIC: in restaurant.
LOCATION: town centre.
CHILDREN: all ages welcomed, extra
bed £15, children's portions.
DOGS: allowed in cottage bedrooms
(£15 a night), not in public areas.
CREDIT CARDS: Amex, MC, Visa.
PRICES: B&B doubles from £100,
cottages from £140. À la carte £45.

Prices may change – check with hotel.

VENTNOR Isle of Wight

MAP 2:E2

HILLSIDE

It may look traditional but this 18th-century thatched country house, with a long conservatory overlooking the sea, has a pleasing Scandi-chic style thanks to its charismatic, art-loving Danish owner, Gert Bach. Rooms of stripped-oak floors, white walls and monochrome furnishings provide an elegant backdrop for Gert's collection of abstract art. Fresh flowers, colourful rugs, bold lighting and a wood-burning stove prevent it from feeling too stark. It 'feels more like a home than a hotel, albeit an incredibly chic one'. Bedrooms, most with sea views, are minimalist (white walls, wood floors), light-filled and have more art, plus 'seriously comfortable' beds covered with bright woollen blankets. Bathrooms are compact; tea/coffee is available downstairs and charged for. The garden with pond and fire pit is perfect for drinks before a simple, tasty two-course supper of dishes such as bouillabaisse and IOW ice cream, roasted trout and lemon brûlée tart; much produce is from the kitchen garden. Their hens produce the eggs for breakfast, a 'surprisingly good' feast with bircher muesli, local sausage and bacon, plates of cheese and meat.

151 Mitchell Avenue,
Ventnor PO38 1DR

T: 01983 852271
E: mail@hillsideventnor.co.uk
W: hillsideventnor.co.uk

BEDROOMS: 12. Plus self-catering apartment.
OPEN: all year.
FACILITIES: restaurant, 2 lounges, conservatory, in-room TV (Freeview), terrace, 5-acre garden (vegetable garden, sheep, beehives), close to tennis club, golf, EV charging, unsuitable for disabled.
BACKGROUND MUSIC: in restaurant in evening but 'not if not wished'.
LOCATION: above village centre.
CHILDREN: not under 12.
DOGS: not allowed.
CREDIT CARDS: MC, Visa.
PRICES: B&B doubles from £176, singles from £88. Brasserie 2 courses £28. Min. 2-night bookings preferred.

Prices may change – check with hotel.

VENTNOR Isle of Wight

MAP 2:E2

THE ROYAL HOTEL

Afternoon tea in the conservatory or on the terrace overlooking sub-tropical gardens is one of many highlights of this venerable Victorian hotel whose legions of loyal guests book their favourite room year after year. With 'lovely rooms looking out over the sea', spacious and elegant public rooms, and staff who are 'so very kind and efficient', many guests feel that 'the Royal is just perfect'. Head gardener Gary Steptoe even dispenses free gardening advice. 'Very comfortable' bedrooms are either classic country house with pretty wallpapers and fabrics, or more contemporary. 'We had a very generous sea view.' Evening meals in the dining room, with its opulent curtains, chandeliers, starched linen and garden views, is a real event. Classic dishes with a modern twist, which some guests rate as 'the best meal' they have eaten, might include monkfish with guacamole and sweet potato, or lamb with pommes Anna and butter lettuce. Other readers would have liked more variety during their six-night stay. Breakfast does not disappoint. Guests who were 'particularly taken with the gardens' often ate theirs outside. (Tony Hall, David Sowden, MW, AS)

Belgrave Road
Ventnor PO38 1JJ

T: 01983 852186
E: enquiries@royalhoteliow.co.uk
W: royalhoteliow.co.uk

BEDROOMS: 51. 1 suitable for disabled.
OPEN: all year.
FACILITIES: lift, lounge, bar, 2 restaurants (vegetarian/vegan menu), conservatory, function rooms, in-room TV, civil wedding licence, terrace, 2-acre grounds, outdoor heated pool, EV charging, public areas/toilet wheelchair accessible.
BACKGROUND MUSIC: in public areas, pianist on peak-season weekends.
LOCATION: short walk from centre.
CHILDREN: all ages welcomed, family rooms, no under-4s at dinner.
DOGS: allowed in some bedrooms (£25 a night, welcome pack), not in restaurants.
CREDIT CARDS: Amex, MC, Visa.
PRICES: B&B doubles from £220, singles from £110, family from £245. Dinner £45. Min. 2-night stay on peak weekends.

Prices may change – check with hotel.

VERYAN-IN-ROSELAND Cornwall

MAP 1:D2

THE NARE

'A year spent without a visit to The Nare is a year wasted,' writes a returning guest of this perennially popular country house hotel overlooking the sands of Carne Bay. Owned by the Ashworth family for more than 30 years, the child- and dog-friendly hotel is traditional yet luxurious. Comfortable, fire-warmed lounges have tartan carpets, bright wallpapers and are hung with political cartoons. Daily complimentary cream tea can be taken inside or on the terrace overlooking lush gardens and sea. 'If this level of thoughtful comfort is "old-fashioned" then count me in!' declares another regular. Large, light bedrooms, many with 'breathtaking' sea views, are elegantly traditional with antiques, and armchairs or sofas. Flowers, fruit and hot-water bottles are standard; 'one of the best-appointed and -furnished rooms we have had anywhere'. Dine either in the jolly Quarterdeck restaurant or the more formal Dining Room on a five-course daily-changing menu with hors d'oeuvre trolley, tableside flame-grilling and dishes such as Portloe lobster and butter-roasted guineafowl. Generous breakfasts mean 'no need for lunch!' (Peter Govier, AK-H, IW)

Carne Beach
Veryan-in-Roseland TR2 5PF

T: 01872 501111
E: stay@narehotel.co.uk
W: narehotel.co.uk

BEDROOMS: 40. Some on ground floor, 1 in cottage, 5 suitable for disabled.
OPEN: all year.
FACILITIES: lift, lounge, drawing room, sun lounge, bar, library, 2 restaurants, conservatory, in-room TV, gym, indoor and outdoor swimming pools, 2-acre grounds, 2 boats, tennis, croquet, EV charging, public rooms wheelchair accessible, adapted toilet.
BACKGROUND MUSIC: none.
LOCATION: 1 mile SW of Veryan.
CHILDREN: all ages welcomed, extra bed £99, no under-7s for evening dining, early suppers available.
DOGS: allowed in bedrooms (£20–£30 a night) and gardens, not in public areas.
CREDIT CARDS: Amex, MC, Visa.
PRICES: B&B doubles from £360, singles from £192. Fixed-price dinner £60.

Prices may change – check with hotel.

WADEBRIDGE Cornwall

MAP 1:D2

TREWORNAN MANOR

A 'delightful B&B up a curving drive, through verdant grounds', Paul and Lesley Stapleton's 'lovely old stone manor house' wins rapturous praise from readers. One thought he saw chef Gordon Ramsay checking it out 'as well he might. Paul Stapleton is a brilliant host and runs the hotel with personal attention to every detail.' Another reader was welcomed with 'tea and home-made lemon cake in the lounge', where 'a fire blazed on a cold, wet day'. Bedrooms, each with an emperor bed, are 'beautifully decorated in muted shades'. Annexe room Finisterre has a separate lounge, a bath and walk-in shower. The smallest, Lundy, had 'a window seat with squashy cushions, little jars of jelly babies and flapjacks' on the tea tray, and 'a huge shower, bathrobe, lovely toiletries'. 'Friendly, efficient' staff even called a reader en route to Cornwall when they heard a last-minute reservation was available in an oversubscribed restaurant he was desperate to visit. 'Breakfast as good as it gets. Table service with generous menu including pastries, smashed avocado on toast, blueberry pancakes, all the usual cooked items.' (Jill Cox, David Hampshire)

Trewornan Bridge
St Minver
Wadebridge PL27 6EX

T: 01208 812359
E: info@trewornanmanor.co.uk
W: trewornanmanor.co.uk

BEDROOMS: 7. 2 in courtyard annexe, 1 on ground floor.
OPEN: all year.
FACILITIES: lounge, snug, dining room, in-room TV (Freeview), civil wedding licence, 25-acre grounds with 8-acre gardens.
BACKGROUND MUSIC: in dining room, lounge at breakfast and evening.
LOCATION: 1 mile N of Wadebridge.
CHILDREN: not under 14.
DOGS: not allowed.
CREDIT CARDS: MC, Visa.
PRICES: B&B doubles from £160, singles from £145.

Prices may change – check with hotel.

WAREHAM Dorset

MAP 2:E1

THE PRIORY

There's certainly nothing monastic about the rooms in this much-loved hotel, standing in four acres of 'beautiful grounds' bordered by the River Frome beside the Saxon priory church. 'Our room exceeded expectations,' writes a reader who stayed in one of the Boat House suites with French doors to a riverside veranda. 'It was beautifully decorated and furnished with polished wood and various artefacts, a super-comfortable bed.' The bathroom had a walk-in shower and what our reader considered to be a slightly impractical spa bath ('the idea was nice, though'). Bedrooms in the main building all have their own character, perhaps toile de Jouy wallpaper and fabrics. Some have views over the garden to the river, others overlook an inner courtyard. In the 'beautiful, airy, modern' new Garden restaurant, Stephan Guinebault's menus include dishes such as turbot, watercress and crème fraîche crushed potatoes. 'The food is particularly good' and service is 'friendly and attentive', although one reader disliked the 'anodyne piped music'. Breakfast brings 'lovely fruit salad and cooked options'. (Jill Cox, Edward Gosnell, and others)

Church Green
Wareham BH20 4ND

T: 01929 551666
E: reservations@theprioryhotel.co.uk
w: theprioryhotel.co.uk

BEDROOMS: 17. Some on ground floor, 4 suites in Boat House, 1 suitable for disabled.
OPEN: all year. Restaurant closed lunch Mon, Tues.
FACILITIES: sitting room, drawing room, snug bar, 2 dining rooms (vegetarian menu), in-room TV (Freeview), spa treatments, 4½-acre gardens, parking, EV charging, restaurant wheelchair accessible, adapted toilet.
BACKGROUND MUSIC: in public rooms, pianist in drawing room Sat evenings and 'special occasions'.
LOCATION: town centre.
CHILDREN: not under 14.
DOGS: not allowed.
CREDIT CARDS: Amex, MC, Visa.
PRICES: B&B doubles from £220, singles from £176. Fixed-price dinner £62. 1-night bookings refused at high season, peak weekends.

Prices may change – check with hotel.

WELLS-NEXT-THE-SEA Norfolk

THE CROWN

At 'a dream address on a square of Georgian houses overlooking a green', this former coaching inn 'feels busy, jolly, and as popular with the locals as with visiting guests'. There is an interesting choice of bedrooms, some in the old living quarters at the rear. The jewel in the Crown, a rooftop suite has a copper bath on a large balcony, though our inspectors were very happy with their more modest room, which had 'lots of interesting touches – a velvet headboard in the shape of an Indian cusp, wooden Venetian blinds, an antique mirrored door on the wall, three little beds for children on an ingeniously designed mezzanine'. Chef/proprietor Chris Coubrough 'clearly loves what he does and runs a happy, tight ship'. A dog-friendly dining area was 'packed with diners, and the odd snoozing Labrador'. In 'a large, light extension with book-lined shelves', a short, modern menu was 'appetising, with plenty of local fish'. For instance, pan-roasted cod on a warm salad of Parmentier potatoes, roast beetroot, green beans, pesto. 'Breakfast brought all the usual favourites, freshly squeezed orange juice, good scrambled eggs.'

The Buttlands
Wells-next-the-Sea NR23 1EX

T: 01328 710209
E: info@crownhotelnorfolk.co.uk
W: crownhotelnorfolk.co.uk

BEDROOMS: 20. 5 in annexe, 2 in barn, 3 on ground floor, 1 suitable for wheelchair-user (wet-room shower, terrace).
OPEN: all year.
FACILITIES: bar, 3 dining rooms, terrace, in-room TV, parking, orangery wheelchair accessible, adapted toilet.
BACKGROUND MUSIC: none.
LOCATION: central, on the Buttlands.
CHILDREN: all ages welcomed, cot £15, extra bed for under-16s £35.
DOGS: allowed in most bedrooms (£10 per night), some public rooms.
CREDIT CARDS: Amex, MC, Visa.
PRICES: B&B doubles from £165, singles from £140. À la carte £40, tasting menu £54.95.

Prices may change – check with hotel.

WEST HOATHLY Sussex

MAP 2:E4

THE CAT INN

'Fabulous as ever', this 16th-century, timber-frame and tile-clad pub-with-rooms has everything you could look for in a village local and makes a good base for exploring the South Downs national park. Several trusted readers stay regularly. We hear high praise of 'great host' Andrew Russell and his 'friendly and efficient' staff. Within, you find oak beams, inglenooks, real ales and quirky contemporary art. Bedroom style is a mix of contemporary and country chic, each with a coffee machine, leaf tea, fresh milk and smart toiletries. One split-level suite has a dining area. 'We stayed in bedroom 3 overlooking the church. Simply but well appointed.' 'Our dog was made most welcome.' Food is served in the dining room and cosy corners, or on the terrace. 'The menu would do justice to a fine-dining restaurant, with seasonal asparagus, Shetland mussels, stone bass alongside steak, mushroom and ale pie', 'superb beer-battered fish and chips'. 'Breakfasts are heroic; muesli, fresh fruit and yogurt followed by a freshly cooked full English.' 'We have already booked to return.' (Simon Rodway, Chris Savory, Idris White, and others)

North Lane
West Hoathly RH19 4PP

T: 01342 810369
E: thecatinn@googlemail.com
W: catinn.co.uk

BEDROOMS: 4.
OPEN: all year except Mon, Tues, 24–26 Dec, lunch only on 1 Jan.
FACILITIES: bar, 3 dining areas, in-room TV (Freeview), terrace (alfresco meals), parking, restaurant wheelchair accessible, adapted toilet.
BACKGROUND MUSIC: none.
LOCATION: in village.
CHILDREN: not under 7 (unless 'well-behaved').
DOGS: allowed in bedrooms (£10 per night), bar, specific dining area.
CREDIT CARDS: Amex, MC, Visa.
PRICES: B&B doubles from £150, singles from £105. À la carte £35.

Prices may change – check with hotel.

WHITEWELL Lancashire   MAP 4:D3

THE INN AT WHITEWELL

Overlooking the River Hodder in the Forest of
Bowland, this sprawling 18th-century manor
house is joyously traditional, with stone-flagged
floors, open fires and bags of atmosphere. Run by
third-generation Bowmans, with 'very friendly
and helpful staff', it is cheery and dog-friendly,
with local ales in the bar and an established
reputation for its food. 'The evening meals in
the bar were excellent.' An 11-strong kitchen
brigade turns out dishes such as slow-roast lamb
shoulder, pan-fried sea bass with olive tapenade,
and a famed fish pie; vegetarian dishes, too. The
bar is 'packed every night' but service is still
slick. Readers praised the 'excellent wine list (and
wine shop)'. Bedrooms, with six in converted
outbuildings, some up a slope, are wonderfully
individual, some verging on the flamboyant.
Expect antiques, deep sofas, thick curtains, books
and handsome artwork. Many have working fires
or wood-burners, some have beams, hand-painted
wallpaper, Victorian cabinet baths and four-
posters. Go fishing (there are seven miles of river
available), borrow an electric bike or enjoy a board
game by the fire.

Whitewell
Clitheroe BB7 3AT

T: 01200 448222
E: reception@innatwhitewell.com
W: innatwhitewell.com

BEDROOMS: 25. 4 in coach house, 2 in
former barn, 150 yds, 2 on ground
floor.
OPEN: all year.
FACILITIES: 3 bars, restaurant,
boardroom, private dining room,
in-house wine shop, spa treatments,
in-room TV (Freeview), civil wedding
licence, 5-acre grounds, terrace
with tables, 7 miles' fishing (ghillie
available), main bar, hall, reception
wheelchair accessible, adapted toilet.
BACKGROUND MUSIC: none.
LOCATION: 6 miles NW of Clitheroe.
CHILDREN: all ages welcomed, cots £6,
extra bed £35.
DOGS: allowed in bedrooms (no
charge), public rooms, not in main
dining room.
CREDIT CARDS: MC, Visa.
PRICES: B&B doubles from £145, singles
from £103. À la carte £40.

Prices may change – check with hotel.

WHITLEY Wiltshire   MAP 2:D1

THE PEAR TREE INN

A beguilingly pretty 17th-century Bath stone inn with stone-mullioned windows and cascading wisteria, this gastropub-with-rooms with atmospheric beamed dining room is set in lovely gardens. There is 'a genial grace to the setting'. House bedrooms, each named after a pear variety, mix contemporary furnishings with original features. Those in a barn conversion have statement wallpaper, comfy seating and a Fired Earth-tiled bathroom. Ground-floor Anjou has a shower; the rest have a bath/shower. A dog-friendly family suite has a king-size bed, two singles on a mezzanine, French doors to a patio. Extra touches include home-made biscuits and luxury toiletries. A larky spirit runs throughout, with jackdaw collections of knick-knacks. There are regular comedy nights, and hostess Jackie Cosens is definitely on the side of fun. They are serious, though, about seasonality and traceability. Chef/patron Adrian Jenkins buys from local farmers and growers, with fish from British waters, to create dishes such as fish pie topped with gratin rösti, or portobello mushroom Kiev burger with red onion marmalade. Breakfast eggs are laid by hens in clover.

Top Lane
Whitley
Melksham SN12 8QX

T: 01225 704966
E: hello@peartreewhitley.co.uk
W: peartreewhitley.co.uk

BEDROOMS: 8. 4 in converted barn, 1 suitable for disabled.
OPEN: all year.
FACILITIES: bar/snug, 2 dining rooms, garden (alfresco dining), in-room TV (terrestrial), parking, EV charging, restaurant wheelchair accessible, adapted toilet.
BACKGROUND MUSIC: in restaurants and bar.
LOCATION: in the heart of the village.
CHILDREN: all ages welcomed, cot free, extra bed for under-12s £15, £25 for 12s and over, high chairs, children's menu.
DOGS: allowed in barn annexe bedrooms (£12.50 per night), bar and Garden Room restaurant (not Sun Room).
CREDIT CARDS: Amex, MC, Visa.
PRICES: B&B doubles from £140. À la carte £35. 1-night bookings refused Fri and Sat.

Prices may change – check with hotel.

WINCHESTER Hampshire

THE OLD VINE

A vine does indeed scramble up the wall of
this Georgian house by the cathedral, in the
historic heart of the city. Now 'a genuinely
unpretentious and enjoyable inn', it has bedrooms
'decorated with taste and discernment and all
sorts of thoughtful touches'. They are named
after designers and are styled accordingly. Nina
Campbell room, overlooking a rear patio, has
twin queen-size mahogany sleigh beds, a mix of
antique and modern furniture, and Campbell's
Peony Place wallpaper. Osborne & Little,
overlooking the cathedral green, has Georgian
plaster panelling and a pencil-point mahogany
four-poster. The menu mixes pub classics with
dishes such as pea and shallot ravioli, lamb kofta
kebabs, and Cornish mussels in a white wine,
garlic and cream sauce. 'Breakfasts were well
prepared with extensive options, NOT self-service
(hurrah!)' – maybe the full English, or smashed
avocado on toasted ciabatta with herby tomato
salsa. On Wednesday evenings, you can raise a
pint of Alfred's Saxon Bronze to the sound of
the world's only diatonic peal of 14 change and
ringing bells. There is just one bum note:
'Parking a pain.' (AW)

8 Great Minster Street
Winchester SO23 9HA

T: 01962 854616
E: reservations@oldvinewinchester.
com
W: oldvinewinchester.com

BEDROOMS: 6. Self-contained 2-bed
apartment, with garage, in annexe.
OPEN: all year except 24/25 Dec.
FACILITIES: bar, restaurant, in-room
TV (Freeview), courtyard with
tables and chairs, parking permits,
restaurant and bar wheelchair
accessible, but not toilets.
BACKGROUND MUSIC: in bar.
LOCATION: town centre, permits
supplied for on-street parking.
CHILDREN: all ages welcomed, under-
3s free, extra bed £30, children's menu,
no under-6s in restaurant or in bar
at night.
DOGS: only in bar.
CREDIT CARDS: Amex, MC, Visa.
PRICES: B&B doubles from £140, singles
from £130. À la carte £35 (fixed-price
£30 for hotel residents).

Prices may change – check with hotel.

WINDERMERE Cumbria

MAP 4: inset C2

CEDAR MANOR

This cosseting and intimate hotel, in a Victorian villa close to Lake Windermere, continues to charm guests with its luxurious bedrooms, thoughtful comforts and faultless, friendly service. Much of Cedar Manor's success is down to 'first-class hosts' Jonathan and Caroline Kaye with their 'lovely warm welcome' and 'attention to detail'. Its location, screened by trees and away from the crowds yet easily reached, helps too. Bedrooms have a contemporary country house style with Herdwick wool carpets, bespoke wood furniture and spoiling touches: bathrobes, fresh milk and chocolates, plus REN products in the ultra-modern bathrooms, some with spa bath; only one is shower only. 'Afternoon tea is a must', with home-made scones and cakes, while simple supper platters offer local produce. Alternatively, it's an easy walk to the Kayes' recommended nearby eateries. 'Delicious' breakfasts have 'many options' including smoked haddock, Cumbrian grill and vegetarian alternative. 'You feel special from start to finish and nothing is too much trouble.' 'Another fabulous stay.' (Peter Laws, Jane Roberts, Janet Hillhouse, Kay Gordon, and many others)

Ambleside Road
Windermere LA23 1AX

T: 01539 443192
E: info@cedarmanor.co.uk
W: cedarmanor.co.uk

BEDROOMS: 10. 1 split-level suite in coach house.
OPEN: all year except 11–26 Dec, 2–19 Jan.
FACILITIES: lounge, lounge/bar, restaurant, in-room TV (Freeview), patio, ¼-acre garden, EV charging, unsuitable for disabled.
BACKGROUND MUSIC: 'very quiet', at mealtimes, in lounge and restaurant.
LOCATION: 5-min. walk from town centre.
CHILDREN: not under 12, extra bed £100.
DOGS: not allowed.
CREDIT CARDS: Amex, MC, Visa.
PRICES: B&B doubles from £155, singles from £135. Afternoon tea £25, supper dishes from £14. Min. 2-night stay at weekends and bank holidays.

Prices may change – check with hotel.

WINDERMERE Cumbria

MAP 4: inset C2

GILPIN HOTEL AND LAKE HOUSE

With its indulgent bedrooms, Michelin-starred dining, attentive staff and guaranteed privacy, Gilpin is considered by many to be the ultimate in Lakeland luxury. Its flagship rooms are extravagantly large glass-cube spa suites that extend over a pond and offer private garden, spa room and circular bath. Elsewhere in the wooded grounds are smaller cedar-clad spa lodges and Scandi-style garden suites with hot tub and sauna. Choose the main Edwardian building for smart country house rooms. For more traditional rooms that are full of charm, opt for the lodge on a nearby estate; guests in the latter share an indoor pool and woodland spa. Dining, too, offers choices: Michelin-starred HRiSHi features Modern British cuisine with an Asian twist, such as vanilla-poached trout with sweet and sour beetroot, while Gilpin Spice has Pan-Asian small and large plates. There's a vast sitting room plump with sofas, a modern cocktail bar plus a peaceful sheltered terrace. Gilpin is different, say readers, because of its long ownership by the Cunliffe family who 'just keep making it better every year'. A member of Relais & Châteaux.

Crook Road
Windermere LA23 3NE

T: 01539 488818
E: hotel@thegilpin.co.uk
W: thegilpin.co.uk

BEDROOMS: 36. 6 garden suites, 10 spa lodges/suites, 6 in Lake House, 1 suitable for disabled.
OPEN: all year.
FACILITIES: Gilpin Hotel: bar, lounge, 2 restaurants (vegetarian menu), patio, 22-acre grounds, public rooms wheelchair accessible, adapted toilet. Lake House: lounge, conservatory, spa (pool), 100-acre grounds; in-room TV, civil wedding licence, EV charging (spa suites).
BACKGROUND MUSIC: in restaurants.
LOCATION: on B5284, 2 miles SE of Windermere.
CHILDREN: no under-7s, extra bed £70.
DOGS: allowed in 2 bedrooms (£30 per night), not in public rooms.
CREDIT CARDS: Amex, MC, Visa.
PRICES: B&B doubles from £255, singles from £210. Set dinner £75, tasting menu £95 (HRiSHi), à la carte £35 (Gilpin Spice). Min. 2-night stay at weekends.

Prices may change – check with hotel.

WINGHAM Kent

MAP 2:D5

THE DOG AT WINGHAM

More a stylish gastropub than a community hub, this historic inn has a following of foodies, who rave about its 'delicious meals'. Owner Marc Bridgen has a passion for local produce, and the kitchen sources ingredients from Kent farmers, growers, butchers and bakers. Senior sous-chef Rob Mantegna has now stepped up as head chef, cooking dishes on his continually evolving menus that might include wild mushroom and feta wellington or rose veal sirloin, bone marrow butter, smoked mash and black garlic mayo. 'The food looked delicious,' reported a Guide insider, who stopped by for a drink outside. 'I had serious lunch envy, but thought the prices a bit high, and we could have done without the 1980s pop/rock from the bar.' Drink and dine in a lounge bar with tub chairs and a log-burner, and when you're dog-tired, head up to one of the stylish bedrooms, where plain paint finishes are enlivened by jazzy cushions and headboards. The cruck-beamed bridal suite has a barley-sugar-twist four-poster. Golf time can be arranged at Royal St George's and other clubs, with transport laid on. Or visit the moon bears at Wingham Wildlife Park. (RS)

Canterbury Road
Wingham
Canterbury CT3 1BB

T: 01227 720339
E: info@thedog.co.uk
W: thedog.co.uk

BEDROOMS: 8.
OPEN: all year, kitchen closes 5 pm Sun.
FACILITIES: lounge bar, restaurant bar, dining room, garden room, terrace (alfresco dining), in-room TV (Freeview), civil wedding licence, golf packages, monthly dining club, unsuitable for disabled.
BACKGROUND MUSIC: in bar and restaurant, live music events.
LOCATION: in village, 7 miles E of Canterbury.
CHILDREN: all ages welcomed.
DOGS: welcomed in 6 bedrooms and in public spaces.
CREDIT CARDS: Amex, MC, Visa.
PRICES: B&B doubles from £150, singles from £99, family from £248. À la carte £50.

Prices may change – check with hotel.

WOODDITTON Cambridgeshire

MAP 2:B4

THE THREE BLACKBIRDS

'If you're after a weekend in the countryside, in a good-value, charismatic pub with excellent food, you can't go wrong here,' a Guide insider advises. The 17th-century thatched pub in the middle of horse-racing country mixes brick-and-beams quaintness with rustic chic. 'The eye-catching main bar is painted with a metallic finish' and there are 'colourful banquettes, contemporary lighting, fern-motif wallpaper on one wall'. Bedrooms, in a new-built 'barn', are 'very contemporary chic – there are even cowhide stools as well as Anglepoise bedside lamps' – with 'muted colour schemes, wood floors and pale wood furniture offset with splashes of colour from the furnishings'. Accessible Juniper has a super-king bed, a rainfall shower, a parking bay outside. In the restaurant, pub classics mix with more ambitious dishes – maybe 'simple but tasty salted baked beetroot with apple and pine nuts', lemon-and-thyme salted hake, a sharing dish of Suffolk pork with chargrilled hispi cabbage, pear, Vichy carrots and mustard mash. Dogs can join their owners in both restaurant and rooms. 'A lovely, cosy place to linger over a long evening meal.'

36 Ditton Green
Woodditton
Newmarket CB8 9SQ

T: 01638 731100
E: info@threeblackbirds.co.uk
W: theblackbirdsinn.com

BEDROOMS: 9. All in self-contained barns, 1 suitable for disabled.
OPEN: all year, bar and restaurant closed Mon, Tues (B&B only on those nights 'for the time being') except bank holidays.
FACILITIES: 2 restaurants, bar, private dining room, in-room TV, garden (outdoor dining), EV charging, 'some challenges for ease of wheelchair access'.
BACKGROUND MUSIC: all day in public areas.
LOCATION: 4 miles SE of Newmarket.
CHILDREN: all ages welcomed, extra bed £15, children's menu.
DOGS: well-behaved dogs allowed (£15 per night) except in 3 dog-free bedrooms.
CREDIT CARDS: Amex, MC, Visa.
PRICES: B&B doubles from £121.50, singles from £108. À la carte £35. 1-night bookings sometimes refused.

Prices may change – check with hotel.

WOOLACOMBE Devon

MAP 1:B4

WATERSMEET

'The location is stunning, with views of the Devon coast with its sandy beaches and tumbled rocks,' writes a reader delighted by this family-friendly hotel, promoted from the Shortlist this year. A former Edwardian gentleman's retreat, it has pools indoors and out, and steps down from the garden to secluded Combesgate beach. The cheapest room has no window, but air conditioning and a sunpipe to channel natural light. The best suites have a sea-view balcony or terrace, an espresso machine, comfy seating. Each has its own style, with a mix of contemporary and period furnishings. 'My spacious, comfortable room had huge windows and the spectacular view.' The staff are 'charming, friendly and helpful'. You can eat outside or in the dining room, which offers sea views as well as a limited menu including dishes such as Exmoor beef sirloin with crisp ox tongue and red wine juice. The 'food is a bit variable' but the 'whole grilled plaice was superb'. For more options visit the bistro. 'Breakfasts were sheer joy. They know how to scramble eggs, and the smoked salmon with them was excellent.' (Ann Lawson Lucas)

Mortehoe
Woolacombe EX34 7EB

T: 01271 870333
E: info@watersmeethotel.co.uk
W: watersmeethotel.co.uk

BEDROOMS: 27. 3 on ground floor, 1 suitable for disabled.
OPEN: all year, except Jan.
FACILITIES: lift, lounge, snug, bar, restaurant, bistro, in-room TV (Freeview), civil wedding licence, function facilities, terrace, ½-acre garden, indoor and heated outdoor swimming pools, treatment room, EV charging, restaurant wheelchair accessible, adapted toilet.
BACKGROUND MUSIC: in public areas.
LOCATION: behind beach, slightly N of village centre.
CHILDREN: all ages welcomed, extra bed £55, family rooms.
DOGS: not allowed.
CREDIT CARDS: MC, Visa.
PRICES: B&B doubles from £170. Fixed-price menu (restaurant) £58–£65 (2/3 courses), à la carte (bistro) £55.

Prices may change – check with hotel.

YARM Yorkshire   MAP 4:C4

JUDGES

A tiny river meanders through the landscaped, wooded grounds of this Victorian country house hotel and photogenic wedding backdrop. Built as a retreat for a wealthy Hartlepool family, it once served as lodgings for circuit judges. Beautiful 'signature' rooms are spacious, with a spa bath and bathroom TV. 'We had a lovely large room with four-poster bed,' a reader tells us. Deluxe rooms might have a sleigh bed, toile de Jouy wallpaper. Even standard rooms have complimentary fresh fruit and sherry. Guilty pleasures include afternoon tea with fizz in a book-lined lounge or on the terrace. New chef Marian (Theo) Padurariu uses produce from the kitchen garden in dishes such as sous-vide guineafowl with baby leek, savoy cabbage and fondant potato. Fridays and Saturdays are 'date nights', when dinner à deux with canapés, cocktails and a bottle of house wine might just lead to a proposal. 'Our wedding day was absolutely perfect!' says one couple who tied the knot here. 'Family and friends had a terrific stay and a lovely breakfast,' relates another. We rest our case. (Mr and Mrs Wilbor, Glynis Pattison, Hannah Shuttleworth, MG, and others)

Kirklevington
Yarm TS15 9LW

T: 01642 789000
E: reception@judgeshotel.co.uk
W: judgeshotel.co.uk

BEDROOMS: 21. Some on ground floor.
OPEN: all year.
FACILITIES: lounge, bar, restaurant, private dining room, in-room TV (Freeview), function facilities, business centre, civil wedding licence, 36-acre grounds (paths, running routes), access to local spa and sports club, EV charging, unsuitable for disabled.
BACKGROUND MUSIC: Radio 4 at breakfast, classical background music in restaurant.
LOCATION: 1½ miles S of centre.
CHILDREN: all ages welcomed, under-4s free, cots £20, extra bed £39.50.
DOGS: guide dogs only.
CREDIT CARDS: Amex, MC, Visa.
PRICES: B&B doubles from £154, singles from £111.50. À la carte (Sun–Thurs) £45, date-night menu (Fri, Sat) £95 per couple.

Prices may change – check with hotel.

YORK Yorkshire

MAP 4:D4

MIDDLETHORPE HALL & SPA

First-time visitors can't help but stand and stare at this exquisite country house, with its William and Mary symmetry and 20 acres of gardens and parkland. Inside, elegant rooms with sash windows and wood panelling are furnished with sofas, paintings and glowing table lamps. It feels 'gorgeous country house' yet York is only a mile away; the racecourse is handily opposite. The house was given to the National Trust in 2008, yet it is not precious; there are newspapers to browse, open fires and a 'really friendly, unstuffy' atmosphere, with thoughtful service. Two cottages contain a small, slightly dated spa. Bedrooms, in the hall and converted outbuildings, are traditional country house with antiques, patterned wallpapers, blankets and eiderdowns. 'Our courtyard room was small but well equipped.' All have books, flowers, fruit and delicious home-made biscuits. Canapés are followed by 'excellent food, imaginatively presented' such as halibut with langoustine bouillabaisse, and chicken with spiced sweet potato. Breakfast offers freshly squeezed juice, leaf tea and cooked dishes such as poached haddock and a full grill. (Michael Lewis)

Bishopthorpe Road
York YO23 2GB

T: 01904 641241
E: info@middlethorpe.com
W: middlethorpe.com

BEDROOMS: 29. 17 in courtyard, 2 in cottage, 1 suitable for disabled.
OPEN: all year, restaurant closed Mon, Tues (light snacks available).
FACILITIES: hall, drawing room, library, 2 dining rooms, private dining rooms, in-room TV, civil wedding licence, terrace, 20-acre grounds, spa (indoor pool), EV charging, public rooms wheelchair accessible, no adapted toilet.
BACKGROUND MUSIC: none.
LOCATION: 1½ miles S of centre.
CHILDREN: not under 6, extra bed £55.
DOGS: by prior arrangement (no charge, welcome pack).
CREDIT CARDS: Amex, MC, Visa.
PRICES: B&B doubles from £245, singles from £160. À la carte 2-course £48, tasting menu £85. 1-night bookings refused at summer weekends.

Prices may change – check with hotel.

SEE ALSO SHORTLIST

YORK Yorkshire

MAP 4:D4

NO. 1 YORK

NEW

This Georgian town house with cool styling and a playful vibe offers comforting Yorkshire food, a cocooning spa and a sunny welcome to all, dogs and children included. Step through the porticoed entrance and 'you know this place is going to be fun', reports a Guide insider. A black-painted hall is lined with violins; a drawing room is full of art; a clubby bar 'buzzes with a toy train, Johnny Cash spinning on a turntable'. The handsome house, a five-minute walk from the city walls, has had a 'radical and daring make-over' while retaining its Georgian good looks: sash windows flood rooms with light, the dining room has a modern elegance. Minimalist bedrooms of milk-coloured walls, floaty muslins and painted floorboards 'make the most of often small-ish spaces' while 'the treats made me smile': a turntable (vinyl library downstairs) and a guest pantry of sweets, cakes, soft drinks. Bathrooms with under-floor heating are 'bright and well thought-through'. Dinner is stylish Yorkshire comfort food such as smoked venison with rhubarb, pork cutlet with herb polenta. Breakfast's 'excellent choice' includes omelette and mushrooms on toast. (HP)

1 Clifton
York YO30 6AA

T: 01904 644744
E: no1.reservations@
   guesthousehotels.co.uk
W: guesthousehotels.co.uk

BEDROOMS: 39. 1 suitable for disabled.
OPEN: all year.
FACILITIES: bar, lounge, dining room, private dining room, spa (5 treatment rooms), kitchen pantry, in-room TV (Freeview), terrace, parking, EV charging, public rooms wheelchair accessible, adapted toilet.
BACKGROUND MUSIC: in public areas.
LOCATION: central York.
CHILDREN: all ages welcomed, under-4s free, extra bed from £25.
DOGS: allowed in designated bedrooms (£25 per night, welcome pack), public rooms apart from dining room and spa.
CREDIT CARDS: Amex, MC, Visa.
PRICES: B&B doubles from £167. À la carte £37. Occasional 2-night min. at weekends.

Prices may change – check with hotel.

SEE ALSO SHORTLIST

ZENNOR Cornwall
MAP 1:D1

THE GURNARD'S HEAD

Friendly, unfussy, effortlessly stylish, Charles and
Edmund Inkin's dining pub 'retains a sense of
the peacefulness, remoteness and wildness that
make this part of the world so very lovely'. Like
sister pubs The Old Coastguard, Mousehole, and
the Felin Fach Griffin, Felin Fach, Wales (see
entries), it is earthed in the community, with a
convivial bar, local staff, work by a Cornish artist
of the month. Bedrooms have views of moors or
ocean, Welsh blankets, books, a Roberts radio,
fresh flowers and Bramley toiletries. Room 8 has
a log-burner and private terrace. Eat inside by the
fire, or on the terrace. 'A real feature of the menus
is fish', with dishes such as hake, curry sauce,
mussels, parsnips, sesame, or otherwise rump cap
of beef, mash, bourguignon sauce. 'Service was
brisk and attentive with a particularly warm and
friendly welcome from the owner.' Breakfast
brings local apple juice, home-made jams, kippers,
a full English. 'An ideal base for walking along
the strenuous but outstandingly beautiful Coastal
Path', it is on the bus route so you can plan walks
without backtracking. 'The place combines style
with some of the best scenery in Cornwall.' (MC)

Treen
Zennor
St Ives TR26 3DE

T: 01736 796928
E: enquiries@gurnardshead.co.uk
W: gurnardshead.co.uk

BEDROOMS: 7.
OPEN: all year except 24 Dec for
dinner, and 25 Dec.
FACILITIES: bar, restaurant, lounge
area, 3-acre garden (alfresco dining),
EV charging, public areas wheelchair
accessible.
BACKGROUND MUSIC: Radio 4 at
breakfast, selected music at other
times, in bar and restaurant.
LOCATION: 7 miles SW of St Ives, on
B3306.
CHILDREN: all ages welcomed, extra
bed £25, children's menus.
DOGS: allowed (no charge, water
bowls, towels and biscuits provided).
CREDIT CARDS: MC, Visa.
PRICES: B&B doubles from £147.50,
singles from £125. Set-price dinner
£42. 1-night bookings refused at
weekends very occasionally.

Prices may change – check with hotel.

SCOTLAND

Glencoe, Highland

ARDUAINE Argyll and Bute

LOCH MELFORT HOTEL

Sit on the deck at this remote hotel, and lose yourself in the views across Asknish Bay to the Sound of Jura and the Inner Hebrides as shaggy Highland cattle graze below. It is, say trusted readers, 'in the middle of nowhere – hence its attraction'. Occupying a mansion built in the 1880s for tea baron J. Arthur Campbell, who planted Arduaine Garden (NT for Scotland) next door, it is perfectly placed for outdoor pursuits, from walking to wild swimming. The Campbells are long gone, but photos, portraits and memorabilia still speak of a family home. House bedrooms, with sea or garden view, range from snug to a master suite. Lodge rooms are more contemporary. Ten have a balcony; ten are dog-friendly with a private deck. Our readers' balcony room was 'very comfortable and adequately equipped'. In the dining room, menu options include burgers, roast loin of venison, local sea trout, and ratatouille-stuffed aubergine. 'We were most impressed with the food and the outstanding service in the dining room.' Another reader, however, felt let down by the food. If you can't get a mobile signal, just detox. (Bill Wood, TH)

Arduaine
Oban PA34 4XG

T: 01852 200233
E: reception@lochmelfort.co.uk
W: lochmelfort.co.uk

BEDROOMS: 30. 20 in lodges, 10 on ground floor, 2 suitable for disabled.
OPEN: Feb Thurs–Sun, Mar to end Nov daily.
FACILITIES: lounge, library, bar/bistro, restaurant (vegetarian/vegan menu), in-room TV (Freeview), wedding facilities, 17-acre grounds, EV charging, public rooms wheelchair accessible.
BACKGROUND MUSIC: in restaurant.
LOCATION: 19 miles S of Oban.
CHILDREN: all ages welcomed, cots free, extra child bed £20.
DOGS: allowed in 10 bedrooms (£10 per night), in public rooms, section of restaurant.
CREDIT CARDS: Amex, MC, Visa.
PRICES: B&B doubles from £70, Apr–Sept weekends D,B&B from £150. À la carte £45 (bistro £30). Min. 2-night stay Fri, Sat Apr–Sept.

Prices may change – check with hotel.

ARINAGOUR Argyll and Bute

MAP 5:C1

COLL HOTEL

The air, the seafood, the views – all are zingingly fresh at this family-run hotel on the Hebridean island of Coll. Next to the ferry landing and with soul-stirring views to Mull, Staffa and the Treshnish Isles, this whitewashed building with a sleek stone and glass extension has been run by the Oliphant family since 1963. Passionate about what they do – 'we were met cheerfully and enthusiastically,' report readers – the family has really made the hotel, with its two friendly bars, a social hub of the island. It's great for wildlife-watching, walking or to blow the cobwebs away. Food is a highlight with commendable local sourcing: shellfish creel-caught off the island, lamb and vegetables from local farms, and fish from nearby waters. Dinner could start with Highland venison croquettes followed by local scallops with chorizo, or langoustines with garlic and lemon butter. Bread, ice cream, desserts and pasta are home made. 'Comfortable and well-equipped' bedrooms have a rustic touch, with tongue-and-groove panelling; ground-floor rooms, some with garden access, are more modern. Most enjoy spectacular views across the bay. (TH)

Arinagour
Isle of Coll PA78 6SZ

T: 01879 230334
E: info@collhotel.com
W: collhotel.com

BEDROOMS: 10. Some on ground floor, 1 suitable for disabled (wet room, Blue Badge parking).
OPEN: all year.
FACILITIES: lounge bar, public bar, restaurant, residents' lounge, in-room TV (Freeview), garden, bicycles, parking, extension room wheelchair accessible, adapted toilet.
BACKGROUND MUSIC: none.
LOCATION: village centre.
CHILDREN: all ages welcomed, extra bed £20.
DOGS: allowed in bar areas, not in restaurant or bedrooms.
CREDIT CARDS: MC, Visa.
PRICES: B&B doubles from £145, singles from £120. À la carte £35.

Prices may change – check with hotel.

GLENAPP CASTLE

At the end of a 'beautiful tree-lined drive', this romantic Victorian Scottish Baronial castle stands in landscaped grounds with views across the Firth of Clyde to Ailsa Craig. A Relais & Châteaux hotel, it has grand public rooms on the first floor with an ambience of 'relaxed luxury'. Bedrooms are below and above, and whether you choose a classic room, a grand sea-view suite or sumptuous master suite, you'll find antiques, artwork and rich fabrics. Readers' garden-view room had 'a large bathroom, a huge bath and shower'. There was no drinks tray, but 'they will readily bring tea and coffee'. A sense of occasion attends dinner in the castle. 'While we enjoyed drinks and canapés in the lounge, a pianist softly played the grand piano.' You can eat less formally, à la carte, among the peach and fig trees in the new Azalea Glasshouse and Bothy restaurant in a 19th-century glasshouse in the kitchen garden. Chef Joe Gould uses home-grown and estate produce in dishes such as heritage baby beetroot salad with whipped goat's cheese; spinach and ricotta ravioli with maple-glazed pecans and wilted spinach; and Pink Lady apple tarte Tatin.

Ballantrae KA26 0NZ

T: 01465 831212
E: info@glenappcastle.com
w: glenappcastle.com

BEDROOMS: 21. 7 on ground floor, 4 in penthouse suite, 1 suitable for disabled, lift to public rooms on first floor.
OPEN: all year.
FACILITIES: lift, drawing room, library, 2 dining rooms, wedding facilities, in-room TV, 36-acre grounds (gardens, lake, tennis, croquet), boat, access to local spa, EV charging, public rooms wheelchair accessible, adapted toilet.
BACKGROUND MUSIC: occasional pianist during meals.
LOCATION: 2 miles S of Ballantrae.
CHILDREN: all ages welcomed, under-7s free, extra bed 7–15s £65.
DOGS: allowed in some bedrooms (£25 per night), not in public rooms.
CREDIT CARDS: Amex, MC, Visa.
PRICES: B&B doubles from £465. Set 3-course dinner £65, 6-course £85, à la carte £42.

Prices may change – check with hotel.

BLAIRGOWRIE Perth and Kinross

MAP 5:D2

KINLOCH HOUSE

Step into the panelled hall of the Allen family's Victorian country house, and it feels like the comfortable home of some outdoorsy friends – albeit with the Relais & Châteaux seal of approval. The situation is lovely amid wooded parkland in soft fruit-growing country. There is nothing corporate here: there is a panelled hall, portrait gallery, lounges with warming fires, comfy sofas, books, board games and malt whiskies. The bedrooms are fittingly traditional with sheets and blankets and Arran Aromatics toiletries. A large suite in shades of apricot has a dual-aspect sitting room, with views over fields, grazed by horses and Highland cattle, to Marlee Loch and the Sidlaw hills. Aperitifs and canapés, coffees and liqueurs bookend dinner. A menu of home-grown and local produce brings dishes such as slow-cooked feather blade of beef with creamed leeks, wild mushrooms, fondant potatoes, roast root vegetables and red wine sauce. 'Attention to detail was second to none.' Hunting, shooting and fishing are all on offer, but if you prefer to stroll in bluebell woods, watching for red squirrels, be their guest.

Dunkeld Road
Blairgowrie PH10 6SG

T: 01250 884237
E: reception@kinlochhouse.com
W: kinlochhouse.com

BEDROOMS: 15. 4 on ground floor.
OPEN: all year except 13–30 Dec.
FACILITIES: bar, lounge, drawing room, conservatory, dining room, private dining room, in-room TV (Freeview), wedding facilities, 20-acre grounds, public areas on ground floor wheelchair accessible, toilet not adapted.
BACKGROUND MUSIC: none.
LOCATION: 3 miles W of Blairgowrie, on A923.
CHILDREN: all ages welcomed, extra bed £40, no under-6s in restaurant at dinner.
DOGS: not allowed.
CREDIT CARDS: Amex, MC, Visa.
PRICES: B&B doubles from £260. Set-price dinner £68. 1-night bookings refused busy periods.

Prices may change – check with hotel.

BRAEMAR Aberdeenshire

THE FIFE ARMS

Swiss gallerists Iwan and Manuela Wirth have had an artistic fling at this Victorian coaching inn in a Cairngorms village famed for its Highland Games. It is 'an extraordinary place that is high Victoriana mixed with contemporary freakishness plus a Bruegel in the dining room, a Picasso in one drawing room and a Lucian Freud in the other'. From a 'croft' single with a cabin bed to a suite with a carved four-poster, copper bath and rain shower, the bedrooms pay homage to luminaries with links to Braemar, such as Robert Louis Stevenson. But one reader's Jekyll is another's Hyde. 'This quirkiness deserves high rating.' 'Bedroom full of clutter and junk … in line with a Victorian brothel', albeit with 'a good selection of teas/coffees, fresh milk'. In a dining room dominated by a stuffed stag, a short menu includes dishes such as wild halibut, white beans, foraged girolles. 'The food was good to excellent.' Morning brings 'an enormous selection of fresh fruit, good porridge with stewed rhubarb, smoked salmon with scrambled eggs', and 'it is not every day that you can have breakfast looking at a Bruegel'. (Dr Sandra Grant, and others)

Mar Road
Braemar AB35 5YN

T: 01339 720200
E: mail@thefifearms.com
W: thefifearms.com

BEDROOMS: 46.
OPEN: all year.
FACILITIES: pub, restaurant, cocktail bar, whisky bar, drawing room, dining room, 2 meeting rooms, wedding facilities, in-room TV (terrestrial), 2-acre gardens, spa, EV charging, public areas wheelchair accessible, adapted toilet.
BACKGROUND MUSIC: in public spaces.
LOCATION: in town centre.
CHILDREN: all ages welcomed, children's menus, family and interconnecting rooms.
DOGS: in some bedrooms (£25 per stay, beds, treats, washing facilities, by prior arrangement), in pub.
CREDIT CARDS: Amex, MC, Visa.
PRICES: B&B doubles from £434, singles from £250. À la carte £65 (Clunie restaurant), £38 (Flying Stag), tasting menu (restaurant) £95.

Prices may change – check with hotel.

CHIRNSIDE Scottish Borders

CHIRNSIDE HALL

Whether you shoot with a 12-bore or a telephoto lens, the gently undulating countryside around this dramatic, Tudor Gothic-style mansion is an irresistible draw. Some bedrooms are huge, with a modern four-poster, a comfy sofa, views across the Tweed valley. 'Our bedroom was spacious, with a lovely view to the Cheviots,' writes a reader. 'There was always plenty of hot water so you could relax in the bath after long walks.' Proud stag heads snoot above you as you descend the grand staircase to peruse a nightly changing, four-course menu over drinks and nibbles by the fire. New chef Kirsty Duff creates dishes such as langoustine tortelloni; roe deer from the estate with girolles and thyme jus; and a vegetarian risotto. 'The menu was always interesting. Soups were excellent, sea bass delicious.' Proprietor Christian Korsten runs the famous Chirnside shoots, while anglers head for the Tweed. Guests say the hotel is 'the perfect base for a perfect walk'. The staff are 'always cheerful' and helpful. 'The kitchen was happy to make us sandwiches on our final morning for the long drive home.' (Sarah Thomas, Bob and Jean Henry)

Chirnside
Duns TD11 3LD

T: 01890 818219
E: reception@chirnsidehallhotel.com
W: chirnsidehallhotel.com

BEDROOMS: 10.
OPEN: all year except early Mar to start of Apr (ring to check Christmas/New Year opening).
FACILITIES: 2 lounges, dining room, private dining room/library/conference rooms, in-room TV (Freeview), billiard room, wedding facilities, 1½-acre grounds, lounges and restaurant wheelchair accessible.
BACKGROUND MUSIC: 'easy listening' in public areas.
LOCATION: 1½ miles E of Chirnside, NE of Duns.
CHILDREN: all ages welcomed, under-5s free, extra bed £50.
DOGS: allowed in some bedrooms (£15 per dog per night), not in public rooms.
CREDIT CARDS: Amex, MC, Visa.
PRICES: B&B doubles from £210, singles from £115. 4-course set-price dinner £48.50.

Prices may change – check with hotel.

THE COLINTRAIVE HOTEL

The road to Colintraive peters out not long after the next village; you come here for the peace, the wildlife, the mesmerising views to the Isle of Bute, and the inn's friendly welcome. Owners Clare Banner and Joe Burnett have brightened up the bedrooms of this stout whitewashed building but kept its much-loved homeliness. The bar, with its stripped-wood floor and wood-burning stove, is a regular haunt of locals; leave plenty of time for a drink here before dinner as most will want a chat. Joe's meals are a treat of local produce (he worked in London under Angela Hartnett); perhaps local langoustines with garlic butter followed by braised ox cheek and mash, or wild mushroom risotto. Desserts include a Scottish cheeseboard with home-made chutney. With sea or fell views, bedrooms are light and airy with local photographs, simple contemporary furnishings and the occasional vintage piece. Some have feature wallpapers; all have fresh milk, locally roasted coffee and smart bathrooms with under-floor heating. Days can be filled with walking, kayaking and cycling, or spotting wildlife such as seals, basking sharks and eagles.

Colintraive PA22 3AS

T: 01700 841207
E: enquiries@colintraivehotel.com
W: colintraivehotel.com

BEDROOMS: 4.
OPEN: all year except Christmas, closed Mon at time of writing but ring to check.
FACILITIES: bar, lounge/bar, restaurant, in-room TV (Freeview), small beer garden, yacht moorings, public rooms wheelchair accessible, no adapted toilet.
BACKGROUND MUSIC: in public areas, occasional live music.
LOCATION: in village, 20 miles W of Dunoon.
CHILDREN: all ages welcomed, extra bed £20.
DOGS: allowed in bedrooms (£10 per night), public rooms, not in restaurant.
CREDIT CARDS: Amex, MC, Visa.
PRICES: B&B doubles from £100, singles from £85. À la carte £40.

Prices may change – check with hotel.

THE COLONSAY

The ferry from Oban brings you to the sole hotel on a beautiful island of fine sandy beaches, heather-clad hills, wild goats, ancient woodland, peat bogs and tidal flats. The 18th-century building overlooking the harbour is a social hub, especially buzzy when it's hosting a festival (books, spring, food and drink, and folk music). 'It was a pleasure to stay,' wrote a reader, who loved the friendly vibe. 'The bar is used by locals, so it has a lovely atmosphere.' There are log fires, painted floors, 'comfy sofas and plenty of space to sit and drink in the bar, before or after dinner'. Here or in the informal restaurant, you can eat pub classics, home-grown salads, steaks, seafood platters, with freshly baked bread. The bedrooms are an essay in simplicity, with oak furniture, artwork, designer fabrics by Jane Churchill, Pierre Frey, Colefax and Fowler and Designers Guild. There is a single overlooking the whitewashed church, with a private bathroom down the passageway. Pig's Paradise – named after dramatic cliffs, home to kittiwake and red-billed chough, black guillemot and razorbill – has an adjoining single room. (CH)
NOTE: As the Guide went to press, the hotel announced it was under new ownership and management.

Isle of Colonsay PA61 7YP

T: 01951 200316
E: manager@colonsayholidays.co.uk
W: colonsayholidays.co.uk

BEDROOMS: 9.
OPEN: Mar–1 Nov, Christmas, New Year.
FACILITIES: conservatory, 2 lounges, log room, bar, restaurant, Wi-Fi on ground floor only, in-room TV (Sky), 1-acre grounds, EV charging, ground-floor public rooms wheelchair accessible, adapted toilet.
BACKGROUND MUSIC: in bar sometimes.
LOCATION: 400 yds W of harbour.
CHILDREN: all ages welcomed, under-12s sharing Pig's Paradise stay free, children's menu.
DOGS: allowed in 2 bedrooms (£30 per stay, bowls, washing facilities), public rooms except restaurant.
CREDIT CARDS: MC, Visa.
PRICES: B&B doubles from £150, singles from £105. Pre-ferry set menus £25–£35 (2/3 courses) Mon, Thurs, Fri, Sat, à la carte £40.

Prices may change – check with hotel.

COUL HOUSE

'A stunning Georgian building with wonderful grounds', this 1820s mansion has been run as a hotel by 'lovely, friendly' hosts Susannah and Stuart Macpherson since 2003. It is a guest-centred place, 'very traditional, tidy, clean, rather old-fashioned'. Public rooms have antiques, log fires, wall-to-wall patterned carpeting, ornate plaster ceilings. Bedroom decor, from small doubles to a four-poster suite, is contemporary. Superior rooms have a roll-top bath and walk-in rainforest shower. 'Bathroom good, with under-floor heating, waterproof TV in bath' – for watching the soaps, maybe. Mountain views are the most sought-after. A warm-water hose awaits your dog's return from a walk to see the giant sequoia. In the impressive octagonal dining room, the chef gives a contemporary spin to classics, in dishes such as corn-fed chicken breast coq au vin in bramble wine jus. Some readers, staying a few nights, weren't blown away by the food at breakfast or dinner, but noted that the restaurant is popular with local diners, and 'Stuart clearly has enormous respect from his team'.

Contin
Strathpeffer IV14 9ES

T: 01997 421487
E: stay@coulhouse.com
W: coulhousehotel.com

BEDROOMS: 21. 4 on ground floor, 1 suitable for disabled.
OPEN: all year excl. 23–26 Dec.
FACILITIES: lounge bar, drawing room, hall, restaurant, in-room TV, conference facilities, wedding facilities, 8-acre grounds (9-hole golf practice area), EV charging, ground floor wheelchair accessible, adapted toilet.
BACKGROUND MUSIC: in lounge bar, restaurant.
LOCATION: 17 miles NW of Inverness.
CHILDREN: all ages welcomed, under-5s free, extra bed 5–15s £25, over-15s £35.
DOGS: allowed in bedrooms (£10 per night), not in restaurant.
CREDIT CARDS: Amex, MC, Visa.
PRICES: B&B doubles from £215 (single occupancy rates on application). À la carte £45. 1-night bookings refused New Year.

Prices may change – check with hotel.

JURA HOTEL

With one single-track road, a single hotel in the island's sole village, and more than 30 deer to every human inhabitant, Jura is one of the UK's last wildernesses. George Orwell, who wrote 1984 in a lonely Jura farmhouse, described it as 'the most un-get-at-able-place', but it's easier now, just a five-minute ferry hop from neighbouring Islay across the Sound of Jura. You come here to walk, to cycle, to fish in the lochs, to scan the skies for golden eagles, perhaps to ascend Beinn an Òir, one of the three iconic, scree-covered 'Paps', for the panoramic views. A warm, simple room awaits your return, with contemporary furnishings and a recently refurbished en suite or private bathroom. A quiet sea-view double has a sleigh bed, comfy seating, a bath, walk-in shower and an extra sofa bed. At the time of writing, a new chef has arrived, and will be working with a wealth of island ingredients – venison, crab, lobster, langoustines, organic vegetables. Guests can dine in the restaurant, pub or lounge bar, and sample local whiskies – the Jura Distillery is a short stroll away.

Craighouse
Isle of Jura PA60 7XU

T: 01496 820243
E: hello@jurahotel.co.uk
W: jurahotel.co.uk

BEDROOMS: 17. 15 en suite, 2 with private bathroom, unsuitable for disabled.
OPEN: all year except Christmas, New Year.
FACILITIES: bar, lounge, restaurant, outdoor eating area, picnic benches, wedding facilities (events shack), EV charging nearby, public areas wheelchair accessible, no adapted toilet.
BACKGROUND MUSIC: all day in bar, restaurant.
LOCATION: in village, opposite Small Isles Bay, 300 yds from passenger ferry terminal, 7 miles from car ferry terminal.
CHILDREN: all ages welcomed, free cots, 5–12s £7.50/over-12s £35 on extra bed.
DOGS: allowed in pub only.
CREDIT CARDS: MC, Visa.
PRICES: B&B doubles from £135, singles from £85. À la carte £36. Min. 2-night stay except in winter.

Prices may change – check with hotel.

DUNVEGAN Highland

THE THREE CHIMNEYS AND THE HOUSE OVER-BY

In the north of Skye, overlooking Loch Dunvegan, this whitewashed former crofter's house with its distinctive three chimneys is the unlikely setting for a celebrated restaurant-with-rooms. Now owned by respected Scottish hotelier Gordon Campbell Gray (see also The Pierhouse, Port Appin), it has been brightened with a cool Scandi-Scots style that doesn't detract either from the food or the views over loch and sea to the mountains of Harris and North Uist. In the restaurant, polished-wood floors, exposed stone and white walls, and tweed-covered chairs keep things smart but simple for short-choice dinners that showcase local produce in imaginative ways: scorched langoustine with cauliflower panna cotta, and roasted hake with nettle sauce. Across the courtyard, spacious rooms, with apex ceilings, natural materials of wool and wood and restful shades of white, grey and sea-blue, have stunning views. Most are split-level between bedroom and sitting area, and all have modern bathrooms with walk-in showers. New arrivals are greeted with tea and home-made cakes, perhaps taken in the garden or the light-filled lounge with wood-burning stove.

Colbost
Dunvegan
Isle of Skye IV55 8ZT

T: 01470 511258
E: eatandstay@threechimneys.co.uk
W: threechimneys.co.uk

BEDROOMS: 6. All on ground floor (5 split-level) in separate building, 1 suitable for disabled.
OPEN: all year except mid-Dec–end Jan.
FACILITIES: lounge/breakfast room, restaurant, in-room TV (Freeview), wedding facilities, garden, EV charging, restaurant and lounge wheelchair accessible, adapted toilet.
BACKGROUND MUSIC: in lounge and restaurant.
LOCATION: 5 miles W of Dunvegan.
CHILDREN: all ages welcomed, extra bed free for under-8s, £100 for 8s and over.
DOGS: assistance dogs only.
CREDIT CARDS: Amex, MC, Visa.
PRICES: B&B doubles from £365. À la carte £75, tasting menu £120.

Prices may change – check with hotel.

EDINBURGH

MAP 5:D2

PRESTONFIELD

With peacocks in the garden, kilt-wearing staff, fire-warmed sitting rooms and antiques at every turn, this 17th-century country house is an indulgent experience. 'It hits all the senses,' says a Guide insider. 'The rich colours, the scent of flowers, walls crammed with art.' Owned by James Thomson of The Witchery by the Castle, it sits in parkland below Arthur's Seat 'yet is only ten minutes from the bustle of Edinburgh's Princes Street'. Glamorous interiors of brocade sofas, tapestries, art, curios and objets are set against deep-red and purple colours. 'Rich and romantic' bedrooms have bold-patterned wallpapers, velvet curtains, beds heaped with cushions – some four-posters require a footstool – rococo mirrors and marbled bathrooms. All spoil with robes, books, magazines, hair straighteners and 'oh joy, Tunnock's tea cakes!' Laze over afternoon tea – on the terrace if warm – 'staff instinctively know where to find you', before dinner of Modern British dishes such as Angus feather blade en croûte or pan-fried sea bream with Parmesan risotto. Breakfast is 'sheer delight' from home-made scones to omelettes and the full Scottish.

Priestfield Road
Edinburgh EH16 5UT

T: 0131 225 7800
E: info@prestonfield.com
W: prestonfield.com

BEDROOMS: 23. 1, on ground floor, suitable for disabled.
OPEN: all year.
FACILITIES: lift, 2 drawing rooms, sitting room, library, whisky bar, restaurant (vegetarian/vegan menus), private dining rooms, in-room TV (Sky), wedding facilities, terraces, tea house, 20-acre grounds, EV charging, public rooms wheelchair accessible, adapted toilet.
BACKGROUND MUSIC: 'as suitable' in public areas.
LOCATION: next to Royal Holyrood Park.
CHILDREN: all ages welcomed, extra bed £25.
DOGS: allowed in bedrooms (no charge), public rooms and park, not in restaurant.
CREDIT CARDS: Amex, MC, Visa.
PRICES: B&B doubles from £375. Set 3-course dinner £50, à la carte £60.

Prices may change – check with hotel.

SEE ALSO SHORTLIST

23 MAYFIELD

Underneath the dramatic landmark of Arthur's Seat, this period gem of a Victorian villa with fine original details and handsome furnishings is a relaxing retreat just ten minutes from the centre. 'Warm and friendly' owners Ross and Kathleen Birnie are clearly proud of their home with its stained-glass windows, cornicing and plasterwork ceilings and have furnished it with antiques and original artwork. The lounge, with its panelling, newspapers and wing armchairs, has the feel of a comfortable gentlemen's club; the books are to borrow, the Georgian chess set to be played and the honesty bar to be used. Bedrooms have mahogany antiques, paintings and polished floorboards, and are warmed with tartan cushions and throws. One has original Punch cartoons, another a chaise longue, and two have four-poster beds. Bathrooms are modern, while all rooms overlook the garden or Arthur's Seat. The top-floor family room has some of the best views. Breakfasts, ordered the night before, 'are made special' with the attention to detail: porridge with flambéed fruit, rare-breed sausages, and plum tomatoes roasted with thyme, among a lengthy menu.

23 Mayfield Gardens
Edinburgh EH9 2BX

T: 0131 667 5806
E: info@23mayfield.co.uk
W: 23mayfield.co.uk

BEDROOMS: 7. 1 on ground floor.
OPEN: all year except Christmas.
FACILITIES: club room, breakfast room, in-room TV (Freeview), terrace, garden, parking.
BACKGROUND MUSIC: at breakfast.
LOCATION: 1 mile S of city centre.
CHILDREN: aged 4 and over welcomed, family room.
DOGS: not allowed.
CREDIT CARDS: MC, Visa.
PRICES: B&B doubles from £180, ring to check single prices. Usually 2-night min. stay but check availability.

Prices may change – check with hotel.

SEE ALSO SHORTLIST

ELIE Fife

MAP 5:D3

THE SHIP INN

The catch of the day could be Shetland hake in the restaurant or nifty fielding on the sands at this pub-with-rooms overlooking the Firth of Forth, with its own beach cricket team. Owned by Rachel and Graham Bucknall, it is a sister venture to The Bridge Inn at Ratho (see Shortlist), and is renowned for its fish and chips, best enjoyed in the salty fresh air as the home team go in to bat against the Obolensky's Heroes or the Battersea Badgers. Two Sea Dog rooms, one on the ground floor with a walk-in shower, are, indeed, dog-friendly. Trade up to a sea-view Captain's room with soft blue tongue-and-groove wall, white shutters, a walk-in shower, or pull rank and ask for the top-floor, bay-view Admiral room with a roll-top bath and separate shower. All rooms have an espresso machine, Laura Thomas bath products. There is a short menu of pub favourites and more imaginative dishes – harissa-spiced Cromarty lamb, say, with a spicy chickpea and tomato casserole, or baba ganoush. An award-winning breakfast includes a full Scottish with tattie scone and haggis, eggs Florentine, a Mull Cheddar omelette or kippers.

The Toft
Elie KY9 1DT

T: 01333 330246
E: info@shipinn.scot
W: shipinn.scot

BEDROOMS: 6. 1 partially accessible on ground floor.
OPEN: all year, except Christmas Day.
FACILITIES: bar, restaurant, in-room TV (Sky, Freeview), wedding facilities, private function room/cricket pavilion, terrace (beach bar, alfresco dining), restaurant, bar, terrace wheelchair accessible, adapted toilet.
BACKGROUND MUSIC: in public areas.
LOCATION: in town, on the bay.
CHILDREN: all ages welcomed, extra bed from £50, children's menu.
DOGS: in 2 bedrooms (£25 per dog per stay), bar, downstairs restaurant.
CREDIT CARDS: MC, Visa.
PRICES: B&B doubles from £160 (£100 in low season). À la carte £35. 1-night bookings refused at New Year.

Prices may change – check with hotel.

GAIRLOCH Highland

MAP 5:B1

SHIELDAIG LODGE

Field-sports fans and whisky aficionados beat a path to this Victorian hunting lodge, in a 'glorious location' on a vast wooded estate by Loch Gairloch. Readers returning after a 38-year absence found much had changed – 'for the better', though they regretted that the fires were not lit. Refurbishment has been 'expensively carried out, in a rather austere, masculine style', with deep leather sofas and modern tartan and tweed furnishings. The lodge is a sister to the very different but similarly characterful Widbrook Grange, Bradford-on-Avon (see entry). Other readers praised the 'friendly staff', the 'tasteful decoration' and the 'first-class comfort'. Some bedrooms have a loch view; a suite has a bay window, a hand-carved four-poster, a roll-top bath on a plinth. Jerome Prodanu's three-course, three-choice menus use estate and home-grown produce to create 'delicious food' such as pan-seared pheasant breast with fondant potato and celeriac. Guests shelling out for a shellfish gastro experience board a creel boat for a tour of the bay, returning with the day's catch to be served up as a feast. (Pauline and David Waterhouse, BW)

Badachro
Gairloch IV21 2AN

T: 01445 741333
E: reservations@shieldaiglodge.com
W: shieldaiglodge.com

BEDROOMS: 12.
OPEN: all year.
FACILITIES: lounge, library, bar, restaurant, snooker/private dining room, in-room TV (Freeview), wedding facilities, garden, 26,000-acre estate (fishing, red deer stalking, falconry centre, motor boat for charter), public areas wheelchair accessible.
BACKGROUND MUSIC: in lounge, bar and restaurant.
LOCATION: 4¼ miles S of Gairloch.
CHILDREN: all ages welcomed, family room.
DOGS: allowed in 2 bedrooms (£20 a night) and bar only.
CREDIT CARDS: Amex, MC, Visa.
PRICES: B&B doubles from £159, singles from £126, family from £190. Set-price menu £49, 5-course tasting menu, on request, £69.

Prices may change – check with hotel.

GLASGOW

MAP 5:D2

GRASSHOPPERS

It feels a bit like finding platform 9¾ but trust us: buzz an intercom to enter a grand, buff-stone railway office block by Glasgow Central, ride the lift to the penthouse and step into a cool city hotel. Created to offer unstuffy, affordable luxury, it is run by a welcoming team, and combines Scandi urban chic with the original features of the classical-style Edwardian Caledonian Chambers. Some bedrooms overlook the station's Victorian glazed roof. All have bespoke ash laminate furniture, a king-size bed, a desk, handmade wallpaper, oak flooring, Pedrali lighting, a Grohe power shower, Arran Aromatics toiletries, bottled water – and Smarties. On arrival guests are offered tea or coffee and home-baked cake, with a constant supply of daily treats such as sausage rolls, gingerbread and ice cream. There is a sitting room with blue panelling and modern artwork, but the kitchen is the hub, a place to relax over a help-yourself deli supper on weekday nights. At breakfast there are cheeses and charcuterie, eggs and bacon, fruit, yoghurts, kedgeree on certain days. Half-price parking nearby is a boon.

87 Union Street
Glasgow G13 TA

T: 0141 222 2666
E: info@grasshoppersglasgow.com
W: grasshoppersglasgow.com

BEDROOMS: 29.
OPEN: all year except week at Christmas, food served Mon–Thurs (weekend suppers, given a day's notice).
FACILITIES: breakfast/supper room, sitting room with small bar, in-room TV (Freeview), discounted car parking, unsuitable for disabled.
BACKGROUND MUSIC: none.
LOCATION: by Central Station.
CHILDREN: all ages welcomed, no charge for cot or extra bed for under-12s if space allows (request at time of booking).
DOGS: small dogs allowed if they can be left in room (no charge, no barking).
CREDIT CARDS: Amex, MC, Visa.
PRICES: B&B doubles from £85, singles from £75, triples from £115. À la carte £17.

Prices may change – check with hotel.

SEE ALSO SHORTLIST

GLENFINNAN Highland

GLENFINNAN HOUSE HOTEL

Gloriously set above Loch Shiel, with views to the evocative Glenfinnan Monument and distant Ben Nevis, this country house hotel is a beacon of traditional Highland hospitality. Readers love it: 'Probably our favourite hotel.' Once home to a veteran of Culloden, it has been run for owners the MacFarlane family for more than 20 years by Manja and Duncan Gibson, manager and chef. Bedrooms have mahogany and oak furniture, and loch, garden or mountain views. The garden-view rooms have a spa bath. Three spacious rooms have a four-poster bed with tartan trim; one of these has an adjoining children's room. No door keys are issued; you are among friends. Lunch and dinner are served in a bar with log-burner and piano. A fire blazes in the hall when it's dreich. In the dining room, Duncan's menus have something for everyone, from fish and chips to vegan haggis hotpot with clapshot, via Glenfinnan estate venison, scallops, langoustine and chargrilled steaks. 'Really excellent dinners, venison stew one night, turbot the next,' wrote a reader. 'Excellent breakfast served on crisp white linen.' (JB, Philip Bright)

Glenfinnan
Fort William PH37 4LT

T: 01397 722235
E: availability@glenfinnanhouse.com
W: glenfinnanhouse.com

BEDROOMS: 14.
OPEN: 12 May–5 Nov.
FACILITIES: drawing room, bar/lounge, playroom, restaurant, wedding facilities, 1-acre grounds (play area), unsuitable for disabled.
BACKGROUND MUSIC: Scottish, in bar and restaurant.
LOCATION: 15 miles NW of Fort William.
CHILDREN: all ages welcomed, under-12s free, extra bed £15.
DOGS: allowed in bedrooms (£15 per night, max. £45 per stay), in some public rooms, not in restaurant or drawing room.
CREDIT CARDS: Amex, MC, Visa.
PRICES: B&B doubles from £165, singles from £145. À la carte (3 courses) £35.

Prices may change – check with hotel.

SEE ALSO SHORTLIST

GRANTOWN-ON-SPEY Highland

MAP 5:C2

CULDEARN HOUSE

Set back from the road in its own mature grounds,
Sonia and William Marshall's Victorian house
stands on the edge of a swathe of the ancient
Scots pine woodland, haunt of the capercaillie,
that surrounds Grantown. The ambience is
more intimate guest house than hotel, with just
six bedrooms, a wide choice of malt whiskies
to sample by the fire, and a locally sourced,
home-cooked four-course dinner cooked by
the hostess. Bedrooms are traditionally and
eclectically furnished (no 'boutique' pretensions
here). Dual-aspect Craigievar has antiques, a
double-ended bath, walk-in shower, views to the
woods and the Cromdale hills. Over drinks in the
drawing room, you can meet fellow guests and
order from an imaginative menu, maybe game
terrine with onion marmalade or West Coast
scallops, guineafowl with pistachio and lemon
stuffing, hill-grazed lamb or the house speciality
steak. After a freshly cooked breakfast of Scottish
produce, head out to explore the Cairngorms
national park, fish in the Spey, visit a falconry
centre or take an exhilarating ride on the funicular
to the summit of Cairngorm mountain.

Woodlands Terrace
Grantown-on-Spey PH26 3JU

T: 01479 872106
E: enquiries@culdearn.com
W: culdearn.com

BEDROOMS: 6. 1, on ground floor, with
wet room, suitable for disabled.
OPEN: all year except Feb, Mar,
Christmas (open New Year).
FACILITIES: drawing room, dining
room, in-room TV (Freeview),
¾-acre garden, parking, public rooms
wheelchair accessible.
BACKGROUND MUSIC: none.
LOCATION: edge of town (within
walking distance).
CHILDREN: aged 10 and upwards
welcomed, younger children by
arrangement.
DOGS: only guide dogs.
CREDIT CARDS: Amex, MC, Visa.
PRICES: B&B doubles from £160,
D,B&B doubles from £220. Four-
course, fixed-price dinner £48.

Prices may change – check with hotel.

THE BONNIE BADGER

The cool Scandi-Scotia design inside this Victorian inn is unexpected in this quiet village close to Scotland's East Lothian coast. Taken over by Michelin-starred chef Tom Kitchin, and his wife, Michaela, it's now a gastropub-with-rooms although the cooking is more honest food done well than fancy flourishes. Dine in the renovated stables, with open beams, exposed stone and designer lighting, on dishes such as pan-fried North Sea cod with roasted fennel, and roast Borders roe deer with apple and parsnip; 'simple food, well cooked'. Pub classics, handsomely done – fish pie, say, or ham, egg and chips – are served in the cool-blue bar with its pale-wood floor, and sea-blue and tan-leather seating. Local sourcing is a big determinant of the menus. Guests are welcomed with afternoon tea – in the terraced garden if fine – and can walk ten minutes to the beach to work up an evening appetite. Bedrooms, some in adjacent cottages, are full of calm colours, retro feature wallpapers and crisp, fuss-free design and an 'outstanding attention to detail'. 'To find hot chocolate and macaroons when we went to bed was a real surprise.'

Main Street
Gullane EH31 2AB

T: 01620 621111
E: info@bonniebadger.com
W: bonniebadger.com

BEDROOMS: 13. 5 in adjacent cottages.
OPEN: all year.
FACILITIES: bar, restaurant, garden room, private dining room, games room, garden area (alfresco dining), in-room TV (Sky), wedding facilities, free parking nearby, bar and restaurant wheelchair accessible, adapted toilet.
BACKGROUND MUSIC: in public areas.
LOCATION: centre of village.
CHILDREN: all ages welcomed (cots free, extra bed £50), children's menu.
DOGS: allowed in specific bedrooms (£25 a night, welcome pack), and public areas.
CREDIT CARDS: Amex, MC, Visa.
PRICES: B&B doubles from £175 (premium prices around key golf event days). À la carte £35–£50.

Prices may change – check with hotel.

INVERGARRY Highland

MAP 5:C2

GLENGARRY CASTLE HOTEL

Turn off the A82 onto a wooded drive and you will pass the emotive ruins of Invergarry Castle in the grounds of this Scottish baronial mansion overlooking Loch Oich. Long run as a hotel by the hands-on MacCallum family, it is old-fashioned in an appealing way. Beyond the pine-panelled reception there are spacious public rooms with deep sofas, comfy armchairs, blazing log fires, oil paintings and, at tea o'clock, freshly baked scones. Bedrooms, from a single to deluxe four-poster rooms, have traditional decor, sprigs, stripes and pelmets, maybe a bay window with a view of the loch and resplendent rhododendrons. Beds are made up with sheets and blankets. Bathrooms have a bath and walk-in shower or an over-bath shower. At night, the menu features local, seasonal and foraged ingredients in dishes such as Shetland crab ravioli with langoustine bisque, samphire and wild sorrel; braised belly and pan-fried loin of lamb, polenta, watercress purée, roasted garlic and breaded sweetbread. There are vegetarian options, too. After breakfast, you can fish for brown trout or stroll to the castle, which twice hosted Bonnie Prince Charlie.

Invergarry PH35 4HW

T: 01809 501254
E: castle@glengarry.net
W: glengarry.net

BEDROOMS: 26.
OPEN: early Apr–late Oct.
FACILITIES: library, lounge with bar service, in-room TV (Freeview), 60-acre grounds (gardens, woodlands, tennis, rowing boats).
BACKGROUND MUSIC: none.
LOCATION: on A82, 1 mile S of A87 junction in Invergarry.
CHILDREN: all ages welcomed, not in deluxe bedrooms (ages 3–12 £40, over-12s £60 on extra bed, children's supper by arrangement).
DOGS: allowed by arrangement in some bedrooms (no charge), and hall, not in deluxe rooms, lounge or library.
CREDIT CARDS: Amex, MC, Visa.
PRICES: B&B doubles from £150, singles from £100. Fixed-price dinner £32–£40 (2/3 courses).

Prices may change – check with hotel.

IONA Argyll and Bute

ARGYLL HOTEL

Overlooking the sea towards Mull, this homely
hotel on the Hebridean island of Iona has a
deserved reputation for its warm welcome,
fresh and creative food, and restorative peace.
Hands-on owners Wendy and Rob MacManaway
and Dafydd and Katy Russon give a 'friendly
personal welcome', reports a reader who returned
for the 'peace and serenity' and 'cosy intimacy'.
Bedrooms, most on the small side, are simple with
pine or oak furniture, neutral colours and local
artwork, all with garden, courtyard or sea views.
No televisions, but guests can 'watch and hear the
birds first thing in the morning and not much
else'. Meals, all made from scratch including the
bread, use kitchen garden produce, sustainably
sourced seafood and meat from local crofters. Hand-
dived Isle of Mull scallops and pan-fried fillet
of cod with parsley mash were 'truly gourmet'.
There are good vegetarian choices, too, and
the presentation 'with flowers and herbs was
always stunning'. There are good walks from the
doorstep, three cosy lounges, one with a fire, and
binoculars in the conservatory for bird-spotting
and wildlife-watching – you may see a dolphin or
two. (Alison Forrester)

Isle of Iona PA76 6SJ

T: 01681 700334
E: reception@argyllhoteliona.co.uk
W: argyllhoteliona.co.uk

BEDROOMS: 17. 7 in linked extension,
all but one en suite, some bath or
shower only.
OPEN: late Mar–late Oct.
FACILITIES: 3 lounges (1 with TV),
conservatory, dining room, wedding
facilities, seafront lawn, free parking
nearby, lounges/dining room
wheelchair accessible, unadapted
toilet, step.
BACKGROUND MUSIC: modern Scottish,
'gentle' jazz, country music in dining
room.
LOCATION: village centre.
CHILDREN: all ages welcomed, under-
5s free, extra bed £20–£40.
DOGS: max. 2 allowed in bedrooms
(£15 per stay, welcome pack on
request) and in 2 lounges.
CREDIT CARDS: Amex, MC, Visa.
PRICES: B&B doubles from £95, singles
from £77. À la carte £37. 1-night
bookings often refused.

Prices may change – check with hotel.

KILBERRY Argyll and Bute

MAP 5:D1

KILBERRY INN

This whitewashed crofter's cottage with a red tin roof, on the scenic, single-track B8024, is the unlikely setting for a much-loved restaurant-with-rooms. Owned by bantering host David Wilson and superlative cook Clare Johnson, it is a welcoming place, with rustic beams, stone walls and a blazing log fire. 'Excellent rooms', with independent access, have an en suite shower room. Two open on to a central courtyard with outdoor seating, raised herb beds, and a fire pit for when it's pure Baltic. Fresh milk, mineral water, home-baked shortbread, books and magazines are all supplied. Clare uses West Coast seafood, Highland beef and lamb from a nearby estate in dishes such as monkfish stew with mussels, croutons and rouille; rib-eye of dry-aged beef, café de Paris butter, watercress, celeriac remoulade. 'Food superb and lovely wines and local gins.' At breakfast there are home-made jams and granola, porridge, a full Scottish with Stornoway black pudding, tattie scones and Kintyre eggs. 'Having learnt that I was wheat intolerant, they made me special granola and got in gluten-free bread.' (MK Webster, and others)

Kilberry
Tarbert PA29 6YD

T: 01880 770223
E: relax@kilberryinn.com
W: kilberryinn.com

BEDROOMS: 5. All on ground floor.
OPEN: Tues–Sun mid-Mar–end Sept, Tues–Sat Oct, Fri/Sat Nov/Dec, New Year (closed Christmas).
FACILITIES: restaurant, snug (wood-burning stove), variable Wi-Fi, 4G signal in car park, in-room TV (Freeview), small garden.
BACKGROUND MUSIC: in restaurant at dinner.
LOCATION: 16 miles NW of Tarbert, on B8024.
CHILDREN: not under 13.
DOGS: allowed by arrangement in 2 bedrooms (bed, towels, bowls, treats, no charge), not in public rooms.
CREDIT CARDS: MC, Visa.
PRICES: D,B&B doubles £265, singles £160. À la carte £38. 2-night bookings preferred at weekends.

Prices may change – check with hotel.

KINGUSSIE Highland

THE CROSS AT KINGUSSIE

Take afternoon tea on the terrace at this former
Victorian tweed mill and you hear nothing but
birdsong and the plash of the Gynack Burn that
once powered the looms. In leafy seclusion on
the edge of town in the Cairngorms national
park, with 'beautiful walks from the door', this
restaurant-with-rooms with 'outstanding food'
and 'hosts that make you feel very much at home'
is 'an excellent place to relax and de-stress'. The
larger bedrooms overlook the burn, one with
French windows to a small balcony. All are
presented in contemporary-cum-cottage style, in
colours inspired by the surrounding hills. After
drinks in one of the cosy lounges, you can eat in
the beamed dining room or alfresco. Chef here
since 2014, David Skiggs wins plaudits for his
imaginative cooking of local, seasonal ingredients.
His fixed-price, three-course menu includes
dishes such as wild halibut with fish velouté and
Parmesan gnocchi. Let them know if you want
veggie options. 'The food was so beautifully
rich that neither of us had room for dessert.' At
breakfast there are local butcher's sausages and
bacon, smoked fish, free-range eggs. (PS, and others)

Ardbroilach Road
Kingussie PH21 1LB

T: 01540 661166
E: relax@thecross.co.uk
W: thecross.co.uk

BEDROOMS: 8.
OPEN: Tues–Sat, Feb–early Jan, closed
Christmas but open for New Year.
FACILITIES: 2 lounges, restaurant,
in-room TV (Freeview), 4-acre
grounds (terraced garden, woodland),
restaurant wheelchair accessible,
adapted toilet.
BACKGROUND MUSIC: none.
LOCATION: 440 yds from village centre.
CHILDREN: all ages welcomed.
DOGS: not allowed.
CREDIT CARDS: Amex, MC, Visa.
PRICES: D,B&B doubles from £200
(B&B sometimes available by
arrangement, from £130). Fixed-price
3-course dinner £60, 6-course tasting
menu £75.

Prices may change – check with hotel.

KIRKBEAN Dumfries and Galloway   MAP 5:E2

CAVENS

Guests love the tranquillity and attentive service at Angus and Jane Fordyce's Georgian mansion, set in open countryside close to the dunes and salt marshes of the Solway coast. 'You feel as if you are welcome guests in someone's much-loved home', surrounded by antiques, paintings and cherished objects. The grandest bedroom, Criffel, named after a local hill that thinks it's a mountain, is huge, with a super-king bed, plus a sofa bed for a child. Ground-floor Solway has a splendid bathroom with bath and walk-in shower. At night, Angus cooks a three-course dinner, and can accommodate special diets. His repertoire includes venison with redcurrant and port sauce, hake with samphire and scallops, and corn-fed chicken with cream and ginger, accompanied by good wines from the well-stocked 18th-century cellar. 'The drawing room, where drinks were served, was well proportioned, airy and had numerous comfy settees.' Breakfasts are 'a highlight, with strong coffee, lovely black pudding and haggis', perhaps a kipper from a smokehouse in Lochmaben, organic eggs from Mrs McMyn's free-ranging Lohmann Browns or the hotel's own hens. (DS)

Kirkbean
Dumfries DG2 8AA

T: 01387 880234
E: enquiries@cavens.com
W: cavens.com

BEDROOMS: 6. 1 on ground floor.
OPEN: Apr–1 Nov, exclusive use by groups at New Year.
FACILITIES: 2 sitting rooms, dining room, wine cellar, meeting facilities, broadband throughout hotel, in-room TV (Freeview), 10-acre grounds.
BACKGROUND MUSIC: light classical all day in 1 sitting room, dining room.
LOCATION: in village, 12 miles S of Dumfries.
CHILDREN: all ages welcomed, free cots, sofa beds in some rooms.
DOGS: allowed by arrangement (£20 per stay), not in public rooms or unattended in bedrooms.
CREDIT CARDS: MC, Visa.
PRICES: D,B&B doubles from £310, singles from £248, family from £435. Dinner £35 for non-residents. 1-night bookings may be refused.

Prices may change – check with hotel.

KYLESKU Highland

MAP 5:B2

KYLESKU HOTEL

In the vast, remote, elemental landscape of Assynt, a 19th-century coaching inn overlooking Loch Glendhu has moved with the times to become a relaxed modern hotel. The tiny car ferry from Kylestrome used to dock on the slipway right outside. Today you just swoosh over the Kylesku Bridge to find a buzzy, dog-friendly place with simple, smart bedrooms painted in soft shades of grey and cinder pink. The cheapest snug attic rooms each have a shower in a private bathroom down a flight of stairs. A first-floor deluxe room in Willie's Hoose annexe has sliding glass doors to a loch-facing balcony and an en suite with walk-in shower. New owners, Highland Coast Hotels, espouse the values of seasonality and provenance. In the bar/restaurant, with magical vistas, the short menus are big on freshly landed seafood, with meat from local crofters. As well as langoustine, oysters, mussels and hand-dived scallops, options include dishes such as sirloin steak and chips and a vegetarian dish. Ask for a picnic and go whale- and dolphin-spotting, kayaking, cycling, or take a self-guided walk along the Coigach Geology Trail.

Kylesku IV27 4HW

T: 01971 910047
E: info@kyleskuhotel.co.uk
W: kyleskuhotel.co.uk

BEDROOMS: 11. 4 in annexe, 1 suitable for disabled.
OPEN: Feb to end of year, ring to enquire about Christmas, New Year.
FACILITIES: lounge, bar, restaurant, in-room TV, small garden (outside eating), area of lounge and dining room wheelchair accessible, toilet not adapted.
BACKGROUND MUSIC: from 10 am in bar, restaurant.
LOCATION: 10 miles S of Scourie.
CHILDREN: all ages welcomed, under-4s stay free, extra bed £25 for 4–12s, £50 for over-12s, children's menu.
DOGS: allowed in bedrooms (£15 a night to max. £60 a stay), public rooms, not in restaurant or bar after 7 pm.
CREDIT CARDS: MC, Visa.
PRICES: B&B doubles from £153, singles from £143, family from £170. À la carte £50.

Prices may change – check with hotel.

LOCHEPORT Western Isles

MAP 5: inset A1

LANGASS LODGE   `NEW`

If you don't see owners Amanda and Niall
Leveson Gower around their small hotel, they
may be at sister venture Hamersay House, or
out diving for scallops and gathering mussels
for supper. On an island of lochs, lochans and
long white-sand beaches, this former shooting
lodge is ideal for outdoorsy families and their
dogs, although readers did not in the least mind
when bad weather forced them inside. 'We loved
it, and plan to go again.' The public rooms are
quaint, with sporting prints, stag heads, and 101
uses for cast antlers. Lodge bedrooms are 'fairly
traditional' and snug. King rooms, built into the
hillside, are more spacious. 'Our room was simple
but comfortable.' You can eat in the bar – maybe
ale-braised beef short rib or monkfish 'scampi'.
In the restaurant, the 'excellent food' includes
dishes such as monkfish and scallop fritter with
pineapple and chilli and lime salsa or hazelnut-
crusted pork fillet. Surfing, wild swimming,
wildlife watching, stalking and fishing are all
available on the doorstep, or just sit in the garden
and take in the view over Loch Eport to Ben
Eaval. (Christine Hughes)

Locheport
North Uist HS6 5HA

T: 01876 580285
E: langasslodge@btconnect.com
W: langasslodge.co.uk

BEDROOMS: 11. Some in extension,
1 suitable for disabled.
OPEN: all year except Feb, Mar, about
10 days over Christmas/New Year.
FACILITIES: conservatory, bar,
restaurant, in-room TV (Freeview),
11-acre garden in 200-acre grounds,
bar and restaurant wheelchair
accessible, adapted toilet.
BACKGROUND MUSIC: in public rooms.
LOCATION: 7½ miles SW of
Lochmaddy.
CHILDREN: all ages welcomed, extra
beds for under-14s £25.
DOGS: allowed in bedrooms (£5 a night),
public rooms, not in restaurant.
CREDIT CARDS: MC, Visa.
PRICES: B&B doubles from £130, singles
from £115, family room from £180.
À la carte (bar) £34, set-price menu
(restaurant) £42–£50 (2/3 courses).

Prices may change – check with hotel.

MEIKLEOUR Perth and Kinross   MAP 5:D2

THE MEIKLEOUR ARMS

On the Marquess of Lansdowne's Meikleour
estate, this Georgian coaching inn amid verdant
woodland comes with fishing rights on the Tay.
Driving north up the A93 you'll pass the longest,
tallest hedge on earth, planted in 1745 by an
ancestor of Sam Mercer Nairne, who owns the
dog-friendly hotel with his Bordeaux-born wife,
Claire. A centuries-old Gallic-Scots alliance is
celebrated in everything from room names to the
cuisine. A reader, returning after several years,
found it had 'changed for the better out of all
recognition'. Hotel bedrooms are individually
styled, with marble bathrooms, chic paint finishes,
maybe toile de Jouy wallpaper, complimentary
sherry, Arran Aromatics toiletries. 'I stayed in one
of the stable cottages, a lovely conversion, built
with anglers in mind, but excellently equipped,'
our reader writes. 'Warm, comfortable, peaceful,'
another concurs. In the restaurant, estate-to-plate
dishes with vegetables from the walled garden,
and East Coast fish, include venison and
chargrilled steaks, all lovely, but more variety
would have been appreciated. 'Excellent breakfast.'
(M K Webster, Christine and Philip Bright)

Meikleour PH2 6EB

T: 01250 883206
E: contact@meikleourarms.co.uk
W: meikleourarms.co.uk

BEDROOMS: 40. 6 in Walled Garden
Cottages, 3 in Roselea Cottage, 20 in
Stable Cottages.
OPEN: all year.
FACILITIES: residents' lounge, pub,
restaurant, private dining room, in-
room TV, beer garden, large grounds
and woodlands, 1.7-mile salmon
fishing beat on river, restaurant
wheelchair accessible, adapted toilet.
BACKGROUND MUSIC: 'at a very low
level' in pub.
LOCATION: 12 miles N of Perth.
CHILDREN: all ages welcomed, extra
bed (max. 1 for under-13s £20).
DOGS: allowed in inn ground-floor and
cottage bedrooms (not unattended, no
charge), restaurant and pub.
CREDIT CARDS: MC, Visa.
PRICES: B&B doubles from £90, singles
from £80. À la carte £32. Min. 2-night
stay in cottages.

Prices may change – check with hotel.

MUTHILL Perth and Kinross

MAP 5:D2

BARLEY BREE

The auld alliance holds firm at this restaurant-with-rooms in a conservation village, where Fabrice Bouteloup gives a French spin to fine Scottish produce. In the 15 years since he and his wife Alison reinvented a handsome, red stone coaching inn, M Bouteloup has won prestigious awards for his modern cooking, inspired by boyhood summers spent on his grandmother's farm in Mayenne. The six smart, street-facing bedrooms vary in size. 'How nice to be here again!' wrote a delighted reader, only regretting that this time he'd missed out on large, dual-aspect room 1, with its super-king-size bed, sofa, roll-top bath and shower. They stayed in smaller room 5, without the swanky bath in the en suite. Lunch and dinner are served in a beamed dining room with a roaring log-burner, and on the terrace. Short, daily-changing menus feature 'beautifully cooked' dishes such as Orkney scallop ceviche with samphire and pink grapefruit, cod and polenta croquette with dill mayo and pickled vegetables, and Hebridean hogget. At breakfast there are free-range eggs, home-baked bread and 'French toast with crispy bacon to die for'. (Bill Wood, and others)

6 Willoughby Street
Muthill PH5 2AB

T: 01764 681451
E: info@barleybree.com
W: barleybree.com

BEDROOMS: 6.
OPEN: all year except 25–27 Dec, various dates throughout year (see website), restaurant closed Mon, Tues.
FACILITIES: lounge bar, restaurant, in-room TV (Freeview), variable Wi-Fi, small terrace and lawn (outdoor seating), drying facilities, gun cupboard, restaurant wheelchair accessible, toilet not adapted.
BACKGROUND MUSIC: none.
LOCATION: village centre.
CHILDREN: all ages welcomed, cot, baby-changing, children's menu, family room.
DOGS: assistance dogs only.
CREDIT CARDS: Amex, MC, Visa.
PRICES: B&B doubles from £115. À la carte £45.

Prices may change – check with hotel.

THE PEAT INN

A dream destination for golfing gourmets, Geoffrey and Katherine Smeddle's restaurant-with-rooms offers Michelin-starred cooking just a 12-minute drive from St Andrews. Whitewash and window boxes at this former Georgian coaching inn seem to speak of a traditional pub, but the interior is smart and contemporary, with modern artwork that complements the decor. Geoffrey Smeddle brings classical training to his creative cooking of seasonal Scottish ingredients, and has had Michelin's seal of approval every year since 2010. A typical dinner might include wild halibut, lime and seaweed butter, scallop mousse, Jersey Royals, asparagus and caviar butter sauce; from a tasting menu, hay-baked onion, braised shoulder of lamb, wild garlic, grain mustard, onion cream, shallot rings, spring truffle. In The Residence, all but one of the suites are split level, with views over the neat garden to fields, a walk-in or over-bath shower. They have a palette of taupe, turquoise and teal, a fridge and tea-/coffee-maker, and a mezzanine lounge in which to enjoy a terrific continental breakfast, delivered by the 'lovely, friendly staff'.

Peat Inn
Cupar KY15 5LH

T: 01334 840206
E: stay@thepeatinn.co.uk
W: thepeatinn.co.uk

BEDROOMS: 8. All suites, on ground floor in annexe, 7 split-level, 1 suitable for disabled.
OPEN: all year except 24–26 Dec and 1–6 Jan, restaurant closed Sun/Mon.
FACILITIES: lounge in restaurant, in-room TV (terrestrial), ½-acre garden, EV charging, restaurant wheelchair accessible, adapted toilet.
BACKGROUND MUSIC: in restaurant.
LOCATION: in hamlet, 7 miles SE of Cupar and 6 miles SW of St Andrews.
CHILDREN: all ages welcomed, extra bed for under-12s £65, no under-7s at dinner.
DOGS: not allowed.
CREDIT CARDS: Amex, MC, Visa.
PRICES: B&B doubles from £275.
À la carte £65/£75 (3/4 courses), tasting menu £95.

Prices may change – check with hotel.

PEEBLES Scottish Borders

MAP 5:E2

CRINGLETIE HOUSE

'Highly recommended for a special occasion', this Victorian Scottish baronial hotel on a 28-acre estate combines luxury with unforced family- and dog-friendliness. Promoted from the Shortlist on the strength of praise from readers, it invites you to relax, with lots of comfy seating around log fires in bar and lounges. Bedrooms are individually styled, with contemporary comforts that respect the building's history. Ranging from very good classic rooms to the Selkirk Suite, which has a spa bath and walk-in jet shower, all are supplied with Scottish-made toiletries. 'Our suite was lovely, with plenty of seating plus a couple of small bottles of the local whisky to enjoy.' In the restaurant, under a painted ceiling depicting a heavenly classical scene, a three-course dinner menu offers such choices as cutlets of Borders lamb, slow-cooked neck, pied de mouton; seared Gigha halibut, sea vegetables, mussel emulsion; tartelette of woodland mushroom. In the grounds you find a walled kitchen garden, dovecote and sundial, modern sculpture, games, a nature trail and woodland, home to a badger colony. (Bill Wood, and others)

off Edinburgh Road
Peebles EH45 8PL

T: 01721 725750
E: enquiries@cringletie.com
W: cringletie.com

BEDROOMS: 13. 1 suitable for disabled, plus 2-bed cottage, with hot tub.
OPEN: all year except 2–3 weeks Jan.
FACILITIES: lift, bar, lounge, conservatory, garden room, restaurant, in-room TV (Freeview), wedding facilities, 28-acre grounds (nature trail, walled garden, woodland), EV charging, hotel fully wheelchair accessible, adapted toilet.
BACKGROUND MUSIC: in public areas.
LOCATION: 2 miles N of Peebles.
CHILDREN: all ages welcomed, children's menu.
DOGS: allowed in most bedrooms (no charge), not in public rooms.
CREDIT CARDS: Amex, MC, Visa.
PRICES: B&B doubles from £265, singles from £252. Set-price menu £65, Sun 7-course tasting menu £130 (incl. wine).

Prices may change – check with hotel.

SEE ALSO SHORTLIST

THE GREEN PARK

Traditional as Burns Night and bannocks, the McMenemie family's Victorian country house hotel stands in well-kept lawned gardens on the shores of Loch Faskally. Guests forget the hurry and scurry of modern life when they come for an 'activity' break, be it crossword or bridge, Scottish nature or music. Staff are 'warm and friendly'. Most of the bedrooms have a loch view, with some in the sympathetically designed Tower Wing and modern Garden Wing extension. Single rooms are available. Your dog (or, indeed, your cat) is welcome to stay in your room but should not set paw in public rooms. From about 11 am every day, a sideboard is laid out with biscuits and flasks of tea and coffee, while home-made cakes arrive in the early afternoon. Binoculars are on hand for wildlife spotters, and there are books and nooks for a quiet read as well as jigsaws. At night, after sherry, long-serving chef Richard Murray's menus include dishes such as Perthshire venison Wellington, or 'delicious and succulent salmon'. 'We very much enjoyed our stay,' writes a reader, 'and look forward to visiting again.' (David Tattersall, and others)

Clunie Bridge Road
Pitlochry PH16 5JY

T: 01796 473248
E: bookings@thegreenpark.co.uk
W: thegreenpark.co.uk

BEDROOMS: 51. 16 on ground floor, 1 suitable for disabled.
OPEN: all year except Christmas.
FACILITIES: 2 lifts, lounge bar, main lounge, sun lounge, in-room TV (BT, Freeview), 3-acre garden, EV charging, public areas wheelchair accessible, adapted toilet.
BACKGROUND MUSIC: none.
LOCATION: ½ mile N of town centre.
CHILDREN: all ages welcomed, under-3s free, extra bed £20–£30.
DOGS: allowed in bedrooms (no charge), not in public rooms.
CREDIT CARDS: MC, Visa.
PRICES: per person B&B from £100 (no supplement for singles). Set-price dinner £33–£40 (3/4 courses).

Prices may change – check with hotel.

SEE ALSO SHORTLIST

PITLOCHRY Perth and Kinross
MAP 5:D2

KNOCKENDARROCH HOTEL

On the leafy edge of Pitlochry, with views to the
Perthshire hills, Struan and Louise Lothian's hotel
has the feel of a Victorian country house in town.
'What a friendly place!' writes a reader, praising
the 'good humour and understanding' with which
post-pandemic arrangements were handled.
Modestly sized top-floor rooms have a furnished
balcony. Another good choice might be a dual-
aspect premier room with both town and country
views. Suites in a 1990s extension have a lounge,
a coffee machine and drinks cooler, smart TV, a
bath and walk-in shower. Dog-friendly rooms can
be found in a new timber annexe, with under-
floor heating and patio doors to a small private
garden. On a cold night, settle in with a dram
by the fire in one of two adjoining lounges. In
both dining room and orangery, a short, modern
menu includes dishes such as braised feather
blade of Highland beef, wild mushroom ragout,
port jus, horseradish mash. At breakfast there are
free-range eggs, smoked salmon, a full Scottish
with potato scone, black pudding and haggis. 'Just
trying to find an excuse to go back.' (Nick Mabbs)

Higher Oakfield
Pitlochry PH16 5HT

T: 01796 473473
E: bookings@knockendarroch.co.uk
w: knockendarroch.co.uk

BEDROOMS: 18. 2 on ground floor, 4 in
annexe.
OPEN: Feb–early Dec.
FACILITIES: 2 lounges, dining room
with orangery extension, in-room
TV (Freeview), 2-acre wooded
garden, bicycle storage, EV charging,
unsuitable for disabled.
BACKGROUND MUSIC: none.
LOCATION: central.
CHILDREN: not under 10.
DOGS: allowed in some annexe rooms
by arrangement (£15 a night up to
max. £60), not in main house.
CREDIT CARDS: Amex, MC, Visa.
PRICES: B&B doubles from £210. Set-
price dinner £49. 1-night bookings
sometimes refused Sat.

Prices may change – check with hotel.

SEE ALSO SHORTLIST

PORT APPIN Argyll and Bute   MAP 5:D1

THE PIERHOUSE

'This is a really lovely hotel in a wonderful location,' writes a reader, after a stay at Gordon Campbell Gray's whitewashed former piermaster's house on the shores of Loch Linnhe, by the jetty where the Lismore ferry docks. It's a sister to Three Chimneys, Dunvegan (see entry), on the Isle of Skye, and its walls are adorned with pieces from the owner's art collection. Enjoy a drink on the terrace, gazing out to Lismore and the mountains of Morven, or eat creel-caught Loch Linnhe langoustine in the sea-facing dining room. The menu is long on fish and shellfish, but you can order a steak, a burger, creative vegan options. 'Great seafood at the restaurant and friendly, helpful staff.' 'Very comfortable room and a luxurious bed.' Bedroom decor is stylish without upstaging the loch views to the fore; cliff-view rooms, looking on to the hillside of Appin Rocks are cheaper. Best is a dual-aspect superior sea-view room with bath and walk-in shower. All have a tea/coffee-maker and room service. At peak season 'the place bustled from mid-morning to late evening with day-trippers', another reader cautions. You can see the attraction. (Peter Gray, and others)

Port Appin PA38 4DE

T: 01631 730302
E: reservations@pierhousehotel.co.uk
W: pierhousehotel.co.uk

BEDROOMS: 12.
OPEN: all year except 24–26 Dec.
FACILITIES: snug, lounge, bar, restaurant (vegan menu), private dining room, in-room TV (Freeview), wedding facilities, sauna, spa treatments, sun terraces, moorings, unsuitable for disabled.
BACKGROUND MUSIC: in bar and restaurant.
LOCATION: in village, 20 miles N of Oban.
CHILDREN: all ages welcomed, extra bed for under-13s £30, cots and high chairs available.
DOGS: well-behaved dogs allowed in 2 bedrooms (not unattended, £15 per night), bar and dining room, not in main restaurant.
CREDIT CARDS: Amex, MC, Visa.
PRICES: B&B doubles from £195. À la carte £45.

Prices may change – check with hotel.

PORTPATRICK Dumfries and Galloway

MAP 5:E1

KNOCKINAAM LODGE

Where the road ends and the Irish Sea begins, this former Victorian hunting lodge with a private cove is secluded, unapologetically traditional and rich in comforts and good food. 'A hotel which is very comfortable in its own skin. Not fussy, no piles of coordinating cushions, just very well run,' reports a fan after their third visit. There are soft carpets, thick floral curtains, a wood-panelled bar and fires in the two lounges. Bedrooms, with sea or garden views, are elegant with pretty patterned wallpapers and fabrics, antiques and good space for armchairs. Some have a window seat, one a tester bed, another views from the bathtub; all have a bath as well as shower. 'Excellent and imaginative' menus highlight seafood and local farm produce and might include grilled salted cod, roast Galloway lamb with rosemary jus, and an 'amazing strawberry soufflé'. Most of the fruit and vegetables are home-grown. Expect sustaining breakfasts with Galloway kippers, kidneys and bacon on the menu. In the summer, guests can dine outdoors. 'Fantastic stay, staff were attentive. We will definitely go back.' (Caroline Thomson, WR, and others)

Portpatrick DG9 9AD

T: 01776 810471
E: reservations@knockinaamlodge.com
W: knockinaamlodge.com

BEDROOMS: 12. 2 in self-catering lodge overlooking beach.
OPEN: all year.
FACILITIES: 2 lounges, bar, restaurant, alfresco dining, in-room TV (Freeview), wedding facilities, 20-acre grounds (garden, beach), EV charging, public areas wheelchair accessible.
BACKGROUND MUSIC: in restaurant in evening.
LOCATION: 3 miles S of Portpatrick.
CHILDREN: all ages welcomed, under-12s extra bed £60 including high tea, 12 and over £130 including dinner, no under-12s in dining room.
DOGS: in some bedrooms (£30 per stay), in grounds, not in public rooms.
CREDIT CARDS: Amex, MC, Visa.
PRICES: D,B&B doubles from £370, singles from £215. Set lunch £42 (Sun £37). 1-night bookings refused on certain weekends, Christmas, New Year.

Prices may change – check with hotel.

VIEWFIELD HOUSE

With porte cochère, crenellated tower and fine Victorian interiors, this country house overlooking Loch Portree is redolent of the history of the Macdonald family, which has lived there for more than 200 years. The grand entrance hall is adorned with animal trophies, the dining room hung with ancestral portraits. A guest sitting room is positively thronged with comfy seating. Bedrooms, spread over three floors, are filled with antiques and original features. None has a TV; most have an over-bath shower. The dual-aspect master bedroom can sleep a family, while two rooms in the stables block stay open throughout the winter. Guests are hosted by Jasper Buxton and his wife, Iona, and can order a light supper of soup and cheese, charcuterie or a vegan platter. In the morning, breakfast on porridge, a full Scottish, a kipper or smoked haddock. Explore the 20-acre grounds, which are home to the Skye Shrubs garden centre, and follow the path down to the village. Skipper Jasper offers half-day sailing trips aboard the yacht Breeze, out to the Sound of Raasay, where you can take in views of the Cuillins over a lunch of smoked salmon and Prosecco.

Viewfield Road
Portree
Isle of Skye IV51 9EU

T: 01478 612217
E: info@viewfieldhouse.com
W: viewfieldhouse.com

BEDROOMS: 13. 1, on ground floor, suitable for disabled, 2 in adjacent converted stables.
OPEN: Apr–Oct.
FACILITIES: drawing room, morning/ TV room, dining room, 20-acre grounds (croquet, swings), public rooms wheelchair accessible.
BACKGROUND MUSIC: none.
LOCATION: S side of Portree.
CHILDREN: all ages welcomed, extra bed for under-12s £10.
DOGS: allowed in bedrooms (£10 charge), drawing room if other guests don't object, not in dining room.
CREDIT CARDS: MC, Visa.
PRICES: B&B doubles from £124, singles from £82. Supper (soup and cheese) £12, (charcuterie plate) £8. 1-night bookings only on application in high season.

Prices may change – check with hotel.

SEE ALSO SHORTLIST

RANNOCH STATION Perth and Kinross

MAP 5:D2

MOOR OF RANNOCH –
RESTAURANT & ROOMS

It's not quite the restaurant at the end of the universe, but there is a great sense of space at Stephanie and Scott Meikle's dog-friendly restaurant-with-rooms. In a wilderness landscape of lochs and lochans, on the edge of Rannoch Moor, it is served by the romantic West Highland line. You can arrive by sleeper from London in time for breakfast, and if it's wild and woolly outside, you'll find it snug and woolly within. Simple bedrooms have a fridge, fresh milk, Arran Aromatics toiletries, binoculars for wildlife spotting – no radio, no TV, no mobile signal, no Wi-Fi. Relax with your dog in a comfy lounge, with books, board games, always a jigsaw on the go. Have a drink from a bar stocked with more than 100 malt whiskies, or enjoy a coffee with home-made shortbread. The dinner menu reflects the fact that the Meikles are passionate about provenance. It might include dishes such as St Bride's roast chicken, shallot marmalade and Lunan Bay asparagus, or Gigha halibut, celeriac, green apple, hazelnut and mussel velouté. In the morning, order a packed lunch. At day's end, marvel at the stars in the darkest of skies.

Rannoch Station PH17 2QA

T: 01882 633238
E: info@moorofrannoch.co.uk
W: moorofrannoch.co.uk

BEDROOMS: 5.
OPEN: Thurs–Mon until 22 Nov 2022, 9 Feb–21 Nov 2023.
FACILITIES: lounge, bar, conservatory dining room, no Wi-Fi or TV, unsuitable for disabled.
BACKGROUND MUSIC: none.
LOCATION: on a single-track, dead-end road, 40 miles W of Pitlochry.
CHILDREN: all ages welcomed, extra bed £40, children's portions (12 and under).
DOGS: welcomed in all areas of the hotel (no charge, max. 2 per room).
CREDIT CARDS: Amex, MC, Visa.
PRICES: D,B&B doubles £340, singles £270. Fixed-price dinner non-residents £70.

Prices may change – check with hotel.

ST OLA Orkney Islands

MAP 5:A3

THE FOVERAN

It's a feast for the eyes as well as the stomach at the Doulls' single-storey restaurant-with-rooms overlooking Scapa Flow and the southern Orkney islands. There are sea views from the residents' lounge and terrace, and from every table in the many-windowed dining room, with its marine palette of soft blue and sand, and paintings inspired by Orkney's ever-changing landscape and skies. It is here that owner Paul Doull uses locally farmed and fished produce in his short menu supplemented by specials, which might include Scapa Flow langoustines; roasted sea bass, lobster and chive sauce; or seaweed-fed North Ronaldsay mutton, four cuts, with an Orkney-style patty. Everything is a family affair here, with Paul's wife, Helen, as the hostess, while his brother and sister-in-law, Hamish and Shirley, keep it all running smoothly. The bedrooms are spruce and comfortable with modern tartans, looking on to countryside or water. After a full Orcadian breakfast or smoked haddock and free-range eggs, visit the enigmatic Neolithic Ring of Brodgar and the Standing Stones of Stenness.

Kirkwall
St Ola KW15 1SF

T: 01856 872389
E: info@thefoveran.com
W: thefoveran.com

BEDROOMS: 8. All on ground floor, 1 single with private bathroom across hall.
OPEN: Apr–early Oct, by arrangement at other times, restaurant closed variable times Apr, Oct.
FACILITIES: lounge, restaurant, in-room TV, 12-acre grounds (private rock beach), restaurant wheelchair accessible, adapted toilet.
BACKGROUND MUSIC: local/Scottish traditional in restaurant.
LOCATION: 3 miles SW of Kirkwall.
CHILDREN: all ages welcomed, ask for details when booking, children's menu and portions.
DOGS: not allowed.
CREDIT CARDS: MC, Visa.
PRICES: B&B doubles from £137, singles from £95. À la carte £38. 1-night bookings refused May–Sept (but phone to check).

Prices may change – check with hotel.

SCARISTA Western Isles

SCARISTA HOUSE

The long drive is worth it to this edge-of-the-world location, where a Georgian manse, with pretty, traditional rooms and superb food, overlooks a long sandy beach. Patricia Martin, co-owner with husband Tim, makes practically everything from scratch – from bread and cakes to pasta and ice cream – and greets guests with afternoon tea before they go for a walk (beach or hills) to work up an appetite for the nightly changing set dinner. Dishes could include monkfish with fennel and pea purée, and cherry clafoutis and almond ice cream. With notice, most diets are imaginatively catered for. There's a pretty blue dining room, a garden room for summer eating, and two sitting rooms with a 'homely atmosphere', squashy sofas and fires; one has 'wall-to-wall bookshelves'. Bedrooms (three in outbuildings) have a no-nonsense traditional style with patterned wallpapers, solid wood furniture and pretty china. All have views of garden, beach or hills; two have sitting areas with sofa and wrap-around windows facing the sea. Sleep to the sound of the sea and wake to 'the lowing of cows and cry of seagulls' and a 'generous breakfast'.

Scarista
Isle of Harris HS3 3HX

T: 01859 550238
E: stay@scaristahouse.com
W: scaristahouse.com

BEDROOMS: 6. 3 in annexe.
OPEN: mid-Feb–end Nov.
FACILITIES: drawing room, library, 2 dining rooms, Wi-Fi not available in some bedrooms, wedding facilities, 1-acre garden, unsuitable for disabled.
BACKGROUND MUSIC: none.
LOCATION: 15 miles SW of Tarbert.
CHILDREN: all ages welcomed, extra bed £25, children's 2-course early supper £15.
DOGS: allowed in bedrooms (£10 per stay) and 1 public room.
CREDIT CARDS: Amex, MC, Visa.
PRICES: B&B doubles from £246, singles from £185. Set dinner £57–£65. Min. 2-night stay (ring to check 1-night availability).

Prices may change – check with hotel.

SCOURIE Highland

EDDRACHILLES HOTEL

Take a drive on the wild side via the North Coast 500 to this small private hotel, a former Church of Scotland manse in a 'magical place right on the water' overlooking Badcall Bay. Some older guests have memories of Youth Hostel stays here in the 1950s, but nostalgia for cold showers, lumpy beds and lumpier porridge melt away in the warmth of the welcome from hosts Fiona and Richard Trevor. 'What a fantastic hotel!' readers write. 'Wonderful porridge.' A complimentary cream tea is served in the conservatory. You have a choice of 60 malt whiskies in the lounge/bar. Six first-floor bedrooms have a king-size bed; four, on the ground floor, have a super-king/twin. Views are over the loch or the courtyard garden. 'The bedrooms have had a complete make-over and have been beautifully decorated.' 'Miracle worker' Trevor Williams cooks a short, nightly changing menu of dishes such as roast lamb rump with red wine jus. 'Breakfast was also lovely.' 'Food and service always exceed expectations.' 'Our dog wants to live there (so do we).' (James Barclay, Roger Meachem, Tina Swanson, Peter Saunders, and many others)

Badcall Bay
Scourie IV27 4TH

T: 01971 502080
E: info@eddrachilles.com
W: eddrachilles.com

BEDROOMS: 10. 4 on ground floor.
OPEN: 3 Apr–21 Oct.
FACILITIES: large reception, bar/lounge, sun lounge, restaurant, in-room TV (Freeview), wedding facilities, 3-acre grounds, public rooms wheelchair accessible, partially adapted toilet.
BACKGROUND MUSIC: 'easy listening' in lounge by bar.
LOCATION: 2 miles S of Scourie, on the North Coast 500 route.
CHILDREN: aged 12 and over welcomed.
DOGS: a limited number of well-behaved dogs allowed in bedrooms by arrangement (£10 per stay), public rooms (part of restaurant, subject to 'three barks' rule).
CREDIT CARDS: MC, Visa.
PRICES: B&B doubles from £145, singles from £120. Set-price dinner £38–£44 (3/4 courses).

Prices may change – check with hotel.

SEE ALSO SHORTLIST

KINLOCH LODGE

It has been an anniversary year at Lord and Lady Macdonald's former hunting lodge 'in a beautiful position' on the shores of Loch Na Dal, with views to the Cuillin mountains. They first opened their family home to guests in 1972, when 17 bedrooms shared three bathrooms. Today, daughter Isabella is at the helm, and all bedrooms have a modern en suite. The best have fine antiques, a separate bath and walk-in shower; all have a king-size bed, posh toiletries. Readers on a return visit felt they should have been warned that access to one of the more contemporary rooms in the new-build extension was via 'an iron spiral staircase, and not easy', although they found the 'bedrooms and the public rooms very comfortable, the food excellent'. In the atmospheric dining room, numerous ancestors look down as you peruse Jordan Webb's nightly menus of Skye produce, with home-grown fruit and vegetables, and dishes such as confit turbot, Sconser scallop, miso broth and mussels. 'Youthful staff were courteous and pleasant.' You can enjoy a drink by the fire pit, sandwiches in the bar, 'and there is also a gracious lounge'. (Christine Hughes, RG)

Sleat
Isle of Skye IV43 8QY

T: 01471 833333
E: reservations@kinloch-lodge.co.uk
W: kinloch-lodge.co.uk

BEDROOMS: 19. 10 in North Lodge, 9 in South Lodge, 3 on ground floor, 1 suitable for disabled.
OPEN: all year.
FACILITIES: 3 drawing rooms, whisky bar, dining room, in-room TV (Sky), wedding facilities, cookery courses, 'huge' grounds on edge of loch, public rooms wheelchair accessible.
BACKGROUND MUSIC: in dining room.
LOCATION: on shore of Loch Na Dal on E coast of Skye, not far off A851.
CHILDREN: all ages welcomed, extra bed £45.
DOGS: in bedrooms only (£20 per night, not unattended).
CREDIT CARDS: MC, Visa.
PRICES: B&B doubles from £320. Set dinner (5 courses) £75.

Prices may change – check with hotel.

SPEAN BRIDGE Highland   MAP 5:C2

SMIDDY HOUSE

'What a fabulous place to stay!' write trusted readers this year of this former Highland village blacksmith's house and workshop, which Robert Bryson and Glen Russell now run as a restaurant-with-rooms. 'We were very warmly welcomed by Robert, with home-made cake and tea.' Four compact house bedrooms are decorated in attractive cottage style. Two have a king-size bed, two a 4ft 6in double. All have handmade soaps and fluffy robes. While two rooms face the road, they are quiet thanks to double glazing. If you want to stay a while, to explore the West Coast, maybe to climb Ben Nevis or take a scenic ride on the Jacobite Steam Train (aka the Hogwarts Express), book the Bryson Suite in the old smithy workshop. It has a ground-floor lounge, double bedroom, a bathroom with shower, and a spiral staircase to a twin-bedded room on a mezzanine. In Russell's restaurant, Glen's menus showcase local produce in dishes such as West Coast scallops au gratin and herb-crusted rump of lamb with pearl barley risotto, or for vegans maybe squash, chickpea and spinach curry. 'The evening meal was delicious.' (John and Val Norris, LM)

Roy Bridge Road
Spean Bridge PH34 4EU

T: 01397 712335
E: enquiry@smiddyhouse.com
W: smiddyhouse.com

BEDROOMS: 5. 1 suite in adjacent cottage.
OPEN: all year except 25/26, 31 Dec, restaurant closed Mon all year, Sun, Tues, Wed, Jan–Mar.
FACILITIES: garden room, restaurant, in-room TV (Freeview), parking.
BACKGROUND MUSIC: in restaurant.
LOCATION: 9 miles N of Fort William.
CHILDREN: not under 7.
DOGS: not allowed.
CREDIT CARDS: MC, Visa.
PRICES: D,B&B doubles from £220, suite from £355, based on 3 sharing. À la carte, min. 2 courses, £45.

Prices may change – check with hotel.

STRACHUR Argyll and Bute

MAP 5:D1

THE CREGGANS INN

It's worth paying extra for a room at the front at this historic whitewashed, dog-friendly inn for the mesmerising views of Loch Fyne. On the borders of Loch Lomond and the Trossachs national park, it was once owned by Sir Fitzroy Maclean, a founding member of the SAS and believed to have been Ian Fleming's model for James Bond. Inside, it is traditional, even a bit old-fashioned, but the views – and especially the sunsets – are breathtaking. Readers this year were disappointed, on arrival, to find no fires lit, and the loch-view dining room closed. Apart from breakfast, you eat, instead, in MacPhunn's bistro, from a menu inspired by produce from the loch and surrounding land. Maybe Cullen skink, mussels marinière, hand-dived scallops, or seared haunch of Ardgay venison with bramble jus. The sun-filled, loch-view reception lounge is a great place to relax with tea or coffee, while in the evening, you can sit with a shot of MacPhunn single malt, which Sir Fitzroy developed. At breakfast there are Loch Fyne kippers, smoked haddock, free-range eggs, a hearty full Scottish with potato scone, Ayrshire bacon and Stornoway black pudding.

Strachur PA27 8BX

T: 01369 860279
E: info@creggans-inn.co.uk
W: creggans-inn.co.uk

BEDROOMS: 14.
OPEN: all year, except Christmas.
FACILITIES: 2 lounges, bar, dining room, bistro, in-room TV (Freeview), 2-acre grounds, moorings for guests arriving by boat.
BACKGROUND MUSIC: all day in bar.
LOCATION: in village.
CHILDREN: all ages welcomed, under-15s on extra bed £15.
DOGS: allowed in bedrooms (not unattended, £10 per night, max. 1 large or 2 small), in bar, not in other public rooms.
CREDIT CARDS: Amex, MC, Visa.
PRICES: B&B doubles from £160. À la carte £30.

Prices may change – check with hotel.

STRATHTUMMEL Perth and Kinross

MAP 5:D2

THE INN AT LOCH TUMMEL

Spectacular views across Loch Tummel to the iconic peak of Schiehallion can be seen from this 'characterful and quirky old coaching inn' ten miles from Pitlochry in Perthshire's big-tree country. Hands-on owners Jade and Alice Calliva 'work incredibly hard to see that everyone is wined, dined and accommodated in the greatest comfort, style and good humour'. It is a supremely relaxing place to stay, say readers. Each room has its own character, mixing hand-picked antiques and artwork with modish paint finishes. Delicate toile de Jouy curtains frame a loch view from one bedroom; another has a sheepskin rug on bare floorboards, folding canvas chairs, a shelf of books. All are supplied with home-made fudge and whisky on arrival, an espresso machine, Scottish Fine Soaps toiletries, robes and biodegradable slippers. An appealing, unpretentious menu offers dishes such as herb-crusted cod, mussels, lemon beurre blanc; roulade of Fife pork belly; burgers meaty and veggie. A full Scottish breakfast includes local sausages and bacon, Stornoway black pudding, Kilduncan eggs. 'This was our third visit, and it has got better every time.'

Queens View
Strathtummel
Pitlochry PH16 5RP

T: 01882 634317
E: info@theinnatlochtummel.com
W: theinnatlochtummel.com

BEDROOMS: 6. 2, on ground floor, suitable for disabled.
OPEN: mid-Feb to mid-Dec, closed Mon, Tues till Nov, then Mon–Wed till mid-Dec.
FACILITIES: bar, snug, restaurant, library, private dining room, large garden and patio, wedding facilities, ground-floor bar and snug wheelchair accessible, no adapted toilet.
BACKGROUND MUSIC: in bar/restaurant and library.
LOCATION: 10 miles W of Pitlochry.
CHILDREN: all ages welcomed, travel cot on request.
DOGS: allowed in bedrooms (£15 per night), public rooms, part of garden.
CREDIT CARDS: MC, Visa.
PRICES: B&B doubles from £200. À la carte £42. 1-night bookings refused at peak weekends.

Prices may change – check with hotel.

STRONTIAN Highland

KILCAMB LODGE

'Very quiet and peaceful' on the shores of Loch Sunart, this family-friendly and dog-friendly country house has an 'exceptional location'. It is surrounded by private meadow and woodlands, home to red deer and pine marten. In a Georgian house bookended by Victorian wings, bedrooms mix contemporary and classic country house styling. From a snug garden-view room to a dual-aspect loch-view room with bath and walk-in shower, all have luxury toiletries and home-made shortbread. You can settle down with a dram by the fire in the drawing room, or enjoy an alfresco afternoon tea. Long-serving head chef Gary Phillips works with locally fished and farmed produce to create dishes such as roast loin of Highland venison with Bourguignon sauce, haggis, neeps and tatties, for his menus in the candlelit restaurant. You can eat more informally in the bar and brasserie, perhaps beer-battered fish and chips, or butternut squash ravioli. Breakfasts include a full Scottish with tattie scone and black pudding, smoked salmon and scrambled eggs on French toast. Work up an appetite by taking a bracing dip. 'We swam every day before breakfast.' (TS)

Strontian PH36 4HY

T: 01967 402257
E: enquiries@kilcamblodge.co.uk
W: kilcamblodge.co.uk

BEDROOMS: 11.
OPEN: all year except 14 Nov–6 Dec, restaurant closed Mon, Tues in Feb and Mar.
FACILITIES: drawing room, lounge/bar, restaurant, brasserie, in-room TV (Freeview), wedding facilities, 22-acre grounds, EV charging, bar, brasserie, restaurant wheelchair accessible, toilet not adapted.
BACKGROUND MUSIC: at dinner.
LOCATION: edge of village.
CHILDREN: all ages welcomed, under-5s free, 5–12s on extra bed £95, with children's menu.
DOGS: allowed in 5 bedrooms (£15 a night), not in public rooms.
CREDIT CARDS: MC, Visa.
PRICES: B&B doubles from £265. Set 5-course dinner £65 (restaurant), à la carte £45 (brasserie). Min. 2-night stay at certain times.

Prices may change – check with hotel.

TARLAND Aberdeenshire

MAP 5:C3

DOUNESIDE HOUSE

This architectural gem – an Edwardian Scots Revival country house – in the fertile Howe of Cromar, with long views to the Grampians, is today a very special country house hotel. It is owned by the charitable MacRobert Trust, set up by Lady MacRobert after the baronetcy died with her three sons in flying tragedies before and in WW2. There is a sense of peace and grace in public rooms, painted in gentle, traditional hues and filled with family portraits and mementos. Bedrooms are a blend of classic and contemporary style. One has a private roof terrace. Loveliest is the dual-aspect Lady MacRobert Suite, under a corner turret. There are dog-friendly apartments and cottages a short walk away. You can dine in the conservatory, looking out over landscaped grounds with stream, rock pools, infinity lawn and beech walk. Rare varieties of organic fruit and vegetables from the walled kitchen garden appear on Matthew Price's short, clever menus of dishes such as spiced East Coast monkfish with cauliflower, couscous, hazelnuts and Atsina cress. Military guests are offered a discount, and all have use of the health club.

Tarland AB34 4UL

T: 01339 881230
E: manager@dounesidehouse.co.uk
W: dounesidehouse.co.uk

BEDROOMS: 23. 9 in cottages, 4 apartments, 2 cottages suitable for disabled.
OPEN: all year excl. 2 weeks Jan, closed Mon, Tues Nov–Mar.
FACILITIES: bar, wine bar, piano lounge, library, conservatory restaurant, in-room TV, wedding facilities, health centre (pool, tennis), 17-acre grounds, public areas wheelchair accessible, adapted toilet.
BACKGROUND MUSIC: in bar, restaurant.
LOCATION: 7 miles NW of Aboyne.
CHILDREN: all ages welcomed, cots free, extra bed £35, children's menu, play park.
DOGS: allowed in cottages, apartments (£25 per stay), not main building.
CREDIT CARDS: MC, Visa.
PRICES: B&B doubles from £260, singles from £243. Set-price dinner £45–£55, tasting menu (Thurs–Sat) £85.

Prices may change – check with hotel.

THURSO Highland

FORSS HOUSE

Under the big skies of Caithness, wrapped in woodland and a curve of the River Forss, this Georgian mansion offers the grandeur of Scottish country house living but with modern-day warmth and comforts. The results are 'excellent' and 'wonderful', say guests who particularly enjoyed the local walking – 'right down to the sea' – and the 'vast bath' perfect for 'a wallow'. Bedrooms are contemporary with traditional touches: soft hues, large headboards, the occasional antique. Those in the main house have big windows overlooking the gardens, those in the lodges are more secluded, some close to the river (with excellent salmon fishing). All have modern bathrooms, the largest with freestanding baths. Relax in the clubby lounge with its panelled walls, chesterfields and tweedy armchairs before the highlight of an 'absolutely superb' dinner served either in the richly decorated main room or light-filled conservatory. Perhaps kick off with Scrabster scallops followed by Scottish beef fillet with ox cheek. Breakfast is thoroughly Scottish and filling, and includes porridge, grilled kippers, and scrambled eggs with double cream.

Forss
Thurso KW14 7XY

T: 01847 861201
E: stay@forsshousehotel.co.uk
W: forsshousehotel.co.uk

BEDROOMS: 14. 3 on ground floor, 6 in neighbouring annexes, 1 suitable for disabled.
OPEN: all year.
FACILITIES: bar, dining room, breakfast room, lounge, in-room TV (Freeview), meeting room, wedding facilities, 19-acre grounds with river and waterfall.
BACKGROUND MUSIC: in public areas breakfast and evening.
LOCATION: 5 miles W of Thurso.
CHILDREN: all ages welcomed, no charge for under-5s, extra bed £20.
DOGS: allowed in sportsmen's lodge bedrooms (£15 a night, welcome pack) and all areas except dining room.
CREDIT CARDS: Amex, MC, Visa.
PRICES: B&B doubles from £142. Fixed-price 3-course dinner £58, 6-course tasting menu £86.

Prices may change – check with hotel.

TORRIDON Highland

THE TORRIDON

'The setting is stunning – the landscape truly breath-taking,' wrote readers on a Munro-climbing jaunt to this remote, baronial-style hunting lodge on a wooded estate at the head of Loch Torridon. There is a wide choice of house rooms, from 'classics' to the Victorian-themed 1887 suite, with emperor-size bed. All are styled with considerable dash, with some costing considerable cash. If you're on a tight budget, book one of the simpler rooms in the old stables, where some on the ground floor are dog-friendly. 'The cheaper rooms were much better value – smaller but not tiny, though they didn't have the spectacular views.' In 1887 restaurant, Paul Green's tasting menus use produce from the Torridon farm, two-acre kitchen garden, local game, fish and shellfish. Meals can also be taken in Bo & Muc brasserie (maybe Torridon farm pork belly, bubble and squeak; a vegan burger or curried cauliflower). 'We ate in the hotel and brasserie. Great food in both, locally sourced and very tasty.' Mountain biking, gorge scrambling, and clay-pigeon shooting are among the activities on offer, or you can just take in the amazing views. (Jo Giddins)

By Achnasheen
Torridon IV22 2EY

T: 01445 791242
E: info@thetorridon.com
W: thetorridon.com

BEDROOMS: 18 in main hotel. Plus 12 in Stables, some adapted for disabled.
OPEN: Feb–Dec (resort); Feb–Nov (Stables, Bo & Muc), may close Mon, Tues off-season.
FACILITIES: ramp, lift, drawing room, library, whisky bar, dining room, wedding facilities, 48-acre estate, EV charging.
BACKGROUND MUSIC: classical at night in dining room.
LOCATION: on W coast, 10 miles SW of Kinlochewe.
CHILDREN: all ages welcomed, extra bed in suites £45.
DOGS: allowed in 1 house room, ground-floor Stables rooms (£15 per stay).
CREDIT CARDS: Amex, MC, Visa.
PRICES: B&B doubles from £190 (Stables), £305 (main house). Tasting menus £85 (1887), à la carte £40 (brasserie). 1-night bookings sometimes refused.

Prices may change – check with hotel.

ULLAPOOL Highland

MAP 5:B1

THE CEILIDH PLACE

Scottish culture and celebration are at the heart
of the Urquhart family's hotel, café, bar and
restaurant near the ferry terminal in a fishing
town and former herring port on Loch Broom.
Launched in a boathouse in 1970 as a café where
musicians could play for a free meal, it has grown
to occupy adjoining cottages, housing a bookshop
and art gallery. Very much a social hub, it hosts
regular live gigs, but no one makes a song and
dance if you want to sit by the log-burner in the
cosy parlour or retire to the first-floor lounge
and help yourself to tea, coffee or a drink from
the honesty bar. Simple, tasteful bedrooms (a few
with no en suite) have a Roberts radio (no TV),
books chosen by customers. Don't expect designer
chic; that's not the point. And if you're on a tight
budget, you can take a bunk in the Clubhouse
opposite. In the restaurant, Scott Morrison
creates short menus of locally sourced dishes –
maybe langoustine, venison/vegan burger, forest
mushroom arancini, hazelnut and nasturtium
pesto; lamb and mint sausage, pan-fried paprika
potatoes, treacle onions. Breakfast includes a full
Scottish or vegan.

12–14 West Argyle Street
Ullapool IV26 2TY

T: 01854 612103
E: stay@theceilidhplace.com
W: theceilidhplace.com

BEDROOMS: 13. 10 with en suite, 3
sharing bath/shower room, plus 11 in
Clubhouse.
OPEN: all year except 5 Jan–9 Feb.
FACILITIES: bar, parlour, lounge, café,
restaurant, bookshop, conference
facilities, wedding facilities, 2-acre
garden, parking, public areas
wheelchair accessible, adapted toilet.
BACKGROUND MUSIC: in public areas.
LOCATION: village centre (car park).
CHILDREN: all ages welcomed, under-
5s free, £30 a night for 5–10s.
DOGS: allowed in bedrooms (£15 per
dog per stay, not unattended) and
throughout.
CREDIT CARDS: MC, Visa.
PRICES: B&B doubles from £159 (£132
with shared bathroom), singles from
£100 (1 single room at £85), Clubhouse
bunk beds £24–£32. À la carte £35.

Prices may change – check with hotel.

SEE ALSO SHORTLIST

WALKERBURN Scottish Borders   MAP 5:E2

WINDLESTRAW

A handsome Edwardian mansion overlooking
the River Tweed in the eastern Scottish Borders,
Windlestraw combines the elegance of its age
with modern comforts and fine dining. Built for a
wealthy mill owner, the house has been turned into
a small luxury hotel by seasoned professionals John
and Sylvia Matthews. Original features such as oak
panelling and carved fireplaces rub shoulders with
light-coloured walls and soft table lamps to create
a relaxed, welcoming atmosphere. Enjoy views
over the gardens and forested slopes from deep
sofas in the fire-warmed lounge or conservatory.
The daily-changing five-course dinner is 'good
and imaginative', kicking off with canapés,
'amongst the best we have had (a Parmesan choux
pastry bite filled with truffle cream was especially
memorable)' and perhaps including Borders
lamb with wild garlic, and hake with mussels and
Prosecco. Breakfast brings home-baked soda bread
and the full Scottish. Light-filled bedrooms have
soft colours, delicately patterned wallpapers, and
rattan and brass bedsteads; most have shower and
bathtub, the latter 'very useful for overwalked
aching legs'. (FT)

Galashiels Road
Walkerburn EH43 6AA

T: 01896 870636
E: stay@windlestraw.co.uk
W: windlestraw.co.uk

BEDROOMS: 6.
OPEN: all year except 18 Dec–31 Mar,
closed Sun/Mon.
FACILITIES: bar, sunroom, lounge/
restaurant, in-room TV (Freeview),
wedding facilities, 3-acre landscaped
gardens, unsuitable for disabled.
BACKGROUND MUSIC: none.
LOCATION: in Walkerburn, 8 miles E
of Peebles.
CHILDREN: all ages welcomed, under-4s
free, additional bed for 12s and under
£62, in own room £170, no under-10s
in restaurant.
DOGS: allowed in bedrooms (max.
2, not unattended, £15 per dog per
night), public rooms, garden, not
restaurant.
CREDIT CARDS: Amex, MC, Visa.
PRICES: B&B doubles from £220, singles
from £200. 5-course set menu £90. At
the time of writing, dinner service was
due to stop in 2023.

Prices may change – check with hotel.

WALES

Ynys Llanddwyn, off Anglesey

HARBOURMASTER HOTEL

Upstaging all the rainbow-hued waterfront houses in a planned Georgian town overlooking Cardigan Bay, this unabashedly blue-fronted boutique hotel is an iconic landmark. After 20 years, Glyn and Menna Heulyn have bowed out, but new owners, local hoteliers Wells and Louise Jones, say there will be no change for change's sake. You can still book the 'nicely furnished, uncluttered bedrooms', ranging from a quirky little single with a good shower room, to the Aeron Queen suite with panoramic views from a balcony, pale-blue walls, purple sofa and teal armchairs, a roll-top bath and walk-in shower. There are suites with private terraces in the adjacent warehouse. All have Frette linen, fine quality toiletries, jazzy Melin Tregwynt fabric headboards. In the restaurant, have a drink at the zinc bar, then dine on locally sourced fish and shellfish, Welsh beef and lamb and organic vegetables. Dishes might include sirloin steak with confit garlic and shallot, or cauliflower risotto with crispy capers and walnuts. 'We love the ambience, the food, the rooms, the whole area!' (Frances Thomas, and others)

Pen Cei
Aberaeron SA46 0BT

T: 01545 570755
E: info@harbour-master.com
W: harbour-master.com

BEDROOMS: 13. 4 in warehouse, 2 in cottage, 1 suitable for disabled.
OPEN: all year except 25/26 Dec.
FACILITIES: lift (in warehouse), bar, restaurant, in-room TV (Freeview), small terrace, limited parking, EV charging, restaurant and bar wheelchair accessible, adapted toilet.
BACKGROUND MUSIC: all day in warehouse and restaurant.
LOCATION: central, on the harbour.
CHILDREN: aged 5 and upwards welcomed, no additional beds, or book cottage.
DOGS: only guide dogs.
CREDIT CARDS: Amex, MC, Visa.
PRICES: B&B doubles from £140, singles from £95. À la carte dinner £40. 1-night bookings refused at most weekends.

Prices may change – check with hotel.

TREFEDDIAN HOTEL

The Cave-Browne-Cave family have kept a welcome in the hillside at their big, white hotel above Cardigan Bay since the days of silent film, when men wore bowler hats to the beach. This 'traditional hotel' moves at its own gentle pace, and 'one gets the impression that that is exactly what guests want', writes a reader. Bedrooms, many with a sea view across road and railway, are decorated in fresh marine colours. 'We had a third-floor room with lovely views over the sand dunes to the sea, but traffic and railway noise was not intrusive.' Most can accommodate an extra bed or cot, some can sleep two adults and three children, and parents can relax at dinner courtesy of a child-listening service. Child-friendliness and flexibility extend to a playroom and outdoor play area, children's supper and all-day lounge menu. 'Staff are enthusiastic and welcoming.' Expect dishes such as Dover sole with prawn mousse and cardinal sauce, slow-roasted belly pork with sauce Albert, or vegetable tagine, with produce from the kitchen garden. On sunny days, you can lunch on the terrace. (Geoffrey Bignell)

Tywyn Road
Aberdovey LL35 0SB

T: 01654 767213
E: info@trefwales.com
W: trefwales.com

BEDROOMS: 59. 1 suitable for disabled.
OPEN: all year except 11 Dec–22 Jan.
FACILITIES: lift, lounge bar, study, family lounge, adult lounge, restaurant, games room (snooker, table tennis, pool table), in-room TV (Freeview), indoor swimming pool, beauty salon, 15-acre grounds (tennis, putting green, children's playground), EV charging, most public rooms wheelchair accessible, adapted toilet.
BACKGROUND MUSIC: none.
LOCATION: ¼ mile N of Aberdovey.
CHILDREN: all ages welcomed, under-10s free, extra bed (aged 10–16) £35–£45, with dinner.
DOGS: allowed in some bedrooms (£15 per dog per night), library.
CREDIT CARDS: MC, Visa.
PRICES: D,B&B from £125 per person (per night for min. 2-night stay, longer stay discounts).

Prices may change – check with hotel.

ABERGAVENNY Monmouthshire

THE ANGEL HOTEL

This handsome Georgian coaching inn, in the centre of Abergavenny, 'the Gateway to Wales', has been whisked into a smart town house hotel with convivial bar, interesting menus and cheerful staff. Expect to meet locals chattering in the bar, a fine affair of wood panelling, chesterfield sofas and glossy ferns. Dine here or in the sleek Oak Room from a 'wide choice of interesting food, well presented and tasty', such as whole lemon sole, seaweed butter and new potatoes, along with vegetarian and pub staples. Bread and patisserie come from the sister bakery next door. The hotel can arrange a taxi to another sister venture, the Michelin-starred Walnut Tree Inn, ten minutes away. 'Comfortable' and 'neat' bedrooms are in neutral shades with good-quality fabrics, space for armchairs – 'a nice place to sit and read after a day out' – and the 'best reading lights ever'. Modern bathrooms feature Villeroy & Boch or Fired Earth fittings. Breakfast includes home-made granola, local sausages and eggs Florentine served by 'very helpful' staff who 'gave us lots of useful ideas for trips out'. (Peter and Anne Davies, and others)

15 Cross Street
Abergavenny NP7 5EN

T: 01873 857121
E: info@angelabergavenny.com
W: angelabergavenny.com

BEDROOMS: 31. 2 in adjacent mews.
OPEN: all year except 24–27 Dec.
FACILITIES: lift, lounge, bar, tea room, restaurant, private function rooms, bakery, in-room TV (Freeview), civil wedding licence, courtyard, parking, EV charging, public rooms wheelchair accessible, adapted toilet.
BACKGROUND MUSIC: in restaurant and tea room, pianist in restaurant Fri and Sat dinner.
LOCATION: town centre.
CHILDREN: all ages welcomed, extra bed (12 and under) £26, free cot.
DOGS: allowed in the Foxhunter bar and courtyard.
CREDIT CARDS: Amex, MC, Visa.
PRICES: B&B doubles from £185.
À la carte £50, 3-course set menu £40.
1-night bookings sometimes refused.

Prices may change – check with hotel.

ABERSOCH Gwynedd

MAP 3:B2

PORTH TOCYN HOTEL

Guide readers are unswervingly loyal to this family-friendly country house by the sea, with peerless views to Snowdonia across Cardigan Bay, run by the Fletcher-Brewer family since opening in 1948. Some who once came for bucket-and-spade holidays now sip G&T on the terrace as the grandkids swim, play table tennis or tuck into high tea. A devotee on their '30th visit to this lovely hotel' sums it up: 'Comfort, good food, good conversation with fellow guests and owners alike are all there in abundance.' Bedroom style is a mix of traditional and contemporary, with a sea or countryside view. Most rooms have an over-bath power shower, some a walk-in shower only. 'Furniture choices were rather eccentric,' notes a less smitten reader, who found the cooking 'hit and miss' – the big hit being 'really excellent fillet steak'. Other menu choices include moules marinière, maybe spiced nut and mushroom balls with herbed couscous, tomato and olive sauce. 'The one lunch we had (alfresco) was very nice.' The staff are 'pleasant and attentive' in this hotel that is 'outstanding as always'. (Dr Helen Parkinson, Steven Parsons, and others)

Bwlchtocyn
Abersoch LL53 7BU

T: 01758 713303
E: bookings@porthtocynhotel.co.uk
W: porthtocynhotel.co.uk

BEDROOMS: 17. 3 on ground floor. 1 shepherd's hut, 1 self-catering cottage.
OPEN: 1 Apr–end Oct.
FACILITIES: sitting rooms, children's snug, small bar, dining room, in-room TV (Freeview), terrace, 20-acre grounds (outdoor pool heated May–Sept, tennis), EV charging, call to discuss wheelchair access.
BACKGROUND MUSIC: none.
LOCATION: 2 miles outside village.
CHILDREN: all ages welcomed, free cots/extra beds, no under-6s at dinner.
DOGS: allowed in bedrooms (no charge), not in restaurant or some public rooms.
CREDIT CARDS: MC, Visa.
PRICES: B&B doubles from £145, singles from £100. À la carte £40, fixed-price dinner £42–£49. 1-night bookings occasionally refused at weekends.

Prices may change – check with hotel.

TY MAWR

'Blessed to be in the beautiful Cothi valley, surrounded by Brechfa Forest', this 16th-century country house hotel has the feeling of a private home. It now belongs to Gill Brown and David Hart, with Gill working as chef and David front of house. They plan to maintain the status quo while upgrading the bathrooms and perhaps adding a bedroom or two. The rustic-chic rooms reflect the tranquil surroundings. Afon Marlais, painted in soft blues, evokes the River Marlais, which borders the property. Dog-friendly Coedwig Brechfa, in a former stable, has its own front door, a seating area, coffee pod machine, sofa bed. All have period furniture, pottery cups and luxury toiletries. Four-legged guests are settled in with biscuits and a bowl. A three-course dinner comes with home-made bread, canapés, sorbet and fruit and veg from the kitchen garden. Gill uses local produce to create dishes such as braised pork cheeks in red wine with apple and mustard compote and pomme purée, perhaps followed by some local Welsh cheese. 'Quiet and peaceful, with easy access to walks,' reports a satisfied guest. (Isaac Romanov, Sue O'Leary)

Brechfa SA32 7RA

T: 01267 202332
E: info@wales-country-hotel.co.uk
W: wales-country-hotel.co.uk

BEDROOMS: 6. 2 on ground floor, 1 with private access.
OPEN: all year.
FACILITIES: sitting room, bar, breakfast room, restaurant, in-room TV (Freeview), wedding licence applied for, 1-acre grounds, EV charging.
BACKGROUND MUSIC: classical in restaurant during dinner.
LOCATION: village centre.
CHILDREN: aged 10 and over welcomed.
DOGS: allowed in some bedrooms (£20 per dog, biscuits, bowls, information on local walks provided), sitting room and bar, breakfast room, not in restaurant.
CREDIT CARDS: Amex, MC, Visa.
PRICES: B&B doubles from £145, singles from £110. À la carte £42.

Prices may change – check with hotel.

BRECON Powys

MAP 3:D3

THE COACH HOUSE

Kayt and Hugh Cooper's top-notch B&B
combines hotel-quality accommodation with
the warmth and intimacy of an owner-run guest
house. A former 19th-century coaching inn, it has
long been championed by friends of the Guide. A
first-floor suite, Brychan, has a super-king bed,
a large bathroom with bath and walk-in shower,
a coffee machine and mini-fridge. The least-
expensive room, top-floor Taliesin, has a double
bed, original artwork, a walk-in shower. Mid-
price Dwynwen has a king-size bed, an over-bath
shower. You can relax in the secluded back garden
or the lounge/library. In the airy breakfast room,
with well-spaced tables, the 'menu is extensive'.
Choices include Welsh rarebit made with local
beer, Welsh cheese and wholegrain mustard;
home-made pancakes with berries; free-range
scrambled eggs with smoked salmon and laver
bread; and a full Welsh with locally sourced
meats, or full veggie. 'I think the rarebit was
better than last time,' repeat visitors reported. And
if that doesn't set you up for the day, you can also
order a packed lunch to take when walking in the
Brecon Beacons national park.

12 Orchard Street
Brecon LD3 8AN

T: 01874 620043
E: reservations@coachhousebrecon.
com
W: coachhousebrecon.com

BEDROOMS: 6.
OPEN: all year except 1 week over
Christmas (open New Year).
FACILITIES: reading room, breakfast
room, lounge (with drinks service), in-
room TV (Freeview), garden, drying
room, parking, secure bicycle storage,
unsuitable for disabled.
BACKGROUND MUSIC: classical or Welsh
harp music in breakfast room.
LOCATION: ½ mile from town centre.
CHILDREN: 16s and upwards
welcomed, guests aged 19 and under
must share a room with an adult aged
20 or over.
DOGS: not allowed.
CREDIT CARDS: MC, Visa.
PRICES: B&B doubles from £89, singles
from £84. Min. 2-night stay.

Prices may change – check with hotel.

PLAS DINAS COUNTRY HOUSE

With its romantic bedrooms and views across the Menai Strait, the former country residence of the Armstrong-Jones family manages to be luxurious yet relaxed. One reader felt 'at home' in this 'incredible historic country house'. Annie and Daniel Perks have preserved the romance of this Victorian home with 17th-century origins, where Princess Margaret and Lord Snowdon spent weekends, while introducing modern comforts. Antiques, family portraits, memorabilia and signed photographs by Lord Snowdon decorate the rooms. Bedrooms, recently fully renovated, are furnished with bold wallpapers, swagged curtains and a mix of antique and bespoke furniture. Some have four-posters or carved beds, others a fireplace or window seat. Bathrooms vary from compact to opulent with gold fittings. Guests gather in the welcoming drawing room with its open fire and plump sofas before dinner. The highly praised monthly-changing menu might include smoked duck breast with five-spice pear, grilled halibut with saffron potato, and 'absolutely glorious' steak. 'The most wonderful country house. I have never felt so relaxed.' (Mrs Duckett, and others)

Bontnewydd
Caernarfon LL54 7YF

T: 01286 830214
E: info@plasdinas.co.uk
W: plasdinas.co.uk

BEDROOMS: 10. 1 on ground floor.
OPEN: all year except Christmas, restaurant closed Sun, Mon Oct–May (incl.) when light snacks available.
FACILITIES: drawing room, restaurant, private dining room, in-room TV (Freeview), civil wedding licence, 15-acre grounds.
BACKGROUND MUSIC: in drawing room and dining room.
LOCATION: 5-min. drive S of town.
CHILDREN: over-12s welcomed, extra bed £50.
DOGS: allowed in 2 bedrooms and drawing room (£15 per night, welcome pack) by arrangement.
CREDIT CARDS: Amex, MC, Visa.
PRICES: B&B doubles from £139. Set dinner £65. 1-night bookings refused New Year's Eve.

Prices may change – check with hotel.

DOLFOR Powys

MAP 3:C4

THE OLD VICARAGE

In the rolling mid-Wales countryside, Tim and Helen Withers' Victorian red brick vicarage is a welcoming base from which to explore a 'wonderful but little-visited part of the world'. The bedrooms are pleasingly styled, with contemporary fabrics and furnishings. Teme has a king-size bed and a roll-top bath with hand-held shower, views over the front lawn to sheep-grazed hills. The Severn Suite, with two doubles, is ideal for a family. Mule ('the local river, not the animal') has a very comfortable five-foot bed, 'nice bedside lights … plenty of space to put things'. You can relax in the residents' lounge, with afternoon tea and quince-and-almond tart on request. At night, by arrangement, a tapas plate brings 'restaurant-standard' house slaw, Serrano ham, Manchego cheese, a Welsh Cheddar soufflé, hake brandade, freshly baked sourdough baguette, and more. 'There is a short wine list which is much appreciated.' Breakfast, 'topped off with toast and home-made quince jelly', is similarly imaginative. 'My wife raved about the omelette with laver bread.' In all, 'we really enjoyed our stay and certainly plan to stay again'. (A and MK)

Dolfor
Newtown SY16 4BN

T: 07753 760054
E: mail@theoldvicaragedolfor.co.uk
W: theoldvicaragedolfor.co.uk

BEDROOMS: 4.
OPEN: all year except last 3 weeks Dec and New Year, reopens 5 Jan.
FACILITIES: drawing room, dining room, in-room TV (Freeview), 1½-acre garden, EV charging, unsuitable for disabled.
BACKGROUND MUSIC: none.
LOCATION: 3 miles S of Newtown.
CHILDREN: all ages welcomed, family room, cot £10, extra bed £20.
DOGS: not allowed.
CREDIT CARDS: Amex, MC, Visa.
PRICES: B&B doubles from £95, singles from £70. Meze plate £14. 1-night bookings refused bank holidays and Royal Welsh Show week.

Prices may change – check with hotel.

AEL Y BRYN

'Creative and immaculate' gardens surround this luxury, adults-only B&B in tranquil countryside, outside the village of 'Egg-lis-oo-roo', with views to the Preseli hills and Carningli mountain. From the shell of a single-storey wartime hostel that once housed land girls, 'consummate hoteliers' Robert Smith and Arwel Hughes have created 'a wonderful, spacious home', with guest lounge/ music room, library and conservatory. 'I'm not surprised you receive rave reviews,' writes a reader, who was warmly welcomed on arrival with tea and 'a plate of delicious fancies'. 'Beautifully furnished' Carn Menyn suite had French doors to a private patio 'where we could sit and watch the swallows skimming over the pond'. We hear perennial praise for the hosts' 'meticulous attention to detail', which includes fresh milk in a mini-fridge. At night, by arrangement, the table is set in the beamed dining room for a dinner cooked 'with love and skill'. Bring your own wine; they charge no corkage. 'Breakfasts are superb with an extensive menu.' (Sheila Mawer, Brian Hughes, and others)

Eglwyswrw
Crymych SA41 3UL

T: 01239 891411
E: stay@aelybrynpembrokeshire.
   co.uk
W: aelybrynpembrokeshire.co.uk

BEDROOMS: 4. All on ground floor.
OPEN: all year except Christmas/New Year.
FACILITIES: library, music room, dining room, conservatory (telescope), in-room TV (Freeview), courtyard, 2½-acre garden (wildlife pond, stream, bowls court, giant chess), public rooms wheelchair accessible.
BACKGROUND MUSIC: none.
LOCATION: ½ mile N of Eglwyswrw.
CHILDREN: not under 16.
DOGS: not allowed.
CREDIT CARDS: Amex, MC, Visa.
PRICES: B&B doubles from £120, singles from £100. Set dinner £29/£35 (2/3 courses). 1-night bookings may be refused.

Prices may change – check with hotel.

FELIN FACH Powys

THE FELIN FACH GRIFFIN

Tucked between the Brecon Beacons and the Black Mountains, this red brick inn glows with a warm welcome and down-to-earth charm that attracts walkers, dogs, families and couples. Brothers Edmund and Charles Inkin believe comfort and good food are key – as at sister properties The Gurnard's Head, Zennor, and The Old Coastguard, Mousehole (see entries) – so expect a series of dining areas with an inviting mix of chunky cottage tables, mustard and teal sofas, flagged or timbered floors, plus open fires or an Aga. The daily-changing menu offers simple food done well such as slow-roasted lamb with couscous, smoked haddock fish pie and a handsome vegetarian choice; many vegetables come from the kitchen garden, meat from local farms. In warmer weather, you can eat outside. Bedrooms, with views to fields or mountains, have a smart but warm cottagey style with bold-coloured walls, tongue-and-groove panelling, country-style furniture and Welsh blankets on beds so comfortable that guests want to take them home. No TVs but fresh flowers, home-made biscuits, fresh milk, Roberts radios and botanical toiletries.

Felin Fach
Brecon LD3 0UB

T: 01874 620111
E: enquiries@felinfachgriffin.co.uk
W: felinfachgriffin.co.uk

BEDROOMS: 8.
OPEN: all year except from 24 Dec evening–26 Dec incl.
FACILITIES: bar, dining rooms, limited mobile signal, 3-acre garden (kitchen garden, alfresco dining), bar/dining areas wheelchair accessible, adapted toilet.
BACKGROUND MUSIC: Radio 4 at breakfast, 'selected music' afternoon and evening.
LOCATION: 4 miles NE of Brecon, in village on A470.
CHILDREN: all ages welcomed, free cot, extra bed £15, children's menu.
DOGS: allowed in bedrooms (no charge, welcome pack), in bar and Tack Room, but not in restaurant.
CREDIT CARDS: MC, Visa.
PRICES: B&B doubles from £160, singles from £127.50. À la carte 3-course set-price £42.

Prices may change – check with hotel.

GLYNARTHEN Ceredigion

PENBONTBREN

Luxury and privacy are guaranteed at this unusual
farmhouse B&B set in gardens, ten minutes from
west Wales beaches and with views to the Preseli
hills. Bedrooms, with comfortable sitting areas,
are in converted outbuildings – stables, barn,
mill and granary – of the Victorian farmhouse.
One is in a charming weatherboard cottage with
window boxes, picket fence and private terrace.
The others, too, have an individual outdoor
space and all blend original features – beams,
low ceilings – with a contemporary cottage style:
light colours, pale oak furniture, Lloyd Loom
chairs and brightly patterned rugs, sofas and
feature wallpapers. A kitchenette with fridge,
microwave and coffee machine means you can
be independent, although it would be a shame
to miss the splendid Welsh breakfasts offered
by Kathryn and Richard Jones. Taken in the
farmhouse dining room, amid pretty china, fresh
flowers and crisp tablecloths, cooked-to-order
dishes highlight Welsh produce and include local
smoked salmon and scrambled eggs, buttermilk
pancakes as well as the full Welsh with vegetarian
option. It makes a great start for tackling the
nearby Wales Coast Path.

Glynarthen
Llandysul SA44 6PE

T: 01239 810248
E: contact@penbontbren.com
W: penbontbren.com

BEDROOMS: 6. 5 in annexe, 1 in garden,
3 on ground floor, 1 family suite,
1 suitable for disabled. Plus self-
catering cottage.
OPEN: all year except 24–26 Dec.
FACILITIES: breakfast room, in-room
TV (Freeview), 4-acre grounds
(croquet lawn), bike storage, public
rooms wheelchair accessible, adapted
toilet.
BACKGROUND MUSIC: classical music at
breakfast.
LOCATION: 5 miles N of Newcastle
Emlyn.
CHILDREN: all ages welcomed, family
suite.
DOGS: allowed in some bedrooms by
prior agreement (£20 per stay), not in
breakfast room.
CREDIT CARDS: Amex, MC, Visa.
PRICES: B&B doubles from £140, singles
from £120, family suite from £165.
1-night bookings occasionally refused
in summer.

Prices may change – check with hotel.

THE FALCONDALE

A 19th-century Italianate villa in 14-acre grounds,
with views across the gently rolling Teifi valley,
is today a hotel and popular wedding venue with
an in-house beauty parlour and romance in its
very fabric. A rebuilding of an older house named
Pant-y-Curyll (valley of the sparrowhawk), it
was designed by Pugin protégé Thomas Talbot
Bury, probably for one JS Harford and his bride,
Mary von Bunsen, who honeymooned in Italy.
The decor is somewhat last century, but rooms
are really spacious, with some good antiques. A
valley-view room has a modern four-poster and
French doors to a Juliet balcony from which
to watch red kites and buzzards. A family can
take the lift to second-floor Room 21, with two
double beds, overlooking the landscaped gardens.
Pleasingly, all rooms have a teapot, cafetière
and shortbread. Readers praise the food. A
seasonal menu inspired by local produce includes
dishes such as venison loin, pan-fried sea bass or
Parmesan linguine. Be sure to bring Fido; they'll
make him so welcome. There are wonderful
walks along the Ceredigion Coast Path or in
the Cambrian mountains. 'A very decent hotel.'
(Peter Anderson)

Falcondale Drive
Lampeter SA48 7RX

T: 01570 422910
E: info@thefalcondale.co.uk
W: thefalcondale.co.uk

BEDROOMS: 17.
OPEN: all year.
FACILITIES: lift (to some bedrooms),
bar, 2 lounges, conservatory,
restaurant, in-room TV (Freeview),
civil wedding licence, beauty
treatment room, terrace, 14-acre
grounds, EV charging, restaurant and
ground floor wheelchair accessible,
adapted toilet.
BACKGROUND MUSIC: in restaurant and
lounges.
LOCATION: 1 mile N of Lampeter.
CHILDREN: all ages welcomed, cots £10,
extra bed £30.
DOGS: allowed in bedrooms (£10 per
night), public areas, not restaurant.
CREDIT CARDS: MC, Visa.
PRICES: B&B doubles from £169, singles
from £145. À la carte £35, fixed-price
menu £38.

Prices may change – check with hotel.

TYDDYN LLAN

There's no mobile signal to distract you at Susan and Bryan Webb's restaurant-with-rooms overlooking the peaceful Vale of Edeyrnion, which means you can concentrate on the excellent food. Although Brian is well into his fifth decade at the stove, his enthusiasm is undimmed. Four nights a week he cooks an eight-course tasting menu and wide-ranging fixed-price menu of dishes such as grilled Dover sole, monk's beard and laver-bread butter sauce, or fillet of venison, creamed polenta and wild mushrooms. Vegetarians will be well taken care of if they give advance notice. Expect traditional, elegant interiors in the extended Georgian house. One of the best bedrooms has an ornate metal four-poster, a sitting area, a slipper bath and walk-in shower; another has patio doors to a private garden. All have home-made biscuits, Gilchrist & Soames toiletries. Breakfast is a feast, with fresh juice, home-made granola, pastries, a full Welsh with rare-breed pork sausages, free-range eggs and laver-bread cake, Loch Fyne smoked salmon, and haddock. If you need more fuel to explore the surrounding countryside, you can order a packed lunch.

Llandrillo
Corwen LL21 0ST

T: 01490 440264
E: info@tyddynllan.co.uk
W: tyddynllan.co.uk

BEDROOMS: 13. 3 with separate entrance, 1, on ground floor, suitable for disabled.
OPEN: all year Thurs–Sun, closed Christmas, last 2 weeks Jan, 1 week Mar, 1 week June, 1 week Sept.
FACILITIES: 2 lounges, bar, 2 dining rooms, in-room TV (Freeview), no mobile signal, civil wedding licence, 3-acre garden, public rooms wheelchair accessible, adapted toilet.
BACKGROUND MUSIC: none.
LOCATION: 5 miles SW of Corwen.
CHILDREN: all ages welcomed, extra bed £30, children's menu.
DOGS: allowed in bedrooms (£15 per dog per night), not in public rooms.
CREDIT CARDS: Amex, MC, Visa.
PRICES: B&B doubles from £190. Fixed-price 3-course dinner £90, tasting menu £110. 1-night bookings refused at Christmas.

Prices may change – check with hotel.

LLANDUDNO Conwy

MAP 3:A3

BODYSGALLEN HALL AND SPA

This Tudor Gothic-style Elizabethan mansion, extended over centuries, overlooks parkland with a rare 17th-century parterre, walled rose garden, cascade, lily pond and follies. Owned by the National Trust, it is now a luxury hotel and spa, part of the Historic House Hotels group (see also Hartwell House, Aylesbury, and Middlethorpe Hall, York). Public rooms have oak panelling, magnificent fireplaces, oil portraits, antiques. Stone-mullioned windows frame views to Conwy Castle and Snowdonia. Bedrooms are presented in traditional country house style. Suites, one with a four-poster, have a sitting room. All have an espresso machine, home-made biscuits, classy toiletries. There are further rooms in charming stone cottages in the grounds, sleeping up to four, some with a private garden, some dog-friendly. Chef Abdalla El Shershaby uses organic produce from the potager in dishes such as roast sea bass fillet with charred aubergine, polenta fritters, Bodysgallen tomato butter. After a full Welsh or continental breakfast, you can request a map at reception and take a woodland walk to a Gothic tower or to an obelisk on top of Pydew mountain.

The Royal Welsh Way
Llandudno LL30 1RS

T: 01492 584466
E: info@bodysgallen.com
W: bodysgallen.com

BEDROOMS: 31. 16 in cottages, 1 suitable for disabled.
OPEN: all year.
FACILITIES: hall, drawing room, library, bar, dining room (vegetarian/vegan menus), in-room TV (Freeview), civil wedding licence, 220-acre park, spa (15-metre heated pool), EV charging, ground floor wheelchair accessible.
BACKGROUND MUSIC: none.
LOCATION: 2 miles S of Llandudno and Conwy.
CHILDREN: no under-7s in hotel, or under-8s in spa.
DOGS: max. 1 large or 2 small, allowed in some cottages by request (no charge).
CREDIT CARDS: Amex, MC, Visa.
PRICES: B&B doubles from £240, singles from £215. Fine-dining menu (Wed–Sat) £74, set-price dinner Mon, Tues £35. 1-night bookings refused at bank holidays.

Prices may change – check with hotel.

SEE ALSO SHORTLIST

LLANGAMMARCH WELLS Powys   MAP 3:D3

LAKE COUNTRY HOUSE HOTEL & SPA

A 'narrow and hairy' road leads to Jan and Pierre Mifsud's hotel in wooded grounds on the River Irfon, with views to the Cambrian mountains. An idiosyncratic Victorian mock-Tudor former fishing lodge, it has 'the kind of calm only found in the back of beyond'. Readers had 'a lovely stay' and were full of praise for the 'very attentive staff'. The ambience is country house comfy, with an abundance of 'chairs and settees, large rugs, lit fires/log-burners, "family" portraits, paintings, cabinets, china … all well cared for'. The best house bedrooms have an in-room spa bath or a separate sitting room. Dog-friendly annexe suites have a bath and shower, double doors opening on to the grounds. You can take afternoon tea in one of several lounges, or alfresco. After 'delicious canapés', 'detailed, inventive' dishes included 'gin-and-tonic-cured chalk stream trout, pickled lemon, tonic gel, rye bread, dill mayo; slow-cooked venison haunch, celeriac mash, pickled walnut ketchup'; tempting veggie options. After an exemplary breakfast, you might fish in the lake or river for trout and grayling. 'Would definitely recommend.' (Carol Jackson)

Llangammarch Wells LD4 4BS

T: 01591 620202
E: info@lakecountryhouse.co.uk
W: lakecountryhouse.co.uk

BEDROOMS: 32. 12 suites in adjacent lodge, 7 on ground floor, 1 suitable for disabled.
OPEN: all year.
FACILITIES: lounge, bar, restaurant (vegetarian menu), breakfast room, in-room TV (Freeview), spa (15-metre swimming pool), civil wedding licence, 50-acre grounds (tennis, trout lake, 9-hole golf course), public rooms wheelchair accessible, adapted toilet.
BACKGROUND MUSIC: none.
LOCATION: 8 miles SW of Builth Wells.
CHILDREN: all ages welcomed, extra bed £25, no under-8s in spa, or restaurant after 7 pm.
DOGS: allowed (£20 per night), not in main lounge, dining room, spa.
CREDIT CARDS: Amex, MC, Visa.
PRICES: B&B doubles from £215, singles from £165. Fixed-price dinner £49.50.

Prices may change – check with hotel.

LLANTHONY Monmouthshire   MAP 3:D4

LLANTHONY PRIORY HOTEL

Peace, stillness and surroundings removed from the buzzing demands of the modern world are guaranteed at this hotel huddled under the Welsh Black mountains. Up the Vale of Ewyas, where the narrow road becomes a track, there is no mobile signal, Wi-Fi or television here. Instead, you'll find comfort, simplicity and a sense of timelessness; the hotel is in the original prior's quarters for the adjoining 12th-century Augustinian Priory, the latter now a roofless but impressive ruin. Rooms are not monastic, but they are simple with whitewashed walls, sparse but solid Victorian furniture – perhaps a marble-topped washstand or four-poster bed – and colourful bedspreads. Four tower rooms up a spiral staircase share two modern shower rooms; the other three share a bathroom. Enjoy walks from the door or relax in the fire-warmed lounge overlooking the Priory. Try a Welsh ale in the stone-flagged and vaulted bar before supper in the equally cosy dining room, gleaming with brass and copper and a fire in the range. Food is homely pub style with a surprisingly large choice that could include beef lasagne, Moroccan chicken and spicy bean goulash.

Llanthony
Abergavenny NP7 7NN

T: 01873 890487
E: llanthonypriory@btconnect.com
W: llanthonyprioryhotel.co.uk

BEDROOMS: 7. All with shared showers/bathrooms.
OPEN: Fri–Sun (Nov–Mar), Tues–Sun (Apr–Oct), 27 Dec–1 Jan, closed Mon except bank holidays.
FACILITIES: lounge, bar, dining room, no Wi-Fi, mobile phone signal or TV, extensive grounds (including priory ruins), unsuitable for disabled.
BACKGROUND MUSIC: none.
LOCATION: 10 miles N of Abergavenny.
CHILDREN: over-10s welcomed, ring for pricing.
DOGS: not allowed.
CREDIT CARDS: MC, Visa.
PRICES: B&B doubles from £110, singles from £85. À la carte 3 courses £21.

Prices may change – check with hotel.

LLYSWEN Powys

LLANGOED HALL

A tree-lined drive leads to this ivy-clad country
mansion – all tall chimneys, vast bay windows
and landscaped gardens, yet its atmosphere is far
from starchy. 'Grand but intimate,' say readers,
'it still has the feel of a private house.' Dating
from the 17th century and remodelled in 1912
in Edwardian Lutyensesque style, it was later
restored to that grandeur in the 1980s by the late
Sir Bernard Ashley, widower of designer Laura
Ashley. It is period-drama perfect with polished-
wood floors and grand fireplaces, plump sofas
and softly lit table lamps, antiques and art, and
luxurious comforts at every turn. Bedrooms
are 'calmly decorated' in classic style with thick
fabrics, pretty florals and some four-posters.
Even the smallest rooms have beautifully draped
beds and space for armchairs; larger rooms have
sofas, and all have robes, a decanter of Madeira,
and home-made Welsh cakes. Elegant dinners
are 'absolutely delicious' – much produce from
the large kitchen garden – with dishes such as
confit monkfish with mushroom risotto, and fillet
of beef with alliums and red wine jus. 'You feel
sheltered from the world.' (Frances Thomas)

Llyswen
Brecon LD3 0YP

T: 01874 754525
E: reception@llangoedhall.com
W: llangoedhall.co.uk

BEDROOMS: 23.
OPEN: all year, Thurs–Sun, open
Christmas and New Year.
FACILITIES: great hall, morning room,
library, bar/lounge, restaurant, billiard
room, function rooms, in-room TV,
civil wedding licence, 17-acre gardens,
EV charging, public areas wheelchair
accessible.
BACKGROUND MUSIC: in restaurant,
pianist on special occasions.
LOCATION: 12 miles NE of Brecon.
CHILDREN: all ages welcomed, extra
bed for under-12s £65 per night, no
under-12s for evening dining.
DOGS: allowed in 2 bedrooms (ring to
check, £25 per night), not in public
rooms, heated kennels (no charge)
available.
CREDIT CARDS: MC, Visa.
PRICES: D,B&B doubles from £350. Set
3-course menu £65, tasting menu £85.

Prices may change – check with hotel.

NARBERTH Pembrokeshire

MAP 3:D2

GROVE OF NARBERTH

Turn off a country lane down a tree-lined drive and your tensions will slip away when you glimpse this white stucco building with its pleasing Georgian symmetry. In 26 verdant acres, with views to the Preseli hills, this country house with Arts and Crafts flourishes is one of Wales's most romantic hideaways. Rescued from semi-dereliction by Neil and Zoë Kedward in 2007, it combines country house hotel comforts – squashy sofas, real fires, fine food, cosseting bedrooms – with a relaxed, modern touch. Lounges have soft colours, Welsh textiles, and antiques – 'comfy rooms to sit and read on wet days'. Fine dining dishes in The Fernery could include sea bass with squid and chilli, and venison with pumpkin and blueberry. Brightly coloured Artisan offers more robust food such as grilled lamb and risottos. 'The cooking is first class,' reported one reader. 'Well served and staff knew their food and wine,' said another. Bedrooms vary from traditional, with William Morris wallpapers, in the main house to a rustic-chic style in the cottages. Enjoy walks, the nearby coast or tea on the terrace. (Peter and Anne Davies, Peter Anderson)

Molleston
Narberth SA67 8BX

T: 01834 860915
E: reservations@grovenarberth.co.uk
W: thegrove-narberth.co.uk

BEDROOMS: 25. 12 in cottages in grounds, 1 suitable for disabled.
OPEN: all year, Fernery closed Sun, Mon, Tues.
FACILITIES: 3 lounges, bar, 2 restaurants (veg/vegan menus), in-room TV, in-room spa treatments, civil wedding licence, 26-acre grounds, EV charging, ground floor wheelchair accessible, adapted toilet.
BACKGROUND MUSIC: in public areas.
LOCATION: 1 mile S of Narberth.
CHILDREN: all ages welcomed, extra bed £45, no under-12s in Fernery.
DOGS: allowed in some bedrooms (£20, welcome pack), lounge, snug.
CREDIT CARDS: Amex, MC, Visa.
PRICES: B&B doubles from £300. Tasting menus (Fernery) from £85, à la carte (Artisan rooms) £46. 1-night bookings refused at peak times.

Prices may change – check with hotel.

SEE ALSO SHORTLIST

CNAPAN

With a home-from-home ambience, this Georgian B&B on Newport's main street is an ideal base from which to explore the Pembrokeshire Coast national park. Perfect hosts Judith and Michael Cooper welcome new arrivals with tea or coffee and home-made Welsh cakes. Interiors are contemporary, spruce and bright. Rear bedrooms overlook the green oasis garden, while those at the front have views of a Norman castle on the slopes of Carningli ('mountain of angels'). They have Welsh wool blankets, works by local artists, fresh milk. The house has a licensed bar, so you can relax with a drink by the log fire in the sitting room or, on fine days, in the sunshine. There is plenty of choice at breakfast – the full Welsh and full vegetarian, a Scottish kipper, smoked salmon, porridge with maple syrup and chia seeds and, for vegans, chickpea and apricot patties, and vegan sausage, grilled tomato, sautéed mushrooms. There are riding stables nearby, or you can hire an electric bike, play golf on Newport links, relax on Newport sands, watch for greenshank and goosander on the Nevern estuary, and at night you'll find plenty of places in which to dine.

East Street
Newport SA42 0SY

T: 01239 820575
E: enquiry@cnapan.co.uk
W: cnapan.co.uk

BEDROOMS: 5. Includes 1 family room. Plus self-catering cottage.
OPEN: all year except Christmas, Feb and early March (ring or check website for dates).
FACILITIES: sitting room, bar, in-room TV (Freeview), small garden, parking, electric bikes to hire.
BACKGROUND MUSIC: none.
LOCATION: town centre.
CHILDREN: all ages welcomed, family room, cots.
DOGS: not allowed.
CREDIT CARDS: MC, Visa.
PRICES: B&B doubles from £90, singles from £70, family room (sleeps 3) from £110. 1-night bookings refused Apr–Nov.

Prices may change – check with hotel.

PENALLY ABBEY

You would need a heart of stone not to be charmed by the creeper-covered facade of this Strawberry Hill Gothic house, with its pretty ogee windows, decorative eaves and hilltop position above gardens tumbling to the sea. Inside doesn't disappoint, either: interior designer Melanie Boissevain and husband Lucas have created stylish, relaxing spaces where antiques mix with French market finds, and blowsy wallpapers with Persian rugs. There are books on the piano, a fire in the sitting room, a cosy bar and a sunroom – take afternoon tea here or on the terrace before a walk 'along the fabulous South Beach to Tenby'. The 'splendid food' is Modern British cooking with both 'variety and taste'. It might include pan-fried scallops with onion sauce, and lamb rump with couscous; fish is landed at Tenby, strawberries from the farm down the road. The romantic dining room, with Arcadian-print wallpaper and candlelight, has views over the bay to the Gower Peninsula. 'Very comfortable' bedrooms are calming spaces of soft colours and pretty fabrics; some with a window seat, coach house rooms are more Scandi. All have indulgent marble bathrooms. (ML)

Penally
Tenby SA70 7PY

T: 01834 843033
E: info@penally-abbey.com
W: penally-abbey.com

BEDROOMS: 12. 4 in coach house, 2 on ground floor.
OPEN: all year.
FACILITIES: drawing room, bar, sunroom, restaurant (vegetarian menu), function room, in-room TV (Freeview), 'limited bandwith' Wi-Fi, civil wedding licence, in-room treatments, terrace, 1-acre lawns.
BACKGROUND MUSIC: 'very gentle' in bar and restaurant.
LOCATION: 1½ miles SW of Tenby.
CHILDREN: all ages welcomed, over-3s on extra bed £25.
DOGS: allowed in coach house bedrooms (not unattended, £15 a night), bar, sunroom, not in restaurant.
CREDIT CARDS: MC, Visa.
PRICES: B&B doubles from £155. À la carte £50 (vegetarian £35). 1-night bookings refused only at Christmas and major sporting event weekends.

Prices may change – check with hotel.

PORTMEIRION Gwynedd

HOTEL PORTMEIRION

The centrepiece of an extraordinary Italianate resort village, this Victorian mansion is on wooded slopes above the Dwyryd estuary in glorious Snowdonia. It opened as a hotel in 1926, as visionary architect Clough Williams-Ellis set out to show how development could enhance the landscape. 'The hotel and scenery are stunning, the food is fabulous and the service is outstanding,' wrote one reader, while a second, returning after ten years, found it 'better than ever'. 'We felt like VIPs, driving through the village to our allocated parking space,' relate others, who also felt that the hotel 'promises more than it delivers'. The bedrooms are a tad old-fashioned, the Peacock Suite sumptuous with a 'wonderful view'. There are more contemporary rooms in Castell Deudraeth, and in other village properties. The Art Deco bar and dining room were recreated in 2005 by Sir Terence Conran. A short fine-dining menu includes dishes such as duck breast and confit, pommes Anna, beetroot, fennel, stem ginger jus. If the hotel divides opinion, all must agree, there is nowhere in the world quite like this. (Kate MacMaster, Stephen D Peters)

Minffordd
Penrhyndeudraeth
Portmeirion LL48 6ER

T: 01766 770000
E: stay@portmeirion-village.com
W: portmeirion.wales

BEDROOMS: 14. Plus 11 in Castell Deudraeth, 34 in village, some on ground floor, 1 suitable for disabled.
OPEN: all year except 10 Jan–1 Feb.
FACILITIES: lift, 4 lounges, bar, restaurant, brasserie in Castell, in-room TV, civil wedding licence, terrace, 130-acre grounds, outdoor heated swimming pool (summer), parking, EV charging, free shuttle service around village, public rooms wheelchair accessible.
BACKGROUND MUSIC: in public areas, occasional live music in lounges.
LOCATION: 2 miles SE of Porthmadog.
CHILDREN: all ages welcomed.
DOGS: only assistance dogs allowed.
CREDIT CARDS: Amex, MC, Visa.
PRICES: B&B doubles from £195. Set-price menu £53/£60 (2/3 courses). Min. 2-night stay at most weekends.

Prices may change – check with hotel.

SANDY MOUNT HOUSE

NEW

The sands of time have seen changes at this formerly drab Edwardian seaside guest house, now a 'beautifully refurbished' contemporary hotel and restaurant. 'The fashionable grey clapboard exterior gives it a North American look,' report our inspectors, who were 'impressed by the quality of the accommodation'. Through the bar and restaurant, up steep stairs, Driftwood room had a sea view, 'a super-king bed with large, padded headboard, stylish art, an espresso machine, china cups, milk in a fridge, a bath with shower over, an old-fashioned washbasin and loo'. It was 'spacious, coastal, bright'. There is 'a breezy, smart, beachy look' to the restaurant, with bench seating, 'Lloyd Loom-type chairs, light shades like lobster pots'. An open kitchen dispensed 'crab hash browns with creamed sweetcorn and smoked chilli dressing (disappointing), exceptionally good mussel chowder; a coarse-ground beef burger as good as any good burger'. In the morning a tray of tea and coffee in flasks, with croissants and juice, was left outside the door before 'the main breakfast, full Welsh or vegetarian, eaten in the restaurant, all enjoyable'.

High Street
Rhosneigr LL64 5UX

T: 01407 253102
E: info@sandymounthouse.co.uk
W: sandymounthouse.co.uk

BEDROOMS: 7.
OPEN: all year, limited hours over Christmas.
FACILITIES: bar, restaurant, conservatory, private dining rooms, in-room TV, terrace, garden, bar and restaurant wheelchair accessible, adapted toilet.
BACKGROUND MUSIC: in bar, restaurant, on front terrace.
LOCATION: in village, close to beach.
CHILDREN: all ages welcomed.
DOGS: allowed by arrangement in 4 bedrooms, bar, on front terrace (max. 2 medium-sized, not unattended, £15 per dog per night).
CREDIT CARDS: Amex, MC, Visa.
PRICES: B&B doubles from £150. À la carte £35.

Prices may change – check with hotel.

TWR Y FELIN HOTEL

On the breezy St Davids peninsula overlooking St Bride's Bay, a 19th-century windmill tower forms the striking centrepiece of a contemporary art hotel. Not everyone is blown away by the 100-plus artwork on display, some of which is meant to be provocative, but 'this is an amazing hotel which offers comfort, good food and especially well-designed bedrooms/bathrooms'. In contrast to the rural setting, interiors are strikingly contemporary, with monochrome colours, hardwood floors and sleek furniture. There is a wide choice of rooms, spread over the main house and Oriel Wing, with 20 in a new annexe and a tower suite over three floors. Minimalist in style, they are generous in facilities, including a super-king bed, coffee machine, mini-fridge, bath, shower, and luxury toiletries. Views are of sea or countryside, the landscaped gardens or the little cathedral city. Some rooms have a terrace, some a Juliet balcony. In Blas restaurant, seasonal Welsh produce stars in dishes such as braised ox cheek, radish and roast onion, or roast brill with cauliflower and brown shrimp. 'Managers and staff were exceptionally friendly.' (MC)

Caerfai Road
St Davids SA62 6QT

T: 01437 725555
E: stay@twryfelinhotel.com
W: twryfelinhotel.com

BEDROOMS: 41. Some on ground floor, some in separate wing, 20 in purpose-built annexe, 2 accessible bedrooms, 1 with adapted bathroom.
OPEN: all year.
FACILITIES: bar, restaurant, lounge, in-room TV (Sky), landscaped grounds, vegan menu, civil wedding licence, EV charging, public areas wheelchair accessible, adapted toilet.
BACKGROUND MUSIC: in public areas.
LOCATION: a few hundred yards from centre of St Davids.
CHILDREN: not under 12.
DOGS: not allowed.
CREDIT CARDS: Amex, MC, Visa.
PRICES: B&B doubles from £250, singles from £210. À la carte £45, vegan £32. Normally 2-night min. stay Fri and Sat, but check for 1-night availability.

Prices may change – check with hotel.

SEE ALSO SHORTLIST

SKENFRITH Monmouthshire

THE BELL AT SKENFRITH

Huddled below wooded hills, beside a stone bridge over the River Monnow, this whitewashed former 17th-century coaching inn is delightfully at ease in the landscape. And that's the same feeling guests experience when they step inside this dog-friendly country inn. 'Smart and fresh' interiors are a blend of original beams and exposed stonework with stripped-wood floors, bottle-green colours, polished rustic tables and spindle-back chairs. Leafy pot plants plus floor-to-ceiling windows in the dining area add to the light and relaxed atmosphere. Dine here or on the terrace on locally sourced food, 'reflected in the quality of the meals', such as Wye valley carpaccio followed by Brecon beef with wild mushroom and peppercorn sauce, and Welsh cheeses for afters. There is a nice vegan menu, too. The comprehensive wine list includes 'a good range by the glass'. Bedrooms, quirkily named after fishing flies, are furnished in soft colours, pretty fabrics and a mix of vintage and contemporary pieces. Larger rooms have freestanding baths; all have views over garden, river or hills. 'Courteous staff were a tonic and a credit to the owners.' (RB)

Skenfrith NP7 8UH

T: 01600 750235
E: reception@skenfrith.co.uk
W: thebellatskenfrith.co.uk

BEDROOMS: 11.
OPEN: all year, except 1 week end Nov, 1 week early Jan, closed Mon and Tues at time of writing (check website).
FACILITIES: 2 bars, restaurant (vegan menu), Wine Room (private dining), in-room TV, 2-acre grounds (terrace, garden, river), EV charging, public rooms and terrace wheelchair accessible, adapted toilet.
BACKGROUND MUSIC: occasionally.
LOCATION: 9 miles W of Ross-on-Wye.
CHILDREN: all ages welcomed, extra bed £20, £24.95 incl. early supper, no under-8s in restaurant after 7 pm.
DOGS: allowed in bedrooms (£20 per night), bar, garden (dog shower/towels).
CREDIT CARDS: MC, Visa.
PRICES: B&B doubles from £175. À la carte £45. 1-night bookings refused Sat.

Prices may change – check with hotel.

PLAS TAN-YR-ALLT

You can lie in an antique four-poster in the William Madocks room at this singular B&B with views over the Glaslyn estuary to the Rhinog mountains, and listen to steam trains puffing along the sea wall. Madocks built not just that wall (the 'Cob'), but Tremadog itself, and incorporated a small house on the hillside above town into the late Georgian villa of today. 'The property is stunning and luxurious; the amount of love and effort that has gone into maintaining it is evident.' Howard Mattingley and Mark White are genial hosts. 'On arrival we were met by Mark, who settled us in and arranged a lovely tea in the drawing room.' The bedrooms are named after former residents. Shelley's Theatre recalls the poet Percy B, who wrote Queen Mab here before doing a flit, claiming someone had tried to assassinate him. Miss Hilda's room honours Hilda Greaves, born at the Plas in 1855, aunt of Clough Williams-Ellis (see Hotel Portmeirion, Portmeirion). All have a coffee machine, mini-fridge, Welsh toiletries. 'A treat to find such a lovely hotel in a beautiful setting.' 'The eggs Royale for breakfast was to die for.' (AB, HH, MH, and others)

Tremadog
Porthmadog LL49 9RG

T: 01766 514591
E: info@plastanyrallt.co.uk
W: plastanyrallt.co.uk

BEDROOMS: 3.
OPEN: all year except 3rd week of Dec to 2nd week of Feb.
FACILITIES: drawing room, dining room, 40-acre grounds, in-room TV (Freeview), unsuitable for disabled.
BACKGROUND MUSIC: in drawing room and dining room.
LOCATION: just above the village of Tremadog.
CHILDREN: not under 18.
DOGS: not allowed.
CREDIT CARDS: MC, Visa.
PRICES: B&B doubles from £190. Min. 2-night bookings Apr–Oct.

Prices may change – check with hotel.

DOLFFANOG FAWR

You could not wish for a more glorious location than you find at Lorraine Hinkins and Alex Yorke's 18th-century farmhouse B&B, with views to Cader Idris and the waters of Tal-y-llyn. Dyfi room has a window seat from which to gaze at the lake, an original fireplace, a large walk-in shower. Mawddach looks across the garden to the Dyfi and Tarren hills, and has three steps down to a bathroom with a shower over a corner bath. All rooms are in contemporary cottage style, with local artwork, a Welsh throw and fine toiletries. There is a well-stocked honesty bar, and an outdoor hydrotherapy hot tub, where you can soak weary limbs after a day's mountain biking, hoping for a glimpse of visiting pine martens. Anglers will find plenty of choice between the lake and rivers. Stable Wi-Fi and high-speed Internet are available; mobile phone coverage is not. A two-course supper may be provided if enough guests request it, and hosts can direct you to local restaurants. In the morning sit down to a full Welsh breakfast with home-baked bread, a Manx kipper, undyed smoked haddock or wild Alaskan smoked salmon.

Tal-y-llyn
Tywyn LL36 9AJ

T: 01654 761247
E: info@dolffanogfawr.co.uk
W: dolffanogfawr.co.uk

BEDROOMS: 4. 1 reached by covered walkway.
OPEN: Mar–Oct, evening meals occasionally available.
FACILITIES: lounge, dining room, in-room TV (Freeview), 1-acre garden (hot tub), unsuitable for disabled.
BACKGROUND MUSIC: background during evening meals.
LOCATION: by lake, 10 miles E of Tywyn.
CHILDREN: not under 11.
DOGS: allowed by arrangement in bedrooms (with own bed, £10 per night, not unattended), and lounge 'if other guests don't mind', not in dining room.
CREDIT CARDS: MC, Visa.
PRICES: B&B doubles from £125. Occasional evening meal when there is sufficient demand, £28 for 2 courses. Min. 2-night bookings preferred.

Prices may change – check with hotel.

THE WHITEBROOK

The beauties of the Wye valley that inspired the Georgian Picturesque movement are all around you at Chris and Kirsty Harrod's Michelin-starred restaurant-with-rooms. It is tucked away on a single-track road, with the eponymous brook rushing by, and the River Wye a stroll away. This is fertile plant-hunting ground, and Chris makes full use of it, devising his menus around foraged ingredients and organic produce from the orchard and kitchen garden. He honed his skills while working for four years at Raymond Blanc's Le Manoir aux Quat'Saisons, Great Milton, England (see entry), and every plate he creates is a work of art. Think Cornish plaice, Jack-by-the-hedge butter, Wye estuary greens and a sauce of the cooking juices, or rare-breed hogget, salsify and valley mushrooms. You can match your meal with a wine flight in the elegant, stripped-back restaurant. Bedrooms are smart and contemporary with a soft, subtle palette. Three have both a double-ended bath and large walk-in shower; one has a stone wet room. Four smaller rooms, overlooking the garden, have an over-bath shower. In such peaceful surroundings, a good night's sleep is assured.

Whitebrook NP25 4TX

T: 01600 860254
E: info@thewhitebrook.co.uk
W: thewhitebrook.co.uk

BEDROOMS: 8.
OPEN: all year, except 24 Dec (rooms), 25/26 Dec, 1 Jan, 2 weeks in Jan, restaurant closed Mon, Tues, Wed, and for lunch on Thurs.
FACILITIES: lounge/bar, restaurant (vegetarian menu), in-room TV (Freeview), terrace, 1-acre garden, restaurant and women's toilet wheelchair accessible.
BACKGROUND MUSIC: 'chill-out' in restaurant and lounge.
LOCATION: 6 miles S of Monmouth.
CHILDREN: all ages welcomed, only over-16s at dinner.
DOGS: only guide dogs allowed.
CREDIT CARDS: Amex, MC, Visa.
PRICES: D,B&B doubles from £390. Fixed-price 3-course lunch £49, tasting menus lunch, 5 courses, £68, dinner, 8 courses £110.

Prices may change – check with hotel.

CHANNEL ISLANDS

Grosnez Castle, Jersey

LITTLE SARK Sark

LA SABLONNERIE

A horse-drawn carriage conveys you over a dramatic, narrow isthmus 80 metres above the sea to this 17th-century farmhouse on a tiny island with no airstrip, no tarmac road and no cars. Since she was in her mid-twenties, the 'charming and charismatic' Elizabeth Perrée has run a hotel begun in 1948 by her family with just three guest bedrooms. Now she presides over 22 rooms, spread over the main house and surrounding cottages. Her motto is 'nothing is impossible, and everything must be tickety-boo', and everything is indeed tickety-boo, but in a very 'traditional and charming' way. That means 'quaintly old-fashioned rooms' with fringed lamps, floral curtains and fresh cut flowers (indeed, we have readers who have been coming here for more than 50 years). You can eat in the rustic, whitewashed dining room, or in the rose-filled garden, among the brimming flower borders. Dishes might include fillet of Sark beef, hand-dived scallops or 'the most amazing lobster', always a vegetarian option or two. Days can be spent cycling, sea-fishing, scuba diving and puffin-spotting off white sandy beaches, while the night sky is something to behold.

Little Sark GY10 1SD

T: 01481 832061
E: reservations@sablonneriesark.com
W: sablonneriesark.com

BEDROOMS: 22. Some in nearby cottages.
OPEN: mid-Apr–22 Oct.
FACILITIES: 3 lounges, 2 bars, restaurant, Wi-Fi by arrangement, civil wedding licence, 1-acre garden (tea garden/bar, croquet), unsuitable for disabled.
BACKGROUND MUSIC: classical/piano in bar.
LOCATION: Little Sark, via boat from Guernsey (guests will be met at the harbour on arrival).
CHILDREN: all ages welcomed, terms on application.
DOGS: allowed in some cottages and bedrooms at hotel's discretion (no charge), not in public rooms.
CREDIT CARDS: MC, Visa.
PRICES: B&B doubles from £97.50. Set menus £35, à la carte £55.

Prices may change – check with hotel.

ST BRELADE Jersey

MAP 1: inset E6

THE ATLANTIC HOTEL

Ocean views are on show through the floor-to-ceiling windows from some of the rooms at this hotel, on a headland above St Ouen's Bay. Designed to recall 1930s marine architecture, it has holiday fun and leisure baked into its DNA. Balconied bedrooms in shades of sea, surf and sand have blond wood furniture. Interconnecting rooms suit families while garden studios have a terrace with access to the landscaped grounds and pool. A reader's executive suite was 'lovely and quiet overnight, and while the ground-floor views may not match those from the first floor, everything was far superior in quality and comfort'. In the Ocean restaurant, you can choose the four-course 'Celebration' tasting menu, the daily three-course market menu, or dine à la carte on dishes such as steamed lemon sole paupiette, lobster tortellini, cucumber 'tagliatelle', samphire, lobster bisque. Cheaper and lighter, the house menu can be ordered anywhere in the hotel or alfresco. Best of all, perhaps, is the gourmet picnic you can order before going off for a day's surfing. Wildlife spotters will thrill to explore La Mielle de Morville nature reserve.

Le Mont de la Pulente
St Brelade JE3 8HE

т: 01534 744101
E: info@theatlantichotel.com
w: theatlantichotel.com

BEDROOMS: 50. Some on ground floor, unsuitable for disabled.
OPEN: all year except 3 Jan–1 Feb.
FACILITIES: lift, lounge, library, cocktail bar, restaurant, private dining room, fitness centre, in-room TV (Sky), civil wedding licence, 10-acre garden (indoor and outdoor heated swimming pools), public rooms wheelchair accessible, no adapted toilet.
BACKGROUND MUSIC: in restaurant, lounge and cocktail bar at night.
LOCATION: 5 miles W of St Helier.
CHILDREN: all ages welcomed, extra bed free.
DOGS: guide dogs only.
CREDIT CARDS: Amex, MC, Visa.
PRICES: B&B doubles from £180, singles from £160. Market menu £60, Celebration menu £90, à la carte £60–£75 (2/3 courses).

Prices may change – check with hotel.

SEE ALSO SHORTLIST

ST PETER Jersey

GREENHILLS COUNTRY HOUSE HOTEL

Time and traffic slow down at the Seymour family's hotel, within Jersey's network of leafy Green Lanes, set around three sides of a flower-filled terrace garden with small pool. Occupying a 17th-century granite house and two new wings, it is 'a very good hotel in virtually every respect', writes a reader on a return visit. The bedroom style is contemporary, with occasional antiques. Some rooms open on to the garden. 'Our superior room looked as if it had been recently decorated. Our bathroom was a fair size, with a bath and a walk-in shower.' Instant coffee and UHT milk came with 'a nice jar of home-made biscuits', and luxury toiletries. Lunch, afternoon tea and light bites can be taken in the bar, lounge or outside. 'Omnicompetent manager' Carmelita Fernandes is assisted by her 'unfailingly cheery and efficient' staff'. In a dining room that harks back to a gentler age, Lukasz Pietrasz's menus include dishes such as Jersey turbot, lobster ravioli and shellfish velouté. 'The food is outstanding. Breakfasts are also good, with cooked-to-order hot dishes.' 'We had no quibbles except one – muzak in public areas.' (Andrew Kleissner)

Mont de l'Ecole
St Peter JE3 7EL

T: 01534 481042
E: reservations@greenhillshotel.com
W: seymourhotels.com/
    greenhills-hotel

BEDROOMS: 33. 10 on ground floor, 1 suitable for disabled.
OPEN: all year except 18 Dec–10 Feb.
FACILITIES: 2 lounges, bar, restaurant (vegetarian/vegan menu), garden, terrace, in-room TV, civil wedding licence, outdoor heated swimming pool, access to leisure club at sister hotel, public rooms wheelchair accessible, adapted toilet.
BACKGROUND MUSIC: in public areas.
LOCATION: 8 miles NW of St Helier.
CHILDREN: all ages welcomed, free cots for under-2s, extra bed 25% of full rate.
DOGS: allowed in 4 ground-floor bedrooms (£10 per dog per night), not in public areas.
CREDIT CARDS: MC, Visa.
PRICES: B&B doubles from £90. Set dinner £35–£42.50 (2/3 courses), à la carte £70.

Prices may change – check with hotel.

ST PETER PORT Guernsey

MAP 1: inset E5

LA FREGATE

High on the cliff-top above St Peter Port, this town house hotel has enviable views over the harbour and neighbouring islands, sleek bedrooms and an established reputation for its food. Interiors of the 18th-century building, sympathetically extended, are contemporary yet the hotel's service levels remain polished and traditional. Expect silver service at dinner in the restaurant with its panoramic windows, striking white and shades-of-blue colours and crisp tablecloths. The monthly changing menu highlights local seafood – Guernsey crab, local sea bass and hand-dived scallops – as well as classics such as steak tartare and shepherd's pie. Drinks on the terrace are the best way to start the evening. All bedrooms enjoy views over the harbour to the islands of Sark, Herm and Brecqhou, and are light and airy with milky colours, accents of lilac and blue, and bleached-wood furniture. Desks and leather armchairs can give them a corporate feel. Book one with a balcony or terrace and you'll be tempted to breakfast in your room to enjoy the morning sun while tucking into cooked options that include kippers, eggs Benedict and omelette.

Beauregard Lane
Les Cotils
St Peter Port GY1 1UT

T: 01481 724624
E: enquiries@lafregatehotel.com
W: lafregatehotel.com

BEDROOMS: 22.
OPEN: all year, closed New Year.
FACILITIES: lounge/bar, restaurant, lift, private dining/function rooms, in-room TV (Freeview), civil wedding licence, terrace (alfresco dining), ½-acre terraced garden, parking, unsuitable for disabled.
BACKGROUND MUSIC: in lounge/bar and restaurant.
LOCATION: hilltop, 5 mins' walk from centre.
CHILDREN: all ages welcomed, ring to check prices for extra bed.
DOGS: guide dogs only.
CREDIT CARDS: Amex, MC, Visa.
PRICES: B&B doubles from £215, singles from £105. À la carte £50.

Prices may change – check with hotel.

SEE ALSO SHORTLIST

ST SAVIOUR Jersey

MAP 1: inset E6

LONGUEVILLE MANOR

'Unbelievably perfect in every way', Malcolm and Patricia Lewis's manor-house hotel (Relais & Châteaux) sits in landscaped gardens with a lake and specimen trees. A forecourt fountain sets the scene as you enter through a grand stone archway. Interiors blend contemporary style with history, with beams thought to have come from the Spanish Armada in one bedroom, an 18th-century French four-poster in another. A reader had a 'well-lit, spacious room', with REN toiletries and scented candles in the bathroom. A suite at the foot of the tower has a separate lounge, a stone bath and oversized walk-in shower as well as direct access to the gardens with outdoor pool. Dine in the Oak Room, its original panels augmented by broken-up carved oak chests, or in the airier Garden Room, choosing wines from an exceptional cellar. Andrew Baird uses produce from the Victorian kitchen garden in dishes such as wild halibut with wakame seaweed, pickled Jersey shiitake, miso – and Jersey Royals, of course. Staff are 'charming and attentive but not OTT'. At breakfast there is freshly squeezed orange juice, apple juice, organic free-range eggs.

Longueville Road
St Saviour JE2 7WF

T: 01534 725501
E: info@longuevillemanor.com
W: longuevillemanor.com

BEDROOMS: 30. 8 on ground floor, suite in cottage.
OPEN: all year except 22 Dec–19 Jan.
FACILITIES: lift, drawing room, snug, cocktail bar, 2 dining rooms, in-room smart TV, conference facilities, spa, 18-acre grounds (croquet, tennis, outdoor heated pool), public areas wheelchair accessible, no adapted toilet.
BACKGROUND MUSIC: in bar and restaurant.
LOCATION: 1½ miles E of St Helier.
CHILDREN: all ages welcomed, extra bed for ages 2–12 £75.
DOGS: allowed in bedrooms (£25, welcome pack), public rooms, not in restaurant.
CREDIT CARDS: MC, Visa.
PRICES: B&B doubles from £225. À la carte £85. 1-night bookings refused at weekends, bank holidays.

Prices may change – check with hotel.

IRELAND

Lough Corrib, Co. Galway

BAGENALSTOWN Co. Carlow

MAP 6:C6

LORUM OLD RECTORY

Bobbie Smith and her daughter Rebecca welcome guests to their Victorian rectory B&B, in a peaceful situation four miles from town on the slopes above the River Barrow. This is very much a home, with cut flowers, blazing fires, chiming clocks, sepia photographs, paintings and curios. The bedrooms, decorated in gentle, fashionable shades, have antiques and artwork, books and ornaments. Both Bobbie and Rebecca are Euro-Toques members, espousing values of seasonality, traceability and tradition in food. On summer weekends, by arrangement, guests gather for drinks in the drawing room, where tall windows frame views of Mount Leinster, before a five-course dinner served by candlelight around a mahogany table in the crimson-walled dining room. A no-choice menu (adapted, with notice, for special diets) might include Parma ham with melon, home-made elderflower sorbet, lamb, or chicken with orange, mustard and balsamic. Breakfast brings fresh fruit, home-baked bread, smoked salmon and scrambled eggs or a full Irish. It is a perfect base for exploring the Barrow valley, the Blackstairs mountains and the South Leinster Way.

Kilgreaney
Bagenalstown R21 RD45

T: 00 353 59 977 5282
E: bobbie@lorum.com
W: lorum.com

BEDROOMS: 3.
OPEN: 14 Apr–14 Oct, all week in July and Aug, weekends only in other months.
FACILITIES: drawing room, study (with TV), dining room, 1-acre garden (croquet) in 18-acre grounds, wedding facilities, unsuitable for disabled.
BACKGROUND MUSIC: none.
LOCATION: 4 miles S of Bagenalstown on R705 to Borris.
CHILDREN: aged 16 and over welcomed.
DOGS: by arrangement in bedrooms (no charge), public rooms but not on furniture or in dining room.
CREDIT CARDS: MC, Visa.
PRICES: B&B doubles from €190, singles from €140. Set 5-course dinner at weekends by arrangement €60. 1-night stays refused at bank holidays.

Prices may change – check with hotel.

BALLINGARRY Co. Limerick

THE MUSTARD SEED
AT ECHO LODGE

Every painting, sculpture and piece of furniture feels cherished and chosen at John Edward Joyce's Victorian country mansion in landscaped gardens. Mantelpieces are crowded with Irish Delft figurines, a jug picked up in Poland, a motley herd of elephants. Vases brim with flowers and artwork crowds walls painted in heritage shades. Traditional-style bedrooms, either in the main house with its hand-carved oak staircase, and in the old school-house wing, have fabrics and wallpaper by Zoffany, Jane Churchill, Cole & Son. All are supplied with Handmade Soap Co toiletries, while an accessible room has doors opening on to the garden. The staff are enthusiastic. 'A waitress furnished us with a vivid description of all the places we must not miss.' In the deep-blue restaurant with wedding-cake plaster ceiling, Angel Pirev's dishes burst with the freshness of the kitchen garden and orchard. They might include squash risotto with asparagus and caramelised baby red onions or guineafowl, nameko mushrooms, leek, mushroom ketchup, fried sage. Breakfast might bring smoked salmon with potato, crème fraîche, and eggs from the pampered hens. (PH)

Ballingarry V94 EHN8

T: 00 353 69 68508
E: info@mustardseed.ie
W: mustardseed.ie

BEDROOMS: 16. 1, on ground floor, suitable for disabled.
OPEN: all year except 24–26 Dec.
FACILITIES: entrance hall, library, restaurant, sunroom, in-room TV (terrestrial), wedding facilities, 12-acre grounds, restaurant and public rooms wheelchair accessible, adapted toilet.
BACKGROUND MUSIC: in restaurant.
LOCATION: in village, 18 miles SW of Limerick.
CHILDREN: all ages welcomed, extra bed no charge.
DOGS: 'well-behaved' pets allowed in designated bedrooms (not unattended, no charge), not in public rooms.
CREDIT CARDS: Amex, MC, Visa.
PRICES: B&B doubles from €180. Classic Dinner (4 courses) €68.

Prices may change – check with hotel.

BALLYCASTLE Co. Mayo

MAP 6:B4

STELLA MARIS

Though it styles itself a 'country house' and stands amid gently rolling hills, the sea provides the drama at Frances Kelly-McSweeney's former coastguard's HQ on the Wild Atlantic Way. A conservatory the length of the facade, with a motley assortment of furniture, is the place from which to gaze out over Bunatrahir Bay, hoping to spot dolphins or enjoying the ever-changing sky. Warmly painted public rooms, opening one into another, have blazing fires on chilly days, comfy seating, old photographs and jolly knick-knacks. Bedrooms, most with an ocean view, have antiques and fascinating architectural features, perhaps a mahogany bed, an original fireplace, a Gothic window set in a three-foot-thick wall (Queen Victoria's Admiralty was taking no chances). In intimate dining rooms, the hostess's contemporary Irish menus showcase fresh locally caught seafood and locally farmed produce, simply prepared. At breakfast there is home-baked bread, free-range eggs, potato rösti, everything cooked to order. Afterwards, swim and scuba-dive off Ballycastle beach, spot puffins and stormy petrels, walk, cycle or spend a day fishing.

Killerduff
Ballycastle F26 YX97

T: 00 353 96 43322
E: info@stellamarisireland.com
W: stellamarisireland.com

BEDROOMS: 11. 1, on ground floor, suitable for disabled.
OPEN: 1 May–30 Sept, restaurant closed Mon evening.
FACILITIES: lounge, bar, restaurant, conservatory, in-room TV (terrestrial), Wi-Fi in public areas, 2-acre grounds, public rooms wheelchair accessible, adapted toilet.
BACKGROUND MUSIC: none.
LOCATION: 1½ miles W of Ballycastle.
CHILDREN: not under 5.
DOGS: not allowed.
CREDIT CARDS: MC, Visa.
PRICES: B&B doubles from €175, singles from €95. À la carte €45.

Prices may change – check with hotel.

BALLYMOTE Co. Sligo

MAP 6:B5

TEMPLE HOUSE

A private drive loops through native woodland and pastures to this classical mansion overlooking a ruined Knights Templar castle and teeming fishing lake in W B Yeats country. Home to Roderick and Helena Perceval and rich in history, it is an endearing mix of the palatial and personal, from its soaring double-height vestibule to snug lounges with log fires. Every surface is crowded with heirloom antiques, ancestral portraits and mementos. The aptly named Hundred Acre has a separate room for a child or two. We hear no complaints about storage space in Porch, with a half-tester bed and 14-foot wardrobe. The former master bedroom has a lake view, a bath and shower, a Victorian lavatory with delayed flush to spare a lady's blushes. Guests gather for aperitifs before a dinner cooked by chef Vicki Scanlon with produce from the walled garden. Expect dishes such as baked salmon fillet hollandaise, couscous, honey-glazed heritage carrots; confit duck leg with kumquat jus. The meal is served communally at a long mahogany table, or separately if you wish, but, as Yeats wrote, 'There are no strangers here. Only friends you haven't yet met.'

Templehouse Demesne
Ballymote F56 NN50

T: 00 353 71 918 3329
E: stay@templehouse.ie
W: templehouse.ie

BEDROOMS: 7. Plus 3 non-B&B reserved for house parties.
OPEN: Apr–mid-Nov.
FACILITIES: morning room, library, dining room, vestibule (table tennis), wedding facilities, 1½-acre garden on 1,000-acre estate, water sports on site, EV charging.
BACKGROUND MUSIC: none.
LOCATION: 12 miles S of Sligo.
CHILDREN: all ages welcomed, extra bed €30, kitchen supper for 3–12s.
DOGS: not allowed.
CREDIT CARDS: Amex, MC, Visa.
PRICES: B&B doubles from €195, singles from €139. Set-price 4-course dinner €59.

Prices may change – check with hotel.

BALLYVAUGHAN Co. Clare

MAP 6:C4

GREGANS CASTLE HOTEL

It may not be a castle but this rambling 18th-century manor house, wrapped in gardens and with views over the otherworldly karst landscape of the Burren, has its own romantic charm. Indeed, author J R R Tolkien was said to have drawn inspiration from the surroundings when he stayed here. Run by the same family since 1976, now headed by Simon Haden and Frederieke McMurray, the hotel is designed to let guests relax and take in the natural beauty, but among modern comforts. Soothing colours, modern art and antiques fill public rooms; the drawing room invites with a fire, books, sofas and large windows overlooking the gardens. Bedrooms are equally calming with fresh colours, original art, more flowers and books. All have views over the garden or towards Galway Bay. Have a drink in the Corkscrew bar with its open fire before moving into the elegant dining room to enjoy Modern Irish dishes that make creative use of local, organic and foraged produce: perhaps beef with salsify, morels and wild garlic. Breakfast on pancakes, eggs Benedict or smoked haddock before a day spent wildlife-spotting or walking the Cliffs of Moher.

Gragan East
Ballyvaughan H91 CF60

T: 00 353 65 707 7005
E: stay@gregans.ie
W: gregans.ie

BEDROOMS: 21. 7 on ground floor, 1 suitable for disabled.
OPEN: mid-Feb–end Nov.
FACILITIES: drawing room, bar, dining room, wedding facilities, 15-acre grounds, EV charging, public areas wheelchair accessible, no adapted toilet.
BACKGROUND MUSIC: in bar and dining room.
LOCATION: 3½ miles SW of Ballyvaughan.
CHILDREN: all ages welcomed, extra bed €25–€50, no under-7s in dining room after 6 pm.
DOGS: allowed in some ground-floor bedrooms by arrangement (€25 per stay), not in public rooms.
CREDIT CARDS: Amex, MC, Visa.
PRICES: B&B doubles from €260. Set menu €85. Min. 2-night booking usually, but ring to check 1-night availability.

Prices may change – check with hotel.

CASTLEHILL Co. Mayo

ENNISCOE HOUSE

Solitary Nephin, Ireland's highest stand-alone mountain, provides a dramatic backdrop to this classic, pink-washed Georgian country house in wooded grounds on Lough Conn. Hosts Susan Kellett and her son DJ are descendants of George Jackson, who built a fortified house on the lough shore in the mid-1700s. The present house (in fact two, one built on to the original, older one) is filled with the treasures of a long, rich past – portraits, antiques, hunting trophies. Three of the spacious bedrooms have a four-poster or canopy bed. The drawing room has an open fire, a wealth of sofas, silk Adam-design wallpaper, faded now from its original blue. At night guests meet over drinks before a dinner cooked by Susan with produce from the organic market garden – maybe onion quiche with salad leaves, carrot and cumin soup, roast pork with walnut and apricot sauce, dessert or Irish cheeses. After breakfast with home-made granola and jams, soda bread and scones, you might fish in the lough (boat and ghillie can be arranged), explore forest paths, or visit the on-site genealogy centre, agricultural museum, smithy and café.

Castlehill
Ballina F26 EA34

T: 00 353 96 31112
E: mail@enniscoe.com
W: enniscoe.com

BEDROOMS: 6. Plus self-catering units behind house.
OPEN: Apr–Oct, possibly closed Mon, Tues nights, but check.
FACILITIES: sitting room, drawing room, dining room, no in-room TV, wedding facilities, 3-acre garden in 30-acre grounds.
BACKGROUND MUSIC: 'background' in hallway during dinner.
LOCATION: 2 miles S of Crossmolina, 12 miles SW of Ballina.
CHILDREN: all ages welcomed, under-12s free, 12–14s €50, sharing with parents.
DOGS: allowed in certain bedrooms (no charge), public rooms, not dining room.
CREDIT CARDS: MC, Visa.
PRICES: B&B doubles from €200, singles from €130. Set menu €50. Sat min. 2-night stay.

Prices may change – check with hotel.

CASTLELYONS Co. Cork

BALLYVOLANE HOUSE

With breakfast served until noon, afternoon tea by the drawing room fire, shooting, fishing and communal dining, a house-party atmosphere prevails at this Georgian country house. Approached along a winding, tree-lined drive, and sitting in parkland, this is the home of third-generation owners and experienced hoteliers Justin and Jenny Green. The interiors are filled with the accumulated treasures of seven decades: quirky antiques, clocks, books, ornaments, paintings. The bedrooms, decorated in fashionable shades, have a coffee machine, home-made cordials, Voya toiletries. One has a vintage, mahogany-encased bath. Produce from the kitchen garden, farm, river and foraged from the estate, appears at night in dishes such as Saddleback pork with crackling, cider jus, cauliflower cheese, gratin potatoes and apple sauce. Vegans and vegetarians are happily accommodated. In the morning you awake to a full Irish with home-baked bread and home-made jam. Children love to collect eggs from the hens. You can take a picnic lunch and explore the grounds. Happy glampers follow the laburnum walk to their bell tent or 'pig ark'.

Castlelyons
Fermoy P61 FP70

T: 00 353 25 36349
E: info@ballyvolanehouse.ie
W: ballyvolanehouse.ie

BEDROOMS: 6. Plus 'glamping' tents May–Sept.
OPEN: all year, but closed Sun, Mon, Tues in winter, Sun, Mon in high season, except for group bookings, Christmas/New Year (self-catering only).
FACILITIES: hall, drawing room, garden hall (honesty bar), dining room, wedding facilities, barn (table tennis), 80-acre grounds (15-acre garden, croquet, tennis, trout lakes).
BACKGROUND MUSIC: none.
LOCATION: 22 miles NE of Cork.
CHILDREN: all ages welcomed, free cots, extra bed €35, high tea for under-13s €15.
DOGS: allowed (max. 1 per room, no charge) but kept on lead during shooting season July–Jan.
CREDIT CARDS: MC, Visa.
PRICES: B&B doubles from €260. Set dinner €70. Min. 2-night stay at some weekends.

Prices may change – check with hotel.

COLLINSTOWN Co. Westmeath

MAP 6:C5

LOUGH BAWN HOUSE

'A long, romantic, tree-lined drive' climbs gently to this classical Georgian house 'overlooking sheep-filled pastures and a glistening lough'. Fourth-generation owner Verity Butterfield 'really seems to enjoy sharing her home with guests', our inspectors say, as it is promoted from the Shortlist. 'When we arrived, tea was produced within minutes, with a plate of home-baked biscuits, and she sat down for a good chat.' Interiors are 'bright and welcoming, with wooden floors, antique patterned rugs, vast gilded mirrors over mantelpieces, displays of wild flowers, walls painted in soft hues, and everywhere something lovely to rest your eyes on'. The 'pretty, elegant bedrooms' have 'electric blankets on large, comfortable beds'. One room has 'sumptuous peacock-pattern wallpaper', while the real things strut their stuff outside. Two rooms share a 'a very nice bathroom, with a roll-top bath and wet-room-style shower'. Readers enjoyed a 'really tasty, beautifully presented' dinner, cooked by Verity, by arrangement. Our inspectors didn't dine, 'but judging by breakfast, there is no reason to doubt the quality'. (Oliver Thomas)

Lough Bane
Collinstown N91 EYX4

T: 00 353 44 966 6186
E: loughbawnhouse@gmail.com
W: loughbawnhouse.com

BEDROOMS: 4. 2 share a bathroom.
OPEN: all year except Dec.
FACILITIES: 2 sitting rooms, dining room, 50-acre parkland, wild swimming lake.
BACKGROUND MUSIC: none.
LOCATION: by Lough Bane, 3 miles from village.
CHILDREN: all ages welcomed.
DOGS: allowed by prior arrangement in 2 bedrooms, public rooms (resident dogs).
CREDIT CARDS: MC, Visa.
PRICES: B&B doubles from €140, singles from €100. Dinner €55 (you can bring your own wine). 2-night min. stay at weekends in May, June.

Prices may change – check with hotel.

DRINAGH Co. Wexford

KILLIANE CASTLE
COUNTRY HOUSE AND FARM

Guests are welcomed with tea or coffee and home-baked biscuits at the Mernagh family's farmhouse B&B beside a 15th-century fortified tower house. This is very much a lived-in and loved home, a place to relax and unwind, perhaps with a glass of wine from the honesty bar. The styling is traditional, with some cherished period pieces, including an antique grandfather clock. There are six house bedrooms, on the first and second floors. Two more, at ground level in the courtyard, have been newly renovated this year. All have spring water from the artesian well, magazines and electric blankets. The views are of the gardens, the working dairy farm and the countryside, with some distant glimpses of the coast. Breakfast brings a wide choice of buffet and cooked dishes, home-baked soda bread and scones, pancakes, a full Irish with black and white pudding, eggs from the hens, honey from the hives, fruit from the garden. Guests can explore the farm, climb the tower, play croquet, tennis, footgolf on the 15-hole course, or try their hand on the driving range.

Drinagh Y35 E1NC

T: 00 353 53 915 8885
E: info@killianecastle.com
W: killianecastle.com

BEDROOMS: 10. 2 in former stable block.
OPEN: mid-Feb–mid-Dec.
FACILITIES: lounge (honesty bar), snug, dining room, in-room TV (Freeview), garden, grounds (nature trail, tennis, croquet, pitch and putt, 300-metre driving range), 230-acre dairy farm, unsuitable for disabled.
BACKGROUND MUSIC: in dining room and reception.
LOCATION: 1½ miles S of Drinagh.
CHILDREN: all ages welcomed, family rooms sleep 1 or 2 children under 12.
DOGS: allowed in grounds, not indoors.
CREDIT CARDS: MC, Visa.
PRICES: B&B doubles from €140, singles from €90.

Prices may change – check with hotel.

DUBLIN

MAP 6:C6

SCHOOLHOUSE HOTEL

More Hogwarts than Dotheboys Hall, this 'charming, rather fairy-tale-like Victorian schoolhouse with turrets and tall chimneys', now a quirky hotel, moves up a grade to the main Guide after a visit from our school inspectors. Interiors are 'quite spectacular', with 'high-beamed and vaulted ceilings, parquet floors, enormous stone fireplaces, William Morris-ish wallpapers'. The bedrooms are 'spacious, in warm tones, with comfortable king-size beds, good bathrooms with marble sinks and powerful showers, Gilchrist & Soames toiletries'. Executive rooms, overlooking the garden, have a canopied half-tester bed. The staff are wonderfully accommodating. 'When we arrived too early for check-in they made us cappuccinos and did not charge for them.' A gastropub menu of dishes such as seafood linguine, steak frites and flatbreads is available in the bar and alfresco by the canal. 'Breakfast was a great spread' with a buffet on a 'huge circular table', alongside cooked options such as 'excellent scrambled eggs and smoked salmon'. 'There is always a member of staff nearby, and they are friendly and prompt.' So a pass with distinction.

2–8 Northumberland Road
Ballsbridge
Dublin D04 P5W8

T: 00 353 1 667 5014
E: reservations@schoolhouse.ie
W: schoolhouse.ie

BEDROOMS: 31. Some on ground floor.
OPEN: all year except 24–26 Dec.
FACILITIES: bar, restaurant, private dining/meeting room, in-room TV, ½-acre garden, limited parking, Gastrobar wheelchair accessible, adapted toilet.
BACKGROUND MUSIC: in bar, restaurant.
LOCATION: in Ballsbridge neighbourhood, 15 mins' walk from St Stephen's Green.
CHILDREN: all ages welcomed.
DOGS: only assistance dogs allowed.
CREDIT CARDS: Amex, MC, Visa.
PRICES: per person B&B from €109. À la carte €42.

Prices may change – check with hotel.

DUBLIN

MAP 6:C6

THE WILDER TOWNHOUSE

'One of Dublin's best boutique hotels', this former home for retired governesses five minutes from the Museum of Irish Literature is now a glamorous hotel with a bookish bent. Styled for hoteliers Frankie and Josephine Whelehan, it is a luxurious blend of classic design and modern comforts. Bedrooms, each with its own colour scheme, are rated according to size and, at 12 square metres, 'shoebox' rooms are indeed snug, but beautiful and characterful. Four suites named after fictional governesses have a marble fireplace, a king-size bed and separate seating area. All rooms have quirky ornaments and art, carefully chosen works by Irish writers such as Oscar Wilde and William Trevor, a marble mosaic bathroom and walk-in rainforest shower, Maison Margiela Paris toiletries. A wide range of gins, light bites such as cheeses and charcuterie, soup and sandwiches, are served in the parquet-floored, Art Deco-inspired Gin and Tea Rooms and outside. In the morning, 'exceptional, well-presented breakfasts' in the Garden Room feature an extensive buffet with cooked dishes to order and 'not a plastic packet in sight'. (AC)

22 Adelaide Road
Dublin D02 ET61

T: 00 353 1 969 65 98
E: stay@thewilder.ie
W: thewilder.ie

BEDROOMS: 42. Some suitable for disabled.
OPEN: all year except 23–27 Dec.
FACILITIES: Gin and Tea Rooms, Garden Room, terrace, in-room TV (terrestrial), 8 parking spaces, public rooms wheelchair accessible, adapted toilet.
BACKGROUND MUSIC: in lobby and bar.
LOCATION: near St Stephen's Green.
CHILDREN: all ages welcomed, but not an ideal place for children, under-3s stay free.
DOGS: not allowed.
CREDIT CARDS: Amex, MC, Visa.
PRICES: B&B doubles from €259.

Prices may change – check with hotel.

GLASLOUGH Co. Monaghan   MAP 6:B6

CASTLE LESLIE ESTATE

The Leslie clan's High Victorian pile overlooking a lake is a stupendous trove of Grand Tour treasures and family lore. On an estate acquired by 'fighting bishop' John Leslie with a bounty from Charles II, it is filled with antiques, arms, ancestral portraits, busts and trophies, while each bedroom has its own story. In the four-poster Red Room, with carved oak furniture from Perugia, in 1914, Lady Marjorie had a beatific visit from her son Norman, killed in battle, though today a knock will more probably presage a visit from housekeeping. A library is filled with books by Leslies, about Leslies. The drawing room has a Della Robbia fireplace, Bishop Leslie's throne, Winston Churchill's christening robe. Bedrooms at the Lodge, by the equestrian centre, have bespoke artwork, a Victorian bath, a shower, a balcony or private courtyard. You can order a picnic, eat in Conor's bar and lounge, or in Snaffles, where Aaron Duffy uses garden produce in dishes such as roast estate venison with buttered sprout leaves, parsnip purée, baby carrot, fondant potato, pickled blackberry and bitter chocolate jus. 'I'll certainly never forget my visit.'

Glaslough H18 RX05

T: 00 353 47 88100
E: info@castleleslie.com
W: castleleslie.com

BEDROOMS: 95 bedrooms. 50 in Lodge (2 suitable for disabled), self-catering cottages.
OPEN: all year except 16–27 Dec.
FACILITIES: drawing rooms, bar, breakfast room, restaurant, conservatory, billiard room, library, private dining, gallery, cinema, some in-room TV, wedding facilities, spa, equestrian centre, 1,000-acre estate (14-acre gardens), public areas wheelchair accessible, adapted toilet.
BACKGROUND MUSIC: in public areas of Lodge.
LOCATION: 7 miles NE of Monaghan.
CHILDREN: all ages welcomed.
DOGS: allowed in Old Stable Mews rooms only (no charge).
CREDIT CARDS: Amex, MC, Visa.
PRICES: B&B doubles from €205. 6-course dinner €68. 1-night bookings sometimes refused.

Prices may change – check with hotel.

HOLYWOOD Co. Down

RAYANNE HOUSE

There is great zest for life at Conor and Bernie McClelland's B&B – a Victorian merchant's house above Belfast lough – from the exuberant décor to Titanic dinners and gargantuan breakfasts. A century after the Southampton-bound Titanic sailed beneath their windows, on selected evenings Bernie cooks the nine-course last dinner served aboard the doomed liner. On other nights, a tasting menu might include Copeland Island crab cakes with prawns and roasted red pepper; lamb rump with lamb and apricot sausage, garden mint and redcurrant and burgundy reduction. Bedrooms are styled with panache. A superior double and a family triple room have a lough-view balcony. The Rory room has a golf-themed bathroom with wet-room shower and a grab bar fashioned from one of Rory McIlroy's clubs. You don't have to stay over to book in for breakfast and enjoy a feast of dishes: chilled cream porridge with raspberry purée; French toast, Clonakilty black and white pudding, apple compote; Co. Down kippers; crockpot oven-baked ham with organic eggs and tomato sauce, and much more. Guests pay discounted green fees at the golf club. Hooray for Holywood!

60 Demesne Road
Holywood BT18 9EX

T: 28 9042 5859
E: info@rayannehouse.com
W: rayannehouse.com

BEDROOMS: 10. 1, on ground floor, suitable for disabled.
OPEN: all year, 'limited service' Christmas/New Year.
FACILITIES: 2 lounges, dining room, conference facilities, wedding facilities, 1-acre grounds, parking, public rooms wheelchair accessible, adapted toilet.
BACKGROUND MUSIC: in dining room.
LOCATION: ½ mile from Holywood town centre, 6 miles NE of Belfast.
CHILDREN: all ages welcomed, under-2s stay free, cots, baby-listening.
DOGS: may be allowed by prior arrangement.
CREDIT CARDS: MC, Visa.
PRICES: B&B doubles from £135, singles from £100, triple from £140. Tasting menu £65 (10% service added), Titanic menu £75, Titanic package, D,B&B £270 for 2 sharing.

Prices may change – check with hotel.

LETTERFRACK Co. Galway

MAP 6:C4

ROSLEAGUE MANOR

Drive under a leafy canopy to this pink-washed manor house 'in rhododendron-filled gardens rolling down to the shore of Ballinakill Bay'. Our inspectors were greeted by Tyson, the Labrador, and checked in by 'a lovely lady who has worked here for 40 years'. Their top-floor room was 'rather like an apartment, with a sitting room and dressing room'. Wonderful views of bay and mountains were framed by 'huge dormer windows', one in the bathroom, 'which you could open while you showered'. Interiors are 'full of curios, antiques, the odd, fun, kitschy object', and the feel is of 'a much-loved home, though it has operated as a hotel since the family bought it in 1968'. Third-generation owner Mark Foyle is 'very much a presence', helping with service in the 'beautiful orange-ochre dining room'. From the imaginative night's menu, 'excellent sirloin with a good helping of vegetables, then poitín ice cream with Irish mist sauce' were enjoyed. Breakfast includes a generous buffet, porridge with cream and honey, kippers and the full Irish. 'We had a great time. I wouldn't hesitate to go back.'

Letterfrack H91 CK26

T: 00 353 95 41101
E: info@rosleague.com
W: rosleague.com

BEDROOMS: 21. 2 on ground floor.
OPEN: mid-Mar–end Oct.
FACILITIES: 2 drawing rooms, conservatory/bar, dining room, in-room TV (terrestrial), wedding facilities, 25-acre grounds (tennis).
BACKGROUND MUSIC: none.
LOCATION: 7 miles NE of Clifden.
CHILDREN: all ages welcomed, extra bed €30, also family rooms.
DOGS: 'well-behaved' dogs allowed in bedrooms (no charge), public rooms.
CREDIT CARDS: MC, Visa.
PRICES: B&B doubles from €190, singles from €113. Set dinner €40/€60 (2/5 courses). Min. 2-night stay at bank holiday weekends.

Prices may change – check with hotel.

LIMERICK Co. Limerick   MAP 6:D5

NO. 1 PERY SQUARE

Once a youth hostel, this hotel at the corner of a
late Georgian terrace has definitely waved away
any thoughts of backpackers' basics, swapping
them for boutique chic. Overlooking the People's
Park, with its Victorian bandstand and towering
Rice Monument, it is filled with period pieces,
chandeliers and elegant decor, with a spa in the
vaulted basement, and a small kitchen garden.
Four glamorous bedrooms in the main house
are named after former Pery Square residents,
each with original features, a handmade brass-
and-gilt bed, a roll-top copper bath and monsoon
shower. Two have park views; two overlook the
kitchen garden and dining terrace. A converted
rates office links the original town house to a
new extension, where smart, contemporary
rooms have super-king or king-size bed and
monsoon shower. All have Voya organic toiletries,
robes, slippers, room service. Meals are served
in the first-floor Sash restaurant where dishes
might include Atlantic cod, clams, consommé,
samphire and sorrel. For something a little less
formal and lighter, go to the Long Room bar, or
eat alfresco in the garden.

Georgian Quarter
1 Pery Square
Limerick V94 EKP9

T: 00 353 61 402402
E: info@oneperysquare.com
W: oneperysquare.com

BEDROOMS: 21. 2 suitable for disabled.
OPEN: all year except 24–26 Dec.
FACILITIES: lift, lounge/bar, drawing
room, restaurant, private dining room,
in-room TV (RTÉ, Virgin), wedding
facilities, small kitchen garden,
terrace, basement spa, car park (free),
public rooms wheelchair accessible,
adapted toilet on floor above, reached
via lift.
BACKGROUND MUSIC: in restaurant and
lounge.
LOCATION: central.
CHILDREN: all ages welcomed, extra
bed €35.
DOGS: 1 dog-friendly bedroom
(€25 per night).
CREDIT CARDS: Amex, MC, Visa.
PRICES: B&B doubles from €175, singles
from €150. À la carte €49.

Prices may change – check with hotel.

LISDOONVARNA Co. Clare

MAP 6:C4

SHEEDY'S

The perfect base for exploring the Wild
Atlantic Way and the Burren's dramatic karst
landscape, the Sheedy family's farmhouse has
been welcoming guests since the 1930s. Third-
generation owners John and Martina Sheedy
are professional hosts, she front-of-house, he as
chef. 'A lovely welcoming place to stay. Martina
is so hospitable,' say readers. Bedrooms have a
traditional elegance, with antique pieces and a
soft palette, and include home-made biscuits and
an espresso machine. Modern bathrooms have
an over-bath power shower. You can take tea
by the fire in the sitting room, sample whiskeys
in the bar, relax in the sunroom. John, who has
worked in a Michelin-starred kitchen, uses locally
fished, farmed and foraged produce, home-grown
vegetables and herbs, in dishes such as roast rack
of Burren lamb or pan-fried fillet of Atlantic hake
with crab risotto. The 'excellent breakfasts' are a
feast: deluxe porridge, crepes, the full Irish with
'my personal favourite, Clonakilty white pudding'.
At close of day, take a short drive to the Cliffs of
Moher to watch the sun go down on Galway Bay.
'We would happily return.' (Sara Hollowell)

Lisdoonvarna V95 NH22

T: 00 353 65 707 4026
E: info@sheedys.com
W: sheedys.com

BEDROOMS: 11. 5 on ground floor.
OPEN: Apr hotel and restaurant
Thurs–Sun, May–Sept daily
(restaurant closed Sun).
FACILITIES: sitting room/library, sun
lounge, bar, restaurant, in-room TV
(terrestrial), ½-acre garden, parking,
restaurant wheelchair accessible,
adapted toilet.
BACKGROUND MUSIC: in restaurant
and bar, Lyric FM at breakfast, 'easy
listening' jazz at dinner.
LOCATION: 20 miles SW of Galway.
CHILDREN: over-12s welcomed.
DOGS: not allowed.
CREDIT CARDS: MC, Visa.
PRICES: B&B doubles from €190.
Set-price menu, dinner, €60. 1-night
bookings refused at weekends in Sept.

Prices may change – check with hotel.

SEE ALSO SHORTLIST

MAGHERALIN Co. Armagh

MAP 6:B6

NEWFORGE HOUSE

There is a happy sense of continuity at this classic Georgian country house, where sixth-generation owners Louise and John Mathers have been welcoming guests since 2005. Standing in extensive, mature gardens, it is filled with heirloom antiques, paintings and mementos. Bedrooms bear the maiden names of past chatelaines. Bijou Waddell (after John's grandmother Emily), overlooking the rockery, has candy-striped wallpaper, a canopy bed draped with toile de Jouy fabric, a marble-floored bathroom. Beaumont has a half-tester bed, floor-to-ceiling windows, a bathroom overlooking the rose garden. In the evening, guests gather in the drawing room for aperitifs – perhaps a Newforge rhubarb and rose gin fizz or apple whisky sour. An accomplished chef, John cooks a seasonally inspired dinner while Lou turns her hand to desserts. Imagine turf-smoked wild salmon, horseradish panna cotta; roast loin of wild halibut, tarragon and dulse beurre blanc; chocolate nemesis, cardamom ice cream, blackberry coulis. After a full Ulster with eggs from the contented hens, have a dander round the grounds, discovering the walled garden and orchard.

58 Newforge Road
Magheralin BT67 0QL

T: 028 9261 1255
E: enquiries@newforgehouse.com
W: newforgehouse.com

BEDROOMS: 6.
OPEN: Feb–mid-Dec, restaurant closed Sun/Mon evenings.
FACILITIES: drawing room, dining room, in-room TV (Freeview), wedding facilities, 2-acre gardens (vegetable garden, wild-flower meadow, orchard, woodland) in 50 acres of pastureland, unsuitable for disabled.
BACKGROUND MUSIC: in dining room.
LOCATION: on edge of village, 20 miles SW of Belfast.
CHILDREN: aged 10 and over welcomed.
DOGS: not allowed.
CREDIT CARDS: MC, Visa.
PRICES: B&B doubles from £155, singles from £125. À la carte £55.

Prices may change – check with hotel.

MOUNTRATH Co. Laois

MAP 6:C5

ROUNDWOOD HOUSE

Rattle over a cattle grid and watch out for roaming ducks and geese as you approach this imposing Palladian villa in native woodland, home to Hannah and Paddy Flynn and their family. 'Do what comes naturally,' Hannah's dad advised when she and Paddy took over as hosts a decade ago, and there is a great sense of warmth, fun and spontaneity here. Reception rooms have tall sash windows, ornate plasterwork, blazing fires, heirloom antiques and auction finds. Six large main-house bedrooms, painted in heritage colours, overlook gardens and the stable yard; four in the older Yellow House overlook a walled garden. Paddy regales guests with jokes and flapjacks, sings, plays the guitar, and cooks a nightly menu of dishes such as seared monkfish with asparagus tips, crispy chorizo, oven-dried heirloom tomatoes, artichoke cream with black olive salsa; roast beef strip loin with caramelised onions, beetroot purée, asparagus and blue cheese compound butter. At breakfast there is freshly squeezed OJ, organic muesli, eggs from the ducks and hens, home-baked bread and griddle scones, Hannah's marmalade, a full Irish or vegetarian.

Mountrath R32 TK79

T: 00 353 57 873 2120
E: info@roundwoodhouse.com
W: roundwoodhouse.com

BEDROOMS: 10. 4 in separate house.
OPEN: all year except 24–26 Dec.
FACILITIES: drawing room, dining room, study, library, 18-acre grounds, unsuitable for disabled.
BACKGROUND MUSIC: none.
LOCATION: 3 miles N of village.
CHILDREN: all ages welcomed, under-6s free, extra bed €30, children's supper €12.50.
DOGS: not allowed.
CREDIT CARDS: Amex, MC, Visa.
PRICES: B&B doubles from €190, singles from €125. Set 4-course dinner €60, supper of soup, cheese and dessert €25.

Prices may change – check with hotel.

NEWPORT Co. Mayo

MAP 6:B4

NEWPORT HOUSE

On a historic estate once home to the O'Donels – a factious crew, by all accounts, transported here by Cromwell – Kieran Thompson's creeper-clad Georgian house has long been a fishing destination. Not that you need to bring rod and line to enjoy the antique-filled interiors, the timeless ambience, the sense of staying with old friends. Tea and cake, elegantly served by the fire on arrival, strike a welcoming note. 'It doesn't seem to have changed at all over the years,' wrote a reader, whose bedroom had 'a fine view towards the estuary'. Some rooms are in nearby houses, one the former holiday home of the late Seán Lemass, fourth Taoiseach. Dinner is a big attraction, 'served in a leisurely fashion, reinforcing the idea that you are more guest than customer'. Fresh, locally farmed and fished, and home-grown ingredients feature in dishes such as poached wild Lough Furnace salmon with champagne sauce or medallions of wild venison with pear purée, red wine and juniper berry sauce. Ask for a picnic lunch and head out to explore the Wild Atlantic Way. Or try your luck at fishing on either eight miles of riverbank or on Lough Beltra.

Newport F28 F243

T: 00 353 98 41222
E: info@newporthouse.ie
W: newporthouse.ie

BEDROOMS: 14. 4 in courtyard, 2 on ground floor.
OPEN: early Apr–early Oct.
FACILITIES: bar, drawing room, sitting room, dining room, Wi-Fi only in reception and some bedrooms, in-room TV, 15-acre grounds, walled garden, private fishery, bicycle hire.
BACKGROUND MUSIC: none.
LOCATION: in village, 7 miles N of Westport.
CHILDREN: all ages welcomed, under-2s free, cots, high chairs, baby monitors provided, €25 for extra bed for child aged 10 or under.
DOGS: allowed in courtyard bedrooms (no charge), not in public rooms.
CREDIT CARDS: Amex, MC, Visa.
PRICES: B&B doubles from €250, singles from €150. Fixed-price 5-course dinner €70.

Prices may change – check with hotel.

OUGHTERARD Co. Galway

MAP 6:C4

CURRAREVAGH HOUSE

'A long private road through woodland' leads to Henry and Lucy Hodgson's Victorian country house, 'lost in time' in 180 acres, overlooking Lough Corrib. 'I've never stayed anywhere like it,' wrote our inspector. 'It was unforgettable to be somewhere so remote, so beautiful, so private.' Enter to find 'thick old carpets, ageing wallpapers, an ancient bagatelle table, fish in glass cases . . .' Bedrooms are 'lovely, some rather faded', with 'comfortable beds, wide views of lough and gardens, large, light bathrooms, no door keys'. An electric shower 'gasped and rattled' but did the job. At 4 pm tea is served with 'delicious, freshly baked cakes'. At night, Henry dispenses drinks and bonhomie before banging a gong to summon all to a dinner cooked by Lucy, of dishes such as crab with apple, fennel, kohlrabi and tomato; lamb with muhammara, carrot, wild garlic; baked Alaska with wild damson ice cream. Breakfast brings a full Irish and more. 'I had baked cannellini beans with barrel-aged feta on sourdough – delicious.' Fishing and boating are among tranquil pastimes. Loyal guests come back year after year. 'I understand why. I adored it.'

Oughterard H91 X3C2

T: 00 353 91 552312
E: rooms@currarevagh.com
W: currarevagh.com

BEDROOMS: 10.
OPEN: 1 Mar–30 Nov.
FACILITIES: sitting room/library, drawing room, dining room, 180-acre grounds (lakeshore, fishing, ghillies available, boating, tennis, croquet), EV charging, nearby golf, riding, unsuitable for disabled.
BACKGROUND MUSIC: none.
LOCATION: 4 miles NW of Oughterard.
CHILDREN: aged 12 and upwards welcomed.
DOGS: allowed in 1 bedroom, not in public rooms.
CREDIT CARDS: MC, Visa.
PRICES: B&B doubles from €180, single occupancy from €110. Set dinner €60.

Prices may change – check with hotel.

RATHMULLAN Co. Donegal

RATHMULLAN HOUSE

Pass the little gate lodge to drive up to this bay-fronted country house in wooded grounds edged by a beach on Lough Swilly. It was a hikers' hostel with no electricity after 8 pm, to encourage early rising, when Bob Wheeler bought it in 1961 and created something far more commodious. Run today by Bob's son Mark and daughter-in-law Mary, it has the feel of a family home, where a full Ulster with fresh-baked bread and Bob's marmalade will tempt you early from your bed. Log fires burn in lounges with comfy sofas, antiques, paintings, photos, exquisite plasterwork, and snacks served all day. Lovely bedrooms with original features are furnished with antiques. The best have a bay window with lough views. More contemporary rooms in a new wing have French doors to a patio or balcony. In the Cook & Gardener restaurant, produce from the walled garden appears with locally landed fish and foraged ingredients in dishes such as seared turbot with champ, beetroot purée, braised fennel, Mulroy Bay mussels and turmeric velouté. Or eat stone-baked pizzas with craft ales under canvas. Wildlife-watchers scan the shores for dolphins and porpoises.

Rathmullan F92 YA0F

T: 00 353 74 915 8188
E: reception@rathmullanhouse.com
W: rathmullanhouse.com

BEDROOMS: 32. Some on ground floor.
OPEN: all year except 24–27 Dec, 6 Jan–6 Feb.
FACILITIES: bar, 2 lounges, library, TV room, playroom, cellar bar/pizza parlour, restaurant, in-room TV, wedding facilities, 15-metre heated indoor swimming pool, 7-acre grounds, EV charging, lounges wheelchair accessible.
BACKGROUND MUSIC: none.
LOCATION: ½ mile N of village.
CHILDREN: all ages welcomed, 6 interconnecting family rooms, cots available.
DOGS: guide dogs only allowed,
CREDIT CARDS: Amex, MC, Visa.
PRICES: B&B doubles from €170, singles from €83. Set-price menu €55 (3 courses). 1-night bookings refused Sat and bank holidays.

Prices may change – check with hotel.

RIVERSTOWN Co. Sligo

MAP 6:B5

COOPERSHILL

Simon and Christina O'Hara and rescue collie
Juno delight in welcoming guests to their
Georgian ancestral home, a mile off-road, on a
500-acre wooded estate with deer park. Interiors
are replete with hunting trophies and antiques
handed down through generations. The newly
renovated Georgian bedroom has a king-size
canopy bed, a 19th-century roll-top bath and
walk-in shower, views to the River Unshin and
Keshcorran mountain. Dual-aspect Jade room
has striking murals, a bathroom with under-floor
heating, bath and large, powerful shower. All
have spring water on tap, top-quality toiletries.
Christina cooks a nightly three-course dinner
with home-reared meats from the free-ranging
fallow deer, sheep and cattle, and produce from
the kitchen garden – maybe Killybegs crab tart;
Atlantic black sole, or rack of lamb with wild
garlic and basil pesto. At breakfast there is Aga-
baked sourdough, Coopershill honey, free-range
eggs. You can take a picnic of home-baked rolls
and cake, Irish cheeses, smoked chicken or salmon
(Christina taught herself the art of smoking in
lockdown) for a day exploring W B Yeats country.

Riverstown F52 EC52

T: 00 353 71 916 5108
E: reservations@coopershill.com
W: coopershill.com

BEDROOMS: 7.
OPEN: Apr–Oct, Tues–Sat, off-season
house parties by arrangement.
FACILITIES: front hall, drawing room,
dining room, snooker room, wedding
facilities, 500-acre estate (garden,
tennis, croquet, woods, farmland,
river with trout fishing), EV charging,
unsuitable for disabled.
BACKGROUND MUSIC: none.
LOCATION: 11 miles SE of Sligo.
CHILDREN: all ages welcomed, extra
bed €50.
DOGS: not allowed.
CREDIT CARDS: MC, Visa.
PRICES: B&B doubles from €275, single
occupancy from €151. Set dinner €62.
1-night bookings refused at weekends.

Prices may change – check with hotel.

SHANAGARRY Co. Cork   MAP 6:D5

BALLYMALOE HOUSE

'We enjoyed a walk in the extensive grounds with the hotel's biodiversity champion,' write readers on a visit to this legendary Irish country house hotel that is passionate about locally sourced food. In the 59 years since the late Myrtle Allen opened the Yeats Room restaurant in the family's Georgian farmhouse, the modest enterprise has grown into a thriving business, with cookery school, café and arts venue. True to the founding principles, head chef Dervilla O'Flynn devises dishes around produce from the farm and walled kitchen garden or locally sourced. For instance, rack and leg of lamb with coriander, lemon and crushed swede; cauliflower with squash and spinach korma, turmeric rice, coconut dahl dumplings and raita. Refurbished bedrooms are charmingly, traditionally styled. 'We had a well-equipped and spacious courtyard room with its own conservatory,' continue our readers, who were also shown the cellars by the sommelier. Breakfast is all that it should be, with home-baked breads, organic, unpasteurised butter, jam from garden fruit, Ballymaloe free-range eggs, labneh with local honey and pistachios. (Tony and Shirley Hall)

Shanagarry P25Y 070

T: 00 353 21 465 2531
E: res@ballymaloe.ie
W: ballymaloe.ie

BEDROOMS: 32. 12 in annexe, 4 on ground floor with wheelchair access.
OPEN: all year except 25/26 Dec, for dinner and Sun lunch (light lunch for residents only, Mon–Sat).
FACILITIES: drawing room, bar, 2 TV rooms, conservatory, restaurant, private dining, wedding facilities, 6-acre gardens, tennis, 5-hole golf course, swimming pool, cookery school, café/kitchen shop, EV charging, restaurant wheelchair accessible, partially adapted toilet.
BACKGROUND MUSIC: none.
LOCATION: 20 miles E of Cork.
CHILDREN: all ages welcomed, extra bed €75.
DOGS: small dogs in 3 bedrooms (no charge), not in public areas.
CREDIT CARDS: Amex, MC, Visa.
PRICES: B&B doubles from €310. Set dinner 5 courses (Mon–Sat) €85, Sun night buffet €70.

Prices may change – check with hotel.

SHORTLIST

The Montenotte Hotel, Cork

LONDON

THE BUXTON

Hip and convivial, this modish Spitalfields gastropub-with-rooms is a stroll up the colourful street from the Whitechapel Gallery. Named after Victorian social reformer, abolitionist and brewer Sir Thomas Fowell Buxton, he would no doubt approve of its sustainable values, vintage styling and selection of local beers. Each of the compact, neatly designed bedrooms has a micro-library of East London-themed books, and handwoven artworks, rugs and blankets made by local weavers. Guests can ascend to the roof terrace for 360-degree views across the East End and the City, or head down to the brick-painted bar and bistro, for seasonally changing British-European menus. (Underground: Aldgate East, Whitechapel)

MAP 2:D4
42 Osborn Street
London E1 6TD
T: 020 7392 2219
W: thebuxton.co.uk

BEDROOMS: 15.
OPEN: all year except 22 Dec–1 Jan.
FACILITIES: pub/bistro, in-room TV, rooftop garden terrace, eating and drinking areas wheelchair accessible.
BACKGROUND MUSIC: all day in public areas.
LOCATION: 2 mins' walk from Aldgate East Underground station.
CHILDREN: all ages welcomed.
DOGS: allowed in pub.
CREDIT CARDS: Amex, MC, Visa.
PRICES: per room B&B (continental) £100–£140. À la carte £28.

Prices may change – check with hotel.

LONDON

CHARLOTTE STREET HOTEL

From its jaunty striped awnings over pavement café tables and bright-patterned dining chairs to its walls hung with contemporary British art, this Firmdale hotel dazzles with colour. Close to Soho and the West End theatres, this is a flashy and family-friendly luxury hotel. Inside, a lounge and library are inviting, with open fires and an honesty bar. Thoughtfully equipped bedrooms and suites (some interconnecting) have strong colours and granite bathrooms. Children receive a welcome gift, and milk and cookies in the evening. Choose the lively restaurant or heated terrace to dine on modern British dishes such as lamb with wild garlic green sauce, plus salads and grills. (Underground: Goodge Street)

MAP 2:D4
15–17 Charlotte Street
Bloomsbury
London W1T 1RJ
T: 020 7806 2000
W: charlottestreethotel.com

BEDROOMS: 52. 1 suitable for disabled.
OPEN: all year.
FACILITIES: bar/restaurant, drawing room, library, private events, in-room TV (Freeview), civil wedding licence, cinema, gym, terrace, ground-floor wheelchair accessible.
BACKGROUND MUSIC: in restaurant and bar.
LOCATION: 5 mins' walk from Goodge Street Underground station.
CHILDREN: all ages welcomed, welcome pack, children's menu.
DOGS: allowed 'on a case-by-case basis'.
CREDIT CARDS: Amex, MC, Visa.
PRICES: room only from £408. Breakfast items £5–£19, à la carte dinner £50.

Prices may change – check with hotel.

LONDON

ECCLESTON SQUARE HOTEL

The classic, white-painted, 19th-century facade of this family-run Pimlico hotel, on a uniformly attractive and tranquil garden square, gives no clue to the high-tech boutique interiors. Neat-sized bedrooms, some with a patio or a balcony, have a monochrome palette and whizzy features: a 'digital concierge' on a tablet, smart-glass shower walls, electronically operated blinds, an adjustable bed with massage settings. Rooms are equipped with a coffee machine; fresh pots of tea are delivered on request. Breakfast and tasty bar food are available; takeaway or room service if you prefer. Guests can use the private gardens, and friendly staff will advise on neighbourhood eateries. (Underground: Victoria)

MAP 2:D4
Pimlico
London SW1V 1PB
T: 020 3503 0692
W: ecclestonsquarehotel.com

BEDROOMS: 39. 2 suitable for disabled. Plus 2-bed town house with patio garden.
OPEN: all year.
FACILITIES: reception/dining area, in-room TV (Sky), lounge/meeting room, time-limited on-street parking (free at weekends), public car park nearby.
BACKGROUND MUSIC: in public areas.
LOCATION: 5 mins' walk from Victoria Underground and rail stations.
CHILDREN: not under 13.
DOGS: not allowed.
CREDIT CARDS: Amex, MC, Visa.
PRICES: room-only doubles from £150. Breakfast £18.50, individual breakfast items from £3.50.

Prices may change – check with hotel.

LONDON

THE FIELDING

A grand jeté from the Royal Opera House, this small hotel is 'remarkably quiet' considering its prime position in bustling Covent Garden. Named after the 18th-century novelist Henry Fielding, it is a 'good-value' option in a central location. Past the pretty, plant-decked Georgian exterior, individually decorated bedrooms, set over four floors, are air conditioned and 'excellently lit'. Each room has a shower room (two rooms also have a bath), plus tea- and coffee-making facilities. Families might ask for a room with an extra sofa bed. No breakfast is provided, but there's plenty of choice on nearby streets – the 'friendly, helpful staff' at reception will point the way. (Underground: Covent Garden)

MAP 2:D4
4 Broad Court
Bow Street
London WC2B 5QZ
T: 020 7836 8305
W: thefieldinghotel.co.uk

BEDROOMS: 25. Some, on ground floor, wheelchair accessible, plus 2 apartments in adjoining building.
OPEN: all year.
FACILITIES: in-room TV (Freeview), free access to nearby spa and fitness centre.
BACKGROUND MUSIC: none.
LOCATION: 3 mins' walk from Covent Garden Underground station.
CHILDREN: all ages welcomed.
DOGS: not allowed.
CREDIT CARDS: Amex, MC, Visa.
PRICES: per room single £112–£125, double £175–£195.

Prices may change – check with hotel.

MAP 2:D4
South Kensington
London SW7 5JW
T: 020 7761 4000
W: 54queensgate.com

LONDON

54 QUEEN'S GATE HOTEL

One in an elegant row of white stucco Edwardian town houses, this small hotel is a short walk from Hyde Park, the Royal Albert Hall and London museums. Within the smartly refurbished Grade II listed building, serene modern bedrooms are each dedicated to a renowned Londoner (Pankhurst, Eliot, Elgar, etc), with air conditioning, dressing gowns and slippers, a coffee machine and a minibar of soft drinks. (Front-facing rooms may have some traffic noise.) A small buffet accompanies a freshly cooked full English at breakfast. After a day out exploring, the lounge, bar and rear terrace are inviting retreats. Plentiful restaurant choice nearby. Part of the Bespoke Hotels group. (Underground: South Kensington)

BEDROOMS: 24.
OPEN: all year.
FACILITIES: lounge, bar, breakfast room, in-room smart TV, terrace.
BACKGROUND MUSIC: none.
LOCATION: 10 mins' walk from South Kensington Underground station.
CHILDREN: not under 16.
DOGS: not allowed.
CREDIT CARDS: Amex, MC, Visa.
PRICES: per room B&B £175–£499.

Prices may change – check with hotel.

MAP 2:D4
35–39 St George's Drive
Pimlico
London SW1V 4DG
T: 020 7834 1438
W: georgianhousehotel.co.uk

LONDON

GEORGIAN HOUSE HOTEL

By turns 'whimsical' and stylish, this Pimlico hotel holds spellbinding surprises for wizards and muggles alike. Spread between the main, Grade II listed building and two town houses nearby, 'light-filled' contemporary accommodation ranges from small single rooms to spacious family apartments. Harry Potter fans of all ages might choose wizard-themed basement 'chambers' in the main house: accessed via a hidden door in a bookcase, they reveal (faux) stained-glass windows, velvet drapes, trunks and tapestries. A café/bar serves breakfast, drinks, snacks and an enchanting afternoon tea. Potion-mixing is a magical option. Stairs are steep; cheerful staff help with luggage. (Underground: Victoria, Pimlico)

BEDROOMS: 45. Some on ground floor, 18 in nearby town houses.
OPEN: all year.
FACILITIES: reception, bar/café, breakfast room, private dining/meeting/function room, 2-person 'cinema', in-room TV.
BACKGROUND MUSIC: in café/bar.
LOCATION: 10 mins' walk from Victoria Underground and train stations.
CHILDREN: all ages welcomed.
DOGS: not allowed.
CREDIT CARDS: MC, Visa.
PRICES: per room B&B £125–£450.

Prices may change – check with hotel.

LONDON
THE GYLE

On the edge of hipster-ish Camden, five minutes from King's Cross and St Pancras International, this quirky, contemporary hotel on leafy Argyle Square fits right in. Converted from three 19th-century town houses, the focus is a bar-lounge with moss on the walls, fake grass on the ceiling and a collection of Scottish malts, wines and craft beers. The sleek green and grey colour palette continues in bedrooms, perked up with quirky details: Scottie-dog cushions, Argyle tartan headboards and repurposed airline trolleys for bathroom storage. Basement rooms have sunken baths; others have balconies. Breakfast is an upmarket continental buffet. (Underground: King's Cross, Eurostar at St Pancras Intl.)

MAP 2:D4
16-18 Argyle Square
Camden
London WC1H 8AS
T: 020 3301 0333
W: thegyle.co.uk

BEDROOMS: 33. Some on ground floor.
OPEN: all year.
FACILITIES: bar/lounge, in-room smart TV, interior courtyard.
BACKGROUND MUSIC: in bar/lounge.
LOCATION: 5 mins' walk from King's Cross St Pancras Underground and rail stations.
CHILDREN: all ages welcomed.
DOGS: allowed in all bedrooms.
CREDIT CARDS: Amex, MC, Visa.
PRICES: B&B doubles from £175.

Prices may change – check with hotel.

LONDON
HAM YARD HOTEL

In an animated neighbourhood, a Tony Cragg bronze sculpture seemingly in motion greets visitors in the tree-lined courtyard of this design-conscious Soho hotel. Inside the modern building, vibrant fabrics, quirky furniture and the latest works from an international roster of artists serve up Kit Kemp's signature Firmdale Hotels flamboyant style. There's top-to-bottom allure, from a residents-only roof terrace to a buzzy basement bar; in between, the well-stocked library and vast restaurant have afternoon teas and leisurely meals. Bedrooms decorated with a sense of upmarket fun take in city or courtyard views via huge windows. A spa and a 1950s bowling alley add to the fun. (Underground: Piccadilly Circus)

MAP 2:D4
1 Ham Yard
Soho
London W1D 7DT
T: 020 3642 2000
W: hotels/london/ham-yard-hotel

BEDROOMS: 91. 6 suitable for disabled.
OPEN: all year.
FACILITIES: lift, bar, restaurant, drawing room, library, meeting rooms, in-room TV (Freeview), civil wedding licence, spa, gym, bowling alley, heated courtyard, rooftop terrace and garden, valet parking (charge).
BACKGROUND MUSIC: in bar.
LOCATION: 3 mins' walk from Piccadilly Circus Underground station.
CHILDREN: all ages welcomed.
DOGS: allowed 'on a case-by-case basis'.
CREDIT CARDS: Amex, MC, Visa.
PRICES: per room from £714. Breakfast from £19, à la carte £60.

Prices may change – check with hotel.

LONDON
HAYMARKET HOTEL

This 19th-century building designed by John
Nash (the architect of Buckingham Palace) is as
classically impressive outside as it is gorgeously
colourful inside. Part of the Firmdale group, it
mixes modern artwork, boldly patterned fabrics
and wallpapers and a cool elegance to create
inviting spaces. The library and conservatory are
made for relaxation; the basement swimming
pool is glamorous. Individually styled bedrooms
have strong colours and granite bathrooms; larger
rooms suit families. Bistro dishes are served in
art-filled Brumus, or on the terrace. It's in the
heart of theatreland with the National Gallery
around the corner, the South Bank an easy walk.
(Underground: Piccadilly Circus)

MAP 2:D4
1 Suffolk Place
London SW1Y 4HX
T: 020 7470 4000
W: haymarkethotel.com

BEDROOMS: 53. Some suitable for
disabled, includes 5-bed town house.
OPEN: all year.
FACILITIES: lift, lobby, library,
conservatory, bar, restaurant, terrace
(honesty bar), in-room TV, civil
wedding licence, indoor swimming
pool, gym, ground-floor rooms
wheelchair accessible.
BACKGROUND MUSIC: in bar and
restaurant.
LOCATION: 5 mins' walk from
Piccadilly Circus Underground
station.
CHILDREN: all ages welcomed.
DOGS: allowed 'on a case-by-case basis'.
CREDIT CARDS: Amex, MC, Visa.
PRICES: room only from £462.
Breakfast hot dishes £9.50–£19. Set
menu 2-course £30, 3-course £35,
à la carte £53.

Prices may change – check with hotel.

LONDON
HOTEL 41

Guests receive royal treatment at this 'superb,
wonderful' and discreet hotel on the fifth floor
of a historic building close to Buckingham
Palace. A pre-arrival questionnaire ensures
residents' preferences are met (pillow firmness, a
humidifier, etc) in the smart bedrooms and suites;
other perks include home-made treats and season-
specific bathrobes. 'Plunder the pantry' of pastries,
cold meats, cheeses and desserts in the clubby
lounge. Dine in opulent surroundings in The
English Grill or for Indian flavours, The Curry
Room, both at sister hotel The Rubens, within the
same building. A pet concierge guarantees dogs
are nobly treated, too. Part of the Red Carnation
group. (Underground: Victoria)

MAP 2:D4
41 Buckingham Palace Road
Victoria
London SW1W 0PS
T: 020 7300 0041
W: 41hotel.com

BEDROOMS: 30. Some suitable for
disabled, if requested.
OPEN: all year.
FACILITIES: lounge, in-room TV (Sky),
room service, butler and chauffeur
service, valet parking, free access to
nearby spa and gym.
BACKGROUND MUSIC: in public areas.
LOCATION: 5 mins' walk from Victoria
Underground and rail stations.
CHILDREN: all ages welcomed.
DOGS: allowed in bedrooms, public
rooms.
CREDIT CARDS: Amex, MC, Visa.
PRICES: per room B&B from £431.

Prices may change – check with hotel.

LONDON
LIME TREE HOTEL

An affordable oasis in one of London's smartest neighbourhoods, Charlotte and Matt Goodsall's peaceful, personably run Belgravia hotel occupies a pair of Grade II listed Georgian town houses and is within walking distance of popular tourist spots. Smartly refurbished bedrooms vary in size, shape and layout, but all retain their original high ceiling, cornices and sash windows. In every room: comfy beds, crisp linens and natural toiletries. Upper-floor rooms are up several flights of stairs (staff will help with luggage). The lounge has guidebooks and magazines; the 'buzzy' Buttery café-restaurant is open for casual all-day dining and has tables in a pretty walled garden. (Underground: Victoria)

MAP 2:D4
135–137 Ebury Street
London SW1W 9QU
T: 020 7730 8191
W: limetreehotel.co.uk

BEDROOMS: 26.
OPEN: all year. Restaurant closed Mon from midday. Dinner Fri and Sat only.
FACILITIES: lounge, restaurant, in-room TV (Freeview), meeting facilities, small garden.
BACKGROUND MUSIC: 'quiet' in lounge, restaurant.
LOCATION: 5 mins' walk from Victoria Underground and rail stations.
CHILDREN: not under 5.
DOGS: only assistance dogs allowed.
CREDIT CARDS: Amex, MC, Visa.
PRICES: per room B&B single £125–£175, double £170–£340. À la carte £40. 1-night bookings sometimes refused Sat and peak periods.

Prices may change – check with hotel.

LONDON
ST JAMES'S HOTEL AND CLUB

This intimate hotel, in a quiet corner of Mayfair, oozes exclusivity from its Michelin-starred restaurant and classy bistro-bar to its sleek bedrooms and smart concierge service. A former diplomats' club, its panelled corridors are hung with fine artworks while the plush bar, with its velvet seating, is renowned for rare ports and wines. Dine here from the bistro menu or in the Seven Park Place restaurant on French-influenced dishes. Bedrooms are understated and fitted with state-of-the-art technology; many have views over neighbourhood rooftops, some from a private balcony. Come morning, 'wellness breakfasts' include green smoothies, almond-milk porridge and quinoa crumpets. (Underground: Green Park)

MAP 2:D4
7–8 Park Place
London SW1A 1LS
T: 020 7316 1600
W: stjameshotelandclub.com

BEDROOMS: 60. 2 on ground floor, some suitable for disabled.
OPEN: all year.
FACILITIES: lounge, bar/bistro, restaurant (closed Sun/Mon), 4 private dining/function rooms, in-room TV, civil wedding licence, public rooms wheelchair accessible, adapted toilet.
BACKGROUND MUSIC: in public areas.
LOCATION: 5 mins' walk from Green Park Underground station.
CHILDREN: all ages welcomed.
DOGS: not allowed.
CREDIT CARDS: Amex, MC, Visa.
PRICES: doubles from £420 (includes £50 food and beverage allowance). Breakfast £27.50. À la carte (bistro) £40, à la carte 2-course £82, 3-course £97, tasting menu £120 (restaurant).

Prices may change – check with hotel.

ALFRISTON Sussex

DEANS PLACE

Hike along the South Downs Way, or meander along a country path to the village green from this dog-friendly, family-run hotel in large grounds on the banks of the Cuckmere river. In good weather, Modern British dishes are served on the terrace. When the temperature dips, retreat to eat in a cosy spot by the log fire in the bar, with a local ale or a glass of Sussex sparkling wine. Or dine in the refined restaurant, open in the evenings and for lunch at weekends. The extensively enlarged old farmhouse has individually styled bedrooms (some recently refurbished) of varying size. The best overlook the well-manicured gardens. After a hearty breakfast, enjoy a dip in the heated outdoor pool (May–Sept).

MAP 2:E4
Seaford Road
Alfriston BN26 5TW
T: 01323 870248
W: deansplace.co.uk

BEDROOMS: 35. 1 suitable for disabled.
OPEN: all year.
FACILITIES: bar, lounge, snug, restaurant, function rooms, in-room TV (Freeview), civil wedding licence, terrace, 4-acre garden, heated outdoor swimming pool (May–Sept).
BACKGROUND MUSIC: in bar and dining room, occasional live jazz at Sun lunch.
LOCATION: in village, 3 miles from coast and walking distance of South Downs.
CHILDREN: all ages welcomed.
DOGS: allowed in some bedrooms, on lead in public rooms, grounds, not in restaurant. Paddock for guests' horses.
CREDIT CARDS: AE, MC, Visa.
PRICES: per room B&B single £82.50–£222, double £99–£235. À la carte £44. 2-night min. stay on certain weekends.

Prices may change – check with hotel.

ALFRISTON Sussex

WINGROVE HOUSE

Charming inside and out, this immaculate 19th-century house is in a pretty village within the South Downs national park. An elegant veranda wraps around the building; inside, an open fire burns in the cosy lounge in winter. Bedrooms, some in an ancient malthouse, are appealingly understated; several have a terrace or balcony; most have verdant views; all have Nespresso machines. Footfall from above may be noticeable. Modern British dishes are served in the bright, 'well-decorated' restaurant (candlelit at night) or on the terrace in good weather. Inspired by seasonal, locally grown produce, menus include interesting vegetarian options, perhaps roasted cauliflower, baba ghanoush, harissa chickpeas.

MAP 2:E4
High Street
Alfriston BN26 5TD
T: 01323 870276
W: wingrovehousealfriston.com

BEDROOMS: 16. 5 on ground floor, plus 3-bed pet-friendly cottage.
OPEN: all year.
FACILITIES: lounge/bar, restaurant, private dining room, in-room TV (Freeview), terrace, walled garden, restaurant wheelchair accessible.
BACKGROUND MUSIC: in restaurant.
LOCATION: at the end of the village High Street, 20 mins' drive from Glyndebourne.
CHILDREN: welcomed in restaurant, not overnight.
DOGS: not in bedrooms, 'although well-behaved dogs are welcome on the terrace'.
CREDIT CARDS: Amex, MC, Visa.
PRICES: per room B&B £110–£260. À la carte £39.

Prices may change – check with hotel.

NEW

MAP 1:B5
Allerford
Minehead TA24 8HW
T: 01643 863403
W: crosslanehouse.com

ALLERFORD Somerset
CROSS LANE HOUSE

Within Exmoor national park, Billy and Ellen Rowlinson's 15th-century farmhouse snuggles in a pretty hamlet on the National Trust's Holnicote Estate. An intimate country retreat, guests can snuggle down by a roaring fire in the comfortable lounge for afternoon tea, a glass of wine or a cocktail. Then settle in a beamed bedroom, simply styled in natural hues and fabrics, and made homely with books, fresh flowers, waffle robes and a radio. A hearty home-cooked meal is available Sunday to Thursday; on other days, cheese and charcuterie boards and small plates, served in the cosy bar and lounge; alfresco in the courtyard garden in summer. The amiable hosts delight in sharing their knowledge of the area.

BEDROOMS: 3.
OPEN: all year, closed Christmas and New Year, restaurant closed Sun–Wed.
FACILITIES: lounge/bar, dining room, free Wi-Fi, in-room TV, 1-acre garden (alfresco dining), unsuitable for disabled, parking.
BACKGROUND MUSIC: in lounge and dining room, late afternoon and evening.
LOCATION: 4¼ miles W of Minehead.
CHILDREN: not under 16.
DOGS: allowed in 2 bedrooms, public rooms.
CREDIT CARDS: Amex, MC, Visa.
PRICES: per room B&B single £120–£150, double £130–£150. 2-night min. stay preferred in peak season.

Prices may change – check with hotel.

MAP 4:A4
22 Northumberland Street
Alnmouth NE66 2RJ
T: 01665 830584
W: redlionalnmouth.com

ALNMOUTH Northumberland
THE RED LION INN

In the sheltered garden of this 18th-century coaching inn, a raised platform makes a perfect spot to watch the tide ebb and flow and the sun go down over the Aln estuary. Family owned, and run by 'friendly' staff, the pub's wood-panelled bar entices with real ales and beers from artisan brewers, and is popular with locals for its simple fare. Pizzas come straight from a wood-fired oven. 'Tasteful, well-appointed' bedrooms on the first floor have modern oak furniture, a 'comfortable' bed and a smart bathroom, plus local teas and biscuits. Breakfast, ordered the night before, includes vegetarian options. Dinner suggestions at village eateries are supplied. Golden beaches are a short walk away.

BEDROOMS: 7. 4 in annexe.
OPEN: all year. Restaurant closed all day Sun, and for dinner on Wed, Fri (pizzas on Friday evening in peak season).
FACILITIES: bar, restaurant, in-room TV (Freeview), beer garden.
BACKGROUND MUSIC: in bar, restaurant, live music events throughout the year.
LOCATION: in village centre.
CHILDREN: all ages welcomed.
DOGS: allowed in bar area, not in restaurant, bedrooms.
CREDIT CARDS: MC, Visa.
PRICES: per room B&B single £103.50–£171, double £115–£190. 2-night min. stay at weekends (Apr–Nov).

Prices may change – check with hotel.

AMBLESIDE Cumbria

ROTHAY MANOR

In landscaped grounds, Jamie and Jenna Shail's Grade II listed manor house pleases, inside and out. Individually decorated bedrooms, 'new and plush, but reflecting the ambience of this period property', are supplied with bathrobes, a coffee machine, Fairtrade tea and a flask of cold milk; some have a balcony with views over the garden to the fells beyond. Chef Daniel McGeorge's ambitious menus in the fine-dining restaurant have excellent vegetarian options; the laid-back lounge has classic fare. 'Meals were superb, and the service courteous and efficient.' Lakeside strolls and hilly hikes are nearby; plus complimentary use of a local health club. The needs of canine companions are well met too.

MAP 4: inset C2
Rothay Bridge
Ambleside LA22 0EH
T: 015394 33605
W: rothaymanor.co.uk

BEDROOMS: 23. 8 in Pavillion, 2 suitable for disabled, 2 with outdoor hot tubs.
OPEN: all year except 2–20 Jan.
FACILITIES: bar, lounge, drawing room, 3 dining areas, in-room TV (Sky), civil wedding licence, boot room, dog wash, terrace, 2-acre gardens, public rooms wheelchair accessible.
BACKGROUND MUSIC: all day in bar, lounge and restaurant.
LOCATION: ¼ mile SW of Ambleside.
CHILDREN: all ages welcomed.
DOGS: allowed in some bedrooms, public rooms, separate area of restaurant.
CREDIT CARDS: Amex, MC, Visa.
PRICES: per room B&B £200–£650. Set dinner, tasting menu (7 courses) £95, à la carte £65. 1-night bookings normally refused Sat, bank holidays.

Prices may change – check with hotel.

ANGMERING Sussex

THE LAMB AT ANGMERING

Between the South Downs and the Sussex coast, the Newbon family's revived village pub enfolds locals and visitors alike in its warmly welcoming atmosphere. Sussex brews, local gins, Sunday roasts and 'delicious' gastropub dishes are served in the oak-floored bar and smart, informal restaurant. In clement weather the decked terrace overlooking St Nicholas Gardens is just the spot for an alfresco meal. Come winter, a log fire burns in the inglenook fireplace. 'Comfortably furnished' bedrooms with vintage touches have a coffee machine, 'electric sockets in sensible places' and country charm in their plaids and florals. Some rooms can accommodate an extra bed for a child. Breakfast is cooked to order.

MAP 2:E3
The Square
Angmering
Littlehampton BN16 4EQ
T: 01903 774300
W: thelamb-angmering.com

BEDROOMS: 8. 1 on ground floor with private entrance.
OPEN: all year, restaurant closed 25 Dec.
FACILITIES: bar, restaurant, in-room TV (Freeview), terrace, garden.
BACKGROUND MUSIC: 'quiet music' in public spaces.
LOCATION: in village, 15 miles E of Chichester.
CHILDREN: all ages welcomed, not in bar area after 9 pm.
DOGS: allowed in pub, on terrace.
CREDIT CARDS: MC, Visa.
PRICES: per room B&B £115–£215. À la carte £36.

Prices may change – check with hotel.

ASKHAM Cumbria

THE QUEEN'S HEAD

Cosy, low-ceilinged and wood fire-warmed, this smartly refurbished 17th-century pub in the centre of a Lake District village is 'friendly, fun and very convivial'. It is owned by the Lowther family, whose Askham Hall, Penrith (see main entry) and Michelin-starred restaurant are a stroll away. Mismatched cushions nudge up along the wooden banquettes, and there are posy-topped tables; five evenings a week, sit down to a five-course menu of refined pub dishes (perhaps twice-baked truffled parmesan soufflé); great selection of wine by the glass. Spacious, country-style bedrooms are made modern with colour; three rooms can accommodate a family. Guests receive free entry to Askham Hall's Grade II listed gardens.

MAP 4: inset C2
Askham
Penrith CA10 2PF
T: 01931 712225
W: queensheadaskham.co.uk

BEDROOMS: 6. 3 on ground floor, 1 suitable for disabled.
OPEN: all year except Christmas, restaurant closed Sun evening–Tues evening.
FACILITIES: bar, restaurant, in-room TV, small beer garden, parking.
BACKGROUND MUSIC: none.
LOCATION: in village, 5½ miles S of Penrith.
CHILDREN: all ages welcomed.
DOGS: allowed.
CREDIT CARDS: Amex, MC, Visa.
PRICES: per room B&B single £118–£178, double £130–£190. 5-course prix-fixe menu £50. 1-night bookings refused at some peak season weekends.

Prices may change – check with hotel.

ASTHALL Oxfordshire

THE MAYTIME INN

Creepers clamber up the honey stone walls of this 17th-century coaching inn, in a peaceful village a short stroll from the River Windrush. Against centuries-old stonework and timbers in the popular bar, a 'good selection' of gins, ales and wines accompany the kitchen's lunchtime seasonal rustic dishes and pub classics. A rear terrace extends out to a walled garden with an outdoor bar, a boules pitch, and views over rolling countryside. Facing the garden or village, 'comfortable, beautifully converted' bedrooms, all on the ground floor, have luxury linens, an iPod docking station and tea- and coffee-making facilities. In the morning, breakfast on eggs laid by happy hens from Daylesford Organic nearby.

MAP 2:C2
Asthall
Burford OX18 4HW
T: 01993 822068
W: themaytime.com

BEDROOMS: 6. All on ground floor.
OPEN: all year, except 25 Dec.
FACILITIES: bar, restaurant, in-room TV (Freeview), private dining, large terrace, garden with outdoor bar, boules pitch.
BACKGROUND MUSIC: in bar, restaurant.
LOCATION: 2 miles from Burford.
CHILDREN: all ages welcomed (not under 18 in own room).
DOGS: allowed in public areas, not in bedrooms.
CREDIT CARDS: MC, Visa.
PRICES: per room B&B £120–£245. À la carte £35–£45.

Prices may change – check with hotel.

AYSGARTH Yorkshire
STOW HOUSE

On the edge of Aysgarth village and with sweeping views over Wensleydale, this Victorian rectory with its lawned gardens gives no clue to the bright and boldly furnished interiors. Phil and Sarah Bucknall have design backgrounds and have created a B&B of colourful rooms with stripped-wood floors, log-burners, contemporary art and piles of books. Bedrooms mix period furniture and modern pieces, perhaps an antique dresser and a statement lampshade. All have countryside views, some have freestanding baths. Walks are on the doorstep; return to one of Phil's classic cocktails. There are two village pubs for supper while breakfasts include freshly squeezed juice, home-baked bread and cooked-to-order dishes.

MAP 4:C3
Aysgarth
Leyburn DL8 3SR
T: 01969 663635
w: stowhouse.co.uk

BEDROOMS: 7. 1 on ground floor.
OPEN: all year except 23–28 Dec.
FACILITIES: sitting room (honesty bar), snug, dining room, in-room TV (Freeview), 2-acre grounds.
BACKGROUND MUSIC: none.
LOCATION: 7 miles from Leyburn, 9 miles from Hawes.
CHILDREN: all ages welcomed.
DOGS: well-behaved dogs allowed in 5 bedrooms, public rooms and garden.
CREDIT CARDS: MC, Visa.
PRICES: B&B doubles from £120. 2-night min. stay at weekends May–Sept.

Prices may change – check with hotel.

BAINBRIDGE Yorkshire
YOREBRIDGE HOUSE

In a 'beautiful Yorkshire Dales setting', an aura of 'laid-back luxury without pretensions' is found at Charlotte and David Reilly's hotel in a former Victorian schoolhouse and headmaster's house by the River Ure. The owners have decorated each spacious bedroom with items that will transport guests to faraway places, perhaps to the Caribbean, the Orient or Greenwich, in the New York style loft suite. Several rooms have a private terrace or riverside garden, plus an outdoor hot tub for a soak while star-gazing. Light bites and afternoon tea are available by day (perhaps with a Yorkshire gin and tonic). In the evenings, 'excellent, well-presented' five-course menus are served in the candlelit dining room.

MAP 4:C3
Bainbridge DL8 3EE
T: 01969 652060
w: yorebridgehouse.co.uk

BEDROOMS: 12. 4 in schoolhouse, 1 suite in village, 5 mins' walk, 6 on ground floor.
OPEN: all year.
FACILITIES: lounge, bar, restaurant, tasting room, in-room TV (Sky), civil wedding licence, function facilities, 5-acre grounds.
BACKGROUND MUSIC: all day in public areas.
LOCATION: village outskirts.
CHILDREN: all ages welcomed.
DOGS: allowed in 2 rooms, by arrangement.
CREDIT CARDS: MC, Visa.
PRICES: per room B&B £250–£400. À la carte, £60.

Prices may change – check with hotel.

BARNSTAPLE Devon

THE IMPERIAL HOTEL

Beside the River Taw, this town-centre hotel has a country house atmosphere. 'Perfect in every way', the Grade II listed Edwardian building set in manicured gardens has 'immaculate', classically decorated bedrooms, some overlooking the water; others, in an annexe, are dog-friendly or interconnect families. 'The excellent lighting and quality of the fittings made our room a real joy.' In the opulent fine dining restaurant, there is good choice from the à la carte, table d'hôte, vegetarian or vegan menus. A lighter meal or a relaxed candlelit dinner is served in the informal military-themed bistro. Guests may use the indoor and outdoor swimming pools at sister Brend Hotel, The Barnstaple, a short drive away.

MAP 1:B4
Taw Vale Parade
Barnstaple EX32 8NB
T: 01271 345861
W: brend-imperial.co.uk

BEDROOMS: 63. 8 in annexe across the car park, 1 suitable for disabled.
OPEN: all year. Closed to non-residents 24–28 Dec.
FACILITIES: lift, lounge, bar, restaurant, bistro, function rooms, in-room TV, room service, civil wedding licence, front terrace.
BACKGROUND MUSIC: classical in bar, restaurant.
LOCATION: in town centre.
CHILDREN: all ages welcomed.
DOGS: allowed in annexe bedrooms, on lead in garden.
CREDIT CARDS: Amex, MC, Visa.
PRICES: per room B&B £190–£320. À la carte £37. 1-night stay sometimes refused. Check with hotel.

Prices may change – check with hotel.

BATH Somerset

THE BIRD

Quirkiness abounds in this chirpy, contemporary hotel close to the centre. Birds of all feathers are displayed on walls, cushions and crockery throughout the remodelled Victorian mansion; vivid artwork and glittering chandeliers add to the eclectic style. Snug or more spacious, the modish bedrooms are supplied with a capsule coffee machine, teas and fancy toiletries to make guests happy as larks; several have views stretching across recreation grounds to Bath Abbey. An all-day menu of Modern British dishes is served in the lower ground-floor Plate restaurant or alfresco on the terrace, amid dining pavilions, domes and fire pits. Not far away, sister hotel Homewood, Bath (see main entry), has country house flair.

MAP 2:D1
18–19 Pulteney Road
Bath BA2 4EZ
T: 01225 580438
W: thebirdbath.co.uk

BEDROOMS: 29.
OPEN: all year, restaurant closed Mon–Thurs lunch.
FACILITIES: lounge, bar, restaurant, conservatory, in-room TV, terrace, garden, parking.
BACKGROUND MUSIC: all day in public areas.
LOCATION: 10 mins' walk from the centre.
CHILDREN: all ages welcomed.
DOGS: 'very warmly welcomed'.
CREDIT CARDS: Amex, MC, Visa.
PRICES: per room B&B £144–£395. À la carte £35. 1-night bookings sometimes refused at peak weekends.

Prices may change – check with hotel.

BIBURY Gloucestershire

THE SWAN

In a setting that elicits admiration, this stylishly updated 17th-century coaching inn stands on the banks of the River Coln, in a village, described by William Morris, as the most beautiful in England. Country-style bedrooms, with views of the river, village or courtyard, are supplied with a coffee machine, and have spacious bathrooms; cottage suites are ideal for larger groups. There's a choice of dining areas: gastropub fare is served in the dog-friendly bar and courtyard; the brasserie has modern European cooking, perhaps Bibury trout. In clement weather, find a sunny spot in the riverside garden across the lane. Part of the Fuller's portfolio; see also Bay Tree Hotel, Burford (Shortlist entry).

MAP 3:E6
Bibury GL7 5NW
T: 01285 740695
W: cotswold-inns-hotels.co.uk/
    the-swan-hotel

BEDROOMS: 22. Some on ground floor, 4 in adjacent garden cottages.
OPEN: all year.
FACILITIES: lift, lounge, bar, brasserie, in-room TV (Freeview), civil wedding licence, function facilities, courtyard, ½-acre garden, EV charging.
BACKGROUND MUSIC: 'subtle' in public spaces.
LOCATION: village centre.
CHILDREN: all ages welcomed.
DOGS: allowed in bar, lounge, garden, some bedrooms.
CREDIT CARDS: Amex, MC, Visa.
PRICES: per room B&B £160–£405. À la carte (brasserie) £36.

Prices may change – check with hotel.

BIRMINGHAM Warwickshire

THE HIGH FIELD TOWN HOUSE

This whitewashed Victorian villa in leafy Edgbaston has been turned into a colourful, boutique-style guest house with sister company, the popular High Field gastropub, next door. The bright sitting room has free newspapers, fresh flowers and fresh coffee; something a little stronger may be found in the honesty bar. Modern bedrooms (some for families) are decorated with well-chosen antiques and retro furnishings. Pop next door to enjoy the lively buzz of the pub and its garden. Alongside cocktails, craft ales and wines, imaginative sharing platters and elevated pub grub might include miso-glazed cod with black rice, and maple-roasted butternut squash, as well as 14-hour-braised beef and ale pie.

MAP 3:C6
23 Highfield Road
Edgbaston
Birmingham B15 3DP
T: 0121 647 6466
W: highfieldedgbaston.co.uk/
    boutique-hotel-stay-birmingham

BEDROOMS: 12. 1 suitable for disabled.
OPEN: all year, except 24/25 Dec.
FACILITIES: sitting room (honesty bar), restaurant/gastropub in adjacent building, private dining, in-room TV (Freeview), terrace, garden, parking, restaurant wheelchair accessible.
BACKGROUND MUSIC: in sitting room.
LOCATION: 10 mins' drive from city centre.
CHILDREN: all ages welcomed.
DOGS: allowed in 2 bedrooms and pub.
CREDIT CARDS: Amex, MC, Visa.
PRICES: B&B doubles from £118. À la carte £37.

Prices may change – check with hotel.

BLACKPOOL Lancashire

NUMBER ONE ST LUKE'S

This stylish South Shore B&B has a boutique-hotel feel with treats such as an outdoor hot tub and state-of-the-art music systems in bedrooms. Run by Mark and Claire Smith, who have many years hospitality experience, the detached period house offers spacious, individually decorated bedrooms each with a king-size bed; snacks and drinks; bathrobes, a power shower and spa bath (plus TV) in the bathroom. A large conservatory overlooks the garden with sun loungers as well as the hot tub. Breakfasts offer a 'full Blackpool' and lighter choices (special diets can be catered for) to set you up for a stroll to the famous promenade and Pleasure Beach. The hosts have good eating out suggestions, too.

MAP 4:D2
1 St Luke's Road
South Shore
Blackpool FY4 2EL
T: 01253 343901
W: numberoneblackpool.com

BEDROOMS: 3.
OPEN: all year.
FACILITIES: dining room, conservatory, in-room TV (Freeview), garden (putting green, hot tub), EV charging, parking.
BACKGROUND MUSIC: none.
LOCATION: 2 miles S of town centre.
CHILDREN: not under 5.
DOGS: 'possibly a small dog', by prior arrangement, allowed in bedroom, not in dining room.
CREDIT CARDS: Amex, MC, Visa.
PRICES: B&B doubles from £130, singles from £80. 1-night bookings occasionally refused weekends.

Prices may change – check with hotel.

BOURNEMOUTH Dorset

THE GREEN HOUSE

Within strolling distance of the town and the beach is this 'friendly', and eco-friendly, hotel in a handsome Victorian clifftop villa. Its many sustainable initiatives include a community veg garden and responsibly sourced furnishings to solar panels and beehives on the roof. Bedrooms (some snug) are smartly decorated in pleasing, earthy tones, 'crisp' organic bed linens on comfortable beds; and bathrobes and slippers; bathrooms have a natural stone handbasin; perhaps even a reclaimed Victorian roll-top bath. Rear rooms are quietest. In Arbor restaurant, uncomplicated but imaginative seasonal dishes use organic, Fairtrade and locally sourced ingredients, and may be served on the terrace in good weather.

MAP 2:E2
4 Grove Road
Bournemouth BH1 3AX
T: 01202 498900
W: thegreenhousehotel.co.uk

BEDROOMS: 32. 1 suitable for disabled.
OPEN: all year.
FACILITIES: lift, bar, restaurant, in-room TV (Freeview), civil wedding licence, private event facilities, 1-acre garden, terrace, parking.
BACKGROUND MUSIC: in public areas.
LOCATION: 5 mins' walk from beach, 10 mins' walk from town centre.
CHILDREN: all ages welcomed, not in restaurant after 7 pm.
DOGS: not allowed.
CREDIT CARDS: Amex, MC, Visa.
PRICES: per room B&B £157–£247. À la carte £35. 1-night bookings refused Sat in peak season.

Prices may change – check with hotel.

BRADFORD-ON-AVON Wiltshire

TIMBRELL'S YARD

An eye-catching 18th-century merchant's house overlooking the River Avon has been imaginatively converted into a relaxed, modern-day inn with designer bedrooms and an industrial-chic bar and restaurant. Snacks, small plates and refined pub food are served in the dining room with its exposed stone walls; the bar has craft spirits, local ales and ciders. Alfresco meals may be taken on the river-facing terrace. Nordic-influenced bedrooms (most with views of the water) are stocked with freshly ground coffee, tea and sweet treats; split-level suites (with 'steep, polished steps') have window seats. Part of the Stay Original Co.; see also The Swan, Wedmore; The Grosvenor Arms, Shaftesbury; and The White Hart, Somerton (Shortlist entries).

MAP 2:D1
49 Saint Margaret's Street
Bradford-on-Avon BA15 1DE
T: 01225 869492
W: timbrellsyard.com

BEDROOMS: 17.
OPEN: all year.
FACILITIES: bar, restaurant, private dining room, in-room TV (Freeview), river-facing terrace, limited parking or permits for nearby public car park.
BACKGROUND MUSIC: in public spaces 'to suit time and ambience'.
LOCATION: in town centre, 3 mins' walk from train station.
CHILDREN: all ages welcomed.
DOGS: allowed in bedrooms, bar.
CREDIT CARDS: MC, Visa.
PRICES: B&B doubles from £95. À la carte £34.

Prices may change – check with hotel.

BREEDON ON THE HILL Leicestershire

BREEDON HALL

Behind high walls, at the end of a crunchy drive, this handsomely proportioned Georgian manor house in the shade of ancient yew trees is both gracious and welcoming. Run as a B&B by Charles and Charlotte Meynell, it has a country house charm with generous sofas in the fire-warmed drawing room, and bedrooms decorated with character. Some rooms have handsome beams; all have garden views. No keys are provided (though bedrooms can be bolted from the inside). 'It's a family home, and feels like one,' the hosts say. Charlotte's breakfasts offer home-made granola and jams, and eggs from the resident hens; pub grub is as near as the end of the drive. The historic market towns Melbourne and Ashby-de-la-Zouch are close.

MAP 2:A2
Breedon on the Hill DE73 8AN
T: 01332 864935
W: breedonhall.co.uk

BEDROOMS: 5. Plus 3 self-catering cottages.
OPEN: all year except Christmas to start Jan, mid-Jan–end Feb, first two weeks July. Often closed Sun, ring to check.
FACILITIES: drawing room (honesty bar), main kitchen, dining room, in-room TV (Freeview), 1-acre grounds, EV charging.
BACKGROUND MUSIC: none.
LOCATION: in village centre.
CHILDREN: preferably not under 12, ring to discuss.
DOGS: well-behaved dogs allowed in bedrooms, public rooms (resident dog).
CREDIT CARDS: MC, Visa.
PRICES: B&B £100–£185. 2-night min. stay.

Prices may change – check with hotel.

BRIGHTON Sussex

BRIGHTONWAVE

A five-minute stroll from the pier, this Kemptown B&B in a row of Victorian town houses has some 'lovely little touches'. Richard Adams and Simon Throp are the helpful, informative owners. Painted in subtle colours, the crisp, contemporary bedrooms (some compact) have 'everything you need': a DVD/CD player, bottles of water, tea- and coffee-making facilities, a little tub of chocolates. One room has a private patio garden with seating; another, a Juliet balcony. Works by local artists decorate the lounge, where there are books to borrow, and a laptop and printer for guests' use. Cooked-to-order breakfasts are served till 10.30 am at the weekend. Vouchers can be purchased for parking on the local streets.

MAP 2:E4
10 Madeira Place
Brighton BN2 1TN
T: 01273 676794
W: brightonwave.com

BEDROOMS: 8.
OPEN: all year except Christmas.
FACILITIES: lounge, in-room TV (Freeview).
BACKGROUND MUSIC: none.
LOCATION: in Kemptown, just off the seafront.
CHILDREN: not under 14.
DOGS: not allowed.
CREDIT CARDS: Amex, MC, Visa.
PRICES: per room B&B £75–£190. 2-night min. stay at weekends, 3-night min. stay on bank holidays, Pride.

Prices may change – check with hotel.

BRISLEY Norfolk

THE BRISLEY BELL

Just the place for watching a Friday-evening cricket match, this 17th-century inn faces the village green. It is owned and run by Norfolk-bred Amelia Nicholson and Marcus Seaman, who restored the old pub and expanded it to include stylish modern bedrooms in converted barns, each with direct access to the large garden, courtyard or herb garden. Two rooms have a freestanding bath; all are supplied with a small bottle of sloe gin and home-made shortbread. Lively groups of locals gather for Norfolk brews, cocktails and wines around original inglenook fireplaces, in the book-lined Garden Room or on a covered patio. Nature trails, country estates and the north Norfolk coastline are all within easy reach.

MAP 2:A5
The Green
Brisley NR20 5DW
T: 01362 705024
W: thebrisleybell.co.uk

BEDROOMS: 6. All on ground floor in converted barns, 1 suitable for disabled.
OPEN: all year, contact inn directly for Christmas and New Year details; food served only on Mon, Tues evenings.
FACILITIES: bar, snug, restaurant, Garden Room, in-room TV (Freeview), pre-bookable in-room massages, covered patio, 2-acre garden (croquet lawn, herb garden, meadow), EV charging.
BACKGROUND MUSIC: none, except for occasional live music events.
LOCATION: just outside village.
CHILDREN: all ages welcomed.
DOGS: allowed in 2 bedrooms, bar, snug, garden.
CREDIT CARDS: MC, Visa.
PRICES: per room B&B £145–£215. À la carte £35.

Prices may change – check with hotel.

BRISTOL
ARTIST RESIDENCE BRISTOL
The latest of Charlotte and Justin Salisbury's young-at-art hotels has kicked off in a former boot factory. On a leafy Georgian square, the Grade I listed building is stripped down to basics, its original features preserved, while leaving exposed brick walls, rough concrete floor amid remnants of its industrial past. Bedrooms have a mix of vintage and distressed furniture. The smallest 'Shoebox' rooms have a leaded, arched window. The Lookout Suite has a spiral staircase up to a roof terrace. All rooms have a coffee machine, radio, bathrobes. The vibe is 'chilled', with a drop-in bar serving all-day drinks and snacks (a restaurant is planned) – a friendly hangout for the creative St Paul's community.

MAP 1:B6
28 Portland Square
Bristol BS2 8SA
T: 0203 019 8623
W: artistresidence.co.uk

BEDROOMS: 22.
OPEN: all year.
FACILITIES: lounge, bar (breakfast, snacks, drinks), in-room TV, table tennis.
BACKGROUND MUSIC: in public rooms.
LOCATION: on garden square, St Paul's.
CHILDREN: all ages welcomed.
DOGS: well-behaved dogs allowed in some bedrooms and guest lounge.
CREDIT CARDS: Amex, MC, Visa.
PRICES: per room £95–£405.

Prices may change – check with hotel.

BROADWAY Worcestershire
THE OLIVE BRANCH
In postcard-perfect Broadway, this 16th-century honeyed-stone building epitomises Cotswold cottage charm with its low-beamed rooms, exposed-stone walls and glinting brasses over the inglenook fireplace. 'Comfortable and well-decorated' bedrooms (some for families) are well equipped; 'welcoming and friendly' hosts Pam and David Talboys have 'thought of everything'. The cosy sitting room has books to borrow, and a wood burner for cool days; in fine weather, the rear garden invites – perhaps with a drink from the honesty bar. Breakfast, taken in the flag-stoned front parlour, includes home-baked breads, smoothies, local jams, and dishes cooked to order. National Trust properties and gardens are nearby.

MAP 3:D6
78 High Street
Broadway WR12 7AJ
T: 01386 853440
W: theolivebranch-broadway.com

BEDROOMS: 8. Some on ground floor, 1 suitable for disabled.
OPEN: all year except 25–27 Dec.
FACILITIES: lounge, breakfast room, in-room TV, ¼-acre garden, gazebo, parking, dining room and lounge wheelchair accessible.
BACKGROUND MUSIC: in lounge, breakfast room.
LOCATION: in village centre.
CHILDREN: all ages welcomed.
DOGS: not allowed.
CREDIT CARDS: MC, Visa.
PRICES: B&B doubles from £120, singles from £95 (with private bathroom). 1-night bookings generally refused weekends in high season.

Prices may change – check with hotel.

BUCKFASTLEIGH Devon
KILBURY MANOR

On the southern edges of Dartmoor, in extensive grounds bordered by the River Dart, Julia and Martin Blundell's B&B guarantees rural peace and restorative walks. Pretty, country-style bedrooms are in the 17th-century Devonshire longhouse or a converted barn across the courtyard; each room is supplied with coffee, tea, hot chocolate, locally bottled water and all-natural toiletries. Breakfast, served by a wood-burning stove on chilly mornings, has fruit, juice and yogurts, plus home-made preserves and compotes; specials such as devilled tomatoes on granary toast are cooked to order. Stretch your legs in their gardens and meadows, explore Dartmoor national park or visit nearby Buckfast Abbey.

MAP 1:D4
Colston Road
Buckfastleigh TQ11 0LN
T: 01364 644079
W: kilburymanor.co.uk

BEDROOMS: 3. 2 in converted stone barn across the courtyard.
OPEN: May–Oct.
FACILITIES: breakfast room, in-room TV (Freeview), 4-acre grounds (garden, meadow, courtyard), bicycle and canoe storage.
BACKGROUND MUSIC: 'gentle classical music played at low level' in breakfast room.
LOCATION: 1 mile from Buckfastleigh centre.
CHILDREN: not under 8.
DOGS: not allowed.
CREDIT CARDS: MC, Visa.
PRICES: B&B £80–£120. 2-night min. stay in peak months.

Prices may change – check with hotel.

BURFORD Oxfordshire
BAY TREE HOTEL

A charmingly refurbished hotel, Bay Tree Hotel is forged from a row of 17th-century houses in picturesque Burford – gateway to the Cotswolds. Past the wisteria-festooned arch, there are huge open fireplaces and a grand galleried staircase; everywhere, staff make visitors feel welcome. In a flourish of florals, checks and tweeds, bedrooms (some with a lounge area), have 'good lighting', a 'large, comfortable bed', an espresso machine, robes and covetable toiletries. Guests with a dog should ask for an adjacent garden room with outdoor access. There are local ales, light meals and board games in the bar; in the restaurant, modern British cuisine. Part of the Fuller's portfolio; see also The Swan, Bibury (Shortlist entry).

MAP 3:D6
Sheep Street
Burford OX18 4LW
T: 01993 822791
W: cotswold-inns-hotels.co.uk/
    the-bay-tree-hotel

BEDROOMS: 21. 2 adjoining garden rooms on ground floor.
OPEN: all year.
FACILITIES: library, bar, restaurant, in-room TV (Freeview), civil wedding licence, function facilities, patio, walled garden, parking.
BACKGROUND MUSIC: 'subtle' in public areas.
LOCATION: 5 mins' walk from Burford High Street.
CHILDREN: all ages welcomed.
DOGS: well-behaved dogs allowed in some bedrooms, public rooms except restaurant.
CREDIT CARDS: Amex, MC, Visa.
PRICES: per room B&B £139–£310. À la carte £38.

Prices may change – check with hotel.

BURLEY Hampshire
BURLEY MANOR

Overlooking a deer park, this eye-catching Victorian manor house with its patterned-brick facades has been stylishly updated as an adult-only retreat with a well-regarded restaurant and two spa treatment rooms. Country-chic bedrooms (most dog friendly) range from snug to capacious; garden suites have a private terrace with seating. At lunch and dinner, 'unusual, eclectic' menus list Mediterranean-inspired and locally sourced small and large plates – local venison with smoked mushroom, perhaps, or grilled octopus with globe artichoke and chilli salsa. There's 'plenty of choice' at breakfast in the conservatory: fruit and yogurts, 'good-quality breads', eggs any way. Burley village is a short stroll away.

MAP 2:E2
Ringwood Road
Burley BH24 4BS
T: 01425 403522
W: burleymanor.com

BEDROOMS: 41. Some in garden wing, 2 suitable for disabled. 1 shepherd's hut.
OPEN: all year, 'house party retreats' over Christmas, New Year.
FACILITIES: drawing room, lounge/bar, restaurant, in-room TV, civil wedding licence, meeting/function facilities, treatment rooms, 8-acre grounds, heated outdoor pool (June–Sept), EV charging, ground floor wheelchair accessible.
BACKGROUND MUSIC: in public rooms.
LOCATION: 7 mins' walk from village.
CHILDREN: no under-13s overnight, welcomed at lunch.
DOGS: allowed in most bedrooms, public rooms, not in restaurant.
CREDIT CARDS: MC, Visa.
PRICES: B&B doubles from £159. À la carte £38. 2-night min. stay at weekends.
Prices may change – check with hotel.

BURY ST EDMUNDS Suffolk
THE NORTHGATE

A red-brick Victorian town house from the outside, glamorous cocktail-bar-and-restaurant-with-rooms from the inside, The Northgate has a relaxed, fun vibe. Spacious, soft-hued bedrooms, including a two-bedroom suite for a family, have French-inspired furniture and statement headboards; garden-facing rooms are quietest. Order a cocktail from the snazzy bar before dining either in the boldly coloured restaurant or on the large terrace. Here, sustainably sourced regional produce informs the modern dishes such as spice-glazed halloumi with beetroot, and Old Spot pork belly with puffed barley. Part of the Chestnut group; see also The Westleton Crown, Westleton, and The Ship at Dunwich, Dunwich (Shortlist entries).

MAP 2:B5
Northgate Street
Bury St Edmunds IP33 1HP
T: 01284 339604
W: thenorthgate.com

BEDROOMS: 9.
OPEN: all year, except 25 Dec, closed Mon/Tues.
FACILITIES: bar/lounge, restaurant, private function room, in-room TV (Freeview), garden, terrace, parking, ground floor wheelchair accessible.
BACKGROUND MUSIC: in public areas.
LOCATION: 6 mins' walk from town.
CHILDREN: all ages welcomed.
DOGS: not allowed.
CREDIT CARDS: Amex, MC, Visa.
PRICES: B&B doubles from £130. À la carte £44.
Prices may change – check with hotel.

CAMBRIDGE Cambridgeshire

GONVILLE HOTEL

Overlooking Parker's Piece common is this large, family-owned hotel with a 'friendly, personable feel'. Smartly updated, it is a 'comfortable' place, with jazz evenings, spa treatments, drinks and meals on the lawn. Air-conditioned bedrooms in the main building and a renovated Victorian villa invigorate classical design with sumptuous textiles. Some have a seating area, or French doors that open on to the garden; others, interconnecting, suit a family. (Set back from a busy road; rooms at the rear are quietest.) On-site parking (extra charge) is a bonus. An easy walk to colleges, shops and cafés; complimentary bicycles are available to borrow; pick-ups and drop-offs in the hotel's Bentley can be pre-arranged.

MAP 2:B4
Gonville Place
Cambridge CB1 1LY
T: 01223 366611
W: gonvillehotel.co.uk

BEDROOMS: 92. Some on ground floor, some suitable for disabled, 8 in Gresham House within the grounds.
OPEN: all year.
FACILITIES: lift, bar, lounge, 2 restaurants, in-room TV (Freeview), spa beauty treatments, parking (£15 council charge), bicycles to borrow.
BACKGROUND MUSIC: in public areas, live jazz in bar, garden on Fri, Sat evenings.
LOCATION: in city centre.
CHILDREN: all ages welcomed.
DOGS: allowed in some bedrooms, reception area.
CREDIT CARDS: Amex, MC, Visa.
PRICES: per room B&B £220–£400. À la carte £60.

Prices may change – check with hotel.

CARBIS BAY Cornwall

THE GANNET

In a pretty village that slopes down to the bay, this 'friendly' inn with a view over the water has 'the feel of a boutique hotel'. Thick armchairs cluster in comfortable groups, some by the wood-burner, in the spacious bar; in the smart dining areas, guests sit down to hearty grills, classic Cornish fare and Sunday lunches. 'Lovely' bedrooms, styled in hues inspired by sand, sea and sky, are cosy, with 'special touches'. Some have views of spectacular seascapes. A short walk down the hill, guests may use the spa, pool and salon at sister property Carbis Bay Hotel before stepping on to the Blue Flag beach; here, too, is the St Ives branch line for the short train ride into town and the Tate St Ives.

MAP 1:D1
St Ives Road
Carbis Bay
St Ives TR26 2SB
T: 01736 795651
W: gannetstives.co.uk

BEDROOMS: 16.
OPEN: all year.
FACILITIES: lounge/bar (darts, pool table), restaurant, in-room TV, civil wedding licence, terrace, beauty salon, yacht charter.
BACKGROUND MUSIC: in public areas.
LOCATION: 1 mile from St Ives.
CHILDREN: all ages welcomed.
DOGS: only assistance dogs allowed.
CREDIT CARDS: Amex, MC, Visa.
PRICES: per room B&B £265–£425. À la carte £40.

Prices may change – check with hotel.

NEW

MAP 1:D4
Chagford TQ13 8HH
T: 01647 432367
W: gidleigh.co.uk

CHAGFORD Devon
GIDLEIGH PARK

At the end of a twisty, country lane and standing high above woodland close to Dartmoor national park, this grand country house in the Arts and Crafts style, is luxurious but surprisingly intimate. 'First-rate' staff and a 'hands-on' General Manager are 'friendly'. Public rooms are rich with original wood panelling, leaded windows, magnificent staircase and 'nice quiet corners'. Bedrooms have antiques, paintings, fresh flowers and modern bathrooms. 'Exquisite' meals offer 'interesting' dishes such as turbot with mixed squash, pumpkin seeds, caviar and seaweed. Enjoy walks, tennis, croquet – and 'excellent' afternoon tea on the terrace. (Relais & Châteaux, part of Andrew Brownsword hotels.)

BEDROOMS: 24. 4 on ground floor, 2 in separate cottage, 1 suitable for disabled.
OPEN: all year, closed Sun/Mon.
FACILITIES: drawing room, bar, conservatory, restaurant, in-room TV, civil wedding licence, 107 acres of grounds (kitchen garden, tennis, 18-hole putting course, river), public rooms wheelchair accessible.
BACKGROUND MUSIC: none.
LOCATION: 23 miles SW of Exeter.
CHILDREN: all ages welcomed, no children in restaurant after 8 pm, children's menu.
DOGS: allowed in some bedrooms (welcome pack) or heated kennels (free), not in public areas apart from grounds.
CREDIT CARDS: Amex, MC, Visa.
PRICES: B&B doubles from £325. À la carte menu £125.
Prices may change – check with hotel.

NEW

MAP 1:D4
Sandy Park
Chagford TQ13 8JN
T: 01647 432282
W: millendhotel.com

CHAGFORD Devon
MILL END HOTEL

Wrapped in woodland, on the banks of the River Teign, this former corn mill is now a tranquil country house hotel with fires in the sitting rooms and a well-regarded restaurant. 'Very comfortable' bedrooms with 'good facilities', and some with a private patio, have views of the gardens and countryside; a charming family room has a window seat overlooking the grounds. Seasonally changing menus include smoked mackerel with beetroot and apple salsa, and herb-crusted lamb with pomme fondant; on warm days, a Devon cream tea may be taken in the garden. 'A little gem', with 'very attentive service'; ideal for exploring Dartmoor, with river path walks to Fingle Bridge and Castle Drogo. Packed lunches available.

BEDROOMS: 20, some on ground floor, 1 suitable for disabled.
OPEN: all year except last 3 weeks Jan.
FACILITIES: 3 lounges, bar, restaurant, 15-acre grounds (river, fishing, bathing), EV charging, ground floor largely wheelchair accessible.
BACKGROUND MUSIC: in public areas.
LOCATION: 21 miles SW of Exeter.
CHILDREN: all ages welcomed.
DOGS: allowed in some bedrooms, in certain public rooms, gardens.
CREDIT CARDS: Amex, MC, Visa.
PRICES: B&B singles from £105, doubles from £115. À la carte 3-course £40, 2-course £35. Min. 2-night stay weekends, May–Oct.
Prices may change – check with hotel.

CHELTENHAM Gloucestershire

COTSWOLD GRANGE

Between town and racecourse in leafy Pittville, Nirav and Dhruti Sheth's friendly hotel is in a fine stone mansion with gardens front and back. The 1830s building retains its original high ceilings, large windows, cantilevered staircase and decorative mouldings; its bijou bar and garden-facing room are stylish spaces in which to enjoy a drink, and the 'very good' breakfast. Individually decorated, pleasing bedrooms vary in size from cosy doubles to spacious rooms that can accommodate an extra bed for a child. Each room has tea- and coffee-making facilities ('with a good size cup'), plus British-made toiletries in a modern bathroom. Shops and eating places in the centre are a 15-minute walk away.

MAP 3:D5
Pittville Circus Road
Cheltenham GL52 2QH
T: 01242 515119
W: cotswoldgrangehotel.co.uk

BEDROOMS: 20.
OPEN: all year except Christmas.
FACILITIES: bar, breakfast room, in-room TV (Freeview), terrace, front and rear gardens, parking.
BACKGROUND MUSIC: in bar, breakfast room.
LOCATION: in Pittville.
CHILDREN: all ages welcomed.
DOGS: in some bedrooms, bar.
CREDIT CARDS: Amex, MC, Visa.
PRICES: per room B&B £70–£250. 2-night min. stay May–Oct.

Prices may change – check with hotel.

CHESTER Cheshire

THE CHESTER GROSVENOR

This grand Victorian hotel, with its columned portico, half-timbering and fluttering flags, holds prime position in the heart of the city, and balances superb service with a charming friendliness. Despite the central location, its 'exceptionally comfortable' bedrooms are 'very quiet'. Whether traditional or more modern, rooms have 'a comfy bed, proper seating and excellent lighting'; 'every amenity' is provided. Informal lunches and dinners are served in the 'likeable' brasserie, alongside its champagne bar. In the smart Arkle restaurant, tasting menus include imaginative vegetarian options. 'Breakfast was good, plenty of choice.' And when you've had enough of the 'charms of the historic centre', head to the hotel's restorative spa.

MAP 3:A4
Eastgate
Chester CH1 1LT
T: 01244 324024
W: chestergrosvenor.com

BEDROOMS: 79. 1 suitable for disabled.
OPEN: all year except 24 (from 4 pm)– 25 Dec.
FACILITIES: lift, drawing room, lounge, bar, brasserie, restaurant, meeting/ private dining rooms, in-room TV (Sky, Freeview), civil wedding licence, function facilities, spa, EV charging, parking (chargeable).
BACKGROUND MUSIC: in public areas.
LOCATION: in city centre.
CHILDREN: all ages welcomed, not under 12 in bar and restaurant (allowed in brasserie), not under 16 in spa.
DOGS: not allowed.
CREDIT CARDS: Amex, MC, Visa.
PRICES: B&B doubles from £171. Tasting menu (restaurant) from £110 (vegetarian, from £95), à la carte (brasserie) £45.

Prices may change – check with hotel.

CHIDDINGFOLD Surrey
THE CROWN INN

This black-and-white timbered medieval inn overlooking Chiddingfold's village green is ridiculously picture-perfect. Step inside and the charm continues with a bar serving pints amidst medieval carvings, oak beams, stained-glass windows and an inglenook fireplace. Dine here or in the oak-panelled dining room on Modern British dishes such as hake and champ mash, as well as pub classics. Bedrooms are contemporary country house in the newer wing or rich and characterful, with four-posters, sloping floors and ancient beams, in the original part. Some have roll-top baths. Breakfast, served late at the weekend, has home-made jams and pastries, and cooked choices from a full grill to avocado and poached egg.

MAP 2:D3
The Green
Petworth Road
Chiddingfold GU8 4TX
T: 01428 682255
W: thecrownchiddingfold.com

BEDROOMS: 8.
OPEN: all year, closed Mon, reopens Tues eve.
FACILITIES: lounge, 2 bars, restaurant, in-room TV (Freeview), private dining, 2 small courtyard gardens, large terrace, parking, public rooms wheelchair accessible.
BACKGROUND MUSIC: 'gentle' in public spaces.
LOCATION: 20 mins from Guildford.
CHILDREN: all ages welcomed.
DOGS: allowed on lead in bar and lounge, not in bedrooms.
CREDIT CARDS: Amex, MC, Visa.
PRICES: B&B doubles from £149, singles from £95. À la carte £35.

Prices may change – check with hotel.

CHURCH ENSTONE Oxfordshire
THE CROWN INN

This picture-perfect Cotswold-stone village inn is all low beams, flagged floors and open fires as befits its 400 years of service. Modern art, courtesy of artist co-owner George Irvine and other local artists, enriches the walls in the bar and restaurant, and the low-ceilinged bedrooms. With valley or village views, these rooms are country-style with modern bathrooms stocked with Cotswolds-made toiletries. George and his wife Victoria ensure there are local ales in the bar. Cream teas and updated pub fare are presented on stoneware crockery in the restaurant and airy conservatory. Out back, the small garden is festive with oversized parasols, beer-barrel tables and pots billowing with flowers in summer.

MAP 2:C2
Mill Lane
Church Enstone
Chipping Norton OX7 4NN
T: 01608 677262
W: crowninnenstone.co.uk

BEDROOMS: 5. Plus 2-bed cottage.
OPEN: all year. Restaurant closed Sun eve, Mon, Tues at time of writing.
FACILITIES: bar, restaurant, conservatory, in-room TV (Freeview), ⅓-acre garden, ground-floor wheelchair accessible with ramps.
BACKGROUND MUSIC: occasionally in public areas.
LOCATION: in village.
CHILDREN: all ages welcomed.
DOGS: allowed in 1 bedroom, bar, garden, cottage.
CREDIT CARDS: MC, Visa.
PRICES: B&B doubles £120–£180. À la carte £35. 2-night min. stay over Sat night.

Prices may change – check with hotel.

CHURCH STRETTON Shropshire

VICTORIA HOUSE

In the centre of a lively market town within walking distance of the Shropshire hills, this 'splendid' B&B is run by Diane Chadwick, a 'wonderfully energetic' and 'cheerful' hostess. The Victorian town house has 'well-priced, convenient' accommodation in 'comfortable' bedrooms, each 'tastefully decorated' with artworks and antiques that lend much character, and generously supplied with bathrobes and toiletries, teas, coffee, hot chocolate, sherry and biscuits. Served in a garden-facing room, breakfast has freshly baked pastries, sausages from locally reared pigs, and 'particularly delicious mushrooms cooked in butter'. Light lunches and sweet treats are taken in the cosy, on-site café, Jemima's Kitchen.

MAP 3:C4
48 High Street
Church Stretton SY6 6BX
T: 01694 723823
W: victoriahouse-shropshire.co.uk

BEDROOMS: 6, 1 with separate bathroom.
OPEN: all year, café open Wed–Sun, 9.30 am–4 pm.
FACILITIES: seating area, breakfast room, café/tea room, in-room TV (Freeview), walled garden, off-street parking and EV charging available at adjacent pay-and-display car park.
BACKGROUND MUSIC: in breakfast room and café.
LOCATION: in town centre.
CHILDREN: all ages welcomed.
DOGS: allowed in all bedrooms, garden.
CREDIT CARDS: Amex, MC, Visa.
PRICES: per room B&B single £74–£94, double £97–£114. 2-night min. stay on weekends.

Prices may change – check with hotel.

NEW

CIRENCESTER Gloucestershire

INGLESIDE

It's no wonder that Ian and Chrissie Carling's hotel is so dramatic. Ardent about performing arts, they created and are patrons of the Barn Theatre next door. They have transformed their Grade II listed building with showy pieces. Exuberant colours and patterns form striking backdrops in the guest lounge and bedrooms. Each has a wide bed, a coffee machine, iron and safe; perhaps an original fireplace painted deep blue or pink, a window seat or free-standing bath. Vivid shades of green vie for attention with flamingo wallpaper in Téatro's restaurant, popular for pre-theatre meals. Make an entrance for cocktails in the piano bar or meet by the firepit in the courtyard. Events may be held at weekends.

MAP 3:E5
5 Beeches Road
Cirencester GL7 1BN
T: 01285 648230
W: inglesidehouse.co.uk

BEDROOMS: 11.
OPEN: all year, except 24 (eve), 25, 26 Dec, restaurant closed Sun eve.
FACILITIES: bar, restaurant, drawing room, lounge, function facilities, in-room TV, civil wedding licence.
BACKGROUND MUSIC: in public rooms.
LOCATION: 15 mins' walk into town.
CHILDREN: all ages welcomed.
DOGS: not in rooms, allowed in bar, outside dining area only.
CREDIT CARDS: MC, Visa.
PRICES: per room B&B £140–£290. À la carte £47.25.

Prices may change – check with hotel.

CLIFTON Cumbria

GEORGE AND DRAGON

A 'convivial' country pub with cosy rooms and 'very good' food, the Lowther family's restored 18th-century coaching inn near Ullswater retains its rural roots. Roaring fires welcome guests in the hop-hung bar and dining areas in cool weather. In sunshine, eat in the courtyard or beer garden. Farm and garden produce from the family estate and sister hotel Askham Hall, Penrith (see main entry) supply the monthly menu. Upstairs, some bedrooms are snug, others family friendly. Light sleepers should ask for a room away from the road. The Lowthers also own The Queen's Head, Askham (see Shortlist entry).

NOTE: As the Guide went to press, the George and Dragon temporarily closed following a serious fire. It plans to reopen in autumn 2022.

MAP 4: inset C2
Clifton
Penrith CA10 2ER
T: 01768 865381
W: georgeanddragonclifton.co.uk

BEDROOMS: 11.
OPEN: all year, except 26 Dec.
FACILITIES: bar, restaurant, in-room TV (Freeview), beer garden, secure bicycle storage, EV charging.
BACKGROUND MUSIC: contemporary in public areas.
LOCATION: on A6, on the edge of the Lake District, 10 mins' drive from Ullswater.
CHILDREN: all ages welcomed.
DOGS: allowed in bedrooms, bar, not in restaurant.
CREDIT CARDS: MC, Visa.
PRICES: per room B&B single £100–£130, double £120–£170. À la carte £40. 2-night min. stay at weekends in high season.

Prices may change – check with hotel.

COLERNE Wiltshire

LUCKNAM PARK

Approached down a mile-long avenue of lime and beech trees, this 'very grand and lovely' Palladian mansion exults in 500 acres of parkland and gardens. There are an arboretum and a rose garden to wander through; trails to explore, on horseback if desired. In a walled garden, the spa has swimming pools and treatments galore. Young visitors are mini VIPs with sports and pony rides, plus indoor and outdoor play areas. At mealtimes, choose between chef Hywel Jones's Michelin-starred fine dining restaurant and the informal contemporary brasserie with sight of the listed dovecote. Wind down afterwards in one of the elegant, classically decorated bedrooms – each is supplied with fluffy robes and slippers.

MAP 2:D1
Colerne SN14 8AZ
T: 01225 742777
W: lucknampark.co.uk

BEDROOMS: 43. 18 in courtyard, 1 suitable for disabled, plus six 3- and 4-bed cottages.
OPEN: all year. Restaurant Hywel Jones closed Sun–Wed. Brasserie open daily.
FACILITIES: drawing room, library, restaurant, brasserie, in-room TV, civil wedding licence, spa, indoor pools, outdoor hydrotherapy and saltwater plunge pools, terrace, tennis, croquet, football pitch, equestrian centre, 5-acre grounds within 500 acres, EV charging.
BACKGROUND MUSIC: in public areas.
LOCATION: 7 miles W of Chippenham.
CHILDREN: all ages welcomed.
DOGS: allowed in 4 bedrooms, cottages, part of brasserie.
CREDIT CARDS: Amex, MC, Visa.
PRICES: per room B&B £469–£1,786. 2-night min. stay at weekends. À la carte (brasserie) £55.

Prices may change – check with hotel.

CORNWORTHY Devon

KERSWELL FARMHOUSE

Spectacular views across the rolling South Hams countryside towards Dartmoor are just one of the joys of Nichola and Graham Hawkins's secluded farm B&B. Two large guest suites are in a converted barn close to the main 400-year-old longhouse and are stylish with a mix of antiques, oak furniture and original art set against white-washed walls and stripped-wood floors. Each has a sitting room, microwave and stocked minibar, bath and separate shower, plus thoughtful extras of bathrobes and fresh flowers; one has a private garden. Breakfast, served in the farmhouse's beamed dining room, includes home-made compote, eggs Benedict and a full Devon with bacon, sausages and eggs from home-reared pigs and hens.

MAP 1:D4
Furze Cross
Cornworthy
Totnes TQ9 7HH
T: 01803 732013
W: kerswellfarmhouse.co.uk

BEDROOMS: 2. In adjacent barn, 1 on ground floor.
OPEN: all year except 22 Dec–4 Jan.
FACILITIES: dining room, in-room TV (Freeview), 14-acre grounds.
BACKGROUND MUSIC: none.
LOCATION: 4 miles S of Totnes, 4 miles N of Dartmouth.
CHILDREN: not under 12.
DOGS: not allowed.
CREDIT CARDS: none accepted.
PRICES: B&B doubles £155–£165. 2-night min. stay, but check for single availability.

Prices may change – check with hotel.

CRAYKE Yorkshire

THE DURHAM OX

With views over the Vale of York, this village inn has all the warmth, character and robust food expected of a 300-year-old country pub. Owners Michael and Sasha Ibbotson ensure guests, and their dogs, are well cared for. The busy dining areas have stone flags, wood panelling and inglenook fireplaces – a 'delightfully decorated' backdrop to the 'excellent' menu of regional pub classics. Alfresco meals may be taken on the heated patio. Most of the 'comfy, well-lit' bedrooms are in stone-built farm cottages behind the pub; some have a terrace with outdoor seating. On clear days, soak in the 'superb' views over a pint of local ale. Maps are available to borrow, for gentle strolls and serious hikes alike.

MAP 4:D4
Westway
Crayke YO61 4TE
T: 01347 821506
W: thedurhamox.com

BEDROOMS: 6. 5 in converted farm buildings, 3 on ground floor, 1 suite accessed via external stairs. Plus 3-bed self-catering cottage in village.
OPEN: all year, except Mon and Tues, Christmas Day.
FACILITIES: 3 bars, restaurant, private dining room, in-room TV (Freeview), function facilities, civil wedding licence, patio, 2-acre grounds, public rooms wheelchair accessible.
BACKGROUND MUSIC: in pub and restaurant.
LOCATION: 2 miles E of Easingwold.
CHILDREN: all ages welcomed.
DOGS: allowed in one of bars, patio, most bedrooms.
CREDIT CARDS: Amex, MC, Visa.
PRICES: B&B £120–£170, D,B&B required on Sat from £270.
À la carte £35.

Prices may change – check with hotel.

DARTMOUTH Devon

STRETE BARTON HOUSE

Steps from the South West Coast Path, Stuart Litster and Kevin Hooper's 'superbly decorated' Jacobean manor house in a small village close to Dartmouth has panoramic sea views stretching over Start Bay. B&B guests come for 'the warmth of welcome' as much as the tea and home-baked cake served on arrival. Overlooking the garden, the lounge has large sofas; a log fire is lit in cool weather. In the main house and a duplex cottage suite, contemporary bedrooms have 'pristine bedding', fresh flowers and biscuits; 'windows open to let in sea air and birdsong'. After a breakfast of 'delicious fruit' and 'beautifully cooked' hot dishes, head for the pine-fringed bay around Blackpool Sands, a 20-minute walk away.

MAP 1:D4
Totnes Road
Strete
Dartmouth TQ6 0RU
T: 01803 770364
W: stretebarton.co.uk

BEDROOMS: 6. 1 in cottage annexe.
OPEN: 7 Apr–end Oct.
FACILITIES: sitting room, breakfast room, library, in-room TV (Freeview), ½-acre garden.
BACKGROUND MUSIC: none.
LOCATION: 5 miles W of Dartmouth.
CHILDREN: not under 8.
DOGS: allowed in cottage suite.
CREDIT CARDS: Amex, MC, Visa.
PRICES: B&B £140–£190. 1-night bookings sometimes refused in high season.

Prices may change – check with hotel.

DELPH Lancashire

THE OLD BELL INN

Nestled below the Pennines in the picturesque village of Delph, this traditional coaching inn, ablaze with hanging baskets, is popular with locals and visitors whether for a drink, a casual meal or a smart night out. The 18th-century stone building shelters a busy bar (with a world record-breaking number of over 1,100 gins), an informal brasserie and a cosy restaurant whose regularly changing menu mixes pub classics with smarter dishes such as duck breast on spinach and pine nuts. Light and neat bedrooms, some with beams, suit leisure and business travellers as well as families; quieter rooms are at the rear. Guests can relax in the first-floor conservatory lounge. Breakfast has hearty cooked options.

MAP 4:E3
Huddersfield Road
Delph
Oldham OL3 5EG
T: 01457 870130
W: theoldbellinn.co.uk

BEDROOMS: 18. 4 in extension.
OPEN: all year.
FACILITIES: bar, lounge, brasserie, restaurant, in-room TV (Freeview), function facilities, terrace, parking, restaurant wheelchair accessible.
BACKGROUND MUSIC: in public areas.
LOCATION: 5 miles from Oldham.
CHILDREN: all ages welcomed.
DOGS: not allowed.
CREDIT CARDS: Amex, MC, Visa.
PRICES: B&B doubles from £130, singles from £79. À la carte £30.

Prices may change – check with hotel.

DEVIZES Wiltshire
THE PEPPERMILL

NEW

In two adjacent ancient buildings (dating from 1452 and 1538), Philip O'Shea's restaurant-with-rooms is in the heart of the historic market town. Modern inside, the restaurant has exposed brick walls and wooden floors, and is popular with locals for its informal lunches, Sunday roasts and evening menus. Meat is supplied by a local master butcher; fish and unusual vegetarian dishes are available too. A wide range of drinks, and snacks, is served in the newly refurbished cocktail bar and lounge, or under umbrellas in the courtyard garden. The clean-lined bedrooms have air conditioning, a safe and dressing gowns; a two-bedroom suite is ideal for a family. There are calm areas upstairs for residents to sit.

MAP 3:E5
40 St John's Street
Devizes SN10 1BL
T: 01380 710407
W: peppermilldevizes.co.uk

BEDROOMS: 16.
OPEN: all year, except Sunday evening.
FACILITIES: 4 bars, 3 sitting rooms, restaurant, in-room TV, function room (lift), private dining, courtyard garden.
BACKGROUND MUSIC: in bars, restaurant.
LOCATION: in town centre.
CHILDREN: all ages welcomed.
DOGS: not allowed.
CREDIT CARDS: MC, Visa.
PRICES: per room B&B £85–£185.
À la carte £38.

Prices may change – check with hotel.

DOUGLAS Isle of Man
THE REGENCY HOTEL

On the promenade of the island's main town (listen out for the clip-clop of horse-drawn trams along the sea front throughout spring and summer), this 'gorgeously panelled' traditional hotel is liked for its amiable staff, who are 'very helpful with local recommendations'. Manx artwork hangs in the lounge. 'Certainly the narrowest lift we've ever been in' takes guests to upper-floor bedrooms (some with 'good' sea views). In L'Experience restaurant, the menu of 'excellent' brasserie classics might include French onion soup and steak au poivre. In a 'very convenient location', a free shuttle takes guests to the town centre.

MAP 4: inset E1
Queens Promenade
Douglas IM2 4NN
T: 01624 680680
W: regency.im

BEDROOMS: 38.
OPEN: all year, restaurant closed Sun.
FACILITIES: lift, lounge, bar, restaurant, in-room TV, civil wedding licence, meeting/function facilities.
BACKGROUND MUSIC: none.
LOCATION: on the promenade.
CHILDREN: all ages welcomed.
DOGS: not allowed.
CREDIT CARDS: Amex, MC, Visa.
PRICES: per room B&B £100–£210.
À la carte £40.

Prices may change – check with hotel.

DUNSFORD Devon
WEEKE BARTON

Jo Gossett and Sam Perry's rustic chic country guest house is just as inviting outside as in, whether you want to play pétanque on the lawn, stroll down to the pond, or on clear nights, settle in to stargaze surrounded by the rolling hills and pastures of the Teign valley. The Grade II listed longhouse has wood-burning stoves, deep sofas, and Dartmoor- and Devon-focused honesty bar; dogs and children are welcome in equal measure. Uncluttered bedrooms have cotton robes, bags of style, rural views from a sheep-skinned window seat. Three nights a week, stay in for a dinner of locally sourced produce (special diets happily catered for); at breakfast, try the award-winning home-made granola.

MAP 1:C4
Dartmoor
Dunsford EX6 7HH
T: 01647 253505
W: weekebarton.com

BEDROOMS: 6. 1 in converted cob barn.
OPEN: all year, dinner available Mon, Thurs and Fri.
FACILITIES: lounge, bar, dining room, in-room flat screens for movies (no TV signal), patio, 4-acre grounds (lawns, paddock, pond, play den for children).
BACKGROUND MUSIC: 'chilled tunes' all day (adjustable volume).
LOCATION: 8 miles SW of Exeter.
CHILDREN: all ages welcomed.
DOGS: allowed (resident dogs).
CREDIT CARDS: MC, Visa.
PRICES: per room B&B single £120–£165, double £130–£175. 2-course fixed menu £25. 2-night min. stay at weekends.

Prices may change – check with hotel.

DUNWICH Suffolk
THE SHIP AT DUNWICH

Once a smugglers' haunt, this creeper-covered inn is close to the unspoiled salt marshes of Dunwich Heath and the RSPB reserves at Dingle Marshes and Minsmere. The red-brick building has a nautical-themed bar and three dining areas for pub favourites and daily specials (Suffolk sausages and parsley mash). An 800-year-old fig tree and iconic fishing boats command admiration in the beer garden where victuals are dispensed from the new Field Kitchen. Bedrooms, some snug, have simple country charm. The best have marsh views; some, in converted outbuildings, are 'perfect for dogs'. Part of the Chestnut group; see also The Northgate, Bury St Edmunds, and The Westleton Crown, Westleton (Shortlist entries).

MAP 2:B6
St James Street
Dunwich IP17 3DT
T: 01728 648219
W: shipatdunwich.co.uk

BEDROOMS: 16. 4 on ground floor in converted stables, 1 suitable for disabled.
OPEN: all year, except 25 Dec.
FACILITIES: bar, restaurant (3 dining areas), in-room TV (Freeview, smart TV in family rooms), courtyard, large beer garden.
BACKGROUND MUSIC: in bar and dining areas.
LOCATION: a few hundred yards from Dunwich beach.
CHILDREN: all ages welcomed.
DOGS: warmly welcomed inside and out.
CREDIT CARDS: MC, Visa.
PRICES: per room B&B £166–£245. À la carte £35. 2-night min. stay at weekends in peak season.

Prices may change – check with hotel.

EAST WITTON Yorkshire
THE BLUE LION

Log fires and settles downstairs, country-style bedrooms up: in this 'sophisticated' 18th-century inn, Paul and Helen Klein offer an 'utterly authentic' slice of rural Wensleydale hospitality. The former coaching house is liked for its 'pleasant, knowledgeable staff' and 'good atmosphere': there are real ales from nearby Masham, and a warm welcome for dogs. In the bar and candlelit restaurant, modern British menus by chef Shaun Best include cassoulet of Yorkshire duck confit. Bedrooms have a more rustic style in the main building, and some have views across the village to the dales; more contemporary 'big and comfortable' rooms are in the converted stables. Nearby are Bolton Castle and Fountains Abbey.

MAP 4:C4
East Witton
Leyburn DL8 4SN
T: 01969 624273
W: thebluelion.co.uk

BEDROOMS: 15. 6 in main building. 9 in courtyard annexe.
OPEN: all year.
FACILITIES: 3 bars, 1 large restaurant, in-room TV (Freeview), 1-acre garden, parking, restaurant, wheelchair accessible.
BACKGROUND MUSIC: none.
LOCATION: in village, 4½ miles from Leyburn.
CHILDREN: all ages welcomed.
DOGS: allowed in bar, garden, some bedrooms.
CREDIT CARDS: MC, Visa.
PRICES: per room B&B £117.50–£175. Children over 2 £15 per night staying overnight in room with parents. 3-course à la carte meal from £51.

Prices may change – check with hotel.

EASTBOURNE Sussex
THE GRAND HOTEL

A 'perfect position for walking on the downs and the beach', this majestic, white Victorian hotel is on the seafront and has views stretching along the coast. 'All is glamorous' inside: there are spacious public rooms, long corridors with patterned carpets, lofty ceilings and heavy drapes at arched windows. Throughout, the many returning guests commend the service from 'friendly and relaxed' staff. 'Beautiful and well-equipped', the bedrooms and suites have towelling robes, an espresso machine and high-end toiletries; 24-hour room service is available. Afternoon tea is served on the terrace, or in the great hall with musical accompaniment; there are two restaurants to choose from at lunch and dinner.

MAP 2:E4
King Edwards Parade
Eastbourne BN21 4EQ
T: 01323 412345
W: grandeastbourne.com

BEDROOMS: 152. 1 suitable for disabled.
OPEN: all year, Mirabelle closed Sun, Mon, first 2 weeks Jan.
FACILITIES: lifts, 5 lounges, bar, 2 restaurants, function facilities, in-room TV (BT, Freeview), civil wedding licence, large terrace, spa/health club (indoor and outdoor pools), 2-acre garden, public areas wheelchair accessible.
BACKGROUND MUSIC: in lounges, live music at weekends.
LOCATION: on the seafront, outside the centre.
CHILDREN: all ages welcomed.
DOGS: allowed in bedrooms.
CREDIT CARDS: Amex, MC, Visa.
PRICES: per room B&B single from £180.50, double £220–£530. À la carte £55 (Mirabelle).

Prices may change – check with hotel.

EDINGTON Wiltshire

THE THREE DAGGERS

With a dash of country cool, this spruced-up pub-with-rooms serves as a vibrant village hub. The enterprise consists of an award-winning microbrewery, a well-stocked deli/farm shop, a hillside spa barn, a restaurant serving modern comfort food, and a trio of rustic-chic bedrooms to fall into at the end of the day. Each room is different – a spacious suite has a claw-footed bath in the bathroom – but all are supplied with natural toiletries and fluffy towels. A continental and cooked breakfast is served in the Garden Room. Above the snug, the residents' lounge has a little kitchen with milk, juice and biscuits. Just beyond the village, scenic trails wind through this stretch of the Salisbury Plain.

MAP 2:D1
47 Westbury Road
Edington
Westbury BA13 4PG
T: 01380 830940
W: threedaggers.co.uk

BEDROOMS: 3. Plus 6-bed self-catering cottage.
OPEN: all year.
FACILITIES: residents' living room/ kitchen, bar, restaurant, private dining room, in-room TV (Freeview), civil wedding licence, garden (direct access to village park), pizza shack (summer months), spa barn, microbrewery, farm shop.
BACKGROUND MUSIC: in the pub.
LOCATION: 10 mins' drive from Westbury.
CHILDREN: all ages welcomed.
DOGS: allowed in bedrooms, public rooms.
CREDIT CARDS: Amex, MC, Visa.
PRICES: per room B&B £120–£160. À la carte £40.

Prices may change – check with hotel.

ELLERBY Yorkshire

THE ELLERBY COUNTRY INN

A mile inland from lovely Runswick Bay, in a quiet Yorkshire village on the edge of the North York Moors, this country inn is a beacon of good service, good value and simple comforts. Owners Mark and Georgie Alderson ensure all are welcome – including dogs, families and walkers – at the long and low sandstone inn, with its window-boxes and colourful garden. Neat and fuss-free bedrooms have large beds, fresh milk, upmarket toiletries and robes, while bathrooms are modern if sometimes small. Relax in the conservatory before a hearty meal – in bar, restaurant or alfresco – of 'superior' pub classics from home-made beef lasagne and pies to steaks and Whitby scampi, plus good vegetarian options.

MAP 4:C5
12–14 Ryeland Lane
Ellerby
Whitby TS13 5LP
T: 01947 840342
W: ellerbyhotel.co.uk

BEDROOMS: 10. 4 on ground floor, 1 suitable for disabled.
OPEN: all year.
FACILITIES: bar, snug, restaurant, conservatory/lounge, garden, in-room TV (Sky), public rooms wheelchair accessible, adapted toilet.
BACKGROUND MUSIC: in public areas.
LOCATION: in village, 8 miles W of Whitby.
CHILDREN: all ages welcomed, under-5s free, extra bed from £20.
DOGS: allowed in 3 bedrooms (£7.50 per night), garden and lounge/ conservatory, not in bar or restaurant.
CREDIT CARDS: MC, Visa.
PRICES: B&B doubles £115–£170, singles £85–£140. À la carte 3-course £32.

Prices may change – check with hotel.

ELY Cambridgeshire

THE OLD HALL

Entering the long drive up to the Old Hall, it's hard to know where to look first; either to the striking tall-chimneyed manor house or the romantic views of Ely cathedral over the Morbey family's farm and woodland estate. Rebuilt from the ruins of a Jacobean brick hall, the family-run B&B, with its beamed ceilings and polished-wood floors, stands in manicured grounds, making it also a popular exclusive-use wedding venue. There are deep sofas, antiques and open fires; several nights a week, the restaurant serves a short menu of Modern British dishes (perhaps coriander chilli crab cake; guinea fowl with smoked mash). Elegant bedrooms with handmade furniture and soft colours overlook the garden and estate.

MAP 2:B4
Stuntney
Ely CB7 5TR
T: 01353 663275
w: theoldhallely.co.uk

BEDROOMS: 15. 2 on ground floor, suitable for disabled.
OPEN: all year except Christmas, restaurant closed Mon, Tues.
FACILITIES: drawing room, main hall, bar, 2 dining rooms, in-room TV (Freeview), civil wedding licence, terrace, 3,000-acre grounds (garden, lakes, farmland).
BACKGROUND MUSIC: 'low-key' in public rooms.
LOCATION: 2 miles S of Ely.
CHILDREN: not allowed.
DOGS: not allowed.
CREDIT CARDS: MC, Visa.
PRICES: B&B doubles from £160. Set dinner £32.95 (2 courses), £38.95 (3 courses).

Prices may change – check with hotel.

FAIRFORD Gloucestershire

THE BULL HOTEL

In lovely soft-coloured Cotswold stone, and with 15th-century origins, the popular and buzzy Bull Hotel stands invitingly in the centre of this market town. Stylishly updated, the pub and hotel (part of the Barkby group), has a stone-walled bar with exposed timbers, local cask ales and plush seating by a crackling fire. A horned bull's head above an open fireplace oversees proceedings. Modern European dishes and steaks are served in the moodily lit dining areas. Contemporary, country-style bedrooms in soft colours are decorated with vintage finds and locally made wool throws. Fishing enthusiasts appreciate the hotel's private stretch of the River Coln; riverside walks are pleasant.

MAP 3:E6
The Market Place
Fairford GL7 4AA
T: 01285 712535
w: thebullhotelfairford.co.uk

BEDROOMS: 21.
OPEN: all year.
FACILITIES: bar, lounge, morning room, 3 dining rooms, function facilities, in-room TV (Freeview), terraces, private fishing rights, free parking nearby.
BACKGROUND MUSIC: in bar, dining rooms.
LOCATION: in town centre.
CHILDREN: all ages welcomed.
DOGS: allowed in bar only.
CREDIT CARDS: Amex, MC, Visa.
PRICES: B&B doubles from £87. À la carte £35. 2-night min. stay preferred at weekends.

Prices may change – check with hotel.

FALMOUTH Cornwall
THE GREENBANK

Life on the water's edge doesn't come much closer than at this large hotel, the oldest in the maritime town. The building is an amalgam of modern additions to a 17th-century sailors' pub; today, coastal light floods into its public spaces, and its bedrooms and suites, some harbour facing, are bright and contemporary. 'We particularly appreciated the Cornish leaf tea, a cafetière with real coffee and a Nespresso machine. Really good lighting too.' Food is served all day in the restaurant (perhaps lamb or seafood classics); in the dog-friendly Working Boat pub, find Sunday roasts and a home brew. Step straight on to a boat from the hotel's pontoons; a ten-minute stroll away, board the ferry to Flushing.

MAP 1:E2
Harbourside
Falmouth TR11 2SR
T: 01326 312440
W: greenbank-hotel.co.uk

BEDROOMS: 61.
OPEN: all year.
FACILITIES: lift, bar, pub, restaurant, lounge, in-room TV, civil wedding licence, spa treatments, EV charging.
BACKGROUND MUSIC: in bar, restaurant.
LOCATION: on Falmouth harbour.
CHILDREN: all ages welcomed.
DOGS: allowed in 9 bedrooms, pub, not in restaurant, bar.
CREDIT CARDS: Amex, MC, Visa.
PRICES: per room B&B £99–£458. À la carte £45. 1-night bookings sometimes refused.

Prices may change – check with hotel.

FERRENSBY Yorkshire
THE GENERAL TARLETON

Open fires and flagstone floors in spruced-up eating and drinking areas make this recently refurbished 18th-century coaching inn a welcoming place. In the bar and conservatory or on the terrace, small and large plates of 'world-inspired' cooking might include mushroom and truffle arancini, spring onion dip, or duo of Yorkshire beef; the fine-dining restaurant, Ralph's, serves a multi-course tasting menu. Overnight guests stay in one of the stylishly updated bedrooms on the first or ground floor, each supplied with tea, coffee and organic toiletries. Residents also have access to a lounge with an honesty bar. Breakfast includes a seasonal smoothie. Harrogate, York and The Dales are an easy drive away.

MAP 4:D4
Boroughbridge Road
Ferrensby HG5 0PZ
T: 01423 340284
W: the-gt.co.uk

BEDROOMS: 15. Some, on ground floor, suitable for disabled.
OPEN: all year, closed Mon, Tues for lunch.
FACILITIES: residents' lounge, bar, 2 restaurants, conservatory, in-room TV (Freeview), terrace, small herb garden, parking.
BACKGROUND MUSIC: all day in public areas.
LOCATION: 4 miles from Knaresborough.
CHILDREN: all ages welcomed.
DOGS: not allowed, except in bar, on terrace.
CREDIT CARDS: Amex, MC, Visa.
PRICES: per room B&B £130–£160. À la carte £50, tasting menu (Ralph's) £60.

Prices may change – check with hotel.

GILSLAND Cumbria
THE HILL ON THE WALL

Elaine Packer's farmhouse B&B overlooks
Hadrian's Wall near Birdoswald, one of the
Roman monument's best-preserved forts. Visitors
praise the welcome they receive at this Georgian
building filled with 'every comfort'. The
traditionally decorated bedrooms are supplied
with bathrobes, freshly ground coffee and a jar
of biscuits; at teatime, there are hot drinks and
home-made cake to be had. On cool days, browse
the library by the wood-burning stove; when
the weather's fine, sit in the 'beautiful' walled
garden and watch the light change over the
North Pennines and the Lakeland Fells beyond.
'So peaceful.' Breakfast on 'gigantic portions' of
home-cooked Northumbrian fare, ordered the
night before.

MAP 4:B3
The Hill
Gilsland CA8 7DA
T: 016977 47214
W: hillonthewall.co.uk

BEDROOMS: 3. 1 on ground floor.
OPEN: Mar–Oct.
FACILITIES: lounge, breakfast room, in-
room TV (Freeview), 1-acre garden,
terrace, secure bicycle storage.
BACKGROUND MUSIC: none.
LOCATION: 1 mile W of Gilsland on
the B6318.
CHILDREN: not under 10.
DOGS: not allowed.
CREDIT CARDS: MC, Visa for online
bookings only.
PRICES: all rooms are £95, irrespective
of dual or single occupancy.

Prices may change – check with hotel.

GOATHLAND Yorkshire
FAIRHAVEN COUNTRY GUEST HOUSE

This large Edwardian house in a North York
Moors village has far-reaching views, and is a
comfortable base for walks and exploring both
moorland and coast, perhaps by the North York
Moors Railway. Peter and Sarah Garnett welcome
guests with tea and home-baked cake in the large
lounge with its open fire; on warmer days guests
can sit in the rear garden. Homely bedrooms,
with pretty wallpapers and views over moorland
and village, are well stocked with hot drinks and
biscuits; fresh milk and filtered water are in the
dining-room fridge. Breakfasts highlight local
produce such as Whitby kippers and smoked
haddock, sausages and home-made granola,
marmalade and jams – plus daily specials.

MAP 4:C5
The Common
Goathland YO22 5AN
T: 01947 896361
W: fairhavencountryguesthouse.co.uk

BEDROOMS: 9. 1 with separate private
bathroom.
OPEN: all year except 1 week over
Christmas.
FACILITIES: lounge, dining room,
in-room TV (Freeview), front terrace,
large garden, secure bicycle storage,
dinner available on certain evenings
in winter, all year for parties of 6 or
more.
BACKGROUND MUSIC: during breakfast.
LOCATION: close to the North York
Moors steam railway, 8 miles from
Whitby.
CHILDREN: all ages welcomed.
DOGS: not allowed.
CREDIT CARDS: MC, Visa.
PRICES: B&B doubles from £105,
singles from £52. 2-night min. during
high season (ring to check 1-night
availability).

Prices may change – check with hotel.

GOSFORTH Cumbria

1692 WASDALE

A relaxing base in the rugged western Lake
District, Faith and Stephen Newell's fantastically
secluded B&B is sleekly designed and has many
modern comforts. Bursts of vibrant colour
complement the high beamed ceilings and timber
and flagstone floors in the stone-built house.
Outside, the breathtaking views stretch across
Wasdale – home to England's deepest lake,
Wastwater, and Scafell Pike, its highest mountain.
An outdoor hot tub soothes aching muscles after
a day's walk. The large lounge has an honesty
bar, a piano, an open fire for cool evenings;
each spacious suite has a private patio. Picnics
and home-cooked dinners may be pre-ordered;
breakfast, served in the courtyard on sunny days,
is 'excellent'.

MAP 4: inset C2
Bolton Head Farm
Gosforth CA20 1EW
T: 019467 25777
W: 1692wasdale.co.uk

BEDROOMS: 6.
OPEN: all year except 23–26 Dec. No
dinner served on Fri, Sun evenings.
FACILITIES: lounge, dining room,
in-room smart TV, courtyard, 3-acre
garden, boot room, sheltered outdoor
hot tub, EV charging.
BACKGROUND MUSIC: in public rooms.
LOCATION: 1½ miles E of Gosforth.
CHILDREN: not under 12.
DOGS: allowed in 3 suites, not in
lounge, dining room.
CREDIT CARDS: MC, Visa.
PRICES: per room B&B single
£155–£175, double £170–£210. À la
carte £35.

Prices may change – check with hotel.

GRANGE-IN-BORROWDALE Cumbria

BORROWDALE GATES

With views down one of the Lake District's
most picturesque valleys, and walks from the
doorstep, this former private country house is now
a charmingly traditional hotel with 21st-century
comforts. Spacious and neatly furnished bedrooms
offer valley and fell views; some with a balcony
or patio, all with refreshment trays and access to
a digital newspaper and magazine library. After a
day's exploring, relax in the open-plan lounge and
bar with wood-burning stove and vast windows
overlooking the garden and valley. A showcase for
Cumbrian produce (Borrowdale trout, fell-bred
lamb), the restaurant offers modern country-
house dishes, vegetarian included. 'Breakfast
sustains walkers through a long day.'

MAP 4: inset C2
Grange-in-Borrowdale
Keswick CA12 5UQ
T: 01768 777204
W: borrowdale-gates.com

BEDROOMS: 32. Some on ground floor.
OPEN: all year.
FACILITIES: lift, open-plan bar/lounge,
dining room, reading room, in-room
TV (Freeview), 2-acre grounds,
terrace, public rooms wheelchair
accessible.
BACKGROUND MUSIC: none.
LOCATION: 5 miles from Keswick, in
the heart of the Borrowdale valley.
CHILDREN: all ages welcomed.
DOGS: allowed in 3 bedrooms, not in
dining room, bar, lounge.
CREDIT CARDS: MC, Visa.
PRICES: B&B single from £137, double
£214–£330. À la carte 2-course £44,
3-course £52.

Prices may change – check with hotel.

GRANGE-OVER-SANDS Cumbria

CLARE HOUSE

In a Victorian house with sweeping views over Morecambe Bay, this comfortable hotel, run by two generations of the Read family, retains the loyal affection of its many returning guests. 'Wonderfully old-fashioned', most of the well-appointed bedrooms have garden and water views. Morning coffee, light lunches and afternoon tea can be taken warmed by open fires in bay-view lounges; under parasols in the 'well-tended' garden in good weather. At dinner, 'beautifully presented' dishes might include broccoli, leek, Gruyère cheese and cream tart; seared and roasted guinea fowl breast, dauphinoise potato. Breakfast is served on linen-dressed tables. 'Friendly staff' readily advise on Lake District day trips.

MAP 4: inset C2
Park Road
Grange-over-Sands LA11 7HQ
T: 015395 33026
W: clarehousehotel.co.uk

BEDROOMS: 17. 1 on ground floor suitable for disabled.
OPEN: mid-Mar–end-Nov.
FACILITIES: 2 lounges, dining room, in-room TV (Freeview), 1-acre grounds, parking.
BACKGROUND MUSIC: none.
LOCATION: in village.
CHILDREN: all ages welcomed, but no special facilities.
DOGS: only assistance dogs allowed.
CREDIT CARDS: MC, Visa.
PRICES: per person D,B&B £110–£135. À la carte £45.

Prices may change – check with hotel.

HALIFAX Yorkshire

SHIBDEN MILL INN

Spilling over with character, this 17th-century country inn lies in the wooded Shibden valley near Red Beck, the stream that once powered its corn and spinning mills. The oak-beamed bar, with thick stone walls and vast open fireplace, offers a range of gins and whiskies, plus Shibden Mill's own brew. Wine recommendations are matched with ambitious, Yorkshire-inspired dishes using produce from the kitchen garden. Homely, individually styled bedrooms (some compact) are supplied with bathrobes, teas and coffee. The wide choice at breakfast includes omelettes, muffin and vegan options; muesli, peanut butter and preserves are all home made. Eat well: circular walks (ask for a map) start from the flowery garden.

MAP 4:D3
Shibden Mill Fold
Halifax HX3 7UL
T: 01422 365840
W: shibdenmillinn.com

BEDROOMS: 11.
OPEN: all year except 25–26 Dec, 1 Jan.
FACILITIES: bar, lounge, restaurant, private dining room, in-room TV (Freeview), small conference facilities, patio, 2-acre garden, parking, complimentary access to local health club.
BACKGROUND MUSIC: in main bar, restaurant.
LOCATION: 2 miles from Halifax town centre.
CHILDREN: all ages welcomed.
DOGS: allowed in bar.
CREDIT CARDS: Amex, MC, Visa.
PRICES: per room B&B single £90–£220, double £95–£238. À la carte £40.

Prices may change – check with hotel.

HARROGATE Yorkshire
THE WEST PARK HOTEL

Overlooking the Stray's 200 acres of open parkland, this jazzily refurbished town-centre hotel was created from a former Victorian coach house. Cocktails and Yorkshire ales are served over a zinc-topped bar; breakfast, light lunches and a seasonal dinner menu are taken in the buzzy brasserie or under fairy lights on the covered, heated terrace. The well-appointed bedrooms, some with a private terrace, are bright and contemporary, with snazzy fabrics. Each room is supplied with teas and a coffee machine, plus bathrobes and good toiletries in a bathroom with under-floor heating. Two spacious duplex suites have a lounge and dining area, and access to the roof terrace. Part of the Provenance Inns & Hotels group.

MAP 4:D4
19 West Park
Harrogate HG1 1BJ
T: 01423 524471
W: thewestparkhotel.com

BEDROOMS: 25. Some suitable for disabled.
OPEN: all year.
FACILITIES: bar, brasserie, meeting/private dining rooms, in-room TV (Freeview), large walled terrace, adjacent NCP car park, pay and display street parking.
BACKGROUND MUSIC: all day in public areas.
LOCATION: in town centre.
CHILDREN: all ages welcomed.
DOGS: well-behaved dogs allowed in some bedrooms, bar.
CREDIT CARDS: Amex, MC, Visa.
PRICES: per room B&B £162–£500. À la carte £35.

Prices may change – check with hotel.

HASTINGS Sussex
THE LAINDONS

In the Old Town, Karen and Malcolm Twist's guest house in a handsome Grade II listed Georgian building has a modern, seasidey feel. Cheery, well-proportioned, high-ceilinged bedrooms have quality linens on a bed handcrafted from reclaimed timber, a period fireplace, perhaps a window seat or chaise longue. Home-made biscuits, organic teas – even earplugs to combat seagull squawks – are welcome extras. The hosts whip up fresh smoothies, bake bread and roast their own coffee for breakfast in the conservatory overlooking the High Street. On the morning menu: a full English, blueberry pancakes, granola with yogurt and home-made compote. In-house treatments, and a three-course dinner (Monday–Thursday) can be pre-booked.

MAP 2:E5
23 High Street
Hastings TN34 3EY
T: 01424 437710
W: thelaindons.com

BEDROOMS: 5. Plus 2 with shared bathroom, suitable for a family or group travelling together.
OPEN: all year except 24–26 Dec, first 2 weeks Jan.
FACILITIES: drawing room (honesty bar), breakfast room, in-room TV (Freeview), parking permits provided.
BACKGROUND MUSIC: 'gentle' in public areas at breakfast.
LOCATION: in the heart of the Old Town.
CHILDREN: not under 10.
DOGS: not allowed.
CREDIT CARDS: Amex, MC, Visa.
PRICES: per room B&B £155–£185, dinner (Mon–Thurs) £30. 2-night min. stay at weekends Apr–Sept.

Prices may change – check with hotel.

NEW

HAWES Yorkshire
STONE HOUSE HOTEL

In a 'beautiful setting', with views stretching across the dales, this family run hotel in an Edwardian country house is on a quiet lane. Panelled walls, grand fireplaces, a billiard table in the library conjure up an era long past, but there is 'nothing stuffy here!' The friendly staff 'have a nice line in chat, and make you feel at home'. Hearty regional produce, in the spacious, modern restaurant, is used for the Yorkshire breakfasts, light lunches and daily changing evening menus; perhaps slow-cooked Wensleydale beef in Black Sheep ale. Bedrooms, in the main house (some with a conservatory and garden access), to one side or in the courtyard, have timeless elegance and a wondrous outlook.

MAP 4:C3
Sedbusk
Hawes DL8 3PT
T: 01969 667571
W: stonehousehotel.co.uk

BEDROOMS: 24. Some accessed from outside main building, 5 in coach house.
OPEN: all year, except 2 weeks in early Jan. Closed for private parties over Christmas, New Year.
FACILITIES: bar, lounge, library/billiard room, in-room TV, courtyard, 1-acre garden.
BACKGROUND MUSIC: in public areas except lounge.
LOCATION: in the Yorkshire Dales national park; on a country lane, 1 mile NE of Hawes.
CHILDREN: all ages welcomed.
DOGS: well-behaved dogs in ground-floor bedrooms, on lead in public areas, not in restaurant.
CREDIT CARDS: MC, Visa.
PRICES: per room B&B £150–£240. Set dinner £34–£40.
Prices may change – check with hotel.

HAWKHURST Kent
THE QUEEN'S INN

Old-meets-new in this revived 16th-century coaching inn with a large front patio, in a historic Wealden village. Against a backdrop of beams, brick walls, and velvet wingback chairs, Kentish wines, ales and ciders headline the drinks list in the bar. Hungry visitors can choose between small plates, savoury waffles, steaks, or sourdough pizzas and pub staples, alongside vegan and vegetarian options in the industrial-chic restaurant. Upstairs, creatively decorated bedrooms (some for families) have coffee and tea, fresh milk, home-made brownies, bathrobes and botanical toiletries. A retro telephone adds a quirky twist. Close to National Trust attractions Scotney Castle and Sissinghurst Castle Garden.

MAP 2:E4
Rye Road
Hawkhurst TN18 4EY
T: 01580 754233
W: thequeensinnhawkhurst.co.uk

BEDROOMS: 8.
OPEN: all year.
FACILITIES: bar, snug, 3 dining areas, in-room TV (Freeview), function facilities, front patio.
BACKGROUND MUSIC: in bar, restaurant.
LOCATION: in village, within the High Weald Area of Outstanding Natural Beauty near Sissinghurst Castle and Gardens.
CHILDREN: all ages welcomed.
DOGS: allowed in bar, part of restaurant.
CREDIT CARDS: Amex, MC, Visa.
PRICES: per room B&B £115–£195. À la carte £35. 2-night min. stay at weekends.
Prices may change – check with hotel.

HEALING Lincolnshire
HEALING MANOR HOTEL
On the edge of the Lincolnshire Wolds, this
centuries-old manor house is in extensive grounds
of landscaped gardens, fields and woodland
with access to country walks and cycle routes.
Individually styled bedrooms are spread among
the main house and converted outbuildings. Some
overlook gliding swans on a willow-draped pond;
others have direct access to a shared courtyard
– though all have a contemporary country air.
Guests have a choice of places to eat: the dog-
friendly Pig & Whistle pub, where accompanying
pooches have their own menu, and the Portman
restaurant, where Steven Bennett's seasonal
à la carte and tasting menus make the most of
locally grown and foraged ingredients. A popular
wedding venue.

MAP 4:E5
Stallingborough Road
Healing
Grimsby DN41 7QF
T: 01472 884544
W: healingmanorhotel.co.uk

BEDROOMS: 37. 24 in converted
outbuildings, 2 suitable for disabled.
OPEN: all year.
FACILITIES: pub, restaurant, function
rooms, in-room TV (Freeview), civil
wedding licence, terrace, 36-acre
grounds (gardens, fields, woodland,
moated island), EV charging.
BACKGROUND MUSIC: all day in dining
areas.
LOCATION: 5 miles W of Grimsby.
CHILDREN: all ages welcomed.
DOGS: allowed in pub, some bedrooms.
CREDIT CARDS: Amex, MC, Visa.
PRICES: per room B&B £95–£200.
À la carte £40.

Prices may change – check with hotel.

HERTFORD Hertfordshire
NUMBER ONE PORT HILL
Filled with vintage glassware, chandeliers,
sculptures and mirrors, Annie Rowley's 'artful'
Georgian house is featured in Pevsner's guide to
Hertfordshire. The B&B has three immaculate
bedrooms on the top floor: one is large, with
a French gilt bed and a raised boat bath in the
bathroom; two are cosy. Plentiful extras include
Belgian hot chocolate, sweet and savoury snacks,
bathrobes and 'eclectic' reading material. Traffic
noise is muted by 'very good' double glazing.
Breakfast, with freshly ground coffee and
home-made preserves, is taken communally, or
under ancient wisteria in the walled garden. A
fine dinner is available some nights. The historic
market town has a wide choice of places to eat.

MAP 2:C4
1 Port Hill
Hertford SG14 1PJ
T: 01992 587350
W: numberoneporthill.co.uk

BEDROOMS: 3.
OPEN: all year except Christmas.
FACILITIES: drawing room, in-room
TV (Sky, Freeview), front and back
gardens, limited street parking.
BACKGROUND MUSIC: none.
LOCATION: 5 mins' walk from town
centre.
CHILDREN: not under 12 ('though
exemptions may be made, if discussed,
for younger children').
DOGS: not allowed.
CREDIT CARDS: MC, Visa.
PRICES: per room B&B £130–£160.
Dinner £45 (dependent on number
of guests).

Prices may change – check with hotel.

HEXHAM Northumberland

BATTLESTEADS

A 'really good experience', Dee and Richard Slade's 'well-run' hotel, restaurant and village pub stand out for their 'laudable' approach to sustainable tourism. Modern menus, 'well cooked and varied', use locally sourced produce and the bounty from the kitchen garden and mushroom farm; the walled garden is a popular spot for birds and red squirrels; the dark sky observatory is simply 'amazing'. Bedrooms are in the main building (part of an 18th-century farmstead) and in wood-built lodges to the rear. Some may be 'on the small side', while others, in the lodges, are 'vast'. Rooms away from the road are quietest. A stroll from the North Tyne River, hosts advise on the best walks for spotting wildlife.

MAP 4:B3
Wark-on-Tyne
Hexham NE48 3LS
T: 01434 230209
W: battlesteads.com

BEDROOMS: 22. 4 on ground floor, 5 in lodges, 2 suitable for disabled.
OPEN: all year except 25 Dec.
FACILITIES: bar, dining room, in-room TV (Freeview), civil wedding licence, function facilities, drying room, 2-acre grounds (walled garden, kitchen garden, dark sky observatory), EV charging.
BACKGROUND MUSIC: in bar, restaurant.
LOCATION: 12 miles N of Hexham.
CHILDREN: all ages welcomed.
DOGS: allowed in public rooms, some bedrooms (resident dog), outdoor dog wash facility.
CREDIT CARDS: Amex, MC, Visa.
PRICES: B&B £135–£195. À la carte £40.

Prices may change – check with hotel.

HITCHIN Hertfordshire

THE FARMHOUSE AT REDCOATS

In serene countryside, this well-restored old farmhouse, its many features dating from the 15th century, stands in large, landscaped gardens. The hotel and restaurant, part of the Nye family's Anglian Country Inns, have intimate sitting areas, and warming fires in inglenook fireplaces. The rustic orangery restaurant opens on to a woodland dell with a 'bug hotel'. Cocktails, wines and real ales accompany chef Sherwin Jacobs's Modern British dishes. Creatively decorated bedrooms are spread over the main house, converted stables and Grade II listed barn across the courtyard, where events are held. In the morning, choose a hearty dish from the farmhouse menu. Circular walks start at the bottom of the garden.

MAP 2:C4
Redcoats Green
Hitchin SG4 7JR
T: 01438 729500
W: farmhouseatredcoats.co.uk

BEDROOMS: 28. 8 in converted stables and coach house, 15 in Grade II listed barn conversion across the yard, some on ground floor.
OPEN: all year.
FACILITIES: bar, lounge, conservatory restaurant, 3 private dining rooms, in-room TV (Freeview), civil wedding licence, events barn, patio, 4-acre grounds.
BACKGROUND MUSIC: 'subtle' in public areas.
LOCATION: 9 mins' drive from Stevenage.
CHILDREN: all ages welcomed.
DOGS: well-behaved dogs allowed in some bedrooms, bar, lounge.
CREDIT CARDS: Amex, MC, Visa.
PRICES: per room B&B single from £95, double £105–£165. À la carte £45.

Prices may change – check with hotel.

HOLKHAM Norfolk
THE VICTORIA INN

'Perfect for exploring the north Norfolk coast', this Victorian flint and brick inn on the Earl of Leicester's Holkham Estate has been transformed into a genteel hotel and restaurant. Hunting trophies are displayed in the bar. Local produce, much of it grown and raised on the estate, dictates the daily specials on the brasserie-style menu. Named after shooting drives, dog-friendly bedrooms and family-friendly suites in the main house have antiques and plenty of perks, including a mini-fridge with complimentary drinks. Ancient House residents also have a walled rose garden to enjoy; two split-level suites have a sitting room. 'One of the most beautiful, isolated beaches' is only a few minutes' walk away.

MAP 2:A5
Park Road
Holkham NR23 1RG
T: 01328 711008
W: victoriaatholkham.co.uk

BEDROOMS: 20. 10 in Ancient House, 150m walk away, 1 on ground floor suitable for disabled.
OPEN: all year.
FACILITIES: bar, lounge, restaurant with conservatory extension, in-room TV, courtyard, garden, children's play area, parking.
BACKGROUND MUSIC:
LOCATION: on the Holkham Estate, 1¾ miles W of Wells-next-the-Sea.
CHILDREN: all ages welcomed.
DOGS: allowed in 10 inn bedrooms, public areas.
CREDIT CARDS: Amex, MC, Visa.
PRICES: per room B&B single £135–£240, double £170–£330. À la carte £40. 2-night min. stay Fri, Sat nights.

Prices may change – check with hotel.

HUDDERSFIELD Yorkshire
MANOR HOUSE LINDLEY

Alluringly redesigned, this Georgian mansion, set back from the High Street in a smart Huddersfield suburb, is brimming with distinctive spaces in which to sit, drink and dine. The hotel has a conservatory-like bistro for daytime comfort food, and a stylish restaurant serving sophisticated dinners (native lobster and salmon ravioli or lavender honey glazed duck). Cocktails may be shaken and stirred in the glitzy lounge, on the roof terrace overlooking St Stephen's church, or in the moody cellar bar. Individually decorated bedrooms and suites are supplied with a capsule coffee machine, a designer scented candle and a dose of contemporary glamour. The fitness studio has classes and a well-equipped gym.

MAP 4:E3
1 Lidget Street
Huddersfield HD3 3JB
T: 01484 504000
W: manorhouselindley.co.uk

BEDROOMS: 11. 1 suitable for disabled, plus duplex apartment.
OPEN: all year, restaurant closed Mon, Tues, bistro closed from 4 pm Mon–Sat, 1 pm on Sun.
FACILITIES: 4 bars, restaurant, bistro, in-room TV (Freeview), civil wedding licence, meeting/function facilities, gym, courtyard, terrace, EV charging.
BACKGROUND MUSIC: 'relaxing' music all day in public areas.
LOCATION: 2 miles NW of Huddersfield town centre.
CHILDREN: all ages welcomed, not under 12 in lounge and restaurant (except at Sunday lunch).
DOGS: allowed in apartment, grounds, not in main building.
CREDIT CARDS: Amex, MC, Visa.
PRICES: per room B&B £139–£299. À la carte £55.

Prices may change – check with hotel.

HURLEY Berkshire

HURLEY HOUSE

A fine base for exploring the Chilterns, this urbane hotel is just outside a picturesque riverside village. Styled in creams and greys, the bedrooms, some with a private patio, have comforts such as air conditioning and under-floor heating; efficient insulation subdues noise from the adjacent busy road. There's a choice of eating areas: the sophisticated restaurant (sleek wood panelling, leather banquettes, oversized artwork) where (Thurs–Sun) guests have their pick from Japanese and British menus, or the smartly rustic, slate-floored bar; and heated garden terraces, ideal for alfresco meals. At breakfast, find a choice of cooked dishes. Within easy reach of historic houses, vineyards and river cruises.

MAP 2:D3
Henley Road
Hurley SL6 5LH
T: 01628 568500
W: hurleyhouse.co.uk

BEDROOMS: 10. Some suitable for disabled.
OPEN: all year, restaurant closed Mon, Tues, Wed.
FACILITIES: bar, snug, restaurant, private dining room, in-room TV (Freeview), function facilities, civil wedding licence, spa treatment room, large terrace, EV charging.
BACKGROUND MUSIC: in public areas until 11 pm, plus live music at weekends.
LOCATION: 5 miles E of Henley-on-Thames, 10 miles NW of Windsor.
CHILDREN: all ages welcomed.
DOGS: allowed in bar, on terrace.
CREDIT CARDS: Amex, MC, Visa.
PRICES: per room B&B £190–£310. À la carte £55.

Prices may change – check with hotel.

ILSINGTON Devon

ILSINGTON COUNTRY HOUSE HOTEL & SPA

In wooded grounds, the Hassell family's country house hotel and 'beautiful' spa impresses with its laudable service and 'very warm welcome'. 'Our dog even received a welcome pack with walk maps and biscuits.' Rooms are decorated in restful shades, with antique pieces and a sleigh bed. Most have a bath and an overhead or walk-in shower. After a game of croquet, guests can take a cream tea on the lawn. In the spacious dining room, where far-reaching views spread to Dartmoor's Hay Tor and the surrounding hills, chef Mike O'Donnell's dishes are an 'excellent' selection of local, seasonal produce and day-boat fish. Desserts are 'impressive'. Breakfast brings fresh fruit salad and eggs from happy hens.

MAP 1:D4
Ilsington
Newton Abbot TQ13 9RR
T: 01364 661452
W: ilsington.co.uk

BEDROOMS: 25. 6 on ground floor.
OPEN: all year except 3–14 Jan.
FACILITIES: lift, 2 lounges, bar, restaurant, bistro, conservatory, function facilities, spa, indoor pool, in-room TV (Freeview), 10-acre grounds, spa/public rooms wheelchair accessible, adapted toilet, ramps.
BACKGROUND MUSIC: in bar, restaurant during day, some areas of spa.
LOCATION: just W of Ilsington village, 7 miles NW of Newton Abbot.
CHILDREN: all ages welcomed.
DOGS: allowed in some bedooms, 1 lounge, bar, conservatory, garden.
CREDIT CARDS: MC, Visa.
PRICES: per room B&B single £110–£185, double £140–£220. Set dinner £36.50–£42.50, tasting menu (Fri, Sat) £58. 1-night bookings refused peak times.
Prices may change – check with hotel.

IRONBRIDGE Shropshire
THE LIBRARY HOUSE

In the heart of town, this 'beautifully decorated'
B&B run by Sarah and Tim Davis is in a once-
upon-a-time library. Neat, pretty bedrooms in
the Grade II listed Georgian town house are
named after writers: Chaucer opens on to a
garden terrace; high-ceilinged Eliot overlooks
the River Severn; spacious Milton has a large
bed and a reading corner. Each is supplied with
waffle robes, fresh milk and a hot-water bottle. A
log-burner blazes in the book-lined sitting room
when the temperature dips; in good weather, take
tea in the terraced garden. Breakfast, with home-
made marmalade, is served at linen-topped tables.
Restaurants and bars are within walking distance;
Ironbridge Gorge, a UNESCO World Heritage
site, is close.

MAP 3:C5
11 Severn Bank
Ironbridge TF8 7AN
T: 01952 432299
W: libraryhouse.com

BEDROOMS: 3.
OPEN: all year.
FACILITIES: sitting room, breakfast
room, in-room TV (Freeview),
courtyard, mature garden, permits for
on-street parking.
BACKGROUND MUSIC: none.
LOCATION: town centre.
CHILDREN: not under 13.
DOGS: not allowed.
CREDIT CARDS: MC, Visa.
PRICES: per room B&B single £75–£95,
double £105–£135. 2-night min. stay
Fri, Sat night, Mar–Oct.

Prices may change – check with hotel.

KELLING Norfolk
THE PHEASANT

In the heart of a sprawling estate of woods and
parkland, this country house hotel is a relaxed,
unstuffy retreat. The staff 'could not have done
more to make our stay a happy one'. Take tea on
the lawn; at lunch and dinner, sample estate-
grown produce in the restaurant or orangery. The
daily changing menu might include smoked duck
salad or Cromer crab thermidore. Among the
classically styled bedrooms (some dog friendly),
some interconnect to suit a family or a group. A
coffee machine and good toiletries are provided.
Two new shepherd's huts in the woods have
king-size beds, clawfoot baths and wood burners
(logs supplied). Varied breakfasts (omelettes,
Cley smoked kippers and more) provide fuel for
exploring coastal walks and nature reserves.

MAP 2:A5
Coast Road
Kelling NR25 7EG
T: 01263 588382
W: pheasanthotelnorfolk.co.uk/
index.html

BEDROOMS: 34. 24 on ground floor,
1 suitable for disabled. 2 shepherd's
huts in the woods.
OPEN: all year.
FACILITIES: bar/lounge, restaurant,
orangery, private dining room,
in-room TV, civil wedding licence,
terrace, 2½-acre garden on 2,000-acre
estate.
BACKGROUND MUSIC: in public areas.
LOCATION: 3½ miles NE of Holt.
CHILDREN: all ages welcomed.
DOGS: allowed in 4 bedrooms, bar,
orangery, not in restaurant.
CREDIT CARDS: Amex, MC, Visa.
PRICES: per room B&B £190–£250.
À la carte £37.50. 2-night min. stay at
weekends July–Aug, bank holidays.

Prices may change – check with hotel.

NEW

KESWICK Cumbria

LYZZICK HALL

Unparalleled fell views are found at this family-friendly spot on the lower slopes of Skiddaw. The early Victorian hotel, recently redesigned, has been owned by the Fernandez family for 37 years, and is co-owned with their daughter and son-in-law, Lucy and David Lake. Many of the modern bedrooms overlook the 'well-maintained' gardens; most also take in the 'stunning scenery' of the fells. Browse books and magazines, or play a board game in the spacious fire-warmed lounge. Dine inside or out: in the orangery or other intimate space, or under a covered area in the garden. Dinners are 'excellent'. 'Dishes are generally elaborate, with many clever combinations beautifully presented.' Walks from the door.

MAP 4: inset C2
Underskiddaw
Keswick CA12 4PY
T: 017687 72277
W: lyzzickhall.co.uk

BEDROOMS: 27. 1 on ground floor.
OPEN: all year, except 24–26 Dec, 3 Jan–5 Feb.
FACILITIES: bar, lounge, orangery, 3 interconnecting restaurants, in-room TV (Freeview), 4-acre grounds.
BACKGROUND MUSIC: 'discreet' in public areas.
LOCATION: 2 miles N of Keswick.
CHILDREN: all ages welcomed.
DOGS: allowed in 1 bedroom.
CREDIT CARDS: MC, Visa.
PRICES: per room B&B £179–£285. À la carte £44.

Prices may change – check with hotel.

KING'S LYNN Norfolk

BANK HOUSE

In a 'fine waterfront setting', this 'distinguished' Georgian building, a former bank, is within strolling distance, along cobbled streets, of historical buildings and squares. Owned by the Goodrich family (see The Rose & Crown, Snettisham, main entry). it is a town hub, where locals gather in its bar and brasserie, and for lively events at festival times. Overnight guests have a choice of individually decorated bedrooms in varying sizes. Most have a river view, some have sight of the iconic Custom House; all have a coffee machine, pampering toiletries, a 'well-researched guide' of local hotspots. Daily-changing menus are served indoors and out, across several dining areas. Pay-and-display parking is close by.

MAP 2:A4
King's Staithe Square
King's Lynn PE30 1RD
T: 01553 660492
W: thebankhouse.co.uk

BEDROOMS: 12.
OPEN: all year.
FACILITIES: bar, 3 dining rooms, meeting/function rooms, vaulted cellars for private functions, in-room smart TV, riverside terrace, courtyard, all public rooms wheelchair accessible, adapted toilet.
BACKGROUND MUSIC: from mid-morning onwards, in public areas (but 'turned off on demand').
LOCATION: on the quayside.
CHILDREN: all ages welcomed.
DOGS: allowed in Counting House, bar, terrace, 2 bedrooms.
CREDIT CARDS: Amex, MC, Visa.
PRICES: per room B&B single £105–£170, double £125–£185. À la carte £36.

Prices may change – check with hotel.

MAP 1:D4
Thurlestone
Kingsbridge TQ7 3NN
T: 01548 560382
w: thurlestone.co.uk

KINGSBRIDGE Devon

THURLESTONE HOTEL

'Stunning' views reach to the sea from the Grose family's hotel, set in 19 acres of sub-tropical gardens along the South Devon National Trust coastline. It is liked for its 'easy blend of tradition, formality, and a relaxed atmosphere that manages to please family parties, individual travellers, young and old alike'. Inside are well-equipped bedrooms (several to accommodate a family) and many 'stylish' areas for lunches, dinners and cream teas. The smart Trevilder is for fine dining; real ales and pub fare are served beneath shipwreck timbers in the 16th-century village inn. Play croquet, tennis or golf in the grounds, book a session in the spa, or head out: coastal walks and rock pools are minutes away.

BEDROOMS: 65. 2 suitable for disabled.
OPEN: all year.
FACILITIES: lift, lounge, bar, restaurant, poolside café, village pub, in-room TV (Sky), civil wedding licence, function facilities, terrace, spa, outdoor heated swimming pool, tennis, 9-hole golf course, children's club during school holidays, EV charging.
BACKGROUND MUSIC: none.
LOCATION: 4 miles SW of Kingsbridge.
CHILDREN: all ages welcomed.
DOGS: allowed in some bedrooms, not in public rooms.
CREDIT CARDS: Amex, MC, Visa.
PRICES: per room B&B from £235.
À la carte £40, tasting menu £70.
2-night min. stay.

Prices may change – check with hotel.

MAP 1:D4
Higher Contour Road
Kingswear TQ6 0AY
T: 01803 752200
w: kaywanahall.co.uk

KINGSWEAR Devon

KAYWANA HALL

Sleek and ultra-modern, Tony Pithers and Gordon Craig's B&B stands in hillside woodland across the estuary from Dartmouth. One of just four in Devon, the 1960s Le Corbusier-inspired 'butterfly house' is a tranquil, adults-only space. Light-filled bedrooms decorated with abstract art each have their own entrance and private terrace with outdoor seating (some reached via steep steps). Well equipped, they have robes and slippers, a mini-fridge, an espresso machine and treats. Breakfast, in a glass-fronted room overlooking the swimming pool, starts with freshly squeezed juices, locally baked bread, fruit compote; eggs Benedict or other cooked dishes follow. Afternoons bring complimentary tea, cakes and snacks.

BEDROOMS: 4.
OPEN: Apr–end Sept.
FACILITIES: Pool House breakfast room and lounge, Wi-Fi in bedrooms, in-room TV (Freeview), 12-acre grounds, 9-metre heated outdoor swimming pool (in summer months), EV charging, parking.
BACKGROUND MUSIC: none.
LOCATION: 5 mins from Dartmouth via ferry.
CHILDREN: not allowed.
DOGS: only assistance dogs allowed.
CREDIT CARDS: Amex, MC, Visa.
PRICES: B&B £210–£245. 2-night min. stay.

Prices may change – check with hotel.

KNARESBOROUGH Yorkshire

NEWTON HOUSE

In a 'fascinating' town, Denise Carter's B&B 'offers good value and plenty of Yorkshire friendliness'. Traditionally furnished bedrooms in the 300-year-old house, stables and adjacent building, are supplied with a hot drinks tray and bottled water; 'the collection of books is a nice touch'. Guests may help themselves to local beers, spirits or soft drinks from the honesty bar in the sitting room. In the evening, light bites might be 'rustled up'; the hostess can recommend nearby eateries for more substantial meals. Home-made sourdough bread, jams and compotes are part of the 'excellent' breakfasts that 'set you up for the day'. The small courtyard garden, and on-site parking are a bonus.

MAP 4:D4
York Place
Knaresborough HG5 0AD
T: 01423 863539
W: newtonhouseyorkshire.com

BEDROOMS: 12. 1 in adjacent building, 2 in converted stables, 2 on ground floor suitable for disabled.
OPEN: all year.
FACILITIES: sitting room (honesty bar), dining room, in-room TV (Freeview), small courtyard garden (wildlife area), parking.
BACKGROUND MUSIC: Classic FM at breakfast.
LOCATION: town centre, 4 miles from Harrogate.
CHILDREN: all ages welcomed.
DOGS: allowed in 2 rooms with outside access, not in public rooms.
CREDIT CARDS: Amex, MC, Visa.
PRICES: per room B&B single £70–£110, double £95–£145. 1-night bookings generally refused weekends.

Prices may change – check with hotel.

LACOCK Wiltshire

SIGN OF THE ANGEL

Think of a quintessential English coaching inn – half-timbered facade, big stone fireplaces, low-beamed rooms, leaded windows, wonky floors – and you could be describing this 15th-century village inn. In the heart of National Trust-owned Lacock, it is more restaurant-with-rooms than pub (the bar is tiny) with a series of fire-warmed dining areas of hefty wooden tables and sea-blue walls. Menus champion local produce with dishes such as pork with glazed beetroot and smoked apple, as well as pub classics. Rustic-chic bedrooms range from snug to superior, with a Roberts radio and home-made cookies. Relax in the panelled sitting room or in the stream-bordered cottage garden, perhaps with an afternoon cream tea.

MAP 2:D1
6 Church Street
Lacock SN15 2LB
T: 01249 730230
W: signoftheangel.co.uk

BEDROOMS: 5.
OPEN: all year except New Year's Eve (phone to check festive dates).
FACILITIES: bar, 3 dining rooms (vegan/gluten-free menu), sitting room, private dining room, no mobile phone signal, free street parking, cottage garden, restaurant and garden wheelchair accessible.
BACKGROUND MUSIC: in restaurant, radio option in sitting room.
LOCATION: in village, 4 miles S of Chippenham.
CHILDREN: all ages welcomed (cot £20, extra bed from £40).
DOGS: allowed in bedrooms (£15 per night), public rooms.
CREDIT CARDS: MC, Visa.
PRICES: B&B doubles from £115, singles from £80. À la carte £42.

Prices may change – check with hotel.

LANCHESTER Co. Durham

BURNHOPESIDE HALL

There are log fires, bucolic views and a warm welcome at this Grade II* listed country house, in a spread of gardens surrounded by acres of farmland and forest. Engineer William Hedley, inventor of Puffing Billy, once lived here. Today, Christine Hewitt, the 'attentive' hostess, offers 'good-value' B&B accommodation in 'clean, quiet and comfortable' traditionally decorated bedrooms (with super-king beds) in the main house, adjoining farmhouse and cottage. Home-made, home-reared and home-grown fare feature at breakfast. The grounds provide generous scope for gentle strolls or for exercising dogs and exuberant children; trails lead to the river and the Lanchester Valley Railway Path. Well placed for visiting Durham.

MAP 4:B4
Durham Road
Lanchester DH7 0TL
T: 01207 520222
W: burnhopeside-hall.co.uk

BEDROOMS: 12. 2-bed apartment on top floor, 5 in adjoining farmhouse, 3 in cottage (all available on a self-catering basis).
OPEN: all year, except when booked for exclusive use.
FACILITIES: sitting room, dining room, library, billiard room, in-room TV (Freeview), 18-acre gardens in 475-acre grounds; farmhouse rooms have a sitting room, dining room; cottages have a sitting room where breakfast can be served; all with log fires, parking.
BACKGROUND MUSIC: none.
LOCATION: 5 miles NW of Durham.
CHILDREN: all ages welcomed.
DOGS: welcomed.
CREDIT CARDS: Amex, MC, Visa.
PRICES: per room B&B single from £95, double £130–£150.

Prices may change – check with hotel.

LEATHERHEAD Surrey

BEAVERBROOK

Nestled in the Surrey hills, this opulent, art- and memorabilia-filled hotel is in a late Victorian mansion, once the rural retreat of press baron Lord Beaverbrook. The politicians and luminaries he entertained here are remembered in elegant bedrooms in the main building; in the Garden House and dog-friendly Coach House, botanical prints and smart rustic features give bedrooms a Victorian cottage feel. Find a spot in the well-stocked library or the fashionably old-world bar; take afternoon tea on the terrace; soak in countryside views from the swimming pool. A trio of restaurants caters for varying tastes, from Japanese fine dining to Anglo-Italian fare to superfood specials in the holistic spa.

MAP 2:D4
Reigate Road
Leatherhead KT22 8QX
T: 01372 227670
W: beaverbrook.co.uk

BEDROOMS: 35. 11 in Garden House, 6 in Coach House, 1 suitable for disabled.
OPEN: all year.
FACILITIES: 2 bars, morning room, 3 restaurants, library, cinema, in-room TV (Sky), civil wedding licence, indoor and outdoor swimming pools, 470-acre grounds, walled garden, cookery school, kids' club, EV charging.
BACKGROUND MUSIC: in restaurant, bar.
LOCATION: on estate, 2 miles from town.
CHILDREN: all ages welcomed.
DOGS: allowed in some bedrooms, public spaces.
CREDIT CARDS: Amex, MC, Visa.
PRICES: per room B&B £600–£3,050. À la carte (Garden House restaurant) £55. 2-night min. stay on Sat, bank holidays, Christmas, New Year's Eve.

Prices may change – check with hotel.

LEDBURY Herefordshire

THE FEATHERS

You can't fail to notice this Tudor building with its striking black-and-white timbered frontage. Inside, the former coaching inn's original features – beams, brickwork and large fireplaces – are combined with bright contemporary furnishings to create a warm welcome. Enjoy tea and cake in the fire-warmed lounge before dinner of small plates and brasserie dishes in the restaurant, dog-friendly bar or alfresco in the courtyard. 'Very comfortable' rooms with a 'cosy atmosphere' have richly patterned fabrics, coffee machines and modern bathrooms; the best have a sitting area. Light sleepers should ask for a room at the rear. In every area, 'the staff are all charming'. Part of the Coaching Inn group.

MAP 3:D5
High Street
Ledbury HR8 1DS
T: 01531 635266
W: feathers-ledbury.co.uk

BEDROOMS: 20. 1 suite in cottage, plus self-catering apartments.
OPEN: all year.
FACILITIES: bar, lounge, restaurant, in-room TV (Freeview), civil wedding licence, function facilities, courtyard garden, parking, restaurant wheelchair accessible.
BACKGROUND MUSIC: mellow music in public areas.
LOCATION: town centre.
CHILDREN: all ages welcomed.
DOGS: allowed in bedrooms, most public areas, not in restaurant.
CREDIT CARDS: Amex, MC, Visa.
PRICES: B&B £110–£240. À la carte £30. 1-night bookings sometimes refused weekends.

Prices may change – check with hotel.

LEVENS Cumbria

HARE AND HOUNDS

Becky and Ash Dewar have transformed a 16th-century hostelry into this family-friendly pub in a Lyth Valley village on the edge of the Lake District. Always welcoming, the beamed bar has cask ales, craft beers and cocktails made with locally produced spirits; pub classics (burgers, pizzas, grills) are served here, in the bright restaurant and on the terrace. Upstairs, and in a spacious barn annexe, contemporary, country-style bedrooms have freshly baked brownies, ground coffee and Cumbrian-made toiletries. At breakfast: fresh fruit, local bread, a choice of hot dishes cooked to order. There are knolls and fells to walk in the area, and the revered topiary of Levens Hall close by.

MAP 4: inset C2
Levens
Kendal LA8 8PN
T: 015395 60004
W: hareandhoundslevens.co.uk

BEDROOMS: 5. 1 in barn annexe.
OPEN: all year, no accommodation 24–25, 31 Dec.
FACILITIES: pub, residents' lounge, restaurant, in-room TV (Freeview), ½-acre beer garden, parking.
BACKGROUND MUSIC: in pub and restaurant.
LOCATION: in village.
CHILDREN: all ages welcomed.
DOGS: allowed in barn annexe, pub, garden, not in restaurant.
CREDIT CARDS: Amex, MC, Visa.
PRICES: per room B&B single £90–£210, double £100–£220. À la carte £38. 2-night min. stay at weekends, unless there is last-minute single-night availability.

Prices may change – check with hotel.

LEWANNICK Cornwall

COOMBESHEAD FARM

Occupying a centuries-old farmhouse and its
surrounding barns, this rustic-chic guest house
and restaurant make an ideal base for exploring
the meadows and woodland around – or simply
for eating 'stupendously' well. It is owned by
chefs Tom Adams and April Bloomfield, who
have won a Michelin green star for the farm-to-
fork cooking. Home-grown, -reared, -smoked,
-cured and -pickled ingredients are paired with
organic Cornish produce and locally foraged food
at dinner and weekend lunch. Butters, yogurts,
cheeses, through to hams, cordials and milling
grains, are made on site. Handsomely countrified
bedrooms are in the farmhouse and a converted
grain store. Bread-making workshops are held in
the sourdough bakery.

MAP 1:D3
Lewannick PL15 7QQ
T: 01566 782009
W: coombesheadfarm.co.uk

BEDROOMS: 9. 1 bunk-bedroom, 4 in
converted grain store, 2 suitable for
disabled. Plus 2-bed self-catering
cottage.
OPEN: all year except Jan, Mon, Tues.
FACILITIES: living room, lounge,
library, dining room, kitchen, civil
wedding licence, farm shop and café
(open Thurs–Sun), 66-acre grounds.
BACKGROUND MUSIC: in the restaurant.
LOCATION: in village, 3 miles from
A30, 6 miles from Launceston.
CHILDREN: not under 12, except at
Sunday lunch, cottage, courtyard café
and farmshop.
DOGS: allowed in 1 bedroom, cottage,
on lead in grounds, not in restaurant.
CREDIT CARDS: Amex, MC, Visa.
PRICES: per room B&B double £195–
£255, single £165–£225. Set dinner £80.
2-night min. stay on Sat.

Prices may change – check with hotel.

LIVERPOOL Merseyside

HOPE STREET HOTEL

With a sleek spa and a private cinema, this
large and contemporary hotel is in the buzzy
Georgian quarter. Its industrial-chic spaces,
transformed from a former Victorian carriage
works, have stripped-back style – glass and
exposed brick walls, pitch pine beams and iron
pillars. Minimalist bedrooms are white with wood
floors and cherry and walnut furniture. They
range from snug double rooms to rooftop suites
with a hot-tub terrace and 'wonderful views' of
city landmarks. Modern British dishes (including
vegan options) are served in the restaurant; in
the bar, sharing platters and easy eats pair with
made-to-order cocktails. The hotel is well placed
for exploring the city; or take a thermal journey
in the spa.

MAP 4:E2
40 Hope Street
Liverpool L1 9DA
T: 0151 709 3000
W: hopestreethotel.co.uk

BEDROOMS: 150. 2 suitable for disabled.
OPEN: all year.
FACILITIES: lift, bar, 2 lounges,
restaurant, private dining rooms,
in-room TV (Sky, Freeview), civil
wedding licence, spa (treatment
rooms, indoor swimming pool,
indoor/outdoor vitality pool), gym,
cinema, limited parking nearby
(charge).
BACKGROUND MUSIC: in restaurants.
LOCATION: in city centre.
CHILDREN: all ages welcomed.
DOGS: allowed in some bedrooms,
public areas, bar side of restaurant.
CREDIT CARDS: Amex, MC, Visa.
PRICES: per room B&B double
£134–£611, single £118.50–£595.
À la carte £41.

Prices may change – check with hotel.

LUDLOW Shropshire

THE CLIVE ARMS

This red-brick Georgian coaching inn, 10 minutes from foodie-central Ludlow, has been smartly updated with a breezy open-plan bar and restaurant, and country-chic bedrooms. It's on the Earl of Plymouth's Oakly Park estate so expect field-to-fork dining with seasonal dishes using produce from the walled garden and surrounding farms. Bedrooms, mainly in the rear courtyard, are individually styled and with pleasing extras: ground coffee, teas, locally baked biscuits; a choice of pillows. Guests sensitive to traffic noise (an A road runs nearby) should call to discuss the best rooms. The Ludlow Farmshop, where breakfast is taken, is steps away; walking maps are available for exploration further afield.

MAP 3:C4
Bromfield
Ludlow SY8 2JR
T: 01584 856565
W: theclive.co.uk

BEDROOMS: 17. 14 in courtyard annexe, some on ground floor, 1 suitable for disabled.
OPEN: all year, restaurant and bar closed Sun eve, Mon, Tues.
FACILITIES: bar, lower bar, restaurant, snug, private dining room, conference room, in-room TV (Freeview), courtyard, beer garden, ground floor wheelchair accessible.
BACKGROUND MUSIC: in public areas.
LOCATION: 4 miles NW of Ludlow.
CHILDREN: all ages welcomed.
DOGS: allowed in public rooms, some bedrooms.
CREDIT CARDS: Amex, MC, Visa.
PRICES: B&B room only from £91.
À la carte £32.

Prices may change – check with hotel.

LUDLOW Shropshire

THE FEATHERS

Fabulously photogenic, this Grade I listed Jacobean building with an ornate, timber-framed facade stands in a 'wonderful position' in the heart of town, a few minutes' walk from the main square and castle. 'The hotel has been completely revamped internally without losing its renowned historical features,' a regular Guide reader, and return visitor, reports. Inside are 'huge fireplaces', 'fine timberwork' and restored oak panelling. It is 'immaculately clean' throughout. Bedrooms are pleasingly modern: while some may be snug, all have a 'very comfortable' bed and a choice of pillows, plus a mini-fridge, coffee and teas. Service at mealtimes is 'fast and cheerful' with a 'decent variety' at breakfast.

MAP 3:C4
Bull Ring
Ludlow SY8 1AA
T: 01584 875261
W: feathersatludlow.co.uk

BEDROOMS: 42. 1 accessible room on the first floor.
OPEN: all year.
FACILITIES: lift, lounge, bar, tea room, restaurant, function rooms, in-room smart TV, civil wedding licence, courtyard, limited parking (charge).
BACKGROUND MUSIC: jazz in public areas.
LOCATION: in town centre.
CHILDREN: all ages welcomed.
DOGS: allowed, not in restaurant.
CREDIT CARDS: MC, Visa.
PRICES: per room £79–£275. Breakfast £11.95, à la carte £40. 1-night bookings occasionally refused in peak season.

Prices may change – check with hotel.

MALVERN WELLS Worcestershire

THE COTTAGE IN THE WOOD

'Fabulous, far-reaching' views spread across the
Severn valley from this hotel in extensive grounds
high above the Malvern hills. The refurbished
Georgian dower house has contemporary public
spaces, and a collection of smart bedrooms in the
main house, and neighbouring Beech Cottage
and the Coach House, some with a patio or
small balcony. Floor-to-ceiling windows in the
restaurant frame a rural panorama that stretches
to the Cotswolds, a fine backdrop for Rob Mason's
'excellent' modern cooking at lunch and dinner.
'The home-made bread was incredibly moreish!'
Casual meals and drinks may also be taken
alfresco on the covered terrace – all the better to
exult in big vistas. The Elgar route is close by.

MAP 3:D5
Holywell Road
Malvern Wells WR14 4LG
T: 01684 588860
W: cottageinthewood.co.uk

BEDROOMS: 32. 4 in Beech Cottage,
19 in Coach House, 10 on ground
floor, 1 suitable for disabled.
OPEN: all year, except 2 weeks in
early Jan.
FACILITIES: bar, restaurant, meeting
room, in-room TV (Freeview),
covered terrace, 8-acre grounds.
BACKGROUND MUSIC: 'ambient' in bar,
restaurant.
LOCATION: 4 miles from Malvern
Wells.
CHILDREN: all ages welcomed.
DOGS: allowed in some bedrooms,
grounds, not in public rooms.
CREDIT CARDS: Amex, MC, Visa.
PRICES: per room B&B £99–£254.
À la carte £45.

Prices may change – check with hotel.

MANCHESTER

DIDSBURY HOUSE

Just 15 minutes from the city centre, this Victorian
town house offers a stylish retreat where cool
design meets relaxing surrounds. Vintage prints,
statement wallpapers and an impressive stained-
glass window form a sophisticated setting for
fresh flowers, books, open fires and deep sofas;
tasteful bedrooms and suites, some set over two
levels, retain original high windows and delicate
cornices. Among amenities in the rooms are a
butler tray with fresh milk, perhaps a roll-top
bath or two. Afternoon tea may be taken in one of
two lounges. A deli menu is served in the bar or
on the atmospherically lit walled terrace; on the
weekend, breakfast continues until late. A sister
hotel is just up the street.

MAP 4:E3
Didsbury Park
Didsbury Village
Manchester M20 5LJ
T: 0161 448 2200
W: didsburyhouse.co.uk

BEDROOMS: 27. Some on ground floor,
1 suitable for disabled.
OPEN: all year.
FACILITIES: bar, 2 lounges, breakfast
room, in-room TV (Sky), civil
wedding licence, meeting/function
facilities, heated walled terrace,
ground floor wheelchair accessible.
BACKGROUND MUSIC: in public
areas, volume adjusted to suit the
atmosphere and time of day.
LOCATION: 6 miles from Manchester
city centre and airport, easy access
to M60.
CHILDREN: all ages welcomed.
DOGS: not allowed.
CREDIT CARDS: Amex, MC, Visa.
PRICES: B&B doubles from £150.
Breakfast from £14. À la carte £30.

Prices may change – check with hotel.

MARAZION Cornwall

THE GODOLPHIN

Across the causeway from St Michael's Mount, light streams into this 'tactfully modernised and enlarged' beachfront restaurant-with-rooms. It is decorated with uplifting coastal colours and local artwork. Smart bedrooms face the village or the sea – the view over Mount's Bay is worth the upgrade. In the breezy restaurant or on the glass-fronted terrace, local fish and seafood feature on the seasonal menus. Breakfast has good choice: a full Cornish, grilled kippers, buttermilk pancakes and more. Children have their own menu; doggy companions receive a welcome pack with treats, a bowl and a blanket. At low tide, walk the historic causeway across to the Mount; when the tide's in, it's a short boat trip away.

MAP 1:E1
West End
Marazion TR17 0EN
T: 01736 888510
W: thegodolphin.com

BEDROOMS: 10. Some suitable for disabled.
OPEN: all year.
FACILITIES: 2 bars, split-level dining area, in-room TV (Freeview), civil wedding licence, function facilities, 2 terraces, parking, dining room wheelchair accessible, parking.
BACKGROUND MUSIC: in public areas, occasional live acoustic music.
LOCATION: 4 miles E of Penzance.
CHILDREN: all ages welcomed.
DOGS: allowed in 2 bedrooms, designated dining area, on terrace.
CREDIT CARDS: MC, Visa.
PRICES: per room B&B £120–£370. À la carte £60. 2-night min. stay at weekends in high season.

Prices may change – check with hotel.

MARCHAM Oxfordshire

B&B RAFTERS

A suntrap garden is just one of the highlights of Sigrid Grawert's inviting B&B, on the outskirts of an Oxfordshire village, within reach of historic houses and the city of dreaming spires. Modern bedrooms (one with a private balcony) have fluffy robes and a power shower in the bathroom; on the landing are honesty-box soft drinks and snacks, and a capsule coffee machine. An award-winning breakfast is taken communally: freshly squeezed orange juice, home-baked sourdough bread, home-made marmalade and jams, a superb porridge menu (the whisky version is not for the faint-hearted). Special diets are willingly catered for. The ever-helpful hostess will happily share local tips.

MAP 2:C2
Abingdon Road
Marcham OX13 6NU
T: 01865 391298
W: bnb-rafters.co.uk

BEDROOMS: 4.
OPEN: all year except Christmas, New Year.
FACILITIES: breakfast room, in-room smart TV (Freeview), garden, parking.
BACKGROUND MUSIC: none.
LOCATION: 3 miles W of Abingdon, 10 miles S of Oxford.
CHILDREN: not under 12.
DOGS: not allowed.
CREDIT CARDS: MC, Visa.
PRICES: per room B&B single from £67, double from £99. 2-night min. stay at bank holiday weekends.

Prices may change – check with hotel.

MATLOCK BATH Derbyshire

HODGKINSON'S HOTEL

Filled with historic interest, Zoe and Chris Hipwell's small town house hotel overlooks a bend of the River Derwent. Most of the restored features (ornate glasswork, a tiled entrance hall, the wood-and-glass bar) date to the ownership of Victorian wine merchant Job Hodgkinson, who stored his wares in the Roman-era cave. The homely bedrooms (some dog-friendly) are traditionally furnished; one has a four-poster bed and a roll-top bath; most have river views. There is a terraced garden with space to sit, and an intimate restaurant serving home-cooked Modern British dishes. Well located for exploring the Peak District, the hotel has 'excellent' walks from the door; stately homes are within an easy drive.

MAP 3:B6
150 South Parade
Matlock Bath DE4 3NR
T: 01629 582170
W: hodgkinsons-hotel.co.uk

BEDROOMS: 8.
OPEN: all year, except Christmas week, restaurant closed Sun–Tues (open on Tues eve for pre-booked guests).
FACILITIES: sitting room, restaurant with bar, in-room TV (Freeview), terraced garden, drying room, limited parking (parking nearby, permits supplied).
BACKGROUND MUSIC: in public areas.
LOCATION: centre of village, 1 mile from Matlock and Cromford.
CHILDREN: all ages welcomed.
DOGS: allowed in some bedrooms, lounge, not in restaurant.
CREDIT CARDS: MC, Visa.
PRICES: per room B&B £95–£165. Set dinner £29.50 (2 courses), £34.50 (3 courses). 2-night min. stay at weekends Easter–Oct.

Prices may change – check with hotel.

MAWNAN SMITH Cornwall

HOTEL MEUDON

Meandering down to a private beach, glorious sub-tropical gardens enfold this secluded Victorian mansion. Recently refurbished, the hotel has plenty of places to repose. Lawns and terraces entice with seating at parasol-covered tables. A cheerful drawing room has colourful sofas, plants, a fire for cooler months. Linking the main house to the 1960s themed bedrooms (some with a terrace or balcony), the Bridge affords wonderful views over the grounds. Cocktails, local gins, small bites and sharing plates are served in Freddie's bar. In the restaurant, local fish and seafood feature on Darren Kerley's inventive set menus. The South West Coast Path is at the end of the garden. Part of Kingfisher Resorts.

MAP 1:E2
Mawnan Smith
Falmouth TR11 5HT
T: 01326 250541
W: meudon.co.uk

BEDROOMS: 29, 16 on ground floor, 2 suitable for disabled, self-catering cottage.
OPEN: all year.
FACILITIES: lift, ramps, 2 lounges, bar, restaurant, in-room TV, private dining, Sanctuary suite (treatments), 8½-acre grounds (gardens, private beach). Wheelchair accessible apart from Freddie's bar.
BACKGROUND MUSIC: jazz-inspired music in public areas.
LOCATION: in secluded grounds, 4 miles from Falmouth.
CHILDREN: all ages welcomed.
DOGS: allowed in selected bedrooms, not in restaurant, on lead in grounds.
CREDIT CARDS: Amex, MC, Visa.
PRICES: per room B&B £139–£459. Set menu £49.

Prices may change – check with hotel.

MINSTER LOVELL Oxfordshire
OLD SWAN

In a village of thatched houses, surrounded by woodland and wildflower meadows and close to a willow-hung riverbank, the 600-year-old Old Swan has a timeless charm. A classic country inn – Oxford is just 15 miles – its cosy nooks, log fires, flagstone floors and sturdy beams form a characterful setting for its famous menu of home-made pies – from beef and ale to lobster and cheese; all paired with a beer. Bedrooms (some with four-posters) have rustic charm in their beams, plaid throws and cushions, plus bathrobes and upmarket toiletries. Enjoy a walk or a spot of fishing; return to take afternoon tea on the terrace. Guests can play tennis, boules and croquet at sister hotel Minster Mill, across the road.

MAP 3:D6
Minster Lovell OX29 0RN
T: 01993 862512
W: oldswan.co.uk

BEDROOMS: 15. 6 on ground floor, plus 3-bed cottage.
OPEN: all year.
FACILITIES: bar, restaurant, in-room TV (Freeview), terrace, civil wedding licence, 65-acre grounds (croquet, fishing), bicycle hire, bar/restaurant wheelchair accessible with ramps.
BACKGROUND MUSIC: none.
LOCATION: in village 3 miles W of Witney, 15 miles from Oxford.
CHILDREN: all ages welcomed.
DOGS: in some bedrooms (welcome pack), bar.
CREDIT CARDS: Amex, MC, Visa.
PRICES: B&B doubles from £145. 2-night min. stay some weekends. À la carte £29.

Prices may change – check with hotel.

MORECAMBE Lancashire
THE MIDLAND

A 'superbly positioned Art Deco wonder', the former railway hotel overlooking the sand flats of Morecambe Bay was restored to its iconic glory by the English Lakes group. Its dining room – 'a joy' – follows the curve of the building; every diner has a 'spectacular' sea view through huge windows. Modern British dishes are served; sandwiches, salads, burgers and tapas platters may be taken on the terrace in the glamorous Rotunda bar. Up a spiral staircase or via a compact lift, red-carpeted corridors lead to urbane, 'surprisingly spacious' bedrooms, many with a view over the sea. The landward side is rather more prosaic. A sister hotel's health club is available to guests. Ideal for the Isle of Man ferry.

MAP 4:D2
Marine Road West
Morecambe LA4 4BU
T: 01524 424000
W: englishlakes.co.uk

BEDROOMS: 44. 2 suitable for disabled.
OPEN: all year.
FACILITIES: lift, lounge, bar, restaurant, in-room TV, function rooms, civil wedding licence, lawns, parking.
BACKGROUND MUSIC: all day in lounge.
LOCATION: overlooking Morecambe Bay, steps from the stone jetty.
CHILDREN: all ages welcomed.
DOGS: well-behaved dogs allowed, not in restaurant.
CREDIT CARDS: Amex, MC, Visa.
PRICES: per room B&B £125–£560. À la carte (The Sun Terrace) £45. 1-night bookings refused Sat.

Prices may change – check with hotel.

NEW

NEWBY BRIDGE Cumbria

THE SWAN HOTEL & SPA

By a stone arched bridge, this 'imposing edifice' is in an idyllic waterside spot, surrounded by gardens that sweep down to the River Leven. The family-friendly hotel, in a former 17th-century coaching house, has been extended with the addition of chic, sustainably furnished accommodation, and a garden spa with outdoor sauna. Bedrooms range from romantic adults-only loft suites to interconnecting family rooms with bunk beds for children. Riotous florals bring playful cheer to the bar and restaurant, where a menu of snacks, grills and brasserie dishes is served. Outside, young imaginations can run wild in the adventure play park or nature trail. A terrace runs along the picturesque riverbank.

MAP 4: inset C2
Newby Bridge LA12 8NB
T: 015395 31681
w: swanhotel.com

BEDROOMS: 86. Some suitable for disabled, plus 4 self-catering cottages.
OPEN: all year.
FACILITIES: sitting room, library, Swan Inn, restaurant, juice bar, in-room TV (Sky), civil wedding licence, function facilities, spa (treatments), 2 indoor pools (1 adults only), gym, terrace, 10-acre grounds, parking, mooring.
BACKGROUND MUSIC: in public areas.
LOCATION: 9 miles from Ulverston, Grange-over-Sands and Bowness-on-Windermere.
CHILDREN: all ages welcomed.
DOGS: allowed in bedrooms, bar, cottages.
CREDIT CARDS: MC, Visa.
PRICES: per room B&B £110–£450.
À la carte £35. 2-night min. stay bank holiday weekends.

Prices may change – check with hotel.

NEW

NEWMARKET Suffolk

THE PACKHORSE INN

Geed up with a sophisticated steer, this inn in a former Victorian pub sits in a rural village near Newmarket by a medieval packhorse bridge. Beyond a glassed-in corridor lie a bar and smart dining areas, with stripped floorboards and wooden tables; outside, a sun-filled garden offers alfresco dining. Your dog-friendly bedroom might have a claw-foot or stone bath, or a view over the village green. Coach house rooms have under-floor heating and open on to a terrace. The well-regarded restaurant uses local vegetables, meats and cheeses for its Modern menus and Sunday roasts. Breakfast brings a Full Suffolk or vegetarian. On race days expect to jockey for position at the bar for a pint of Woodforde's Wherry.

MAP 2:B4
Bridge Street
Moulton
Newmarket CB8 8SP
T: 01638 751818
w: thepackhorseinn.com

BEDROOMS: 8. 4 on ground floor in coach house, 3 suitable for disabled.
OPEN: all year, except 25 Dec.
FACILITIES: bar, restaurant, function room, in-room TV (Freeview), courtyard, public areas wheelchair accessible, adapted toilet, parking.
BACKGROUND MUSIC: in dining areas.
LOCATION: opposite green in Moulton village, 3 miles from Newmarket.
CHILDREN: all ages welcomed.
DOGS: allowed in courtyard rooms, restaurant and bar.
CREDIT CARDS: Amex, MC, Visa.
PRICES: per room B&B £112–£256.
À la carte £45.

Prices may change – check with hotel.

NEWQUAY Cornwall

THE HEADLAND HOTEL

Standing majestically above Fistral beach with
far-reaching Atlantic ocean views, this well-loved,
family hotel is an engaging mix of the grand
and the contemporary with diversions a-plenty.
Whether you want to chill out or be active, the
landmark Victorian building and its swish Aqua
Club can provide: six indoor and outdoor pools; a
host of spa treatments; buckets and spades for the
beach; games, books and DVDs for duvet days.
A golf course and surf school round out the offer.
Most bedrooms have coastal hues and views; some
have a balcony, too. Day or night, varied menus
and venues – on the waterfront terrace, in the
sophisticated Samphire restaurant, or poolside –
highlight Cornish produce in season.

MAP 1:D2
Headland Road
Newquay TR7 1EW
T: 01637 872211
W: headlandhotel.co.uk

BEDROOMS: 91. 1 suitable for disabled,
plus 39 self-catering 1-, 2- and
3-bedroom cottages in the grounds.
OPEN: all year.
FACILITIES: 5 lounges, bar, 3 restaurants,
in-room TV (Freeview), civil wedding
licence, conference/event facilities,
10-acre grounds, spa, gym, indoor and
outdoor heated pools, EV charging,
public rooms wheelchair accessible.
BACKGROUND MUSIC: 'easy listening' in
restaurants.
LOCATION: on a headland overlooking
Fistral beach.
CHILDREN: all ages welcomed.
DOGS: allowed in bedrooms (welcome
pack), public rooms, not in restaurants
except Terrace.
CREDIT CARDS: Amex, MC, Visa.
PRICES: B&B doubles £195–£655.
À la carte £40.

Prices may change – check with hotel.

NEWQUAY Cornwall

LEWINNICK LODGE

On the craggy Pentire headland, this seaside-
chic hotel looking north along the Cornish coast
dispenses 'fabulous' views and soothing Atlantic
sounds. Sleek and stylish inside, it has 'friendly,
helpful and efficient' staff and a laid-back
atmosphere. Most bedrooms take in a 'fabulous'
vista towards Towan Head and Fistral beach.
Each room has home-made biscuits, binoculars
and high-tech features. Bathrooms have robes,
organic toiletries, perhaps a slipper bath. The
restaurant and bar are popular with locals. In the
dining room and on the terrace above the ocean,
Cornish ingredients are given a contemporary
twist and include vegan and vegetarian options.
A pebble's throw from the South West Coast Path.

MAP 1:D2
Pentire Headland
Newquay TR7 1QD
T: 01637 878117
W: lewinnicklodge.co.uk

BEDROOMS: 17. Some suitable for
disabled.
OPEN: all year.
FACILITIES: lift, bar, snug, restaurant,
in-room smart TV (Sky, Freeview)
and Bluetooth speakers, in-room spa
treatments, terraced beer garden, EV
charging.
BACKGROUND MUSIC: all day in public
spaces.
LOCATION: 3 miles W of Newquay
centre.
CHILDREN: all ages welcomed.
DOGS: allowed in some bedrooms, bar,
terrace, not in restaurant.
CREDIT CARDS: MC, Visa.
PRICES: per room B&B £180–£370.
À la carte £29.50. 1-night bookings
sometimes refused high season.

Prices may change – check with hotel.

NORTHALLERTON Yorkshire
THE CLEVELAND TONTINE

On the western edge of the North York Moors, head to this handsome Georgian coaching inn for its friendly atmosphere and 'good' Yorkshire fare. Seasonal menus in the 'busy' restaurant focus on produce from its own kitchen garden at Mount St John and regional farmers. Afternoon tea may be taken on the garden terrace or in the morning room overlooking the Cleveland Hills. Bedrooms, decorated with arresting wallpaper, are supplied with tea- and coffee-making facilities, plus bathrobes in a bathroom with under-floor heating. Continental or cooked breakfasts include vegetarian options. Part of the Provenance Inns & Hotels group; see The Carpenters Arms, Felixkirk (main entry), and The West Park Hotel, Harrogate (Shortlist entry).

MAP 4:C4
Staddlebridge
Northallerton DL6 3JB
T: 01609 882671
W: theclevelandtontine.com

BEDROOMS: 7.
OPEN: all year.
FACILITIES: bar, 2 lounges, morning room, bistro, in-room TV (Freeview), room service, function facilities, small garden, parking.
BACKGROUND MUSIC: in public rooms.
LOCATION: 8 miles NE of Northallerton.
CHILDREN: all ages welcomed.
DOGS: allowed in bar, 1 lounge.
CREDIT CARDS: Amex, MC, Visa.
PRICES: per room B&B £149–£310. À la carte £36.

Prices may change – check with hotel.

NEW

OBORNE Dorset
THE GRANGE AT OBORNE

Built of stone from the Purbeck hills, this 200-year-old house on the edge of the village stands in formal gardens (floodlit at night). 'Quite delightful', the family-run hotel is owned by Karenza and Ken Mathews, their daughter, Jennifer, and her husband, Jonathan (who manage on a day-to-day basis), and are 'always around, busy looking after their guests'. The bedrooms are decorated in traditional and modern style; some have an original fireplace, some a balcony with views of the Dorset hills, or patio doors on to the garden, 'perfect for a summer stay'. Chef Simon Clewlow's award-winning seasonal dishes are served in a candlelit dining room. Well placed for Sherborne and the surrounding area.

MAP 1:C6
Oborne
Sherborne DT9 4LA
T: 01935 813463
W: thegrange.co.uk

BEDROOMS: 18. 1 suitable for disabled.
OPEN: all year, except 2 weeks at Easter, 2 weeks in Oct/Nov.
FACILITIES: lounge, bar/snug, restaurant, 2 function rooms, in-room TV (Freeview), civil wedding licence, ½-acre garden, parking.
BACKGROUND MUSIC: none.
LOCATION: 2 miles NE of Sherborne by A30.
CHILDREN: all ages welcomed.
DOGS: not allowed.
CREDIT CARDS: Amex, MC, Visa.
PRICES: per room B&B single £79–£199, double £99–£219. Set dinner £40. 1-night bookings sometimes refused at weekends in summer.

Prices may change – check with hotel.

OUNDLE Northamptonshire

LOWER FARM

On the edge of a tranquil village, yet only ten minutes from historic Oundle, the Marriott family offers comfortable B&B rooms in converted buildings on their traditional arable farm. Robert and his brother, John, run the farm while Caroline is the 'friendly, accommodating' hostess. Arranged around a neatly landscaped courtyard with seating, up-to-date bedrooms occupy the former milking parlour and stables; connecting rooms suit a family. Hearty breakfasts might include porridge with fresh cream, or avocado with locally sourced sausages and eggs – fuel for tackling the walking and cycling tracks from the door. The Nene Way footpath runs through the farm; the 300-year-old village pub is a short stroll away.

MAP 2:B3
Main Street
Barnwell
Oundle PE8 5PU
T: 01832 273220
W: lower-farm.co.uk

BEDROOMS: 10. All on ground floor, 1 suitable for disabled.
OPEN: all year, except Christmas, New Year.
FACILITIES: breakfast room, in-room TV (Freeview), courtyard garden, 300-acre farm, public rooms wheelchair accessible.
BACKGROUND MUSIC: radio 'if guests wish' in breakfast room.
LOCATION: at one end of the village, 3 miles from Oundle.
CHILDREN: all ages welcomed.
DOGS: allowed in 2 bedrooms, not in public rooms. Farm walks.
CREDIT CARDS: Amex, MC, Visa.
PRICES: B&B £65–£95.

Prices may change – check with hotel.

PAKEFIELD Suffolk

THE HOG HOTEL

Walking maps and a picnic are supplied for the many glorious beach and inland walks from this hotel, restaurant and bar in an old maritime village on the Suffolk coast. Decorated in a palette of grey, with wood flooring, the former farmhouse has a 'clean-lined' look. Bedrooms (some with their own entrance) vary in size; some can accommodate a family. 'Our suite overlooking the well-kept garden had an extremely comfy bed. In the bathroom: fluffy towels, super-soft robes, a wonderful drench shower.' The modern bar serves light-bite lunches, ales, cider and cocktails. For dinner in the restaurant there is good choice, perhaps a duo of Gressingham duck or chargrilled rack of lamb; vegetarian options too.

MAP 2:B6
41 London Road
Pakefield
Lowestoft NR33 7AA
T: 01502 569805
W: thehoghotel.co.uk

BEDROOMS: 16. 6 accessed from outside, 1 suite suitable for disabled.
OPEN: all year, except 25–30 Dec. Restaurant closed Sun eve.
FACILITIES: bar, restaurant, conservatory, in-room smart TV, function facilities, terrace, garden.
BACKGROUND MUSIC: jazz, classical, 'easy listening' in public areas.
LOCATION: in village, 2 miles S of Lowestoft.
CHILDREN: all ages welcomed.
DOGS: welcomed in 4 bedrooms, garden, not in main hotel, bar, restaurant.
CREDIT CARDS: Amex, MC, Visa.
PRICES: per room B&B £120–£260. À la carte £35.

Prices may change – check with hotel.

PENZANCE Cornwall

ARTIST RESIDENCE CORNWALL

A short uphill walk from the harbour, this revitalised Georgian coach house brims with a sense of stylish fun. Set across three floors, beach-shack chic bedrooms (some snug; some to suit an accompanying dog or a family) are styled with bright artworks and vintage pieces. Downstairs, eating, drinking and merry-making take place in the informal bar and restaurant with its wood-burner, retro sofas and reclaimed furniture. Menus feature Cornish produce, and meat and fish from the on-site smokehouse. In summer, a Seafood Shack is set up in the sunny garden. Part of Justin and Charlotte Salisbury's eclectic hotel collection (see main entries for Artist Residence in London, Brighton and Oxfordshire, and Shortlist entry for Bristol).

MAP 1:E1
20 Chapel Street
Penzance TR18 4AW
T: 01736 365664
W: artistresidence.co.uk

BEDROOMS: 19. Plus 3-bed cottage in grounds.
OPEN: all year.
FACILITIES: bar, restaurant, in-room TV (Freeview), terrace, beer garden (outdoor seafood shack and bar in summer).
BACKGROUND MUSIC: in public areas.
LOCATION: in town centre.
CHILDREN: all ages welcomed.
DOGS: allowed in some bedrooms, restaurant.
CREDIT CARDS: Amex, MC, Visa.
PRICES: per room £85–£625. Breakfast £4–£10.50, à la carte £35. 1-night stay sometimes refused weekends.

Prices may change – check with hotel.

PENZANCE Cornwall

VENTON VEAN

This modern B&B has a pleasing mix of contemporary, local art and vintage furnishings, the stylish whole set against the period features of the immaculately restored Victorian house. Spacious bedrooms have king- or super-king beds, stripped wood floors and welcome extras (refreshments, bathrobes); books are available to borrow in the airy sitting room. When it comes to food, 'our emphasis is on special and unusual dishes', the hosts say: home-made corn tortillas and refried beans at breakfast, perhaps, or a Sri Lankan hodi broth with fresh Newlyn mussels at dinner. Vegan and vegetarian diets are willingly catered for. By Penlee Park; good-sized garden with unusual plants.

MAP 1:E1
Trewithen Road
Penzance TR18 4LS
T: 01736 351294
W: ventonvean.co.uk

BEDROOMS: 5. 1 with adjoining single room, suitable for a family.
OPEN: all year except 25–26 Dec.
FACILITIES: sitting room, dining room, in-room smart TV, garden.
BACKGROUND MUSIC: at breakfast in dining room.
LOCATION: 7 mins' walk from the centre of Penzance and seafront.
CHILDREN: not under 5.
DOGS: not allowed.
CREDIT CARDS: MC, Visa.
PRICES: per room B&B single £80–£115, double £90–£125. Dinner by request. À la carte £30. 2-night min. stay.

Prices may change – check with hotel.

RAMSGATE Kent

ALBION HOUSE

This chic and stylish small hotel in a restored Regency building has an enviable clifftop position overlooking the beach and Royal Harbour. Owners Ben and Emma Irvine have retained the building's grandeur – in the past it was favoured by politicians, actors, even Princess Victoria – in the high ceilings, ornate cornices and carved fireplaces but added modern elegance. Public spaces have mirrors, plants, walls painted deep heritage shades; a lounge is a 'welcoming' spot. Most of the light-filled bedrooms, some high up in the eaves, have views towards the water. A busy road at the front may affect light sleepers. In the restaurant, seasonal produce, including locally caught seafood, dictates the menu.

MAP 2:D6
Albion Place
Ramsgate CT11 8HQ
T: 01843 606630
W: albionhouseramsgate.co.uk

BEDROOMS: 14. 1 suitable for disabled.
OPEN: all year.
FACILITIES: 2 lounges, bar/restaurant, snug, in-room TV (Freeview), private dining room, electric bicycle hire, paid/free parking nearby, ground floor wheelchair accessible.
BACKGROUND MUSIC: all day in public areas.
LOCATION: above Ramsgate Main Sands beach.
CHILDREN: all ages welcomed.
DOGS: allowed in bedrooms, public rooms, welcome pack.
CREDIT CARDS: MC, Visa.
PRICES: B&B £89–£300. À la carte £75. 1-night bookings refused weekends in July, Aug.

Prices may change – check with hotel.

RIPLEY Surrey

BROADWAY BARN

'Nigh on perfect', Mindi McLean's 'superb B&B with every taste catered for' is in a restored 200-year-old barn at the heart of a historic village. Decorated with a blend of characterful antiques and artwork, bedrooms (one with a roll-top bath) are equipped with little luxuries: dressing gowns, slippers, flowers and home-made shortbread. In the morning, guests find a feast in the bright conservatory, 'a gorgeous setting' overlooking a small walled garden. The 'friendly and attentive' host provides an 'exceptional' spread of home-made breads, jams and granola, and house-recipe chipolatas, and has places to recommend for the evening in this foodie area. RHS Garden Wisley is ten minutes down the road.

MAP 2:D3
High Street
Ripley
Woking GU23 6AQ
T: 01483 223200
W: broadwaybarn.com

BEDROOMS: 3. Plus self-catering flat and cottages.
OPEN: all year.
FACILITIES: conservatory sitting room/breakfast room, in-room TV (Freeview), small garden, parking.
BACKGROUND MUSIC: 'subtle' at breakfast.
LOCATION: village centre.
CHILDREN: not under 12.
DOGS: not allowed.
CREDIT CARDS: Amex, MC, Visa.
PRICES: B&B from £130.

Prices may change – check with hotel.

ST ALBANS Hertfordshire

SOPWELL HOUSE HOTEL

The former country home of Lord Louis Mountbatten is 'well run', with contemporary bedrooms, cosseting suites, a good choice of eating and drinking spaces, and a magnificent spa. Bedrooms in the extended Georgian manor house have king-size beds and ESPA bath products; upmarket mews suites, in landscaped gardens in a gated compound, offer extra privacy. The 'bustling', light-drenched brasserie has classic bistro dishes ('seemingly something for everyone'); a new pan-Asian restaurant serves sharing plates. Besides the state-of-the-art Cottonmill spa, several walled gardens provide space for relaxation and reflection. 'Plentiful' breakfasts are 'nicely served'.

MAP 2:C3
Cottonmill Lane
St Albans AL1 2HQ
T: 01727 864477
W: sopwellhouse.co.uk

BEDROOMS: 128. 16 mews suites, some with outdoor hot tubs.
OPEN: all year, brasserie open all week, restaurant open Wed–Sun for dinner.
FACILITIES: cocktail lounge, bar, 2 restaurants, sitting room, in-room TV (Sky, BT), civil wedding licence, meeting and conference facilities, spa, indoor pool, gym, 12-acre grounds, EV charging.
BACKGROUND MUSIC: in lobby and restaurants.
LOCATION: 1½ miles from the city centre and rail station.
CHILDREN: not under 12 to stay, not under 16 in spa or swimming pool.
DOGS: not allowed.
CREDIT CARDS: Amex, MC, Visa.
PRICES: per room B&B £229–£799. À la carte £45.

Prices may change – check with hotel.

ST IVES Cornwall

TREVOSE HARBOUR HOUSE

This Victorian mid-terrace B&B, overlooking the harbour, zings with light from its whitewashed exterior to its blue-and-white colour scheme and original paintings by St Ives artists. Angela and Olivier Noverraz have mixed vintage finds and upcycled furniture with a New England style to create restful interiors. Most bedrooms, with their sleek furnishings, have sea views. All have filtered water, coffee, tea and organic toiletries; a split-level annexe room has a separate seating area. There are books and an honesty bar in the snug; a terrace has seating for a sunny day. At breakfast, local produce is highlighted: Cornish cheeses, smoked salmon from St Mawes, home-made granola and preserves.

MAP 1:D1
22 The Warren
St Ives TR26 2EA
T: 01736 793267
W: trevosehouse.co.uk

BEDROOMS: 6. 1 in rear annexe.
OPEN: Apr–end Oct.
FACILITIES: snug (honesty bar), breakfast room, in-room TV, in-room treatments, 2 terraces, limited parking close by.
BACKGROUND MUSIC: in snug.
LOCATION: in town centre.
CHILDREN: not under 12.
DOGS: not allowed.
CREDIT CARDS: Amex, MC, Visa.
PRICES: B&B doubles from £220, singles from £210. 2-night min. stay (ring to check occasional 1-night availability).

Prices may change – check with hotel.

ST LEONARDS-ON-SEA Sussex

THE CLOUDESLEY

Creatively arranged, Shahriar Mazandi's eclectic B&B reflects his interests as a photographer, award-winning gardener and holistic therapist. The drawing room is stocked with art, gardening and photography books; the walls are hung with his photographs. Decorated with works of art, the serene bedrooms have a large, comfortable bed and a compact shower room; no TV, but Wi-Fi and plenty to read. In the bright dining room or on the sunny bamboo terrace, inventive breakfasts, seasoned with Himalayan pink salt, include an impressive omelette menu (sausage, sage and courgette; fruit and Armagnac). In-room therapies (massages, reiki, reflexology) are available. The town, train station and seafront are close by.

MAP 2:E4
7 Cloudesley Road
St Leonards-on-Sea TN37 6JN
T: 07507 000148
W: thecloudesley.co.uk

BEDROOMS: 4.
OPEN: all year.
FACILITIES: drawing room (honesty bar), dining room, in-room spa treatments, ¼-acre garden, patio.
BACKGROUND MUSIC: none.
LOCATION: 10 mins from St Leonards-on-Sea town centre.
CHILDREN: well-behaved children accepted.
DOGS: not allowed.
CREDIT CARDS: MC, Visa.
PRICES: per room B&B £90–£150. 2-night min. stay preferred at weekends.

Prices may change – check with hotel.

ST MARTIN'S Isles of Scilly

KARMA ST MARTIN'S

Overlooking the white sands of St Martin's and with views across the waters to Tresco, this long and low stone-built hotel offers a luxurious yet laidback retreat with a private jetty for the ferry from St Mary's. It is the only hotel on the island, and dogs and children are welcomed. Classic British meets contemporary style in the bedrooms with vintage-style furnishings, books and freshly ground Cornish coffee; large windows offer restful sea views. In the restaurant, or alfresco in the sub-tropical garden, lobster rolls and platters of freshly caught seafood are menu mainstays. Accompanying dogs relish a dish from the Kanine Kitchen. Hire a day boat or snorkel with seals; soothing spa treatments also available.

MAP 1: inset C1
Lower Town
St Martin's TR25 0QW
T: 01720 422368
W: karmaresorts.com

BEDROOMS: 30. 12 on ground floor, 5 suitable for disabled.
OPEN: Easter–end Oct.
FACILITIES: bar, restaurant, 2 lounges, in-room TV (Freeview), civil wedding licence, treatment room, children's games room, 7-acre grounds, terrace, bar and restaurant wheelchair accessible.
BACKGROUND MUSIC: jazz in bar, restaurant, muted on request.
LOCATION: 2 mins' walk from Lower Town Quay.
CHILDREN: all ages welcomed.
DOGS: allowed in some bedrooms (welcome packs), upper dining room and grounds.
CREDIT CARDS: Amex, MC, Visa.
PRICES: B&B doubles from £275. À la carte £55.

Prices may change – check with hotel.

NEW

MAP 2:D2
Minster Street
Wilton
Salisbury SP2 0BH
T: 01722 743328
W: pembrokearms.co.uk

SALISBURY Wiltshire

THE PEMBROKE ARMS

Across from Wilton House, seat of the earls of Pembroke (admission discount for staying guests), an 18th-century inn overlays old-style comforts with buzzy charm. Well-worn leather seating, heritage-colour walls, dark wood tables and chairs inside; in the garden, under umbrellas or awnings, the Garden Kitchen and Tap Room provide dining and drinking space, serving handmade shortcrust pies, hand-stretched pizzas with locally sourced toppings, and regular pub staples, vegetarian and vegan dishes, along with draught beer, cider, cocktails and wines. From small and cosy to spacious yet quaint, a mix of bedrooms includes a large room with two double beds that would suit a family. Salisbury is a bus ride away.

BEDROOMS: 9.
OPEN: all year, except Tues.
FACILITIES: bar, dining room, private dining room, large garden (alfresco eating), parking.
BACKGROUND MUSIC: in public areas.
LOCATION: in village, 3 miles from Salisbury.
CHILDREN: all ages welcomed.
DOGS: not allowed.
CREDIT CARDS: MC, Visa.
PRICES: B&B £114–£133. Dinner £32.

Prices may change – check with hotel.

NEW

MAP 3:A5
1 Hightown
Sandbach CW11 1AG
T: 01270 762013
W: wheatsheafsandbach.co.uk

SANDBACH Cheshire

THE WHEATSHEAF

In the centre of a 'pleasant' town, famous for its Anglo-Saxon crosses, this revitalised 19th-century inn with an 'informal atmosphere' is a popular gathering point. The handsome building, refurbished by the Pear family, has hunting lodge elements inside: deep leather armchairs beside open fires; muted plaids and antler motifs throughout. On the second floor, soft-toned, well-equipped bedrooms have oak beams and 'enjoyably quirky features'. Home-made gastropub dishes, steaks, and vegan menus are served by 'a very professional, cheerful young crew' in the well-supplied bar, a spacious, modern restaurant or on a covered terrace. Easy access from the M6; Tatton Park (NT) is close.

BEDROOMS: 18.
OPEN: all year.
FACILITIES: bar, restaurant, covered terrace.
BACKGROUND MUSIC: live music on terrace on Sat nights.
LOCATION: in town centre.
CHILDREN: all ages welcomed.
DOGS: allowed, in 2 rooms.
CREDIT CARDS: Amex, MC, Visa.
PRICES: per room B&B £95–£165. À la carte £36.

Prices may change – check with hotel.

SEDGEFORD Norfolk

MAGAZINE WOOD

In a swath of green countryside, Pip and Jonathan Barber's chic B&B looks over the village towards the Norfolk coast. Just right for cocooning, each spacious, newly refurbished suite has a private entrance and terrace; a large bed and mood lighting, plus a deep bath and separate shower in the bathroom. Books, DVDs and binoculars are provided; a tablet computer serves as an online concierge, to download a newspaper or create an itinerary. The day begins 'anytime': a well-stocked cupboard contains muesli, cereals, fruit and croissants; milk and organic yogurts are in the fridge. Cooked breakfasts (charged extra and ordered the night before) are brought to the room. A dining pub is within walking distance.

MAP 2:A5
Peddars Way
Sedgeford
Hunstanton PE36 5LW
T: 01485 750740
W: magazinewood.co.uk

BEDROOMS: 3. All on ground floor, 2 in converted barn.
OPEN: all year except Christmas.
FACILITIES: in-room TV (on-demand movies), in-room spa treatments, 3-acre grounds, parking.
BACKGROUND MUSIC: none.
LOCATION: 5 miles from Hunstanton.
CHILDREN: infants welcomed.
DOGS: allowed (not unattended) in 1 bedroom, in grounds if well behaved.
CREDIT CARDS: MC, Visa.
PRICES: per room B&B (continental) £115–£149. Cooked breakfast £7.50. 2-night min. stay most weekends.

Prices may change – check with hotel.

SHAFTESBURY Dorset

THE GROSVENOR ARMS

This former coaching inn, in a hilltop Dorset town, combines Georgian features with a contemporary style to create an intimate feel. The wood-floored bar has a wood burner and well-worn leather armchairs; in the buzzy restaurant, or courtyard, dishes on the locally sourced menus might include flat-iron chicken, Somerset Camembert, squash and chestnut pie, or a pizza from the wood-fired oven. 'Attractive' bedrooms and suites are well equipped with teas and a capsule coffee machine; some rooms are spacious enough for families. Throughout, staff make guests feel that 'nothing is too much trouble'. At breakfast, stoke up on Old Spot sausage and bacon, smoky beans and hash browns for the climb up Gold Hill. Part of the Stay Original Co.

MAP 2:D1
The Commons
Shaftesbury SP7 8JA
T: 01747 850580
W: grosvenorarms.co.uk

BEDROOMS: 16. 2 on first floor accessible by lift.
OPEN: all year.
FACILITIES: lift to first-floor rooms, bar, lounge, restaurant, conservatory, private dining room, ballroom, in-room TV (Freeview), courtyard garden, parking permits supplied for local car park, bar and restaurant wheelchair accessible, adapted toilet.
BACKGROUND MUSIC: in public areas.
LOCATION: in town centre, 1-min. walk from Gold Hill.
CHILDREN: all ages welcomed.
DOGS: allowed in bedrooms (welcome pack), bar, conservatory, courtyard, not in restaurant.
CREDIT CARDS: Amex, MC, Visa.
PRICES: B&B £95–£240. À la carte £37.

Prices may change – check with hotel.

SHANKLIN Isle of Wight
HAVEN HALL HOTEL
Breakfast on the terrace looking out to sea from this sprawling, cliff-top Edwardian house is 'a wonderful start to each day'. David and Arielle Barratt have furnished their guest house with carefully chosen period pieces that give the luxurious and spacious bedrooms and suites, many with marble bathrooms, an Arts and Crafts appeal. Nearly all rooms have views over the water. Breakfast is a spread of fruit, cereals, breads, jams and home-made compotes, plus eggs cooked how you like, enjoyed either indoors or outdoors. There are landscaped gardens to wander, a swimming pool and grass tennis court, while Sandown Bay is a short stroll on the nearby Coast Path. The owners will advise guests on dining options.

MAP 2:E2
5 Howard Road
Shanklin PO37 6HD
T: 07914 796494
W: havenhallhotel.com

BEDROOMS: 14. 3 on ground floor, 7 available for self-catering.
OPEN: Apr to beginning Oct.
FACILITIES: bar, lounge, dining room, in-room TV (Freeview), outdoor pool (heated May–Sept), grass tennis court, croquet, 2-acre grounds, EV charging, parking.
BACKGROUND MUSIC: none.
LOCATION: on E. side of island, overlooking the English Channel.
CHILDREN: over 12 welcomed.
DOGS: welcomed in 3 bedrooms and on main lawn.
CREDIT CARDS: Amex, MC, Visa.
PRICES: B&B £420–£1,250. 2-night min. stay. À la carte £40.

Prices may change – check with hotel.

SHANKLIN Isle of Wight
RYLSTONE MANOR
Surrounded by both private and public gardens, this handsome Victorian, former gentleman's residence, with its large leaded windows, offers a relaxing B&B with glimpses of Sandown Bay. Carole and Mike Hailston have created a welcoming and homely style in keeping with the building's age; the bar and sitting rooms sport rich hues and period furnishing while bedrooms are traditionally styled with handsome wallpapers and flowing curtains. Some offer glimpses of the sea through trees; others have window seats, perfect for spotting a red squirrel in the garden from which steps lead to the beach. Mike prepares breakfast; both have excellent knowledge of the island and can also arrange ferry bookings.

MAP 2:E2
Popham Road
Shanklin PO37 6RG
T: 01983 862806
W: rylstone-manor.co.uk

BEDROOMS: 8.
OPEN: Apr–early Oct.
FACILITIES: drawing room, bar, breakfast room, in-room TV (Freeview), terrace, ¼-acre garden in 4-acre public gardens.
BACKGROUND MUSIC: none.
LOCATION: in Shanklin Old Village.
CHILDREN: not under 16.
DOGS: only assistance dogs allowed.
CREDIT CARDS: MC, Visa.
PRICES: B&B doubles from £140, singles from £110. 3-night min. stay June–Aug 'unless space allows'.

Prices may change – check with hotel.

SHERBORNE Dorset

THE EASTBURY HOTEL & SPA

Close to the Abbey, Peter and Lana de Savary's dog-friendly hotel in a handsome Georgian town house makes a 'comfortable and characterful' retreat in the historic market town. Cosy sitting rooms have games to play. Bedrooms (classic, or with a chic edge) have bathrobes and slippers, a whisky decanter; Alexa for music or calling reception. In the garden, five green-roofed suites, all dog friendly, each have a private terrace. Afternoon teas and snacks are served in the bar and lounge, or on the terrace when fine. In the 'quaint' dining room, chef Matthew Street's creative fine-dining and tasting menus are a high point. 'Immaculately served, and all delicious.' A snug spa is tucked away in the garden.

MAP 2:E1
Long Street
Sherborne DT9 3BY
T: 01935 813131
w: theeastburyhotel.co.uk

BEDROOMS: 26. 5 in walled gardens, 2 suitable for disabled. Plus 3-bed self-catering cottage with hot tub.
OPEN: all year.
FACILITIES: bar/dining room, morning room, drawing room, library, private dining room, in-room TV (Freeview), wedding/function facilities, spa (hydrotherapy pool, outdoor hot tub), terrace, 1-acre walled garden.
BACKGROUND MUSIC: in bar, restaurant.
LOCATION: in town centre.
CHILDREN: all ages welcomed.
DOGS: allowed in 9 bedrooms, on lead in morning room, part of restaurant, garden.
CREDIT CARDS: Amex, MC, Visa.
PRICES: per room B&B £155–£410. À la carte £40. 1-night bookings sometimes refused.

Prices may change – check with hotel.

SHIPSTON-ON-STOUR Warwickshire

THE BOWER HOUSE

Formed from an 'amazing' conversion of several shops on the pretty square of a historic market town, this restaurant-with-rooms is decorated with 'immense panache'. Against brick or richly coloured walls, 'an impressive assortment of pictures and eclectic furniture' fills the public areas. But its biggest attraction is the elevated cooking for set lunches or dinner in the bistro: perhaps Dorset lamb rump, smoked aubergine, panisse, wild garlic, crispy sweetbreads. Through a separate entrance, 'elegant' bedrooms are up a steep staircase. They're worth the climb, for 'every possible need has been thought of' – tea and coffee, Scrabble, books and playing cards among them. Breakfast is served until late.

MAP 3:D6
Market Place
Shipston-on-Stour CV36 4AG
T: 01608 663333
w: thebowerhouseshipston.com

BEDROOMS: 5.
OPEN: all year except 25–26 Dec, restaurant closed Mon, Tues.
FACILITIES: bar, dining rooms, in-room TV (Freeview), dining areas wheelchair accessible.
BACKGROUND MUSIC: in restaurant.
LOCATION: in town centre.
CHILDREN: all ages 'warmly welcomed'.
DOGS: allowed in bar area of restaurant.
CREDIT CARDS: Amex, MC, Visa.
PRICES: per room B&B from £120. À la carte £49. 2-night min. stay bank holidays, summer weekends.

Prices may change – check with hotel.

SHREWSBURY Shropshire

LION AND PHEASANT

On a street of 16th- and 17th-century buildings near the English Bridge, this coaching inn has been updated with a fresh, pale grey and white New England look. 'Young, friendly staff' dish out regional real ales in the 'thrumming' bar; a fire burns in the inglenook fireplace in cooler months. On two levels, the restaurant serves Shropshire produce, uplifted by head chef Kaife O'Reilly's innovative cooking – perhaps treacle cured salmon, pickled shallots and lemongrass. Breakfasts are 'generous'. Staying guests choose bedrooms with contemporary country chic set against original dark beams; bathrooms are 'spic and span'. Some rooms also have river views. Close by are riverside walks and Tudor streetscapes.

MAP 3:B4
50 Wyle Cop
Shrewsbury SY1 1XJ
T: 01743 770345
W: lionandpheasant.co.uk

BEDROOMS: 22.
OPEN: all year except 25–26 Dec.
FACILITIES: bar, wine bar, restaurant, function room, in-room TV (Freeview), garden terrace, parking (narrow entrance).
BACKGROUND MUSIC: in public areas, occasional live music in bar.
LOCATION: in town centre.
CHILDREN: all ages welcomed.
DOGS: can stay in studios and allowed on garden terrace.
CREDIT CARDS: MC, Visa.
PRICES: per room B&B £160–£240. À la carte £45.

Prices may change – check with hotel.

NEW

SISSINGHURST Kent

SISSINGHURST CASTLE FARMHOUSE

A draw for garden-lovers, this serene Victorian farmhouse B&B is sheltered by a National Trust estate of ancient woodland, farmland and Vita Sackville-West's acclaimed gardens (tickets for Sissinghurst Castle may be purchased at the gate). Country-style bedrooms mix contemporary and period furniture; large windows look out at the estate or towards Sissinghurst Castle's Elizabethan tower. Guests are welcomed with tea and home-baked cake served in the sitting room or on the south-facing lawn. Pre-ordered farmhouse platters are available in the evening. 'Amazing' breakfasts 'power you through the day'. A game of croquet can be enjoyed in the garden, or take a walk around the estate.

MAP 2:D4
Biddenden Road
Sissinghurst
Cranbrook TN17 2AB
T: 01580 720992
W: sissinghurstcastlefarmhouse.co.uk

BEDROOMS: 9. 1 suitable for disabled.
OPEN: Feb–Dec.
FACILITIES: lift, sitting room, dining room, free Wi-Fi, in-room TV, small functions, ¾-acre garden.
BACKGROUND MUSIC: none.
LOCATION: on the National Trust estate known as Sissinghurst Castle, a mile from the centre of Sissinghurst village.
CHILDREN: children over 8 welcomed.
DOGS: not allowed.
CREDIT CARDS: MC, Visa.
PRICES: per room B&B £160–£300.

Prices may change – check with hotel.

SOMERTON Somerset
THE WHITE HART

A foodie spot in a friendly town skirting the
Somerset Levels, this updated pub-with-rooms
on the market square draws tourists and locals
with its 'good atmosphere' and 'generous'
West Country menus. The wood-floored
restaurant is bright and spacious; here, diners
tuck in to modern gastropub dishes – Somerset
Camembert, squash and chestnut pie. Cocktails,
local ciders and organic wines are quaffed in
the wood burner-warmed bar. 'Well-presented'
and individually styled bedrooms upstairs. At
breakfast: wood-roasted kippers, Old Spot
sausages are served. Part of the Stay Original
Co.; see also Timbrell's Yard, Bradford-on-Avon;
The Swan, Wedmore; and The Grosvenor Arms,
Shaftesbury (Shortlist entries).

MAP 1:C6
Market Place
Somerton TA11 7LX
T: 01458 272273
W: whitehartsomerton.com

BEDROOMS: 8.
OPEN: all year.
FACILITIES: bar, restaurant, in-room
smart TV, large courtyard garden,
bicycle storage.
BACKGROUND MUSIC: in bar.
LOCATION: in town centre.
CHILDREN: all ages welcomed.
DOGS: 'very welcome' in bedrooms,
bar, terrace and garden.
CREDIT CARDS: MC, Visa.
PRICES: per room B&B £85–£160.
Dinner, bed and breakfast £35
more than B&B includes a £55 food
allowance. Dogs £15 per stay.

Prices may change – check with hotel.

SOUTH ALKHAM Kent
ALKHAM COURT

Home-made cake is the welcome treat from
'wonderful, engaging' Wendy and Neil Burrows
at their award-winning Alkham valley farmhouse
B&B, and their warm thoughtfulness lasts for the
entire stay. Country-style bedrooms each have a
private entrance, and extras within: flowers, robes
and slippers, a coffee machine, biscuits and sherry.
Guests also have use of a spa barn with a hot tub
and sauna, and the hosts 'have a love for the area',
and can advise on things to do on the Kent Downs
and along the coast. Packed lunches and, in the
evening, soup with warm, crusty rolls can also be
provided. Breakfast wins fans with a spread of
local produce, plus home-made preserves, freshly
baked muffins and a large choice of hot dishes.

MAP 2:D5
Meggett Lane
South Alkham
Dover CT15 7DG
T: 01303 892056
W: alkhamcourt.co.uk

BEDROOMS: 4. 3 on ground floor, 1
suitable for disabled. Plus 2 vintage
shepherd's huts for self-catering.
OPEN: all year except 1 Nov–31 Jan.
FACILITIES: sitting/breakfast room,
in-room TV (Freeview), spa barn (hot
tub, sauna), large garden, 60-acre farm.
BACKGROUND MUSIC: none.
LOCATION: in a rural location near
Dover; 5 mins from M20, 10 mins
from Eurotunnel.
CHILDREN: all ages welcomed.
DOGS: allowed (not unattended) in
1 bedroom, on lead at all times outside
because of livestock.
CREDIT CARDS: Amex, MC, Visa.
PRICES: per room B&B single £85–£100,
double £140–£170. 2-night min. stay in
summer, 3-night min. stay over bank
holidays.
Prices may change – check with hotel.

SOUTH HARTING Sussex

THE WHITE HART

In a peaceful village near the South Downs Way, ramblers join locals at this dog- and family-friendly 16th-century inn. There's character in the beams and log fires of the wood- and flagstone-floored bar, a setting that's just right for the ales, wines and spirits on offer; in the walled garden, picnic tables and parasols await clement weather. Hearty meals include classic fish pie or a grilled aubergine, mushroom and chimichurri burger. In the main building and a converted barn at the rear, well-refurbished bedrooms and family suites have rustic charm in their exposed timbers, plaids and patterns; all have smart TVs, radios and coffee machines. The National Trust's Uppark House and Garden is close by.

MAP 2:E3
The Street
South Harting GU31 5QB
T: 01730 825124
W: the-whitehart.co.uk

BEDROOMS: 7. 4 in annexe.
OPEN: all year except evenings of 25 and 26 Dec, 1 Jan.
FACILITIES: bar, restaurant, snug, in-room TV, terrace, garden, parking.
BACKGROUND MUSIC: in public areas.
LOCATION: in village, 4½ miles SE of Petersfield.
CHILDREN: all ages welcomed.
DOGS: allowed in some bedrooms, bar, snug, garden.
CREDIT CARDS: Amex, MC, Visa.
PRICES: per room B&B £89–£204. À la carte £30.

Prices may change – check with hotel.

SOUTHLEIGH Devon

GLEBE HOUSE

There's a bohemian charm to Olivia and Hugo Guest's Georgian house with its colourful interiors and its smallholding and rolling Devon views. Outside are gardens, a heated pool and tennis court; inside are bold-patterned fabrics and walls, and original art. Bedrooms mix designer pieces with antiques, and overlook gardens and countryside. Most have freestanding baths; one has a wood-burner. Dinner is either a home-grown or locally sourced, one-course 'kitchen' supper or (Thursdays to Sunday lunch) an Italian-inspired menu: wild mushroom tagliatelle, perhaps. Neither offers a choice, which surprised some guests. Snacks are offered on Sundays. Breakfast has home-made pastries and granola and changing cooked options.

MAP 1:C5
Southleigh
Colyton EX24 6SD
T: 01404 871276
W: glebehousedevon.co.uk

BEDROOMS: 6. 1 in annexe.
OPEN: all year except 23 Dec–31 Jan, exclusive use over New Year. Kitchen-style supper Mon–Wed, 4-course dinner Thurs–Sun lunch.
FACILITIES: 2 sitting rooms, 4 dining areas, 15-acre grounds, heated outdoor swimming pool, tennis court, restaurant wheelchair accessible.
BACKGROUND MUSIC: in public areas.
LOCATION: 3 miles W of Colyton.
CHILDREN: all ages welcomed.
DOGS: allowed in 1 bedroom, elsewhere on lead, except in fields around house.
CREDIT CARDS: Amex, MC, Visa.
PRICES: B&B doubles from £139, singles from £118. Supper £20, 4-course fixed menu £55, Sun lunch £40. 2-night min. weekends (but check 1-night availability).

Prices may change – check with hotel.

SOUTHWOLD Suffolk

THE SWAN

Bright and jazzy, this Southwold stalwart, which has stood on the market square for centuries, has a hip, modern feel with a colourful sofa or two on stripped oak floorboards. It is owned by Adnams, and guests may tour the on-site brewery and distillery. Panelled bedrooms (some in the garden) are supplied with 'very nice touches', such as an espresso machine, good biscuits, a small bottle of gin. Pub classics mix with imaginative options in the banquette-lined Tap Room. The 'pleasantly lit' Still Room restaurant has a 'particularly smart' copper-topped bar. 'Friendly staff are found throughout.' An 'excellent' breakfast precedes a stroll to the pier. Or borrow picnic rugs and deckchairs and head for the beach.

MAP 2:B6
Market Place
Southwold IP18 6EG
T: 01502 722186
W: theswansouthwold.co.uk

BEDROOMS: 35. 12 in garden extension, 1 suitable for disabled.
OPEN: all year.
FACILITIES: 2 restaurants, lounge, private dining rooms, in-room TV, civil wedding licence, large garden, bicycle hire, EV charging, parking.
BACKGROUND MUSIC: in restaurant.
LOCATION: on market square.
CHILDREN: all ages welcomed.
DOGS: allowed in garden rooms, not in main hotel building.
CREDIT CARDS: MC, Visa.
PRICES: per room B&B double £220.50–£373.50, single from £195.50. À la carte £35. 1-night bookings generally refused in summer.

Prices may change – check with hotel.

STOW-ON-THE-WOLD Gloucestershire

THE OLD STOCKS INN

The classic Cotswold-stone exterior of this 17th-century inn reveals cool and fun interiors that successfully blend wooden beams and ancient floorboards with cocktails, Scandi-chic furnishings and a family-friendly feel. Past the board games in the bar, colourful bedrooms range from cosy doubles to spacious garden rooms that open on to a terrace, and have a coffee machine, fresh milk and local snacks. 'We like the location, the ambience, the staff and the quirky features' – exposed stone walls in one room; a private, slanted staircase in another; 'some creaks and footfalls from neighbouring rooms'. Hearty British cuisine in the restaurant includes interesting vegetarian and vegan options.

MAP 3:D6
The Square
Stow-on-the-Wold GL54 1AF
T: 01451 830666
W: oldstocksinn.com

BEDROOMS: 16. 3 in garden annexe.
OPEN: all year except 24–25 Dec, restaurant closed for lunch Mon–Fri.
FACILITIES: restaurant, bar, library, coffee shop, private dining room, in-room TV (Freeview), terrace, parking.
BACKGROUND MUSIC: in public areas.
LOCATION: in town centre.
CHILDREN: all ages welcomed.
DOGS: allowed in 3 bedrooms, bar, library, coffee shop.
CREDIT CARDS: Amex, MC, Visa.
PRICES: B&B £129–£299. À la carte £40. 1-night bookings usually refused Sat night.

Prices may change – check with hotel.

STRATFORD-UPON-AVON Warwickshire

WHITE SAILS

'Lots of little details made this an outstanding
stay.' Within a 20-minute stroll of Shakespeare's
birthplace, Tim and Denise Perkin's B&B is in a
suburban house well placed for visiting historic
cottages and theatres alike. The 'very welcoming'
hosts maintain a home-away-from-home
atmosphere, with help-yourself extras (sherry,
espresso coffee, home-made treats) in the compact
lounge, and a neat garden to sit in on warm days.
'Immaculate' bedrooms have bathrobes, a digital
radio and home-baked cake; chilled water and
fresh milk are in a silent fridge. Breakfast has
yogurt, fruit and compotes, plus home-made
granola, bread and cakes; cooked-to-order dishes
include smoked haddock with poached eggs.

MAP 3:D6
85 Evesham Road
Stratford-upon-Avon CV37 9BE
T: 01789 550469
W: white-sails.co.uk

BEDROOMS: 4.
OPEN: all year except 25 Dec, 1 Jan.
FACILITIES: lounge, dining room, in-
room TV (Freeview), garden, bicycle
storage, parking.
BACKGROUND MUSIC: in breakfast room.
LOCATION: 1 mile W of centre.
CHILDREN: not under 12.
DOGS: not allowed.
CREDIT CARDS: Amex, MC, Visa.
PRICES: per room B&B single £95–£120,
double £110–£135. 2-night min. stay
May–Sept.

Prices may change – check with hotel.

SUMMERHOUSE Co. Durham

THE RABY HUNT
RESTAURANT AND ROOMS

Past fields of grazing cows, arrive at this Grade
II listed 19th-century drover's inn, light glinting
on its strikingly modern zinc extension on sunny
days. In a rural hamlet, the small restaurant-with-
rooms is as surprising inside as out. It is owned
by James Close, a self-taught chef, who has two
Michelin stars for his innovative, global-inspired
cooking. An open-view kitchen in the restaurant
lets diners watch the drama as a busy team
prepares the tasting menu of some 15 succinctly
described courses: suckling pig, perhaps, or
halibut. A chocolate skull provides a theatrical
finish. Up close, the Kitchen Table has front-row
seats for six. Stay for breakfast: there are five
spacious, contemporary bedrooms.

MAP 4:C4
Summerhouse
Darlington DL2 3UD
T: 01325 374237
W: rabyhuntrestaurant.co.uk

BEDROOMS: 5.
OPEN: all year except Christmas, New
Year, restaurant closed Sun–Tues.
FACILITIES: restaurant, in-room TV.
BACKGROUND MUSIC: in restaurant.
LOCATION: 6 miles NW of Darlington.
CHILDREN: not under 12.
DOGS: not allowed.
CREDIT CARDS: Amex, MC, Visa.
PRICES: per room B&B £225–£275.
Tasting menu (14–18 courses) £230,
Kitchen Table menu £300.

Prices may change – check with hotel.

TAUNTON Somerset

THE CASTLE AT TAUNTON

The 150-year-old wisteria covering the facade
of this historic building with its tower and
crenellations attests to its longevity as a well-
loved hotel at the heart of the county town.
Much extended and rebuilt over the centuries
since its medieval origins, today it is run by the
third generation of the Chapman family, who
have owned it since 1950. 'Cheerful' bedrooms
and suites, some newly refurbished in a 'retro
chic' style, vary in size and shape; larger or
interconnecting rooms suit a family. In the
buzzy brasserie, menus might include Quantock
lamb, Brixham lamb or the signature home-made
fishcakes. Breakfast on home-made jams and muesli,
and 'excellent' cooked dishes such as eggs Benedict.

MAP 1:C5
Castle Green
Taunton TA1 1NF
T: 01823 272671
W: the-castle-hotel.com

BEDROOMS: 44.
OPEN: all year, except 2 weeks in Jan,
restaurant closed Sun/Mon.
FACILITIES: lift, lounge/bar, snug,
restaurant, private dining/meeting
rooms, in-room TV (Freeview), civil
wedding licence, ¼-acre garden, EV
charging, public rooms wheelchair
accessible, adapted toilet.
BACKGROUND MUSIC: 'easy listening' in
bar, restaurant.
LOCATION: in town centre.
CHILDREN: all ages welcomed.
DOGS: allowed in bedrooms, bar.
CREDIT CARDS: Amex, MC, Visa.
PRICES: B&B doubles from £150, singles
from £101. À la carte £46, set menu
2 courses £25, 3 courses £30.

Prices may change – check with hotel.

NEW

THORNHAM Norfolk

ANNA'S HOUSE

On the north Norfolk coast, Thornham's
saltmarshes and unspoiled beaches are a paradise
for birdwatchers and walkers. Every bit as
blissful, is this chic bolthole with a garden hot
tub near the town's artisan shops and restaurants.
Named after a previous resident, the house
retains the feel of a private home. Smartly styled
bedrooms, some cosy, might have extra space for
sitting or a bathroom with a deep bathtub; each
has access to a terrace. Guests help themselves to
complimentary coffee or a drink from the honesty
bar in the foyer; a discount is offered at the deli
over the road or other eateries, where breakfast
is taken. Owned by Pip and Jonathan Barber (see
also Magazine Wood, Sedgeford, Shortlist entry).

MAP 2:A5
High Street
Thornham
Hunstanton PE36 6LX
T: 01485 750707
W: annasnorfolk.co.uk

BEDROOMS: 5.
OPEN: all year except eve of 24-26 Dec.
FACILITIES: foyer with seating,
complimentary coffee, honesty bar
and wine chiller, terraces, garden.
BACKGROUND MUSIC: none.
LOCATION: in village, 4½ miles NE of
Hunstanton.
CHILDREN: all ages welcomed.
DOGS: welcomed (1 dog only) in
ground floor bedrooms.
CREDIT CARDS: MC, Visa.
PRICES: per room £119–£189. Sun-
Thurs min. stay sometimes refused.

Prices may change – check with hotel.

THORNHAM Norfolk

THE LIFEBOAT INN

Gaze out to sea and over the salt marshes from
this 16th-century beer house, which takes in the
changing landscape from its 'spectacular' location
facing the north Norfolk coast. In a white-painted
building, the family-friendly, dog-welcoming
inn has an oak-beamed bar with settles and open
fires; a relaxed restaurant serving seasonal dishes
and daily specials; a conservatory crowned by a
200-year-old vine; and up-to-date bedrooms with
views of countryside or coast. A pitch-penny slot
in a bar bench adds extra character. Sit down to
a hearty meal, or head out to Holme Dunes for
the company of migrating birds, natterjack toads
and dragonflies. Part of Agellus Hotels (see also
Tuddenham Mill, Tuddenham, main entry).

MAP 2:A5
Ship Lane
Thornham PE36 6LT
T: 01485 512236
W: lifeboatinnthornham.com

BEDROOMS: 16. 1 on ground floor, 1 in
cottage. 14 on first floor.
OPEN: all year.
FACILITIES: bar, 2 lounge areas,
conservatory, restaurant, meeting
room, private dining room, in-room
smart TV, terrace, garden, parking.
BACKGROUND MUSIC: all day in
restaurant, bar.
LOCATION: in a small coastal village,
4½ miles NE of Hunstanton.
CHILDREN: all ages welcomed.
DOGS: allowed in bedrooms, public
rooms.
CREDIT CARDS: MC, Visa.
PRICES: per room B&B £160–£240.
À la carte £28. 2-night min. stay
preferred.

Prices may change – check with hotel.

THORNTON HOUGH Merseyside

MERE BROOK HOUSE

A 'home away from home' for its many returning
guests, this B&B is run with 'thoughtful
hospitality' by Lorna Tyson and her husband,
Donald, a farmer, who are keen to treat visitors
to the bounty of their land. The Edwardian
country house is a 'peaceful haven' set within a
dell of mature trees, and has pretty bedrooms
(supplied with home-baked cake), overlooking
garden or countryside in the main building and
in a converted coach house 20 yards away. Both
buildings have their own lounge and kitchen
stocked with cheese, home-made chutneys, juice
and hot drinks. A 'generous' breakfast in the
conservatory brings more super-local treats: honey
from garden beehives, apple juice or cider from
orchard fruit.

MAP 4:E2
Thornton Common Road
Thornton Hough CH63 0LU
T: 07713 189949
W: merebrookhouse.co.uk

BEDROOMS: 8. 4 in coach house, 3 on
ground floor, 2 wheelchair accessible.
OPEN: all year, limited availability over
Christmas, New Year.
FACILITIES: 3 lounges, conservatory,
dining room, guest kitchens, in-room
TV (Freeview), wedding/function
facilities, 1-acre garden in 4-acre
grounds (paddocks).
BACKGROUND MUSIC: none.
LOCATION: centre of Wirral peninsula,
20 mins' drive from Chester and
Liverpool.
CHILDREN: all ages welcomed.
DOGS: only assistance dogs allowed.
CREDIT CARDS: MC, Visa.
PRICES: B&B £89–£139.

Prices may change – check with hotel.

TISBURY Wiltshire

THE COMPASSES INN

Welcoming and peaceful, Ben Maschler's traditional country pub-with-rooms occupies a thatched 14th-century inn, hidden down rural lanes bordered by hedgerows. Flagstone floors and ancient beams lend it much character. There are nooks and crannies, and candles lit on wooden tables; a fire burns in the inglenook fireplace when the mercury dips. Come hungry, as the locals do, for the 'exceptional' cooking: sophisticated pub standbys are ably accompanied by cocktails and local ales. Above the pub, 'simple but more than adequate' bedrooms are pleasingly pared-back; modern bath- and shower rooms are stocked with British-made toiletries. The Nadder valley's footpaths and sheep trails start from the door.

MAP 2:D1
Lower Chicksgrove
Tisbury SP3 6NB
T: 01722 714318
W: thecompassesinn.com

BEDROOMS: 4. Plus 3-bed self-catering cottage.
OPEN: all year except 25 Dec.
FACILITIES: bar, restaurant, in-room TV (Freeview), terrace, ⅓-acre garden.
BACKGROUND MUSIC: none, occasional live music events.
LOCATION: 2 miles E of Tisbury.
CHILDREN: all ages welcomed.
DOGS: allowed in bedrooms, public areas.
CREDIT CARDS: MC, Visa.
PRICES: per room B&B single from £95, double from £120. À la carte £38. 2-night min. stay bank holidays and summer weekends.

Prices may change – check with hotel.

TOPSHAM Devon

THE SALUTATION INN

In an old ship-building town on the Exe estuary, this contemporary restaurant-with-rooms is in a handsome 18th-century coaching inn with a notable porte cochère. The enterprise, including a wet fish deli, is run by chef/patron Tom Williams-Hawkes and his wife, Amelia. 'Adventurous' menus are served in the glass-covered atrium café or in the intimate restaurant. Perhaps hand-dived scallops, rhubarb, saffron and brown crab espuma; pan-roasted brill, sumach cauliflower, pomme purée, black pudding, fish red wine sauce. Clean-lined bedrooms (some snug, with a 'bijou' shower room) are modern and restrained. Guests may help themselves to drinks, snacks and continental breakfast items in a shared kitchen.

MAP 1:C5
68 Fore Street
Topsham
Exeter EX3 0HL
T: 01392 873060
W: salutationtopsham.co.uk

BEDROOMS: 6.
OPEN: all year, except 1 week in Autumn, 25–28 Dec (restaurant, café), 1–4 Jan. Restaurant and café closed Sun, Mon evenings.
FACILITIES: 2 lounges, restaurant, café, meeting/function room, in-room TV (Freeview), walled yard with seating, wet fish deli, parking.
BACKGROUND MUSIC: in public areas.
LOCATION: in town centre, 5 miles SE of Exeter.
CHILDREN: all ages welcomed.
DOGS: not allowed; in courtyard only.
CREDIT CARDS: MC, Visa.
PRICES: per room B&B single £100–£140, double £114–£228. À la carte £55. 2-night min. stay at weekends May–Sept.

Prices may change – check with hotel.

TORQUAY Devon

THE MEADFOOT BAY

A 'home-away-from-home' atmosphere is encouraged at Phil Hartnett and Vicki Osborne's stylish adults-only hotel in a Victorian villa close to the beach and South West Coast Path. Past a light-filled sitting room, graceful with its chandelier and deep sofas, 'comfortable, spotless' bedrooms and suites have teas and coffee; fresh milk and chilled water in a mini-fridge. Three rooms have a private terrace. Before dinner, sit on the front terrace with a gin mixed with botanicals from Meadfoot beach. In the brasserie, Modern British menus might include butter-roasted halibut or aged West Country beef. 'Good' cooked-to-order breakfasts follow home-made muesli and granola. It's a 15-minute downhill walk into town.

MAP 1:D5
Meadfoot Sea Road
Torquay TQ1 2LQ
T: 01803 294722
W: meadfoot.com

BEDROOMS: 14. 1 on ground floor.
OPEN: all year.
FACILITIES: lounge, bar, dining room, library, in-room TV (Freeview), terrace, parking.
BACKGROUND MUSIC: in public areas.
LOCATION: 3 mins' walk behind Meadfoot beach, 15 mins' walk from Torquay harbour.
CHILDREN: not under 15.
DOGS: allowed in 1 bedroom with own entrance, not inside main hotel.
CREDIT CARDS: Amex, MC, Visa.
PRICES: per room B&B £96.50–£352. À la carte £40. 2-night min. stay in high season and on bank holidays.

Prices may change – check with hotel.

TRESCO Isles of Scilly

THE NEW INN

Sporting a fresh new look in bedrooms and dining areas, the only pub on this family-owned, car-free island still retains its innate charm. At the heart of the community, close to the harbour, locals and visitors enjoy the all-day dining in the bar with its marine paraphernalia, more intimate Pavilion or on the terrace. Menus feature robust dishes such as island-caught lobster and ale-battered fish and chips. In the summer, there's an outdoor grill. Contemporary rustic bedrooms have tongue-and-groove panelling, bespoke wooden furniture and country colours. All have walk-in showers, robes, and home-made biscuits; two have baths and private terraces. Guests have free entry to Tresco Abbey Garden.

MAP 1: inset C1
Tresco TR24 0QQ
T: 01720 422849
W: tresco.co.uk/staying/the-new-inn

BEDROOMS: 16. Some on ground floor.
OPEN: all year, limited opening in winter months.
FACILITIES: bar, residents' lounge, restaurant, in-room TV (Freeview), pavilion, beer garden, terrace, use of nearby Tresco Island Spa facilities.
BACKGROUND MUSIC: in bar and restaurant, occasional live music events.
LOCATION: near New Grimsby harbour.
CHILDREN: all ages welcomed.
DOGS: in bar, beer garden, assistance dogs only allowed in bedrooms.
CREDIT CARDS: MC, Visa.
PRICES: B&B doubles £185–£295. À la carte £45.

Prices may change – check with hotel.

TRUSHAM Devon

THE CRIDFORD INN

Tucked away down single-track roads, this thatched and whitewashed pub with its low ceilings, slate floors and inglenook fireplaces looks to have been here forever. Mentioned in the Domesday Book, the Devon longhouse, on the edge of Dartmoor national park, has charm by the bucket-load. Owners Paul and Ness Moir ensure a welcome to all-comers – dogs, walkers, families – as well as a convivial spot for locals. There are Sunday roasts and everyday lunches and dinners (good vegetarian choices) in the bar and restaurant; alfresco meals and drinks on the suntrap terrace. Up the stairs, recently revamped bedrooms retain their sloping ceilings and exposed beams. Restorative country walks start from the door.

MAP 1:D4
Trusham
Exeter TQ13 0NR
T: 01626 853694
W: thecridfordinn.co.uk

BEDROOMS: 4. Plus two 2-bed cottages.
OPEN: all year.
FACILITIES: bar, restaurant, function room, in-room TV (Freeview), terrace, drying shed, bar and restaurant wheelchair accessible.
BACKGROUND MUSIC: 'appropriate' in pub and restaurant, occasional live music.
LOCATION: 12 miles SW of Exeter.
CHILDREN: all ages welcomed.
DOGS: allowed in 1 bedroom and cottage, bar, dog-friendly eating area.
CREDIT CARDS: MC, Visa.
PRICES: B&B doubles from £99. À la carte £30. 1-night bookings refused weekends in high season.

Prices may change – check with hotel.

TUNBRIDGE WELLS Kent

THE MOUNT EDGCUMBE

Greenery surrounds this family-run pub with a restaurant and joyful bedrooms in a Grade II listed house overlooking the Common and Mount Edgcumbe rocks. The Georgian building has been updated in contemporary style with a douse of eccentricity. Downstairs, wood floors, exposed brick and interesting curiosities surround the real-ale connoisseurs and gastropub diners in the informal, split-level restaurant; a 6th-century sandstone cave shelters a snug bar. In warm weather, parasols spring up over picnic tables on the large patio. On the top floor, bedrooms of all sizes decorated in subtle colours with eye-catching fabrics, and have antique furniture and leafy views. The town centre is a short walk away.

MAP 2:D4
The Common
Tunbridge Wells TN4 8BX
T: 01892 618854
W: themountedgcumbe.com

BEDROOMS: 6.
OPEN: all year, restaurant closed 25 Dec.
FACILITIES: bar, restaurant, cave, in-room TV (Freeview), garden.
BACKGROUND MUSIC: in bar, restaurant.
LOCATION: ½ mile from Tunbridge Wells train station.
CHILDREN: all ages welcomed.
DOGS: in bar, downstairs restaurant, garden, not in bedrooms.
CREDIT CARDS: Amex, MC, Visa.
PRICES: per room B&B £90–£230. À la carte £35–£40.

Prices may change – check with hotel.

ULVERSTON Cumbria
THE BAY HORSE

Watch the tide race in from Robert Lyons and
Lesley Wheeler's traditional pub-with-rooms
overlooking the Levens estuary – it's a thrilling
sight that harks back centuries to when the inn
was a stopover for coaches and horses before they
crossed the sands to Lancaster. The 'amiable'
place draws in birdwatchers, cyclists, dog owners,
fishermen and walkers on the Cumbria Way.
Regular visitors praise 'the friendly atmosphere,
Bob's cooking and the wonderful view of the
bay'. Homely bedrooms are supplied with board
games and books; six rooms have an estuary-view
balcony. There are casual bar meals, or candlelit
dinners in the 'airy' conservatory restaurant that
opens on to a small garden by the water's edge.

MAP 4: inset C2
Canal Foot
Ulverston LA12 9EL
T: 01229 583972
W: thebayhorsehotel.co.uk

BEDROOMS: 9.
OPEN: all year, except 24–26 Dec, first
week of Jan; restaurant closed Mon
lunchtime (light bites available).
FACILITIES: bar/lounge, conservatory
restaurant, in-room TV (Freeview),
picnic area, parking, bar and
restaurant wheelchair accessible.
BACKGROUND MUSIC: in bar, restaurant.
LOCATION: 1½ miles from town centre.
CHILDREN: not under 10.
DOGS: well-behaved dogs allowed in
bedrooms, bar area, not in restaurant.
CREDIT CARDS: Amex, MC, Visa.
PRICES: per room B&B £110–£125.
À la carte £40. 2-night min. stay on
Saturdays Easter–Sept, bank holidays.

Prices may change – check with hotel.

NEW

WARMINSTER Wiltshire
BISHOPSTROW HOTEL & SPA

Rolling countryside surrounds this Grade II
listed Georgian mansion in extensive grounds
of meadows and woodland; a tunnel leads to the
river Wylye. Part of the Kaleidoscope Collection
(see main entry for Homewood, Bath, and
Shortlist entry for The Bird, Bath), the family-
friendly hotel has a heated outdoor pool ('lovely
to swim in, even in December!'), a large hot tub
and a tennis court. Indoor types can relax by a
warming fire in a cosy lounge, or try a Rasul mud
treatment in the spa. Bedrooms, many recently
refurbished, have opulent touches, and verdant
views. They vary in size from snug spaces to
duplex suites; two suites have a hot tub. A modern
menu is served in the restaurant, where large
windows look out over the terrace and garden.

MAP 2:D1
Boreham Road
Warminster BA12 9HH
T: 01985 212312
W: bishopstrow.co.uk

BEDROOMS: 32. Some in courtyard.
OPEN: all year.
FACILITIES: bar, lounges, restaurant,
private dining room, in-room TV
(Freeview), spa (indoor and outdoor
pools, thermal suite, treatments, gym),
tennis court, 27-acre grounds.
BACKGROUND MUSIC: in public spaces.
LOCATION: 1½ miles from Warminster
railway station.
CHILDREN: all ages welcomed.
DOGS: welcomed.
CREDIT CARDS: Amex, MC, Visa.
PRICES: per room B&B from £160.
À la carte £42.

Prices may change – check with hotel.

WARTLING Sussex

WARTLING PLACE

In beautiful landscaped gardens with views to the South Downs, this Grade II listed Georgian rectory offers a tranquil retreat yet is still close to the Sussex coast, historic houses and Glyndebourne. Guests praise the thoughtful ways Rowena and Barry Gittoes ensure everyone has what they need. The drawing room is inviting with pictures, books, objets d'art and comfortable seating; bedrooms are traditional country house, two with antique four-posters. All have garden views, and nice touches such as bathrobes and DAB radios. In the garden-facing dining room, breakfast includes smoked salmon from Hastings, local sausages and eggs, and home-grown herbs. Return from a day's exploring to relax on the terrace.

MAP 2:E4
Herstmonceux
Wartling
Hailsham BN27 1RY
T: 01323 832590
W: wartlingplace.co.uk

BEDROOMS: 3. Plus 2-bed self-catering cottage, suitable for disabled.
OPEN: all year.
FACILITIES: drawing room, dining room, in-room TV (Freeview), 3-acre garden, parking.
BACKGROUND MUSIC: none.
LOCATION: 5 miles E of Hailsham.
CHILDREN: not under 12.
DOGS: not allowed.
CREDIT CARDS: Amex, MC, Visa.
PRICES: B&B doubles £150–£175, singles from £105. 2-night min. stay.

Prices may change – check with hotel.

WARWICK Warwickshire

PARK COTTAGE

By the entrance to Warwick Castle, Janet and Stuart Baldry's wonderfully wonky Grade II listed 15th-century house is festooned with hanging baskets of colourful blooms. The welcoming owners exhibit 'truly attentive care and concern' for their B&B guests. Most of the 'comfortable' bedrooms, all different, are accessed across sloping floors and up a steep, narrow staircase. One has an antique four-poster bed under original beams; two can accommodate a family. A room on the ground floor has access to the pretty patio garden, home to a 300-year-old listed yew tree. 'Splendid' breakfasts, 'expertly cooked' by the host, are served at tables set on the original sandstone floor of the former castle dairy.

MAP 3:C6
113 West Street
Warwick CV34 6AH
T: 01926 410319
W: parkcottagewarwick.co.uk

BEDROOMS: 4. 1 on ground floor. Plus 2 self-catering cottages.
OPEN: all year except Christmas, New Year.
FACILITIES: reception/sitting area, breakfast room, in-room TV (Freeview), patio, parking.
BACKGROUND MUSIC: radio at breakfast.
LOCATION: in town centre.
CHILDREN: all ages welcomed.
DOGS: allowed by prior arrangement in Potting Shed apartment, 2-night min stay (not unattended, own bed required, water bowl provided), on lead in public areas.
CREDIT CARDS: Amex, MC, Visa.
PRICES: per room B&B from £96. 1-night bookings sometimes refused.

Prices may change – check with hotel.

WATCHET Somerset

SWAIN HOUSE

In the heart of the historic harbour town that inspired poet Samuel Taylor Coleridge, Jason Robinson's chic, 'immaculate' B&B is an ideal place in which to be 'as idle as a painted ship upon a painted ocean'. Ramble along the Mineral Line or West Somerset Coast Path, or explore the heritage West Somerset Railway. Alternatively, simply cocoon yourself in one of the large, comfortable bedrooms in this refurbished 18th-century house. Each has been thoughtfully supplied with teas, coffee and fresh milk; waffle bathrobes and high-end toiletries; a freestanding slipper bath and walk-in shower. Breakfasts include a full veggie option; in the evening, a light cheese or charcuterie supper is available.

MAP 1:B5
48 Swain Street
Watchet TA23 0AG
T: 01984 631038
W: swain-house.com

BEDROOMS: 4.
OPEN: all year except Christmas, New Year.
FACILITIES: lounge/dining room, in-room TV (Freeview), public car park 20 yards away.
BACKGROUND MUSIC: none.
LOCATION: 100 yards from harbour marina.
CHILDREN: not under 12.
DOGS: not allowed.
CREDIT CARDS: Amex, MC, Visa.
PRICES: per room B&B single from £125, double from £140.

Prices may change – check with hotel.

NEW

WATH-IN-NIDDERDALE Yorkshire

THE SPORTSMAN'S ARMS

A country lane across a packhorse bridge leads to this fine-looking village inn in classic dales countryside, as popular with diners as with overnight guests. With its creeper-covered facade, smart banquettes in the bar, squashy sofas in the lounge (both with fires) and crisp napery in the restaurant, it's more hotel than pub. Run by the Carter family for over 40 years, it's dotted with fishing paraphernalia, wall-clocks and hunting prints. 'Very good' 'Yorkshire portion' dinners are proudly local – Nidderdale trout, lamb and venison; wines extensive. Bedrooms in the barn conversions are neat and modern, those in the pub more characterful. Night-time is 'so quiet', a sound sleep is guaranteed.

MAP 4:D3
Wath-in-Nidderdale
Harrogate HG3 5PP
T: 01423 711306
W: sportsmans-arms.co.uk

BEDROOMS: 11, 6 in converted outbuildings.
OPEN: all year, closed Mon/Tues.
FACILITIES: bar, restaurant, lounge, private dining room, in-room TV, patio, large lawned gardens.
BACKGROUND MUSIC: none.
LOCATION: on banks of River Nidd, 2 miles NW of Pateley Bridge.
CHILDREN: all ages welcomed (no extra beds provided).
DOGS: allowed in 2 bedrooms, bar.
CREDIT CARDS: MC, Visa.
PRICES: B&B double from £140. À la carte £37. 2-night min. stay usually required at weekends.

Prices may change – check with hotel.

WEDMORE Somerset

THE SWAN

Go where the locals go, in this lively village in the Somerset Levels: this bring-the-dog, kids-in-tow pub-with-rooms bustles with a 'lovely, informal atmosphere'. There are real ales and ciders, plus an all-day snack menu, in the bar; at lunch and dinner, perhaps eaten alfresco on the garden terrace, the menu of unfussy gastropub dishes might include such vegetarian options as spiced squash Wellington. Staying guests spend the night in one of the rustic-chic bedrooms upstairs. 'Breakfast is a real treat.' Beyond the village, walking and cycling paths reach out into lush landscapes. Part of the Stay Original Co.; see also Timbrell's Yard, Bradford-on-Avon, and The White Hart, Somerton (Shortlist entries).

MAP 1:B6
Cheddar Road
Wedmore BS28 4EQ
T: 01934 710337
W: theswanwedmore.com

BEDROOMS: 7.
OPEN: all year.
FACILITIES: bar, restaurant, in-room TV, civil wedding licence, function facilities, terrace, large garden, parking.
BACKGROUND MUSIC: in bar.
LOCATION: in village centre.
CHILDREN: all ages welcomed.
DOGS: allowed in bedrooms, public rooms.
CREDIT CARDS: MC, Visa.
PRICES: B&B £75–£195. À la carte £27.

Prices may change – check with hotel.

WESTGATE Co. Durham

WESTGATE MANOR

A haven of comfort, Kathryn and Stuart Dobson's 'thoroughly relaxing' guest house is in a Victorian manor in a small Weardale village. Huge windows in the wood burner-warmed lounge look out over the valley – spot grazing sheep, strolling pheasants, rabbits or deer. On the first floor, high-ceilinged and traditionally decorated bedrooms have mood lighting, and green views. Two rooms have a grand four-poster bed; all have underfloor heating, a walk-in shower and a roll-top bath in the bathroom. Breakfast is taken in the book-lined orangery; evening meals may be ordered in advance. The terrace is a fine spot for afternoon tea or a drink. The North Pennine hills, ancient woodland and waterfalls await.

MAP 4:B3
Westgate DL13 1JT
T: 01388 517371
W: westgatemanor.co.uk

BEDROOMS: 5.
OPEN: all year except Christmas, New Year.
FACILITIES: lounge, dining room, orangery, garden room, in-room TV (Freeview), patio, secure bicycle storage.
BACKGROUND MUSIC: in reception, dining room.
LOCATION: 25 miles W of Durham.
CHILDREN: all ages welcomed.
DOGS: not allowed.
CREDIT CARDS: Amex, MC, Visa.
PRICES: per room B&B £189–£215. À la carte £34.

Prices may change – check with hotel.

WESTLETON Suffolk

THE WESTLETON CROWN

Ramblers, twitchers and wildlife enthusiasts seek out this refreshed 12th-century coaching inn, on the edge of a common in a quiet Suffolk village. Wood fires, deep armchairs, snug corners and a dog-friendly approach create an informal atmosphere in the bar and lounge; at mealtimes, diners sit in the cosy pub parlour, conservatory or terraced courtyard for unfussy modern dishes – 'beautifully cooked fish' served by 'enthusiastic young staff'. Bedrooms, in the pub and outbuildings, are decorated in an updated rustic style; duplex rooms have bunk beds for young guests. RSPB Minsmere is a ten-minute drive away; a circular walk calls for a pit stop at sister inn The Ship at Dunwich, Dunwich (see Shortlist entry).

MAP 2:B6
The Street
Westleton
Southwold IP17 3AD
T: 01728 648777
W: westletoncrown.co.uk

BEDROOMS: 34. Most in cottages, converted stables and purpose-built blocks in grounds, 1 suitable for disabled.
OPEN: all year.
FACILITIES: bar, lounge, snug, 2 dining areas, in-room TV (Freeview), civil wedding licence, terraced garden.
BACKGROUND MUSIC: all day in dining areas.
LOCATION: in countryside, 6 miles SW of Southwold, 3 miles from Dunwich beach.
CHILDREN: all ages welcomed.
DOGS: allowed in some bedrooms, bar/lounge.
CREDIT CARDS: Amex, MC, Visa.
PRICES: per room B&B from £139.50. À la carte £42. 2-night min. stay at weekends.
Prices may change – check with hotel.

WILLIAN Hertfordshire

THE FOX AT WILLIAN

By the parish church in a quiet village mentioned in the Domesday Book, this inviting pub is a popular gathering place, liked for its 'relaxed, jolly atmosphere'. All-day refreshments, pub classics and inspired-by-the-seasons dishes, cooked by chef Piran Dewey, are served in the pared-back bar and dining room, or alfresco under heated parasols, overlooking the green. A garden bar serves draft beer, quality gins, and English sparkling wine. Overnight guests sleep in contemporary bedrooms, where rustic features mix with modern amenities (air conditioning, a rainfall shower). Dog-friendly garden rooms have outside seating. Part of Anglian Country Inns; see also The White Horse, Brancaster Staithe (main entry).

MAP 2:C4
Willian SG6 2AE
T: 01462 480233
W: foxatwillian.co.uk

BEDROOMS: 8. 5 rooms on the ground floor and 3 on the first floor.
OPEN: all year, restaurant closed Sun eve (bar food available on Sunday until 4 pm).
FACILITIES: bar (Sky TV), restaurant, conservatory, in-room TV (Freeview), 2 terraces, garden; restaurant, bar, garden bedrooms wheelchair accessible.
BACKGROUND MUSIC: in bar and restaurant.
LOCATION: in village, 2 miles S of Letchworth Garden City.
CHILDREN: all ages welcomed.
DOGS: small dogs (and cats) allowed in garden bedrooms, bar, in garden on lead.
CREDIT CARDS: Amex, MC, Visa.
PRICES: B&B £115–£165. À la carte £34.

Prices may change – check with hotel.

WOLD NEWTON Yorkshire

THE WOLD COTTAGE

This 'cottage' is in fact a handsome Georgian manor house set in landscaped gardens with peaceful views over the Yorkshire Wold. Interiors are gracious with high-ceilinged rooms, fine paintings and furnishings, yet by no means formal. Owners Katrina and Derek like guests to feel they can curl up with a book next to a log fire in the sitting room. Bedrooms, divided between the main house and a converted barn, range from traditional with antiques to more contemporary, where neutral colours are jazzed up with bright wallpaper or a bold throw. Breakfast, in the large dining room with its Georgian-red walls, includes porridge with Yorkshire whisky, smoked haddock and poached egg, plus locally made preserves.

MAP 4:D5
Wold Newton
Driffield YO25 3HL
T: 01262 470696
W: woldcottage.com

BEDROOMS: 6. 2 in converted barn, 1 on ground floor, 1 has option of self-catering apartment. 3 self-catering cottages.
OPEN: closed Dec and Jan.
FACILITIES: lounge, dining room, in-room TV (Freeview), 3-acre gardens (croquet) in 240-acre grounds (farmland, woodland), public rooms wheelchair accessible.
BACKGROUND MUSIC: occasionally.
LOCATION: just outside village.
CHILDREN: all ages welcomed, only in family room.
DOGS: not allowed.
CREDIT CARDS: MC, Visa.
PRICES: B&B single £70–£100, double £90–£165. Min. 2-night bookings.

Prices may change – check with hotel.

WOLTERTON Norfolk

THE SARACEN'S HEAD

Hidden down country lanes, Tim and Janie Elwes's inn is in 'a beautifully rural setting' yet close to the north Norfolk coast. The ivy-covered, 19th-century building was designed to mimic a Tuscan farmhouse; it has bright public spaces, cosy-making wood burners, and books and maps to browse. Simply and cheerily decorated, bedrooms have a well-supplied drinks tray, plus Norfolk toiletries; a family room comfortably accommodates four people. Beers and gins are local; so too, roast leg of Wolterton lamb or a bouillabaisse of line-caught grey mullet, pollock, Brancaster mussels on head chef Sam Rush's seasonal menus. Beaches, stately homes and day boats along the River Bure are all within reach.

MAP 2:A5
Wall Road
Wolterton
Erpingham NR11 7LZ
T: 01263 768909
W: saracenshead-norfolk.co.uk

BEDROOMS: 6.
OPEN: all year except 5 days over Christmas, 2 weeks in early Mar. Restaurant closed Sun eve–Wed lunch Nov–late Apr.
FACILITIES: lounge, bar, restaurant, in-room TV (Freeview), courtyard garden, restaurant and bar wheelchair accessible, no adapted toilet.
BACKGROUND MUSIC: in bar and dining rooms.
LOCATION: 5 miles N of Aylsham.
CHILDREN: all ages welcomed.
DOGS: allowed in bedrooms, back bar (booking required), not in restaurant.
CREDIT CARDS: MC, Visa.
PRICES: per room B&B single £75–£90, double £110–£130. À la carte £40.

Prices may change – check with hotel.

WOODCHESTER Gloucestershire

WOODCHESTER VALLEY VINEYARD

Fiona Shiner's family-owned vineyard, winery and B&B are surrounded by the green fields of the Stroud valleys. Light-filled, spacious duplex suites in a sympathetically restored barn each have a mini-kitchenette and a log burner-warmed sitting area that also has underfloor heating; a trio of private terraces takes in far-reaching views across the valley and vine-covered hills. Set off on the walking or cycling routes that wind through this part of the south Cotswolds; return for a pre-booked vineyard tour and a tasting of the award-winning wines. Breakfast hampers (charged extra) include freshly baked bread, croissants, preserves, yogurt, fruit and juice. A local caterer can provide dinner.

MAP 3:E5
Convent Lane
Woodchester
Stroud GL5 5EY
T: 07808 650883
W: woodchestervalleyvineyard.co.uk

BEDROOMS: 3. plus 2-bed farmhouse available for self-catering.
OPEN: all year.
FACILITIES: tasting room, in-room TV (Sky), 40-acre vineyard, winery (tours, tutored tastings), EV charging.
BACKGROUND MUSIC: none.
LOCATION: 3 miles from Stroud.
CHILDREN: children of any age not allowed in the vineyard barn guest suites.
DOGS: allowed only in the self-catered farmhouse.
CREDIT CARDS: Amex, MC, Visa.
PRICES: per room single £135–210, double £160–£240. Continental breakfast hamper starts at £25. 2-night min. stay at weekends.

Prices may change – check with hotel.

WORCESTER Worcestershire

THE MANOR COACH HOUSE

In a 'peaceful' rural hamlet near Worcester, Chrissie Mitchell greets guests at her well-cared-for B&B with tea and cake and a warm welcome. Set around a courtyard, 'immaculate' bedrooms with 'excellent' lighting are in converted outbuildings, each with their own entrance. Fresh milk for tea and coffee, bathrobes and toiletries are supplied. A duplex family suite (suitable for children over four because of the stairs) also has a kitchenette. For breakfast, there's fruit salad, yogurt, a selection of breads, pastries and preserves, and a full English or an omelette; special diets can be catered for. For dinner, pubs are within walking distance; the city centre and cathedral are four miles away.

MAP 3:C5
Hindlip Lane
Hindlip
Worcester WR3 8SJ
T: 01905 456457
W: manorcoachhouse.co.uk

BEDROOMS: 5. All in converted outbuildings, 3 on ground floor, plus 2 self-catering units.
OPEN: all year except Christmas.
FACILITIES: breakfast room, in-room TV (Freeview), 1-acre garden.
BACKGROUND MUSIC: none.
LOCATION: 4 miles from city centre.
CHILDREN: all ages welcomed, over 4 in duplex suite.
DOGS: not allowed.
CREDIT CARDS: MC, Visa.
PRICES: per room B&B double £75–£105, single £75–£90.

Prices may change – check with hotel.

YELVERTON Devon
CIDER HOUSE

In the sprawling grounds of the National Trust's Buckland Abbey, this handsomely decorated property is run with bonhomie by Bertie and Bryony Hancock. Once the medieval abbey's brew house – the granite supports for the old cider press are still in place – the stone-built home is a bright, birdsong-accompanied place to be. There are flowers and deep sofas in the drawing room; country-chic bedrooms have restorative views through mullioned windows. Residents receive passes for the abbey, and can explore its gardens outside public visiting times. B&B accommodation is limited as the house is also run on a self-catering basis for up to eight guests. Home-cooked meals on the Aga may be provided on request.

MAP 1:D4
Buckland Abbey
Yelverton PL20 6EZ
T: 01822 259062
W: cider-house.co.uk

BEDROOMS: 4. Plus 2 adults-only self-catering shepherd's huts.
OPEN: all year.
FACILITIES: drawing room, in-room TV (Freeview), terrace, garden, 700-acre grounds, EV charging, parking.
BACKGROUND MUSIC: none.
LOCATION: 1 mile from village, 4 miles N of Plymouth.
CHILDREN: all ages welcomed.
DOGS: not allowed.
CREDIT CARDS: MC, Visa.
PRICES: per room B&B £140–£190, from £1,468 for a self-catering midweek stay or long weekend in low season.

Prices may change – check with hotel.

YORK Yorkshire
BAR CONVENT

York's most unusual and, arguably, best-value B&B is part of England's oldest working convent, where guests can share the sisters' peaceful garden and visit their striking domed chapel. Neat bedrooms in the Grade I listed building close to the city's walls have pine furniture, light colours, fresh milk for teas and coffees, and modern, shower-only bathrooms. Cooked-to-order breakfasts, light lunches, afternoon teas and home-made cakes are served in the café and in the adjoining Victorian atrium. On warm days, the suntrap garden is ideal for alfresco dining or reading. There's a communal kitchen for DIY dinners, and York's eateries are on the doorstep. Guests receive a discount to the on-site heritage museum.

MAP 4:D4
17 Blossom Street
York YO24 1AQ
T: 01904 643238
W: bar-convent.org.uk

BEDROOMS: 20. 16 en-suite and 4 with shared bathrooms.
OPEN: all year except some days over Christmas, café closed Sun except for residents' breakfast.
FACILITIES: lift, sitting room, guest kitchen, licensed café, meeting rooms, in-room TV (Freeview), ¼-acre garden, 18th-century chapel, museum, shop.
BACKGROUND MUSIC: none.
LOCATION: 5 mins' walk from the railway station.
CHILDREN: all ages welcomed (guest kitchen, with use of washing machine for small additional charge).
DOGS: only assistance dogs allowed.
CREDIT CARDS: MC, Visa.
PRICES: B&B doubles from £109 (£76 shared bathroom), singles from £75 (£42 shared bathroom).

Prices may change – check with hotel.

ALLANTON Scottish Borders
ALLANTON INN

In a sleepy village in the Scottish Borders, Katrina and William Reynolds's 'friendly village inn' is an 'excellent-value' base for walkers, cyclists, fisherfolk and visitors in search of a rural break. Family run for more than a decade, it has 'a happy blend of modern furnishings and artwork, and the feel of a traditional country pub'. At mealtimes, expect local produce: home-baked breads and Scottish seafood platters among the 'generous portions of first-class food'. Dinner in a beer garden pod with farmland views 'is a real treat'. Up-to-date bedrooms have Scottish biscuits, Highland toiletries and information on local walks; the helpful owners have tips to share.

MAP 5:E3
Main Street
Allanton TD11 3JZ
T: 01890 818260
W: allantoninn.co.uk

BEDROOMS: 6.
OPEN: all year except for 2 weeks from Christmas Eve.
FACILITIES: bar, 2 restaurant areas, in-room TV (Freeview), wedding/function facilities, large beer garden, wooden heated pods and garden marquee restaurant in summer, bicycle storage, drying room.
BACKGROUND MUSIC: in bar, restaurant.
LOCATION: in village centre.
CHILDREN: all ages welcomed.
DOGS: allowed in some areas, by prior arrangement.
CREDIT CARDS: Amex, MC, Visa.
PRICES: per room B&B £80–£120. À la carte £30.

Prices may change – check with hotel.

APPLECROSS Highland
APPLECROSS INN

'Surely a one-off.' Judith Fish's lively hostelry in an 'enchanting village' is reached by the scenic, 'hair-raising' Bealach na Bà, a single-track road that winds across the Applecross peninsula. Low-key charm and cheer spill on to the shoreside terrace, where views stretch across the Inner Sound of Raasay. Inside, malt whiskies, Scottish gins and Applecross ale are just right for sipping by the peat fire. In the small dining room or alfresco, feast on 'excellent' seafood, perhaps prawns and king scallops, straight from the bay; in spring and summer, a food truck sells fish and chips, coffees and ice cream. The simple bedrooms have no TV, but superlative water views. Cyclists, walkers and kayakers welcomed.

MAP 5:C1
Shore Street
Applecross IV54 8LR
T: 01520 744262
W: applecrossinn.co.uk

BEDROOMS: 7. 1 on ground floor.
OPEN: all year (some exceptions over Christmas, New Year).
FACILITIES: bar, dining room, beer garden, bicycle storage, bar, dining room wheelchair accessible, adapted toilet.
BACKGROUND MUSIC: 'easy listening' and traditional Scottish in bar.
LOCATION: 85 miles W of Inverness, opposite the Isle of Skye, approx. 2 hours' drive.
CHILDREN: all ages welcomed, not in bar after 9 pm.
DOGS: allowed in bedrooms (own bedding required), in bar/dining area.
CREDIT CARDS: Amex, MC, Visa.
PRICES: per room B&B single £90–£170, double £140–£170. À la carte £45.

Prices may change – check with hotel.

BALLYGRANT Argyll and Bute
KILMENY COUNTRY HOUSE

The number of returning guests to Margaret and
Blair Rozga's whitewashed farmhouse with its
stunning views over Islay's hills and glens says all
you need to know about their warm hospitality.
At the island's heart, surrounded by green acres
of family farm, the large home is handsomely
furnished in country house style. Traditionally
decorated bedrooms have antiques, pretty
wallpapers and fabrics, and far-reaching views.
Most have separate baths, and all welcome with
home-made biscuits, fresh milk and binoculars.
Some rooms are capacious (a suite with its own
kitchen suits a family). Substantial breakfasts
include home-made bread and preserves, eggs
Florentine and smoked Argyll salmon.

MAP 5:D1
Ballygrant
Isle of Islay PA45 7QW
T: 01496 840668
W: kilmeny.co.uk

BEDROOMS: 6. 3 on ground floor.
OPEN: Mar–Oct.
FACILITIES: drawing room, dining
room, sun lounge, in-room TV
(Freeview), ½-acre garden.
BACKGROUND MUSIC: none.
LOCATION: ½ mile S of Ballygrant,
10 mins' drive to Port Askaig.
CHILDREN: not under 6.
DOGS: allowed in some bedrooms, not
in public rooms.
CREDIT CARDS: none accepted.
PRICES: B&B £140–£195, 1-night
bookings sometimes refused.

Prices may change – check with hotel.

BALQUHIDDER Stirling
MONACHYLE MHOR

In a 'beautiful' situation overlooking lochs
and hills, this remote restaurant-with-rooms is
surprisingly glamorous inside. It has a bar with
colourful Italian stools and a white lounge with
vintage chairs. Main bedrooms range from coolly
rustic with blanket throws, exposed-stone walls
and splashes of colour, to sprawling affairs with
designer lighting and an egg-shaped bath. Quirky
options in the grounds include a three-storey
'pod' in the trees, a 1950s wagon, a ferry cabin
and yurts. 'Elaborate' dishes on the three-course
menus feature local venison and produce from
their farm. Breakfast on Inverawe smoked trout
with scrambled egg, while enjoying 'stunning
views', before embarking on a wild walk down a
single-track lane skirting Loch Voil.

MAP 5:D2
Balquhidder
Lochearnhead FK19 8PQ
T: 01877 384622
W: monachylemhor.net

BEDROOMS: 18. 5 on ground floor, 11 in
courtyard, 1 in modular three-storey
'pod', 1 suitable for disabled. Plus 3
yurts and self-catering lodge, wagon,
bothy and cabin.
OPEN: all year.
FACILITIES: lounge, living room, bar,
conservatory restaurant, in-room TV,
wedding/function facilities, garden,
2,000-acre estate, EV charging, public
rooms wheelchair accessible.
BACKGROUND MUSIC: all day in public
areas.
LOCATION: 4 miles off A84.
CHILDREN: all ages welcomed, under-3s
free, extra bed from £30.
DOGS: allowed in 3 bedrooms (£10 per
stay), bar and lounge.
CREDIT CARDS: Amex, MC, Visa.
PRICES: B&B doubles £260–£370. Set
menu £75.

Prices may change – check with hotel.

BARCALDINE Argyll and Bute
ARDTORNA

By Loch Creran, Karen and Sean O'Byrne's super-modern, eco-friendly house has 'lovely views' over the water. B&B guests are welcomed with scones fresh from the oven; home-made whisky cream liqueur is further temptation. Light and bright inside, loch-view bedrooms have a vaulted ceiling and under-floor heating, a king-size bed, plus bathrobes and good toiletries. Start breakfast with a fruit smoothie in the glass-fronted dining room. Then choose among adventurous egg dishes, sweet and savoury pancakes, or a Scottish platter of sausage, bacon, egg, tomato, black pudding, haggis and hash brown. The 'very helpful' hosts assist with planning day-trips to castles and islands and the best spots for a dram.

MAP 5:D1
Mill Farm
Barcaldine
Oban PA37 1SE
T: 01631 720125
W: ardtorna.co.uk

BEDROOMS: 4. Plus self-catering accommodation in adjacent building.
OPEN: all year.
FACILITIES: sitting room, dining room, in-room TV (Freeview), outdoor hot tub (charge), 1-acre farmland.
BACKGROUND MUSIC: traditional in dining room.
LOCATION: 12 miles N of Oban.
CHILDREN: not under 12.
DOGS: not allowed.
CREDIT CARDS: MC, Visa.
PRICES: per person B&B £80–£110.

Prices may change – check with hotel.

BRUICHLADDICH Argyll and Bute
LOCH GORM HOUSE

On this southernmost island of the Inner Hebrides, florist Fiona Doyle runs her 'immaculate, beautifully furnished' B&B in a stone-built house, steps from the shores of Loch Indaal. Cosily decorated, the bedrooms have 'stunning views' over the bay or across the large garden. 'Our room had fresh flowers, an amazing selection of teas and a good shower.' 'Delicious' scones are offered on arrival; breakfasts are praised, too. 'Friendly and helpful', the hostess has a wealth of local information to share, recommending restaurants and walking routes. Wellies, coats and beach towels may be borrowed for coastal wanderings. The Bruichladdich distillery 'makes a visit a necessity'. Jura is a short ferry ride away.

MAP 5:D1
Bruichladdich
Isle of Islay PA49 7UN
T: 01496 850139
W: lochgormhouse.com

BEDROOMS: 3.
OPEN: all year.
FACILITIES: drawing room, dining room, in-room TV (Freeview), 1-acre garden, drying facilities.
BACKGROUND MUSIC: none.
LOCATION: on seafront, outside village.
CHILDREN: all ages welcomed.
DOGS: well-behaved dogs by special arrangement, not in bedrooms.
CREDIT CARDS: MC, Visa.
PRICES: per room B&B £155–£180.

Prices may change – check with hotel.

COVE Argyll and Bute

KNOCKDERRY HOUSE HOTEL

'Scottish baronial at its best: all towers and turrets', Beth and Murdo Macleod's 'very well-organised', dog-friendly hotel stands in manicured lawns by the shores of Loch Long. Within the listed building are handsome rooms with original fireplaces, wood carvings, tartan carpets and notable stained glass. Several have views over the water towards the Argyllshire hills. 'Imaginative' four-course dinners are served in the loch-facing, panelled restaurant; more informal meals may be taken in the lounge bar. There are novels and board games to entertain. Outdoor adventure is found in the Arrochar Alps and Loch Lomond & The Trossachs national park. In Helensburgh, explore Charles Rennie Mackintosh's Hill House.

MAP 5:D1
Shore Road
Cove
Helensburgh G84 0NX
T: 01436 842283
W: knockderryhouse.co.uk

BEDROOMS: 15. 4 in an integrated modern extension.
OPEN: all year except Christmas.
FACILITIES: lounge bar, 2 dining rooms, library/billiard room, in-room TV, civil wedding licence, function facilities, terrace, ½-acre garden, dining areas wheelchair accessible, private moorings.
BACKGROUND MUSIC: 'soft classical' in restaurant.
LOCATION: on a peninsula in the Firth of Clyde, 17 miles from Helensburgh.
CHILDREN: all ages welcomed.
DOGS: in 5 bedrooms, public rooms, dog-friendly dining room.
CREDIT CARDS: Amex, MC, Visa.
PRICES: per room B&B £124.50–£326.50. À la carte £45. 1-night bookings refused over New Year.

Prices may change – check with hotel.

DRUMNADROCHIT Highland

THE LOCH NESS INN

Hikers and cyclists stop for the simple comforts of this 'friendly' 160-year-old coaching inn, a 'busy and bustling' local gathering place in a village on the Great Glen Way. There are Scottish whiskies and gins, and local real ales in the bar. In the slate-floored restaurant with its wood-burning stove, classic pub dishes and smarter options are on the menu. Throughout, nature paintings add interest. Accommodation is in light and neat bedrooms made homely with wool throws and tweedy cushions, tea and coffee, Scottish toiletries; budget-friendly bunkhouse rooms overlooking the River Coiltie suit groups or a family. Hearty breakfast choices include porridge, eggs Benedict and a 'full Highland' or vegetarian.

MAP 5:C2
Lewiston
Drumnadrochit IV63 6UW
T: 01456 450991
W: staylochness.co.uk

BEDROOMS: 20. 4 in annexe, 1 on ground floor suitable for disabled, plus bunkhouse.
OPEN: all year except 25 Dec.
FACILITIES: bar, restaurant, in-room TV, wedding facilities, beer garden, public rooms wheelchair accessible.
BACKGROUND MUSIC: in bar, restaurant.
LOCATION: off the A82, in village 16 miles SW of Inverness.
CHILDREN: all ages welcomed.
DOGS: clean, well-behaved dogs allowed in 1 bedroom, bar.
CREDIT CARDS: Amex, MC, Visa.
PRICES: B&B doubles/singles from £100. À la carte £28.

Prices may change – check with hotel.

DUNNING Perth and Kinross

THE KIRKSTYLE INN & ROOMS

In a conservation village with history in its ancient stones, this popular, dog-friendly inn ticks all the boxes for a traditional pub brimming with genial hospitality. Well-worn leather armchairs, eclectic bits and pieces and a fire in the hearth are found in the stone-walled bar where drinks include the pub's own Risky Kelt beer. Modern pub favourites feature on the weekly changing menu; a blackboard lists daily specials. Next door to the pub, large and light bedrooms with vintage and contemporary furniture have modern bathrooms, some with slipper bath. Choose a continental breakfast (freshly baked croissants, muesli, yogurt, fruit) or full Scottish. The café/farm shop has sandwiches and sweet treats.

MAP 5:D2
Kirkstyle Square
Dunning PH2 0RR
T: 01764 684248
W: thekirkstyleinn.co.uk

BEDROOMS: 4. All in adjacent building.
OPEN: all year except 25–26 Dec, 1 Jan.
FACILITIES: bar, snug, lounges, dining room, Garden Larder café/farm shop, pizza bar, in-room TV (Freeview), wedding facilities, beer garden, free street parking.
BACKGROUND MUSIC: in public areas, occasional live fiddle music.
LOCATION: in village, 10 miles SW of Perth.
CHILDREN: all ages welcomed.
DOGS: 'very welcome' in all areas, not on beds.
CREDIT CARDS: Amex, MC, Visa.
PRICES: B&B £100–£155 (cooked breakfast £10 per person extra). À la carte £40.

Prices may change – check with hotel.

EDINBURGH

THE BALMORAL

This landmark Edinburgh building towering over Princes Street and Waverley Station is one of the city's grand hotels, with kilted doormen and a choice of dining, subterranean spa and legendary Palm Court tea room. Part of Rocco Forte Hotels, its elegant and uncluttered bedrooms have been designed by Olga Polizzi in soft Scottish countryside colours such as Hebridean blue and heathery purple; most overlook the city, some towards Edinburgh Castle or Arthur's Seat. All have Scottish artwork or photography, and a marble bathroom. Choose fine dining in Number One restaurant or classic French dishes in Brasserie Prince. Round off the evening in Scotch, the whisky bar. Galleries, castle and Old Town all walkable.

MAP 5:D2
1 Princes Street
Edinburgh EH2 2EQ
T: 0131 556 2414
W: roccofortehotels.com/hotels-and-resorts/the-balmoral-hotel

BEDROOMS: 187. 3 suitable for disabled.
OPEN: all year.
FACILITIES: drawing room, tea lounge, 2 bars, restaurant (closed Tues/Wed), brasserie, in-room TV (Freeview), wedding facilities, function rooms, indoor pool, spa, gym, valet parking (charge), ground floor wheelchair accessible.
BACKGROUND MUSIC: in public areas.
LOCATION: in city centre.
CHILDREN: all ages welcomed.
DOGS: allowed in bedrooms (welcome pack), public areas except where food and drink are served.
CREDIT CARDS: Amex, MC, Visa.
PRICES: B&B doubles from £403. Tasting menu £115 (restaurant), à la carte £47 (brasserie).

Prices may change – check with hotel.

EDINBURGH
BARONY HOUSE

The Arts and Crafts movement is lovingly nurtured in this restored Victorian terraced house in a conservation area. Run as a B&B by Brisbane natives Susan and Paul Johnson, the hostess, who is an artist and a descendant of John Ruskin, has painted decorative friezes in the elegant, high-ceilinged bedrooms; William Morris fabrics adorn eye-catching oversized headboards. Down stone steps, a separate entrance leads to two rooms (one with a private garden) that share a lounge and a kitchen. A lounge upstairs has a bar and hot drinks. Served on linen-dressed tables, breakfast includes home-baked bread, fruit and Aussie pikelets. Hosts have a wealth of local information; buses and taxis connect to the city centre.

MAP 5:D2
20 Mayfield Gardens
Edinburgh EH9 2BZ
T: 0131 662 9938
W: baronyhouse.co.uk

BEDROOMS: 6. 2 in 'Servants' Quarters' with shared lounge and kitchen.
OPEN: all year except 1 week over Christmas; open for Hogmanay.
FACILITIES: 2 honesty bars, dining room, in-room TV (Freeview).
BACKGROUND MUSIC: classical in public rooms.
LOCATION: in Mayfield, 20 mins' walk from city centre; buses and taxis available.
CHILDREN: not under 10.
DOGS: not allowed.
CREDIT CARDS: MC, Visa.
PRICES: per room B&B £119–£200. 3-night stays preferred in summer.

Prices may change – check with hotel.

NEW

EDINBURGH
THE BONHAM

In one of the New Town's elegant terraces, within ten minutes of Princes Street yet 'sufficiently quiet for a good night's sleep', the stylish Bonham is hidden within three Victorian town houses. Interiors are bold and colourful with velvet-upholstered chairs and wood panelling in the lounge, glittering wallpaper in the bar and chandeliers in the dining room, with a striking art collection throughout. At weekends, dine on brasserie dishes such as chicken with wild garlic pesto, or smoked salmon fishcakes. 'Surprisingly large', 'very well-appointed bedrooms' are elegant with muted colours and smart fabrics; all have fresh milk and shortbread; many have views to the street's gardens or Firth of Forth.

MAP 5:D2
35 Drumsheugh Gardens
Edinburgh EH3 7RN
T: 0131 226 6050
W: thebonham.com

BEDROOMS: 49. 6 on ground floor, 1 suitable for disabled.
OPEN: all year, restaurant only Fri/Sat eve and Fri/Sat/Sun lunch.
FACILITIES: lift, reception lounge, bar, restaurant, in-room TV (Freeview), conference/wedding facilities, secure car park (charge), public rooms wheelchair accessible.
BACKGROUND MUSIC: in public areas.
LOCATION: West End.
CHILDREN: all ages welcomed.
DOGS: not allowed.
CREDIT CARDS: Amex, MC, Visa.
PRICES: B&B doubles from £223. À la carte £35. 1-night bookings sometimes refused.

Prices may change – check with hotel.

EDINBURGH
THE DUNSTANE HOUSES

The epitome of tweed chic, two handsomely
refurbished Victorian villas – Dunstane House,
and Hampton House, opposite – make up one
smart hotel, in a peaceful area just beyond the
city centre. From 'cosy wee singles and doubles'
to luxurious, high-ceilinged suites, bedrooms
(some dog friendly) are kitted out in heather-
toned heritage style and supplied with Scottish
bath products and home-made shortbread. In
Ba' bar, find monochrome photographs and a
wide selection of rare and vintage craft spirits;
in the clubby lounge, velvet armchairs and sofas.
Modern Scottish dishes, including promising
vegan and vegetarian options, are available all day.
Buses to the centre and the airport stop outside.

MAP 5:D2
4 West Coates
Edinburgh EH12 5JQ
T: 0131 337 6169
W: thedunstane.com

BEDROOMS: 35. 18 in Hampton House,
opposite.
OPEN: all year.
FACILITIES: lounge/bar, conservatory,
residents' lounge and breakfast
room in Hampton House, in-room
smart TV, wedding facilities, garden,
parking.
BACKGROUND MUSIC: in bar, lounge.
LOCATION: in Murrayfield, just W of
city centre.
CHILDREN: all ages welcomed.
DOGS: allowed in some bedrooms (not
unattended), conservatory, garden.
CREDIT CARDS: Amex, MC, Visa.
PRICES: per room B&B single
£149–£395, double £184–£790.
Prix fixe menu £32 (2 courses), £36
(3 courses). 2-night min. stay preferred
Sat in peak season.

Prices may change – check with hotel.

EDINBURGH
FINGAL

In shipshape order, this luxury floating hotel
aboard a revamped former Northern Lighthouse
supply ship is berthed in a working dock in
Edinburgh's trendy Leith district. Once serving
Scottish islands, the now-luxury liner serves
up cocktails and refined dining before rocking
guests to sleep in decadent berths. All curving
wood, thick carpets and glossy brass, the Art
Deco interiors glamorously gleam. Porthole-lined
cabins have a huge bed draped in a custom-woven
throw; bathrobes, a rain shower, under-floor
heating. First-class cabins open on to the deck;
those on the starboard have the best views. At
breakfast, haggis and black pudding complete the
full Scottish.

MAP 5:D2
Alexandra Dock
Leith
Edinburgh EH6 7DX
T: 0131 357 5000
W: fingal.co.uk

BEDROOMS: 23.
OPEN: all year except 25 Dec.
FACILITIES: bar, restaurant, in-room
TV, deck, parking.
BACKGROUND MUSIC: none.
LOCATION: berthed at the port of Leith.
CHILDREN: all ages welcomed.
DOGS: not allowed.
CREDIT CARDS: Amex, MC, Visa.
PRICES: per room B&B £300–£1,200.
À la carte £50.

Prices may change – check with hotel.

ELGOL Highland
CORUISK HOUSE

A scenic, single-track road in a remote part of the
island leads to Clare Winskill and Iain Roden's
romantic restaurant-with-rooms, where guests
are welcomed with a glass of sparkling wine.
The original Skye 'black house' has quaintly low
ceilings, a stone-walled snug and a conservatory
dining room with views towards mountains and
the islands of Rum and Eigg. Modern-rustic
bedrooms and suites are upstairs and in the house
next door. A four-course set menu of flavoursome,
island ingredient-led cooking is served at 7 pm.
Dishes might include lobster bisque or venison
fillet, and ice creams made with herbs and fruit.
After a fortifying breakfast, set off on a walk or
take a dip in a wild swimming cove nearby.

MAP 5:C1
Elgol
Isle of Skye IV49 9BL
T: 01471 866330
w: coruiskhouse.com

BEDROOMS: 5. 2 suites (one with 2
bedrooms) in The Steading, next door.
OPEN: Mar–end Oct. Open for private
dining for 4 or more, Nov–15 Dec,
15 Jan–end Feb.
FACILITIES: sitting room/snug, 2 dining
rooms (1 conservatory), in-room
TV (Freeview) in 2 suites, humanist
wedding facilities, front lawn,
restaurant wheelchair accessible.
BACKGROUND MUSIC: none.
LOCATION: ½ mile NE of Elgol,
22 miles SW of Kyle of Lochalsh.
CHILDREN: not under 14.
DOGS: well-behaved dogs allowed in
hall of 1 suite; on lead outside.
CREDIT CARDS: MC, Visa.
PRICES: per room B&B £160–£450,
4-course set menu £65.

Prices may change – check with hotel.

GLASGOW
CATHEDRAL HOUSE

This fine baronial house, opposite the Necropolis,
and with the cathedral as a backdrop, was built
in 1896 as a halfway hostel for female prisoners
and is now a comfortable B&B. The owners,
Shane and Laura McKenzie, have refurbished the
interior with a streamlined, contemporary look. A
spiral staircase leads to plainly styled bedrooms in
well-considered colours and different sizes. Grand
rooms are the most spacious and have inspiring
cathedral views; all rooms have crisp white linen
on a handmade bed, and a well-stocked tea tray
with Tunnock's biscuits. Downstairs, under
separate management, Celentano's restaurant
serves Italian-inspired food in an impressive split-
level dining room, or alfresco in the garden.

MAP 5:D2
28-32 Cathedral Square
Glasgow G4 0XA
T: 0141 552 3519
w: cathedralhouseglasgow.com

BEDROOMS: 8.
OPEN: all year, except over Christmas.
Restaurant closed Mon, Tues.
FACILITIES: bar, restaurant, in-room
TV, covered heated area in garden.
BACKGROUND MUSIC: in public areas.
LOCATION: opposite the Necropolis.
CHILDREN: all ages welcomed.
DOGS: not allowed.
CREDIT CARDS: MC, Visa.
PRICES: per room B&B £85–£150.
À la carte £40.

Prices may change – check with hotel.

GLASGOW
15GLASGOW

Opposite private gardens, Lorraine Gibson's
'guest-centred' B&B occupies an 'elegant' 19th-
century terrace house close to Kelvingrove Park.
Original fireplaces, sash windows and intricate
cornicing in the former merchants' home are
complemented by well-considered modern decor.
Spacious, high-ceilinged bedrooms have a large
bed, mood lighting and a Scottish cast; from two
vast suites, huge windows overlook gardens front
or rear. Ordered the night before, breakfast is
eaten in the room, or communally in the lounge.
Expect freshly squeezed orange juice, a fruit salad
'bursting with variety', a 'piping hot' full Scottish
– 'all first class'. Museums are within walking
distance; recommended eateries are close.

MAP 5:D2
15 Woodside Place
Glasgow G3 7QL
T: 0141 332 1263
W: 15glasgow.com

BEDROOMS: 5.
OPEN: all year.
FACILITIES: lounge, in-room TV
(Freeview), small garden, limited
parking.
BACKGROUND MUSIC: none.
LOCATION: between town centre and
West End.
CHILDREN: not under 6.
DOGS: allowed in bedrooms, not in
public rooms.
CREDIT CARDS: MC, Visa.
PRICES: per room B&B £145–£170.

Prices may change – check with hotel.

GLENEGEDALE
GLENEGEDALE HOUSE

Graeme and Emma Clark's hospitable guest
house on the Isle of Islay basks in uninterrupted
views over the Mull of Oa; guests often bask in
the comfort – and indulgent treats – the hosts
provide. Handsome bedrooms with tweedy
touches are stocked with spoiling extras (Scottish-
blended teas, Highland chocolates); a residents'
bar holds Islay malts and Scottish gins. In the
evening, a platter of charcuterie, cheese or local
seafood with home-baked bread and oatcakes is
available for the asking. Breakfast, and its whisky-
laced porridge, wins awards. The consummate
hosts have local knowledge to share, perhaps over
a dram by the peat fire. Close to the island's small
airfield; ferry terminals are a short drive.

MAP 5:D1
Glenegedale
Isle of Islay PA42 7AS
T: 01496 300400
W: glenegedalehouse.co.uk

BEDROOMS: 4. 1 on ground floor, plus
4-bed self-catering house.
OPEN: all year except Christmas and
New Year. No meals on Sunday
evenings.
FACILITIES: bar, morning room,
drawing room, dining room, music
room, in-room TV (Freeview),
wedding facilities, garden, public
rooms wheelchair accessible.
BACKGROUND MUSIC: classical, jazz and
instrumental music, 'played very low',
in dining room.
LOCATION: 4 miles from Port Ellen,
6 miles from Bowmore.
CHILDREN: not under 12.
DOGS: not allowed.
CREDIT CARDS: Amex, MC, Visa.
PRICES: B&B £160–£210. À la carte £45.

Prices may change – check with hotel.

GLENFINNAN Highland
THE PRINCE'S HOUSE

Close to Loch Shiel, this old coaching inn has welcomed travellers along the Road to the Isles since the 17th century. Today it is a welcoming small hotel run by 'friendly, attentive' hosts Ina and Kieron Kelly. Traditionally decorated bedrooms are on the first floor, under sloping ceilings. The best, with a Jacobean four-poster bed, is equipped with bathrobes, flowers and a decanter of whisky mac. Book ahead to dine on Kieron's six-course tasting menu in the panelled restaurant: his well-regarded dishes highlight locally sourced ingredients such as fish and shellfish from the boats at Mallaig, and beef from Highland butchers. Simpler fare is found in the Stage House bistro. The ferry to Skye is close by.

MAP 5:C1
Glenfinnan
Fort William PH37 4LT
T: 01397 722246
W: glenfinnan.co.uk

BEDROOMS: 9.
OPEN: mid-Mar–end Oct, restaurant open Easter–end Sept, except Sun, Mon.
FACILITIES: restaurant, bistro/bar, in-room TV (Freeview), small front lawn.
BACKGROUND MUSIC: in bar, bistro.
LOCATION: 17 miles NW of Fort William.
CHILDREN: all ages welcomed.
DOGS: not allowed.
CREDIT CARDS: Amex, MC, Visa.
PRICES: per room B&B single £95–£150, double £175–£295. 6-course set menu (restaurant) £75, à la carte (bistro) £40.

Prices may change – check with hotel.

INNERLEITHEN Scottish Borders
CADDON VIEW

'An excellent base for exploring the lowlands', Lisa and Steve Davies's 'great-value' Victorian guest house is in a small town surrounded by 'beautiful rolling countryside'. Guests, including many returnees, laud the friendly welcome and home-baked treats. 'Clean, pleasant and comfortable', bedrooms have a simple country air, a modern bathroom and all the amenities (tea- and coffee-making facilities, fresh milk, a radio/alarm clock); secondary glazing reduces traffic noise. There are 'lovely' walks nearby. The hosts provide books, board games, and a blazing fire in the drawing room. Seasonal Scottish dishes are served at dinner in the conservatory café several nights a week; breakfast is 'beautiful'.

MAP 5:E2
14 Pirn Road
Innerleithen EH44 6HH
T: 01896 830208
W: caddonview.co.uk

BEDROOMS: 8.
OPEN: all year except Christmas and New Year, café closed Mon, Tues, Sun evenings, dinner available at or before 7 pm Wed–Sat, reservations essential.
FACILITIES: snug bar, drawing room, breakfast room, café/bistro, in-room TV (Freeview), ½-acre garden, bicycles/fishing gear storage, parking.
BACKGROUND MUSIC: local radio in café, 'a CD at night if desired'.
LOCATION: 400 yds from town centre.
CHILDREN: well-behaved children of all ages welcomed.
DOGS: allowed in 1 bedroom, drawing room, café, bar, not in breakfast room.
CREDIT CARDS: MC, Visa.
PRICES: per room B&B £60–£135. Set menus £28. 1-night bookings refused weekends in peak season.

Prices may change – check with hotel.

NEW

INVERKEILOR Angus

GORDON'S

In a tiny village close to the North Sea coast, Maria Watson and her son, Garry, combine gracious hospitality with 'outstanding' cooking at their restaurant-with-rooms. Their Victorian terrace house has an intimate dining room with stone walls and a wood-burning stove, and five comfortable, modern bedrooms, each with its own emphatic style. Thistle has Timorous Beasties' Grand Thistle wallpaper, a roll-top bath and separate shower. A spacious suite in the annexe has ground-floor access. Garry's well-regarded tasting menus make use of Scotland's abundant larder, and might include Shetland turbot, and rib cap of Aberdeen Angus beef. In the vicinity, discover castles, a distillery, beaches and wildlife.

MAP 5:D3
Main Road
Inverkeilor DD11 5RN
T: 01241 830364
W: gordonsrestaurant.co.uk

BEDROOMS: 5. 1 on ground floor in courtyard annexe.
OPEN: all year (incl. 25 and 31 Dec), closed Jan, Mon and Tues in summer, Sun–Tues 31 Oct–31 Mar.
FACILITIES: lounge, restaurant, in-room TV (terrestrial), small garden and patio, only restaurant wheelchair accessible.
BACKGROUND MUSIC: in restaurant.
LOCATION: in hamlet, 6 miles NE of Arbroath.
CHILDREN: over-12s welcomed (no family rooms).
DOGS: not allowed.
CREDIT CARDS: MC, Visa.
PRICES: per room B&B £110–£165. 7-course tasting menu £80.

Prices may change – check with hotel.

INVERNESS Highland

BUNCHREW HOUSE

On the tranquil shore of the Beauly Firth, this traditional country house, in part dating to the 17th century, stands in gardens and woodland laced with paths. Rooms have period details of wood-panelling and carved fireplaces; sink into sofas in the fire-warmed drawing room, or enjoy a fine malt whisky in the clubby bar. The restaurant, with its sea views, offers 'very good' Scottish dishes that might include salmon, venison, wild mushrooms and samphire; the wine list is 'comprehensive and reasonably priced'. 'Stylish and welcoming' bedrooms are comfortably traditional, with views over garden or lake. Breakfast on a Scottish grill or pancakes with maple-glazed bacon before a walk to try and spot brown hares and roe deer.

MAP 5:C2
Bunchrew
Inverness IV3 8TA
T: 01463 234917
W: bunchrewhousehotel.com

BEDROOMS: 16. 1 on ground floor.
OPEN: all year except mid-Jan.
FACILITIES: bar, drawing room, restaurant, private dining room, civil wedding licence, in-room TV (Freeview), terrace, garden, woodlands, EV charging, public areas wheelchair accessible.
BACKGROUND MUSIC: in public areas.
LOCATION: on the A862 Beauly/ Dingwall road, 3 miles from Inverness city centre.
CHILDREN: all ages welcomed.
DOGS: allowed in bar, not in restaurant.
CREDIT CARDS: Amex, MC, Visa.
PRICES: B&B £95–£395. Set-price dinner £45 (2 courses), £55 (3 courses).

Prices may change – check with hotel.

KELSO Scottish Borders

THE OLD PRIORY BED AND BREAKFAST

This classic Georgian house, overlooking Kelso's cobbled market square, surprises with its peaceful rear walled garden adjacent to the old parish church. The Girdwoods' family home, it is run as a comfortable and spacious B&B with traditionally furnished bedrooms of antiques, thick curtains and colourful bedspreads. Most rooms overlook the pretty walled garden; a suite with a separate twin-bedded room is ideal for a family. Breakfast, in the light-filled, wood-floored dining room, has a wide range of cooked choices and includes vegetarian options. The hosts have good local knowledge, and there's a light-filled conservatory as well as the garden for relaxing. Kelso Abbey and many restaurants are a stroll away.

MAP 5:E3
33/35 Woodmarket
Kelso TD5 7AT
T: 01573 223030
w: theoldpriorykelso.com

BEDROOMS: 5. 2 on ground floor.
OPEN: Feb–Dec, New Year.
FACILITIES: dining room, conservatory/ sitting room, in-room TV (Freeview), garden, parking.
BACKGROUND MUSIC: none.
LOCATION: in town centre.
CHILDREN: all ages welcomed (in family room).
DOGS: allowed in 1 bedroom (resident dogs).
CREDIT CARDS: not accepted.
PRICES: B&B £90–£125, singles from £82.

Prices may change – check with hotel.

KINLOCH RANNOCH Perth and Kinross

DUNALASTAIR HOTEL SUITES

Against the wildly beautiful forest and mountain scenery around remote Loch Rannoch in the Scottish Highlands, this Victorian hotel brings a surprising cocoon of modern, understated luxury. A stroll from the loch shores, in the centre of a stone-built village, this is a place for outdoor adventurers – hiking, cycling, bird-watching – who like their creature comforts. Lounge and dining rooms are calm, contemporary spaces of natural materials and tawny tones. Sleek bedrooms, in restful whites, greys and inky blues – many with mini-kitchens – have modern bathrooms. All have robes, fresh milk and home-made cookies. Enjoy fine dining menus in the Library or well-crafted Modern Scottish dishes in Monadh.

MAP 5:C2
1 The Square
Kinloch Rannoch PH16 5PW
T: 01882 580444
w: dunalastairhotel.com

BEDROOMS: 32. 2 suitable for disabled.
OPEN: all year. Library restaurant temporarily closed at time of writing (Monadh restaurant open).
FACILITIES: lounge, 2 restaurants, in-room TV, wedding/function facilities, courtyard, EV charging, brasserie and lounge wheelchair accessible.
BACKGROUND MUSIC: in public rooms.
LOCATION: in village at E end of Loch Rannoch.
CHILDREN: all ages welcomed.
DOGS: not allowed.
CREDIT CARDS: Amex, MC, Visa.
PRICES: B&B doubles from £170 (continental), £189 (cooked breakfast). À la carte (Monadh) £53, 7-course tasting menu (Library) £69.95. 2-night min. stay at bank holiday weekends.

Prices may change – check with hotel.

LASSWADE Midlothian

MELVILLE CASTLE

Lush greenery along a sweeping tree-lined drive 'soothes the soul' as towers and crenellations of an 18th-century castle come into view. Inside, guests are beguiled by the sweet smell of wood smoke from an open hearth, and the 'disciplined informality' of welcoming, 'guest-centred' staff. Decorated with richly patterned wallpaper and fabrics, bedrooms are embellished with ornate beds, table lamps and mirrors. For afternoon tea, there are three tiers of sweet and savoury treats. Dinner is taken in the 'graceful' ballroom, or at candlelit tables in the vaulted cellars. South of the Edinburgh city bypass, in acres of park and woodland, the castle is a popular venue for weddings. Part of the Original Collection.

NEW

MAP 5:D2
Gilmerton Road
Lasswade
Edinburgh EH18 1AP
T: 0131 654 0088
W: melvillecastle.com

BEDROOMS: 33. 1 wheelchair accessible.
OPEN: all year.
FACILITIES: lift, bar, lounge, 2 restaurants, in-room TV, garden, 54-acre grounds, parking.
BACKGROUND MUSIC: none.
LOCATION: on an estate, 3 miles from Arthur's Seat.
CHILDREN: all ages welcomed.
DOGS: welcomed in some bedrooms, public areas, not in restaurant.
CREDIT CARDS: MC, Visa.
PRICES: per room B&B £99–£600. À la carte £35.

Prices may change – check with hotel.

MELROSE Scottish Borders

BURT'S

The whitewashed 18th-century building with its distinctive black window mouldings has long been a popular landmark of this pretty Borders town. Run by the Henderson family, Burt's is popular with locals and visitors alike. Neat bedrooms are decorated in soothing shades with bright pops of colour and tweedy accents; each room has tea- and coffee-making facilities and Scottish toiletries. Dine either on bistro and lighter dishes in the bar, or smarter options, such as lamb rump with barley risotto and roast fennel, in the restaurant. A sustaining breakfast supports the next day's activities: golfing, walking, fishing on the River Tweed, or exploring Melrose. The Hendersons also own The Townhouse opposite.

MAP 5:E3
Market Square
Melrose TD6 9PL
T: 01896 822285
W: burtshotel.co.uk

BEDROOMS: 20.
OPEN: all year, no accommodation 24–26 Dec.
FACILITIES: lobby lounge, residents' lounge, bistro bar, restaurant, private dining room, in-room TV (Freeview), wedding facilities, function facilities, ½-acre garden, EV charging, parking.
BACKGROUND MUSIC: in public areas.
LOCATION: in town centre.
CHILDREN: all ages welcomed, not under 8 in restaurant.
DOGS: allowed in some bedrooms (welcome package), bistro bar, not in restaurant.
CREDIT CARDS: Amex, MC, Visa.
PRICES: B&B doubles from £148, singles from £79. À la carte £30 (bistro), £45 (restaurant).

Prices may change – check with hotel.

MOFFAT Dumfries and Galloway

HARTFELL HOUSE & THE LIMETREE RESTAURANT

Robert and Mhairi Ash offer 'very good-value' accommodation, deemed 'excellent' all round, in their 'lovely' 1850s Gothic Revival house, in a conservation town popular for outdoor activities. A highlight here is the Michelin-rated Limetree restaurant (Tues–Sat, booking essential), where chef Matt Seddon cooks 'thoroughly enjoyable' Modern Scottish dishes. Vegetarian and other diets are well catered for, with advance notice. 'Well-appointed and comfortable', the traditionally furnished bedrooms have tea- and coffee-making facilities and Scottish toiletries. Some rooms are snug; others accommodate a family. Easy access to the M74; the Southern Upland Way passes nearby.

MAP 5:E2
Hartfell Crescent
Moffat DG10 9AL
T: 01683 220153
w: hartfellhouse.co.uk

BEDROOMS: 7. Plus self-catering cottage in the grounds.
OPEN: all year, except Mon, restaurant closed Apr–Oct, Sun, Mon.
FACILITIES: lounge, restaurant, in-room TV (Freeview), garden, cooking classes, bicycle storage, parking.
BACKGROUND MUSIC: in restaurant.
LOCATION: 5 mins' walk from town centre.
CHILDREN: all ages welcomed.
DOGS: not allowed.
CREDIT CARDS: MC, Visa.
PRICES: per room B&B single £60–£90, double £90–£100. Set menu £29 (2 courses), £36 (3 courses).

Prices may change – check with hotel.

NAIRN Highland

SUNNY BRAE

Within easy reach of dolphins, dunes and whisky distilleries, John Bochel and Rachel Philipsen's 'good-value' B&B stands before 'the panorama of the sea' on the Moray coast. There's 'a domestic feel' at this house across the road from the beach: books are available for borrowing; the pretty suntrap gardens have plentiful seating. 'Airy, comfortable' bedrooms, some with views over the Moray Firth, are supplied with bathrobes and a hospitality tray. Local produce features in the 'very good' breakfast, with sausages from the town butcher and seasonal fruit from a farm shop; vegetarian and vegan diets are happily catered for. 'Friendly and personable', the hosts have a wealth of local information to share.

MAP 5:C2
Marine Road
Nairn IV12 4EA
T: 01667 452309
w: sunnybraenairn.co.uk

BEDROOMS: 8. 1 suitable for disabled.
OPEN: Mar–end Oct.
FACILITIES: lounge, dining room, in-room TV (Freeview), terrace, front and rear gardens, parking, electric vehicle charging.
BACKGROUND MUSIC: none.
LOCATION: 5 mins' walk from town centre, 2 mins from beach.
CHILDREN: all ages welcomed.
DOGS: only guide dogs allowed.
CREDIT CARDS: MC, Visa.
PRICES: per room B&B £85–£145. À la carte £35.

Prices may change – check with hotel.

PEEBLES Scottish Borders
THE TONTINE

In a busy, arty town on the River Tweed, Kate and Gordon Innes's comfortable hotel is liked for its 'friendly atmosphere'. Locals and tourists pop in for afternoon teas and evening cocktails; at weekends, ramblers, keen cyclists and golfers gather over real ales beside the open fire in the lounge. A drying room deals with wet clothing. Informal bistro food includes Border lamb casserole or pie of the day. Seasonal menus are served in the 'beautiful' high-ceilinged, chandelier-lit restaurant. Bedrooms are spread between the main 19th-century building and a more modern annexe (connected by a glass-sided corridor); dogs in annexe rooms have a blanket, bowl and treat. Maps point the way to rural walks.

MAP 5:E2
High Street
Peebles EH45 8AJ
T: 01721 720892
W: tontinehotel.com

BEDROOMS: 36. 20 in Riverside Lodge annexe.
OPEN: all year.
FACILITIES: lift, bar, lounge, bistro, restaurant, private dining/meeting room, in-room TV (Freeview), wedding facilities, 2 garden areas, drying room, secure bicycle storage, parking, all public rooms wheelchair accessible.
BACKGROUND MUSIC: in public areas.
LOCATION: in town centre.
CHILDREN: all ages welcomed.
DOGS: allowed in 10 annexe bedrooms, bar, bistro, garden.
CREDIT CARDS: MC, Visa.
PRICES: per room B&B £130–£160. À la carte from £25.

Prices may change – check with hotel.

PITLOCHRY Perth and Kinross
CRAIGATIN HOUSE AND COURTYARD

Pheasants wander the enclosed gardens and woodland of this stone-built Victorian house, within easy walking distance of the town. Once the home of a respected community doctor, it is now owned and amiably run as a modern B&B by Lynne Fordyce and John Watters, and has bright rooms and a lofty, glass-fronted extension facing the neat lawn. In the main house and converted stables, contemporary bedrooms are thoughtfully supplied with hot drinks, bottles of water and locally made biscuits. A log-burning stove warms the spacious lounge. The Scottish breakfasts offer plenty of choice: home-made compotes and Perthshire honey, whisky and cream porridge, omelettes and apple pancakes.

MAP 5:D2
165 Atholl Road
Pitlochry PH16 5QL
T: 01796 472478
W: craigatinhouse.co.uk

BEDROOMS: 14. 7 in courtyard, 2 on ground floor, 1 suitable for disabled.
OPEN: Feb–end Oct, New Year.
FACILITIES: lounge, 2 breakfast rooms, in-room TV (Freeview), 2-acre garden, parking, lounge/breakfast room wheelchair accessible.
BACKGROUND MUSIC: in lounge, breakfast rooms.
LOCATION: 10 mins' walk to town centre.
CHILDREN: not under 14.
DOGS: not allowed.
CREDIT CARDS: Amex, MC, Visa.
PRICES: per room B&B single £105–£135, double £115–£145. 1-night bookings sometimes refused Sat.

Prices may change – check with hotel.

PITLOCHRY Perth and Kinross

PINE TREES HOTEL

A private drive winds through wooded grounds to this stately Victorian mansion which feels deep in the country, yet Pitlochry town centre is only a ten-minute walk. Full of old-world charm, it features oriental carpets, deep armchairs, single malt whiskies and a judicious use of tartan. An impressive wood-and-wrought iron staircase leads to bedrooms both traditional and more contemporary in style. Ground-floor rooms are in a converted coach house and annexe nearby. In the garden-facing restaurant, hearty dishes use Scottish produce, perhaps local lamb with wild mushroom polenta cake, and poached salmon with mussels. Roe deer and red squirrels are often spotted; fishing, golf and hill walking are close by.

MAP 5:D2
Strathview Terrace
Pitlochry PH16 5QR
T: 01796 472121
w: pinetreeshotel.co.uk

BEDROOMS: 32. 7 on ground floor, 6 in coach house, 3 ground floor rooms in annexe plus 2-bed apartment above, 1 self-contained cottage.
OPEN: all year.
FACILITIES: bar, 2 lounges, restaurant, in-room TV (Freeview), 7-acre grounds, restaurant wheelchair accessible.
BACKGROUND MUSIC: in bar, restaurant.
LOCATION: ¼ mile N of town centre.
CHILDREN: all ages welcomed, children's menu.
DOGS: well-behaved dogs allowed in bedrooms, 1 lounge.
CREDIT CARDS: Amex, MC, Visa.
PRICES: B&B doubles from £149, singles from £99. Set price à la carte 2 courses £48.50, 3 courses £55 (£49 for 3 courses if booked in advance).

Prices may change – check with hotel.

NEW

PORTREE Highland

CUILLIN HILLS HOTEL

Arguably, this former Victorian shooting lodge has the best location in Portree with views over the bay and Sound of Raasay and to the Cuillin mountains. Screened by mature grounds, it feels secluded yet is only a ten-minute walk from the centre. The hotel has been run by the Wickman family for 25 years, and the 'hands-on management really shows', with luggage whisked to rooms and staff who 'take a pride in their work'. After a day's exploring, relax in the warmly coloured lounge with chesterfields and log fire before an 'excellent' dinner of Scottish classics such as Skye mussels followed by roast venison, rounded off with one of over 130 whiskies. Smart contemporary rooms include fruit and local shortbread; many have sea views.

MAP 5:C1
Portree
Isle of Skye IV51 9QU
T: 01478 612003
w: cuillinhills-hotel-skye.co.uk

BEDROOMS: 39 bedrooms, 15 on ground floor, 1 suitable for disabled.
OPEN: all year.
FACILITIES: Drawing room, restaurant, bar, private dining/meeting facilities, in-room TV, 15-acre ground, ground floor wheelchair accessible.
BACKGROUND MUSIC: in public areas.
LOCATION: in 15-acre grounds overlooking Portree Bay.
CHILDREN: all ages welcomed.
DOGS: only assistance dogs.
CREDIT CARDS: Amex, MC, Visa.
PRICES: B&B £99–£450. À la carte £45.

Prices may change – check with hotel.

RATHO Midlothian

THE BRIDGE INN AT RATHO

Expect a 'cheerful welcome' at this gastropub-with-rooms, which stands by a bridge over the Union Canal in a conservation village. Fires burn in a bar popular with locals; in the 'inviting' dining room, produce from local suppliers and the walled garden influences the menu of pub classics (fish and chips; pie of the day) and more elaborate dishes (duck breast, confit leg, celeriac purée, pickled pear, chicory). There's an outdoor terrace for sunny days. Upstairs, 'snug', pleasingly simple bedrooms have a canal view. Breakfast brings sausages from rare-breed pigs, and freshly laid chicken and duck eggs from Ratho Hall. Convenient for Edinburgh Airport. Sister hotel The Ship Inn is in Elie (see main entry).

MAP 5:D2
27 Baird Road
Ratho EH28 8RA
T: 0131 333 1320
W: bridgeinn.com

BEDROOMS: 4.
OPEN: all year except 25–26 Dec.
FACILITIES: 2 bars, restaurant, in-room TV (Freeview), wedding facilities, terrace (beer garden, boat shed), bar and restaurant wheelchair accessible, adapted toilet.
BACKGROUND MUSIC: 'relaxed' all day, monthly live music nights.
LOCATION: in village, 7 miles W of Edinburgh.
CHILDREN: all ages welcomed.
DOGS: allowed in 2 bedrooms and public rooms.
CREDIT CARDS: MC, Visa.
PRICES: per room B&B single £80–£210, double £90–£220. À la carte £45.

Prices may change – check with hotel.

ST ANDREWS Fife

RUFFLETS

'Nothing seems too much trouble' at this turreted 1920s mansion, one of Scotland's first country house hotels, owned by the same family for 70 years. 'It's not inexpensive, but the staff are welcoming and helpful, the food is good, the guest lounges, bar (which stocks 110 whiskies) and dining areas are attractive and comfortable, and the grounds are delightful – what more can you ask of a hotel?' Those who do ask for more find 'superb' dog- and family-friendly bedrooms packed with thoughtful touches; a popular afternoon tea; and modern Scottish lunches and dinners, served inside and out, featuring kitchen garden produce. Just beyond is the historic seaside town of St Andrews.

MAP 5:D3
Strathkinness Low Road
St Andrews KY16 9TX
T: 01334 472594
W: rufflets.co.uk

BEDROOMS: 23. Some in Gatehouse and Rufflets Lodge, 4 on ground floor, 1 suitable for disabled, 2 with private balconies, plus 3 self-catering cottages in gardens.
OPEN: all year.
FACILITIES: bar, drawing room, library, restaurant, in-room TV (Freeview), wedding/function facilities, yoga studio, 10-acre grounds (formal gardens, kitchen garden and woodland), bicycle hire.
BACKGROUND MUSIC: in bar, restaurant.
LOCATION: 2 miles W of town.
CHILDREN: all ages welcomed.
DOGS: allowed in some bedrooms, bar.
CREDIT CARDS: Amex, MC, Visa.
PRICES: per room B&B £145–£375. À la carte £40.

Prices may change – check with hotel.

ST FILLANS Perth and Kinross
ACHRAY HOUSE

With 'wonderful views' over Loch Earn and the hills beyond, this small, peaceful hotel, which is part of Loch Lomond & The Trossachs national park, offers fine cooking and a good base for walking and wildlife. Most of the 'very comfortable' bedrooms, with their feature wallpapers, coffee machines and large bathrooms, have loch views and binoculars – watch the ospreys in season. Deep sofas in the lounge are inviting after a day's exploring. More loch views in the restaurant accompany a menu of modern Scottish dishes, such as mackerel ceviche, and lamb rump with couscous and amaretto. Lighter dishes are offered in the conservatory. 'Very good' breakfasts, highlighting local produce, set you up for the day.

MAP 5:D2
On Loch Earn
St Fillans PH6 2NF
T: 01764 685320
W: achrayhouse.com

BEDROOMS: 9. Plus self-catering cottage.
OPEN: all year, except mid-Jan to mid-Feb, closed Tues/Wed Nov–end Feb.
FACILITIES: lounge, bar, conservatory, restaurant, in-room TV (Sky), civil wedding licence, terrace, large foreshore, EV charging, bar and restaurant wheelchair accessible.
BACKGROUND MUSIC: in lobby, bar, restaurant.
LOCATION: at E end of Loch Earn, 6 miles W of Comrie.
CHILDREN: 'not ideal for small children, but call to discuss.'
DOGS: allowed in 5 bedrooms, conservatory, bar.
CREDIT CARDS: Amex, MC, Visa.
PRICES: B&B doubles from £79. À la carte £38.

Prices may change – check with hotel.

SCOURIE Highland
SCOURIE HOTEL

Genuine Scottish hospitality, spectacular scenery and the thrill of some of Scotland's finest wild brown trout fishing lure visitors to the Campbell family's old coaching inn on the scenic North Coast 500 road route. Wonderfully wild, it's surrounded by majestic mountains, white sandy bays, and lochs and lochans of wild trout and salmon. Bonhomie begins with fireside tea and scones in lounges full of fishing memorabilia; tall tales are exchanged over drinks in the bar before a set dinner of local seafood, game and meat, and home-grown veg. Drift off to sleep in a neat and bright bedroom; no TV to spoil the peace. Large grounds encompass walled gardens and an orchard; a path leads down to the harbour.

MAP 5:B2
Scourie IV27 4SX
T: 01971 502396
W: scouriehotel.com

BEDROOMS: 21. 2 in garden annexe.
OPEN: mid-Apr–mid-Oct.
FACILITIES: 2 bars, 2 lounges, restaurant, 7-acre grounds (gardens, paddock, orchard), fishing beats (permits supplied, boats to hire, ghillies available).
BACKGROUND MUSIC: none.
LOCATION: in a village on the North Coast 500 route.
CHILDREN: all ages welcomed.
DOGS: allowed, not in dining area.
CREDIT CARDS: MC, Visa.
PRICES: B&B £125–£195. Set dinner £42.

Prices may change – check with hotel.

SOUTH GALSON Western Isles

GALSON FARM GUEST HOUSE

On the north-west coast of the Isle of Lewis, Elaine Fothergill and Richard Inger invite you to their traditional Hebridean farmhouse to switch off, unwind and relax. A short walk from the sea, the sky is vast here; the birds, wild. Bedrooms with views of rugged coast or moorland crofts have a modern rustic feel, with locally made ceramics, crafts and furniture; fresh milk and cold drinks are in the fridge. Guests can relax in a TV lounge (with a fire) or a quieter reading room overlooking the surging Atlantic. Home-cooked evening meals or sharing platters can be ordered in advance while the Aga-fresh breakfast – porridge, kippers or a full grill – fuels exploration of beaches, mountains and burns.

MAP 5:B1
South Galson
Isle of Lewis HS2 0SH
T: 01851 850492
W: galsonfarm.co.uk

BEDROOMS: 4. Plus self-catering cottage.
OPEN: all year except Christmas, New Year. Evening meals May–end Sept, Tues, Thurs, Sat, Sun only.
FACILITIES: 2 lounges, dining room, ¼-acre garden, drying facilities, bicycle storage.
BACKGROUND MUSIC: in dining room, lounge.
LOCATION: on the coast, 7½ miles SW of the port of Ness, 20 miles from Stornoway.
CHILDREN: not under 14.
DOGS: only assistance dogs allowed (animals on site).
CREDIT CARDS: Amex, MC, Visa.
PRICES: B&B doubles from £115. Pre-booked dinner £27 (2 courses), sharing platter for 2 £55. 2-night min. stay.

Prices may change – check with hotel.

STIRLING

VICTORIA SQUARE

In the shadow of Stirling Castle, and overlooking a tree-lined square in the town's conservation area, this Victorian house offers boutique-style bedrooms and fine dining. Kari and Phillip Couser have created bedrooms with William Morris-designed wallpapers and period-style furnishings; superior rooms might have bay-window seating or a view towards the castle. Modern comforts include underfloor-heated bathrooms, Scottish mineral water, bathrobes and upmarket toiletries. In the orangery restaurant, dinner (served Wednesday to Saturday) offers dishes such as venison with tarragon boulangère; in-room picnics are also an option each night. Breakfast includes porridge, eggs Benedict and Scottish smoked salmon.

MAP 5:D2
12 Victoria Square
Stirling FK8 2QZ
T: 01786 473920
W: victoriasquare.scot

BEDROOMS: 10. 1 on ground floor.
OPEN: all year except Christmas, restaurant closed Sun, Mon, Tues.
FACILITIES: lounge, breakfast room, orangery restaurant, in-room TV (Freeview), limited parking, payable street parking.
BACKGROUND MUSIC: quiet, in restaurant.
LOCATION: ½ mile from town centre.
CHILDREN: not under 12.
DOGS: not allowed.
CREDIT CARDS: MC, Visa.
PRICES: B&B £75–£250. À la carte £43.

Prices may change – check with hotel.

THORNHILL Dumfries and Galloway
TRIGONY HOUSE

In a 'beautiful' setting, Jan and Adam Moore's dog-friendly country hotel in an 18th-century sporting lodge looks out over the hills and is surrounded by trees. Past fire-warmed sitting areas, 'perfectly pleasant and comfortable' bedrooms are supplied with home-made shortbread, fresh coffee and organic toiletries; a garden suite has a conservatory and private garden. Guests sensitive to noise (an A road runs close by) should ring in advance to discuss best options. Dinner has good choice for vegetarians and vegans; breakfast is 'excellent'. Arm yourself with the hotel's richly informative guide of walks before striding out, or simply relax: a Finnish sauna cabin and hot tub are in the grounds.

MAP 5:E2
Closeburn
Thornhill DG3 5EZ
T: 01848 331211
W: trigonyhotel.co.uk

BEDROOMS: 9. 1 on ground floor.
OPEN: all year except 24–26, 31 Dec.
FACILITIES: bar, lounge, 2 dining rooms, in-room TV (Freeview), spa treatment room (outdoor hot tub, sauna cabin), wedding facilities, 4-acre grounds, ramp, EV charging.
BACKGROUND MUSIC: in bar in evening.
LOCATION: 1 mile south of Thornhill.
CHILDREN: all ages welcomed.
DOGS: well-behaved dogs 'not only allowed but welcomed' in bedrooms, bar, 1 dining room, grounds. Beds, bowls, dog breakfast, washing area provided, on-site dog sitting and dog training by pre-arrangement.
CREDIT CARDS: Amex, MC, Visa.
PRICES: per room B&B single £110–£155, double £135–£180. À la carte £35. 1-night bookings sometimes refused Sat.

Prices may change – check with hotel.

NEW

ULLAPOOL Highland
THE DIPPING LUGGER

Surprises spring up in Robert and Helen Hicks's restaurant with rooms, crafted from an 18th-century manse on the waterfront. Beyond a plain white exterior, the house (named after a type of sailing vessel) is lushly decorated with dark parquet floors, velvet and leather seating, swashbuckling wallpaper. Tweed blankets and landscape views across Loch Broom bring the Highlands into three smart bedrooms upstairs, each supplied with bathrobes and an espresso machine. Along a corridor, discover a hoard of treats in an honesty bar and 'Sweet Shop'. In the restaurant, terse menus create anticipation for chef David Smith's fine gourmet dishes. The owners' gin can be sampled in the intimate Tasting Room.

MAP 5:B1
4 W Shore Street
Ullapool
IV26 2UR
T: 01854 613344
W: thedippinglugger.co.uk

BEDROOMS: 3.
OPEN: Thurs–Sun. Restaurant open Fri–Sun for lunch, Thurs–Sun for dinner.
FACILITIES: lounge, Sweet Shop/ honesty bar, restaurant, tasting room.
BACKGROUND MUSIC: in restaurant, tasting room; vinyl collection in lounge.
LOCATION: on shores of Loch Broom.
CHILDREN: welcomed, cots provided for babies; no additional beds or children's menus.
DOGS: not allowed.
CREDIT CARDS: MC, Visa.
PRICES: Per room (for 2 people) DB&B £410. Set menu, lunch £35, optional wine pairing £30; dinner £75, optional wine pairing £50.

Prices may change – check with hotel.

ABERYSTWYTH Ceredigion

NANTEOS MANSION

Standing in graceful seclusion in wooded grounds with a walled garden, this family-friendly Grade I listed manor house offers a tranquil country retreat combining Georgian elegance and modern comforts. Sympathetically restored, it has retained historic features of stained glass, plasterwork ceilings, carved fireplaces and a grand staircase. Bedrooms and sumptuous suites are decorated in keeping with the period of the house, but with modern bathrooms with bath as well as shower. In the chandelier-lit dining room, after cocktails in the library bar, a Modern Welsh menu is served Friday and Saturday evenings – perhaps salmon with mango and lime salsa. Pre-ordered breakfast includes kippers and a full Welsh.

MAP 3:C3
Rhydyfelin
Aberystwyth SY23 4LU
T: 01970 600522
W: nanteos.com

BEDROOMS: 22. 3 on ground floor, 1 suitable for disabled. Plus 4-bed mews house.
OPEN: all year except Sun eve, all Mon. Restaurant open Fri and Sat only.
FACILITIES: lounge, bar, restaurant, private dining room, billiard room, in-room TV (Freeview), civil wedding licence, 30-acre grounds (gardens, woodland), EV charging, public rooms wheelchair accessible.
BACKGROUND MUSIC: in reception, bar.
LOCATION: 4 miles SE of Aberystwyth.
CHILDREN: all ages welcomed.
DOGS: allowed in 4 bedrooms, not in restaurant.
CREDIT CARDS: Amex, MC, Visa.
PRICES: B&B doubles from £165, singles from £140. À la carte £49.

Prices may change – check with hotel.

AMROTH Pembrokeshire

MELLIEHA GUEST HOUSE

In a forested valley, a short walk from the sea, Julia and Stuart Adams 'warmly welcome' B&B guests with tea and a home-baked treat. The house stands in large, well-cared-for grounds with a natural pond – a tranquil scene to take in from the sunny terrace. 'Comfortable' bedrooms have views over the garden and valley, or towards Carmarthen Bay. They vary in size, but all of them are 'thoughtfully' supplied with fresh milk for morning coffee or tea. One room has a private terrace, another, its own balcony. Breakfast (perhaps cockles and laverbread) is ordered the night before. 'The best I have ever had.' There is easy access to the Pembrokeshire Coast Path, and the 'informative hosts' have circular walks to share.

MAP 3:D2
Amroth SA67 8NA
T: 01834 811581
W: mellieha.co.uk

BEDROOMS: 4.
OPEN: all year except over Christmas, New Year.
FACILITIES: lounge, breakfast room, in-room TV, no mobile signal, 1-acre garden, parking.
BACKGROUND MUSIC: none.
LOCATION: 150 yards from Amroth seafront, 2 miles E of Saundersfoot.
CHILDREN: not under 12.
DOGS: only assistance dogs allowed.
CREDIT CARDS: MC, Visa.
PRICES: per room B&B single £65–£85, double £95–£135. 2-night min. stay preferred at weekends May–Sept.

Prices may change – check with hotel.

BALA Gwynedd
PALE HALL

On the edge of Snowdonia national park, this
stately Victorian mansion, with its tower, tall
chimneys and terraced lawns, does not disappoint
once inside. Oak panelling and a sweeping
staircase dominate the Grand Hall while,
throughout, antiques sit amongst traditional
furnishings. Gracefully decorated bedrooms
combine original features with luxurious modern
comforts; suites in the outbuildings are more
contemporary; all have organic toiletries and
complimentary Madeira. Seasonal produce
inspires tasting menus in the dining room and
more informal meals in the bistro. Sustainably
run, the hotel is powered by one of the country's
oldest-running hydro-electric plants, and bottles
its own spring water.

MAP 3:B3
Palé Estate
Llandderfel
Bala LL23 7PS
T: 01678 530285
W: palehall.co.uk

BEDROOMS: 22. 4 in barn, coach house
and cottage, 1 suitable for disabled.
OPEN: all year.
FACILITIES: Grand Hall, lounge, library,
restaurant, bar/bistro, family/private
dining room, in-room TV (Freeview),
function facilities, civil wedding
licence, 50-acre grounds, EV charging,
public rooms wheelchair accessible.
BACKGROUND MUSIC: in Grand Hall,
restaurants.
LOCATION: 2 miles from Bala.
CHILDREN: all ages welcomed.
DOGS: allowed in 7 bedrooms, Grand
Hall, bistro, on lead in gardens and
public areas.
CREDIT CARDS: Amex, MC, Visa.
PRICES: B&B doubles from £295. Tasting
menu £95 (8 courses), à la carte £45.

Prices may change – check with hotel.

NEW

BLAENAU FFESTINIOG Gwynedd
PLAS WEUNYDD HOTEL

Nostalgia seeker or adrenaline junkie? Zipwire
thrills, underground explorations, mountain bike
trails lie on the doorstep of this easy-going hotel
on UNESCO's newest World Heritage site in
Snowdonia. The distinctive 19th-century black
and white building stands high above the almost
'other-worldly' landscape of a slate quarry and
the old Llechwedd mine. The house has been
refurbished in modern style, its spacious rooms
given colourful walls to offset works by Welsh
artists; a terrace affords far-reaching views and
stunning sunsets. Charcuterie and vegetarian
sharing platters, and 'generously topped' pizzas,
satisfy after a day's activity. A little further,
mountains and beaches are waiting to be explored.

MAP 3:B3
Llechwedd
Blaenau Ffestiniog
LL41 3NB
T: 01766 610006
W: plasweunydd.co.uk

BEDROOMS: 24. 6 glamping tents.
OPEN: all year.
FACILITIES: bar, restaurant, sitting
room, in-room TV, terrace, parking.
BACKGROUND MUSIC: none.
LOCATION: in the heart of Snowdonia,
at the entrance to Zip World
Llechwedd.
CHILDREN: all ages welcomed.
DOGS: welcomed, by request.
CREDIT CARDS: MC, Visa.
PRICES: per room B&B £105–£150.

Prices may change – check with hotel.

CARDIFF

NEW HOUSE COUNTRY HOTEL

Just north of the city, magnificent views over Cardiff and Vale of Glamorgan spread below this hotel with the air of a country retreat. A tiered fountain fronts the creeper-covered Grade II listed manor house. Stone steps lead to elegant rooms with high windows that look out on to lush greenery. Afternoon tea may be taken in the lounges; at mealtimes, Modern Welsh dishes in the restaurant or under the glass pergola might include baby pear, Per Las cheese, pickled walnut salad, or braised blade of Welsh beef. Colourful and contemporary bedrooms are supplied with Welsh toiletries. Part of the Town & Country Collective; see also The Bear, Cowbridge, and The West House, Llantwit Major (Shortlist entries).

MAP 3:E4
Thornhill
Cardiff CF14 9UA
T: 02920 520280
W: townandcountrycollective.co.uk/
new-house-home

BEDROOMS: 37. 29 in annexe, connected via lounges.
OPEN: all year except 26 Dec, 1 Jan.
FACILITIES: 3 lounges, library, restaurant, in-room TV (Freeview), civil wedding licence, meeting/function facilities, gym, 9-acre grounds.
BACKGROUND MUSIC: in restaurant.
LOCATION: in Thornhill suburb, 7 miles from Cardiff city centre.
CHILDREN: all ages welcomed.
DOGS: allowed in 3 bedrooms, 2 lounges, parts of garden, not in restaurant.
CREDIT CARDS: Amex, MC, Visa.
PRICES: per room B&B £99–£165. À la carte £35.

Prices may change – check with hotel.

COWBRIDGE Vale of Glamorgan

THE BEAR

In the heart of Cowbridge, with its fashionable shops and a few miles from the Wales Coast Path, this former coaching inn is popular with locals and visitors alike. The panelled lounge and grill bar (spot the medieval fireplace) buzz with chatter; when the sun's out, find a table in the courtyard. You can also eat in the atmospheric Cellars restaurant; menus of modern dishes feature Welsh produce. Up-to-date bedrooms, with bright throws and feature wallpapers, have Welsh toiletries; some can accommodate a dog or a family. Residents have gym access at a leisure centre nearby. Part of the Town & Country Collective; see also The West House, Llantwit Major, and New House Country Hotel, Cardiff (Shortlist entries).

MAP 3:E3
63 High Street
Cowbridge CF71 7AF
T: 01446 774814
W: townandcountrycollective.co.uk/
the-bear-home

BEDROOMS: 33. Some on ground floor, some in annexe, plus self-catering apartments.
OPEN: all year.
FACILITIES: lounge/bar, grill/bar, restaurant, in-room TV, civil wedding licence, function rooms, courtyard, secure bicycle storage, parking.
BACKGROUND MUSIC: in restaurant.
LOCATION: in town centre.
CHILDREN: all ages welcomed.
DOGS: allowed in bedrooms, bar.
CREDIT CARDS: MC, Visa.
PRICES: B&B doubles from £135, singles from £95. À la carte £35.

Prices may change – check with hotel.

FISHGUARD Pembrokeshire

THE MANOR TOWN HOUSE

Behind Helen and Chris Sheldon's pastel blue-painted B&B is a secluded garden terrace with 'spectacular' views over Lower Town harbour and across Cardigan Bay. The listed Georgian town house is furnished in contemporary style with comfy seating, books, magazines, 'interesting' antiques and an honesty bar. Bedrooms have bright fabrics, and maybe a patterned headboard or an accent wall of deep blue. Some rooms are snug; two are large enough for a family. A continental breakfast includes home-baked bread and granola, and fresh fruit skewers. A packed lunch and a cream tea may be ordered. Bike hire can be arranged, or you can walk the Pembrokeshire Coast Path that runs below or hop on a coastal bus.

MAP 3:D1
11 Main Street
Fishguard SA65 9HG
T: 01348 873260
W: manortownhouse.com

BEDROOMS: 6.
OPEN: all year except 23–28 Dec.
FACILITIES: 2 lounges, breakfast room, in-room TV (Freeview), small walled garden, bicycle storage, parking in public car park, unsuitable for disabled.
BACKGROUND MUSIC: none.
LOCATION: town centre.
CHILDREN: all ages welcomed, cots free, extra bed £25.
DOGS: not allowed.
CREDIT CARDS: Amex, MC, Visa.
PRICES: per room B&B single £90, double £140–£180. 2-night min. stay Apr–Oct and some peak weekends.

Prices may change – check with hotel.

HARLECH Gwynedd

CASTLE COTTAGE INN

At the top of one of the world's steepest streets, this inn occupies two 16th-century buildings just above Edward I's formidable castle (faint hearts, take the High Street route). An aviation-themed bar serves snacks and small plates alongside local ales and spirits. New owners have brought a more casual approach to dining in the sleekly renovated restaurant, and a Thai influence to the Modern British menu; perhaps grilled fillet of cod, oriental noodles, green curry and coconut sauce. In the bedrooms, fine linens and tea, coffee and biscuits. Contemporary decor and modern oak furniture contrast with original features; ask for a room with a view of sea, castle or the Snowdonia mountain range.

MAP 3:B3
Y Llech
Harlech LL46 2YL
T: 01766 780479
W: castlecottageinnharlech.com

BEDROOMS: 7. 4 in annexe, 2 on ground floor.
OPEN: all year.
FACILITIES: bar/lounge, restaurant, in-room TV (Freeview), limited parking, public car park within 30 yards.
BACKGROUND MUSIC: in bar and restaurant at mealtimes.
LOCATION: in town centre.
CHILDREN: all ages welcomed.
DOGS: not allowed.
CREDIT CARDS: MC, Visa.
PRICES: per room B&B single £85–£125, double £130–£175. À la carte £30.

Prices may change – check with hotel.

LAUGHARNE Carmarthenshire

BROWN'S HOTEL

A favourite watering hole of Dylan Thomas, this refurbished 18th-century inn, in a lively coastal town, remains a characterful place. The timber-beamed pub is inviting with its wood stove, candle-topped tables, old photos and Thomas memorabilia; there are Welsh ales, Penderyn whisky, board games, books. 'Good' grills are served in Dexters, the wood-panelled restaurant. Dapper bedrooms, each different, are decorated in deep shades and equipped with all the modern amenities (mini-fridge, coffee machine, eco-friendly toiletries). They hold charm in their creaky wood floors, exposed stonework and beams, though 'showers over baths were awkward'. Down a green lane, Thomas's boathouse is a ten-minute stroll away.

MAP 3:D2
King Street
Laugharne SA33 4RY
T: 01994 427688
W: browns.wales

BEDROOMS: 14. 2 on ground floor, 4 in annexe, 2 wheelchair accessible.
OPEN: all year.
FACILITIES: bar, restaurant, reading room, in-room TV, function facilities, small beer garden, electric car charging points, parking.
BACKGROUND MUSIC: in bar, restaurant.
LOCATION: in town centre.
CHILDREN: all ages welcomed.
DOGS: allowed in most bedrooms, not in areas where food is served.
CREDIT CARDS: MC, Visa.
PRICES: per room B&B single £75–£110, double £130–£180. À la carte £40.

Prices may change – check with hotel.

LLANDDEINIOLEN Gwynedd

TY'N RHOS

Deep in the countryside, the Murphy family's 'beautifully situated' hotel is in a former farmstead turned country house overlooking the Isle of Anglesey. Sheep and cattle graze in fields beyond the gardens; binoculars are provided for watching the varied bird life. 'Comfortable, well-equipped' bedrooms are in the creeper-covered house or around the courtyard; some open on to the garden. Pre-dinner drinks are enjoyed in the bar, lounge or bright conservatory, or on the terrace in fine weather. 'It's great!' The staff are 'brilliant', the food is 'excellent' (marinated wild trout, harissa roast aubergine, duck breast, lemon cream dessert). Breakfast includes haddock with Welsh rarebit.

MAP 3:A3
Seion
Llanddeiniolen LL55 3AE
T: 01248 670489
W: tynrhos.co.uk

BEDROOMS: 19. 7 in converted outbuilding, some on ground floor.
OPEN: all year except Sun, Mon, Christmas, New Year.
FACILITIES: lounge, bar, restaurant, conservatory, in-room TV, terrace, 1-acre garden.
BACKGROUND MUSIC: in public areas.
LOCATION: 4 miles from Bangor and Caernarfon. 12 mins' drive from the Llanberis train.
CHILDREN: all ages welcomed, no 'small children' in restaurant in evening.
DOGS: allowed in some bedrooms, garden.
CREDIT CARDS: MC, Visa.
PRICES: per room B&B £160–£210. 2-night min. stay. Dinner £46.

Prices may change – check with hotel.

LLANDUDNO Conwy

ESCAPE

Above the town, this design-conscious B&B occupies a white stucco Victorian villa close to the Great Orme Tramway. The owners, Gaenor Loftus and Sam Nayar, have filled it with modern and vintage furnishings set against a backdrop of period features such as stained-glass windows and oak panelling; bedrooms have plenty of personality and a touch of glamour. Choose a room decorated with coastal flair or one with botanical or William Morris-style wallpaper; two of the best rooms have seating in a wide bay window. In every room: high-end toiletries and high-spec technology. Breakfast offers veggie options, alongside sausages from the local butcher. The beach and the pier are a short downhill stroll away.

MAP 3:A3
48 Church Walks
Llandudno LL30 2HL
T: 01492 877776
W: escapebandb.co.uk

BEDROOMS: 9.
OPEN: all year except 18–26 Dec.
FACILITIES: lounge (honesty bar), breakfast room, in-room TV (Freeview), front garden, limited parking.
BACKGROUND MUSIC: at breakfast.
LOCATION: 1 mile from town and coast.
CHILDREN: not under 10.
DOGS: not allowed.
CREDIT CARDS: Amex, MC, Visa.
PRICES: per room B&B £135–£160. 2-night min. stay at weekends, 3 nights on bank holidays.

Prices may change – check with hotel.

LLANDUDNO Conwy

OSBORNE HOUSE

'Splendid' public rooms decorated with oil paintings and gilded mirrors give this small hotel on the promenade an air of 'impressive grandeur'. On the upper floors, some of the 'characterful' suites have glorious sea views. The hotel has been owned for more than 20 years by the Maddocks and Waddy families, Llandudno hoteliers who have been at the helm of neighbouring sister hotel The Empire since 1946. Each well-supplied suite has a sitting room, a marble bathroom, and a gas fire in a marble fireplace; continental breakfasts are taken in the room. There's a Modern British menu in the 'ornate' Victorian dining room; guests may also have a cooked breakfast, swim, work out and step into the sauna at The Empire.

MAP 3:A3
17 North Parade
Llandudno LL30 2LP
T: 01492 860330
W: osbornehouse.co.uk

BEDROOMS: 7 suites.
OPEN: all year except Sun, Mon, Christmas.
FACILITIES: lounge/bar, restaurant, in-room TV (Freeview), small patio, parking.
BACKGROUND MUSIC: in public rooms.
LOCATION: on the promenade.
CHILDREN: only allowed in rear family suite.
DOGS: not allowed.
CREDIT CARDS: MC, Visa.
PRICES: per room B&B £150–£240. À la carte £27.50. 2-night min. stay at weekends, 3-night min. stay over bank holidays, 2-night min. stay July-Oct.

Prices may change – check with hotel.

LLANSTEFFAN Carmarthenshire
MANSION HOUSE LLANSTEFFAN

Overlooking the Tywi estuary, this contemporary restaurant-with-rooms in a restored Georgian mansion is enjoyed for its 'really lovely hospitality, food and accommodation'. It is owned and run by Carmarthenshire native Wendy Beaney and her husband, David Stylish. Uncluttered bedrooms with garden or river views are supplied with bathrobes and Welsh toiletries. Two ground-floor rooms interconnect; one has a private garden terrace. From the period dining room, the 'excellent' view is a fine accompaniment for Paul Owen's seasonal menus of locally farmed vegetables, Welsh meats and Carmarthen Bay seafood. Discover Norman castles at Llansteffan, and, half an hour's drive away, Dylan Thomas landmarks in Laugharne.

MAP 3:D2
Pantyrathro
Llansteffan SA33 5AJ
T: 01267 241515
W: mansionhousellansteffan.co.uk

BEDROOMS: 9. 2 interconnecting rooms on ground floor, 1 suitable for disabled.
OPEN: all year, restaurant closed Sun eve except for residents, also Mon, Nov–mid-Feb.
FACILITIES: large open-plan bar/reception area, lounge, restaurant, in-room TV (Freeview), civil wedding licence, conference facilities, 5-acre grounds, EV charging, parking.
BACKGROUND MUSIC: in public areas.
LOCATION: 2 miles to Llansteffan village, beach and castle.
CHILDREN: all ages welcomed.
DOGS: not allowed.
CREDIT CARDS: Amex, MC, Visa.
PRICES: per room B&B £150–£275. 1-night bookings refused at Christmas. À la carte £30.

Prices may change – check with hotel.

LLANTWIT MAJOR Vale of Glamorgan
THE WEST HOUSE

Within meandering reach, down green lanes and pathways, of the Glamorgan Heritage Coast, this modern hotel is in a quiet town that was once an unrivalled centre of scholarship. Countrified bedrooms vary in size and decor; guests travelling with their dog may request one of the Fido-friendly rooms – they're supplied with a dog bed, towel and treats, and have access to the walled garden. Sandwiches, light bites and straightforward British classics are served in the restaurant, along with interesting vegetarian options. Pubs and cafés are close by. Part of the Town & Country Collective; see also New House Country Hotel, Cardiff, and The Bear, Cowbridge (Shortlist entries).

MAP 3:E3
West Street
Llantwit Major CF61 1SP
T: 01446 792406
W: townandcountrycollective.co.uk/the-west-house-home

BEDROOMS: 17. 1 on ground floor.
OPEN: all year, restaurant closed Sun eve.
FACILITIES: bar, restaurant, snug, conservatory, in-room TV, civil wedding licence, meeting/function facilities, terrace, front and rear gardens, parking.
BACKGROUND MUSIC: in public areas.
LOCATION: 10 mins' walk from town centre.
CHILDREN: all ages welcomed.
DOGS: allowed in some bedrooms, separate eating area.
CREDIT CARDS: MC, Visa.
PRICES: per room B&B £129–£149. À la carte £25.

Prices may change – check with hotel.

MOYLEGROVE Pembrokeshire
THE OLD VICARAGE B&B

With views to the sea and hills of north Pembrokeshire, and minutes from the region's Coast Path, Meg and Jaap van Soest's airy B&B suits walkers and those wanting a quiet escape. They have refurbished their hilltop Edwardian vicarage to take advantage of its high ceilings and light-filled rooms. There are books, maps and guides in the spacious sitting room, plus chess for a fireside game. Upstairs, uncluttered bedrooms with soothing colours have Welsh woollen blankets on large beds, and bright-white shower rooms. For supper, a Spanish tapas hamper – with wine – can be arranged. Breakfast on home-baked breads, local bacon and sausages, good veggie options, and views over the valley to the sea.

MAP 3:D2
Moylegrove SA43 3BN
T: 01239 881711
W: oldvicaragemoylegrove.co.uk

BEDROOMS: 5. Plus birch huts in grounds available for self-catering.
OPEN: all year.
FACILITIES: sitting room, dining room, in-room TV (Freeview), 1-acre garden.
BACKGROUND MUSIC: in dining room in evening.
LOCATION: 500 yards from village, 13 miles N of Fishguard.
CHILDREN: all ages welcomed.
DOGS: allowed, not in dining room.
CREDIT CARDS: MC, Visa.
PRICES: B&B doubles from £110, 2-night min. summer weekends.

Prices may change – check with hotel.

NARBERTH Pembrokeshire
CANASTON OAKS

Praised for its spacious, modern bedrooms and award-winning breakfasts, this 'very good' B&B is run by friendly owners Eleanor and David Lewis, with their daughter, Emma Millership. Accommodation is in a lake-view lodge and converted barns set around a courtyard. Each thoughtfully supplied room (dressing gowns, candles, etc) is different: some have a conservatory seating area; a family suite opens on to a terrace with wide countryside views. Breakfast has thick Welsh yogurt, heather honey and poached fruit; hot dishes include porridge with Penderyn whisky, and smoked haddock fishcakes. Charcuterie and pizzas (except Sundays) may be taken in the room or on the patio. Narberth is a short drive away.

MAP 3:D2
Canaston Bridge
Narberth SA67 8DE
T: 01437 541254
W: canastonoaks.co.uk

BEDROOMS: 10. 7 on ground floor around courtyard, 2 suitable for disabled, plus 1-bed self-catering apartment.
OPEN: all year except Christmas.
FACILITIES: lounge (honesty bar), dining room, in-room TV (Freeview), 1-acre grounds, parking.
BACKGROUND MUSIC: 'mainly easy listening or classical' in dining room.
LOCATION: 2 miles W of Narberth.
CHILDREN: all ages welcomed.
DOGS: well-behaved dogs allowed in 3 barn suites, not in dining area, on lead in all public areas.
CREDIT CARDS: MC, Visa.
PRICES: per room B&B £100–£250. Evening meals Mon–Sat, must be ordered by 10 am. 1-night bookings sometimes refused at peak times.

Prices may change – check with hotel.

ROCH Pembrokeshire

ROCH CASTLE HOTEL

On a rocky outcrop, high above the Pembrokeshire landscape, stands a 12th-century castle with contemporary B&B accommodation and spectacular panoramas. Reached via a curving staircase, sleek bedrooms have 21st-century comforts: luxury towels and toiletries, slippers and a coffee machine. The best room has double-aspect windows to take in the views. Still higher, the Sun Room, with floor-to-ceiling glass walls and an open-air viewing platform, merits the climb. Modern artworks inspired by Welsh history and landscapes provide extra visual interest. For dinner, free transfers take guests to sister hotel Twr y Felin, St Davids (see main entry); in the morning, breakfast includes laverbread and local honey.

MAP 3:D1
Roch
Haverford West SA62 6AQ
T: 01437 725566
W: rochcastle.com

BEDROOMS: 6.
OPEN: all year.
FACILITIES: lounge, study, breakfast room, Sun Room (honesty bar), in-room TV (Freeview), civil wedding licence, 19-acre grounds, EV charging.
BACKGROUND MUSIC: classical and 'easy listening' in lounges, breakfast room.
LOCATION: 7 miles NW of Haverfordwest.
CHILDREN: not under 12.
DOGS: not allowed.
CREDIT CARDS: Amex, MC, Visa.
PRICES: per room B&B £230–£280. 2- or 3-night min. stay at weekends and peak times, also available for exclusive use.

Prices may change – check with hotel.

ST DAVIDS Pembrokeshire

CRUG-GLAS

Eco-friendly heating is newly installed at this peaceful, relaxed restaurant-with-rooms, run by the Evans family with 'warm concern for their guests'. 'They went out of their way to prepare a favourite dish for our birthday celebration,' a Guide reader reports. The Georgian farmhouse on the family farm is full of photographs and inherited pieces; a generations-old dresser houses the honesty bar. Large bedrooms each have their own country style, though all share tranquil rural views. A short walk through the grounds, a spacious suite in a converted barn offers extra privacy. Seasonal dinner menus include beef from home-reared cows; breakfast has good choice. The Pembrokeshire Coast Path is nearby.

MAP 3:D1
Abereiddy
St Davids SA62 6XX
T: 01348 831302
W: crug-glas.co.uk

BEDROOMS: 7. 1 in converted barn, 1 on ground floor.
OPEN: all year except 23–27 Dec.
FACILITIES: drawing room, dining room, in-room TV (Freeview), civil wedding licence, function facilities, hair salon, 1-acre garden on 600-acre farm.
BACKGROUND MUSIC: in public rooms.
LOCATION: 3½ miles NE of St Davids.
CHILDREN: babes-in-arms and over-11s welcomed.
DOGS: allowed in coach house suite.
CREDIT CARDS: MC, Visa.
PRICES: per room B&B single £150, double £170–£250. À la carte £40.

Prices may change – check with hotel.

ST DAVIDS Pembrokeshire

PENRHIW PRIORY

Close to St Davids and its cathedral, this tranquil retreat is enveloped by acres of landscaped gardens, woodland paths, a river and a wildflower meadow. Built in 1882 as a Tudorbethan rectory, it is modern inside, with soberly decorated rooms and dramatic abstract artwork inspired by local landscapes. Bedrooms are supplied with cosseting extras (bathrobes and slippers, aromatherapy toiletries, quality bedding); a suite in the coach house has a private terrace and views of Carn Llidi. Drinks and snacks are available in the honesty bar. At dinnertime, complimentary transfers to the well-regarded Blas restaurant at sister hotel Twr y Felin (see main entry), on the other side of town, can be arranged.

MAP 3:D1
St Davids SA62 6PG
T: 01437 725588
W: penrhiwhotel.com

BEDROOMS: 8. 2 in coach house, 1 on ground floor.
OPEN: all year.
FACILITIES: lounge, drawing room, breakfast room, study, in-room TV, treatment room, civil wedding licence, 12-acre grounds, EV charging.
BACKGROUND MUSIC: soft jazz/classical in breakfast room.
LOCATION: 10 mins' walk from St Davids cathedral and town centre.
CHILDREN: not under 12, except for exclusive-use bookings.
DOGS: not allowed.
CREDIT CARDS: Amex, MC, Visa.
PRICES: per room B&B £200–£280. À la carte £55. 2-night min. stay in summer months.

Prices may change – check with hotel.

SAUNDERSFOOT Pembrokeshire

ST BRIDES SPA HOTEL

High above the town, a modern hotel with 'exceptional' seascapes, as restorative, perhaps, as the calm that washes over guests in the award-winning spa. Four terrace areas overlook the beach, harbour and Carmarthen Bay. Light floods in through floor-to-ceiling windows; fresh sea air through glass doors. Bedrooms are breezily styled in blue and white; some rooms have a balcony. Residents get a 90-minute session in a thermal suite and marine infinity hydropool in the spa; ocean-inspired treatments can be booked. In the restaurant and bar, or on the terrace, Pembrokeshire produce and locally landed fish feature. A downhill stroll away, a chippy and beach barbecue in the village are offshoots.

MAP 3:D2
St Brides Hill
Saundersfoot SA69 9NH
T: 01834 812304
W: stbridesspahotel.com

BEDROOMS: 34. 1 suitable for disabled. Plus six 2-bed apartments in grounds, 12 self-catering in village.
OPEN: all year.
FACILITIES: lift, lounge, bar, restaurant, Gallery dining area, meeting/function rooms, in-room TV, civil wedding licence, 4 terraces, art gallery, spa (treatments, infinity hydropool), EV charging.
BACKGROUND MUSIC: all day in public areas.
LOCATION: 3 mins' walk to village.
CHILDREN: all ages welcomed.
DOGS: allowed in some ground-floor apartments.
CREDIT CARDS: Amex, MC, Visa.
PRICES: per room B&B single £145–£230, double £200–£390. À la carte £40.

Prices may change – check with hotel.

ST ANNE Alderney

THE BLONDE HEDGEHOG

Down the pretty cobbled streets of St Anne, this contemporary hotel makes a chic base from which to experience island life. The popular restaurant, marble-topped bar and modish bedrooms span a Victorian pub and a Georgian town house. A log-burner warms the cosy snug; there's a room for playing games and watching movies. Driven by the seasons, unfussy dishes are cooked to order and served in the stylish, rustic restaurant and terraced garden. Eat well, then retire to one of the well-equipped, handsome-hued bedrooms or suites; some have an original fireplace or a free-standing bathtub. Island activities (bird-watching, island-hopping, sea kayaking, etc) can be arranged, with a picnic to take along.

MAP 1: inset D6
6 Le Huret
St Anne
Alderney GY9 3TR
T: 01481 823230
W: blondehedgehog.com

BEDROOMS: 9. 5 in adjacent town house, 2 on ground floor, plus 3-bed cottage opposite, and 4-bed farmhouse.
OPEN: all year, except 25 Dec.
FACILITIES: bar, snug, restaurant, in-room TV, cinema/games room, terrace, ¼-acre garden, ground-floor public rooms wheelchair accessible.
BACKGROUND MUSIC: in bar, restaurant.
LOCATION: in town centre.
CHILDREN: all ages welcomed.
DOGS: allowed in bar, garden, cottage, assistance dogs allowed throughout.
CREDIT CARDS: Amex, MC, Visa.
PRICES: per room B&B single £150–£300, double £190–£420. À la carte £40. 1-night bookings refused during Alderney Week.

Prices may change – check with hotel.

NEW

ST BRELADE Jersey

ST BRELADE'S BAY HOTEL

In a 'fabulous' position, this large hotel in lush subtropical gardens overlooks a 'magnificent' sandy bay. It is run by 'extremely friendly, helpful and well organised' staff. Tasteful, and decorated in neutral tones, the 'very comfortable and well equipped' bedrooms range in size from a small single to a room suitable for a family or a spacious suite; most sea-facing rooms have a small balcony. Locally caught seafood and seasonal vegetables feature in the traditional restaurant. Excellent facilities include an outdoor heated swimming pool, a spa and a health club. For children there is a play area, a games room and a kids' pool. Descend to the beach for activities by the water and extensive walks.

MAP 1: inset E6
La Route de la Baie
St Brelade JE3 8EF
T: 01534 746141
W: stbreladesbayhotel.com

BEDROOMS: 77.
OPEN: all year.
FACILITIES: lift, ramps, bar, lounge, sun lounge, restaurant, in-room TV, toddlers' room, games room, snooker room, function room, wedding facilities, 5-acre grounds (outdoor restaurant, 2 heated swimming pools (19 by 9 metres, 1 for children), tennis, parking.
BACKGROUND MUSIC: jazz in bar, pianist in restaurant.
LOCATION: overlooking St Brelade's Bay.
CHILDREN: all ages welcomed.
DOGS: not allowed.
CREDIT CARDS: all major cards.
PRICES: per room B&B £130–£279, set dinner £35–£40, à la carte £45.

Prices may change – check with hotel.

ST PETER PORT Guernsey

LA COLLINETTE HOTEL

A short uphill stroll from the boats in the harbour, the Chambers family run their unpretentious, family-friendly hotel in a 19th-century house set in expansive grounds. Walls in the clubby, recently refurbished La Collinette bar and restaurant display black-and-white photos of the island's history and sporting links. Up the stairs, bedrooms are bright, simply decorated, and most have sea views. Uncomplicated dishes, perhaps with Guernsey lobsters and scallops, are served in the restaurant; in good weather, eat alfresco on the poolside terrace. Visit the German Naval Signals HQ, in former bunkers under today's self-catering accommodation, then head, with calling seagulls, to historic Candie Gardens.

MAP 1: inset E5
St Jacques
St Peter Port GY1 1SN
T: 01481 710331
W: lacollinette.com

BEDROOMS: 23. Plus 14 self-catering cottages and apartments.
OPEN: all year.
FACILITIES: lounge, bar, restaurant, in-room TV (Sky, Freeview), 2-acre garden, terrace, outdoor heated swimming pool, children's pool, play area, gym, sauna, spa treatments, restaurant and bar wheelchair accessible.
BACKGROUND MUSIC: in bar, restaurant.
LOCATION: less than 1 mile W of town centre.
CHILDREN: all ages welcomed.
DOGS: allowed only in self-catering accommodation, by arrangement.
CREDIT CARDS: MC, Visa.
PRICES: per person B&B £60–£160. Set dinner £20, à la carte £30.

Prices may change – check with hotel.

BELFAST
THE OLD RECTORY

A welcoming home away from home, Mary Callan's guest guest house is in a conservation area just south of the centre. The late Victorian former rectory is set back from the road behind a row of mature trees. The 'nicely furnished' drawing room has books, board games, and a hot toddy for cool days. Bedrooms are supplied with tea, coffee, biscuits and magazines; there's fresh milk in a mini-fridge on each landing. A light supper (soup, frittata) may be requested in advance. In the morning, 'generous' breakfasts taken by an open fire include Irish home-baked breads and home-made preserves. The bus to the city stops right outside; the hostess shares her local knowledge. Hillsborough Castle is 15 minutes' drive away.

MAP 6:B6
148 Malone Road
Belfast BT9 5LH
T: 028 9066 7882
W: anoldrectory.co.uk

BEDROOMS: 5. 1 on ground floor, suitable for disabled.
OPEN: all year except Christmas, New Year's Eve.
FACILITIES: drawing room, dining room, in-room TV (Freeview), garden, parking.
BACKGROUND MUSIC: traditional Irish music in breakfast room.
LOCATION: 2 miles from city centre.
CHILDREN: all ages welcomed.
DOGS: not allowed.
CREDIT CARDS: MC, Visa.
PRICES: per room B&B single £75–£108, double £108–£159. 2-night min. stay at weekends, bank holidays.

Prices may change – check with hotel.

BELFAST
RAVENHILL HOUSE

Handsomely restored, this double-fronted, red-brick B&B is just a short bus ride from the city centre. It is owned by Olive and Roger Nicholson, who welcome arriving guests with tea and oven-fresh treats. Individually decorated in keeping with the style of the Victorian house, bedrooms have good seating, home-baked shortbread, a vintage Hacker radio and modern facilities. A wide-ranging breakfast is served in a book-lined room with a wood-burning stove. The Nicholsons mill their own flour from organic Irish wheat grain for the freshly baked sourdough bread; there are also home-made marmalades and jams, spiced fruit compotes and good vegetarian options. Shops, restaurants and a leafy park are close by.

MAP 6:B6
690 Ravenhill Road
Belfast BT6 0BZ
T: 028 9028 2590
W: ravenhillhouse.com

BEDROOMS: 6.
OPEN: Feb–15 Dec.
FACILITIES: sitting room/breakfast room, in-room TV (Freeview), small garden, parking.
BACKGROUND MUSIC: classical music/ Radio 3 at breakfast.
LOCATION: 2 miles S of city centre.
CHILDREN: not under 10.
DOGS: not allowed.
CREDIT CARDS: Amex, MC, Visa.
PRICES: per room B&B £105–£150. 2-night min. stay in spring and summer.

Prices may change – check with hotel.

BUSHMILLS Co. Antrim

BUSHMILLS INN

Travellers have been enjoying the traditional comforts of this coaching inn, along the Causeway Coastal Route, since the 17th century, and still feel revived by its robust food, convivial bar, cosy nooks and spacious bedrooms. Some bedrooms have river views, others exposed beams, while all have space for armchairs or a sofa, and spoil with bathrobes, slippers and a dressing area. 'Our room was excellent, and very quiet.' Dine on modern dishes in the garden-facing restaurant – on the patio if warm – or hunker down in the Gas Bar, still lit by Victorian gas light, for simpler pub food; on Saturdays live music, too. The world's oldest distillery is a short stroll away.

MAP 6:A6
9 Dunluce Road
Bushmills BT57 8QG
T: 028 2073 3000
W: bushmillsinn.com

BEDROOMS: 41. Some, on ground floor, suitable for disabled.
OPEN: all year, no accommodation 24–25 Dec.
FACILITIES: lift, bar, lounge, restaurant, loft, cinema, in-room TV (Freeview), conference facilities, patio, 1-acre garden, parking, public areas wheelchair accessible.
BACKGROUND MUSIC: in public areas, live traditional Irish music sessions every Sat in bar.
LOCATION: in village centre, 2 miles from Giant's Causeway.
CHILDREN: all ages welcomed.
DOGS: allowed on patio.
CREDIT CARDS: Amex, MC, Visa.
PRICES: B&B doubles from £140.
À la carte £60 (in restaurant), 2 courses £25 in bar.

Prices may change – check with hotel.

CARAGH LAKE Co. Kerry

ARD NA SIDHE
COUNTRY HOUSE HOTEL

On the wooded shores of Lough Caragh, the extensive gardens of this Irish sandstone manor house are ripe for discovery: hidden paths lead to the water and the mountains beyond. The serene hotel has handsome bedrooms in the main house and around a rustic courtyard. Each has antique furnishings and a deep mattress; no TV, but, perhaps, the sound of water coming to shore. On crisp white linen, candlelit dinners are served in the elegant restaurant; regional dishes use fish from the Atlantic, local meat and cheeses. Afternoon tea is taken in the fire-warmed lounge, or on the terrace in fine weather. Complimentary boating and fishing on the lake can be arranged, along with a picnic hamper.

MAP 6:D4
Caragh Lake
Killorglin V93 HV57
T: 00 353 66 976 9105
W: ardnasidhe.com

BEDROOMS: 18. 1 on ground floor, suitable for disabled, 8 in Garden House.
OPEN: 21 Apr–15 Oct (closed Sun–Wed in Oct).
FACILITIES: lounge, library, restaurant, terrace, 32-acre grounds.
BACKGROUND MUSIC: in lounge, library.
LOCATION: on Lough Caragh, 8 km SW of Killorglin.
CHILDREN: all ages welcomed.
DOGS: not allowed.
CREDIT CARDS: Amex, MC, Visa.
PRICES: per room B&B double €245–€355. À la carte €60.

Prices may change – check with hotel.

CARLINGFORD Co. Louth
GHAN HOUSE

Beneath Slieve Foy mountain, stepping distance
from the sea and within walled gardens, the
Carroll family's Georgian house affords views
at every turn. 'A tree's length' from medieval
Carlingford, the house is filled with family
photographs and heirlooms, fresh flowers and
squashy sofas. Traditionally decorated bedrooms,
sprinkled with antiques, have home-made biscuits
to go with those views; most have a roll-top bath
and a power shower in a modern bathroom. After
a walk up the hills or along the seashore, return to
a fire in the drawing room. Modern Irish dishes
such as local salmon with salsa verde are served
in the dining room, elegant with candles. At
breakfast: home-made jams and marmalades.

MAP 6:B6
Carlingford A91 DXY5
T: 00 353 42 937 3682
W: ghanhouse.com

BEDROOMS: 12. 8 in garden annexe,
4 on ground floor.
OPEN: all year except 24–26, 31 Dec,
1–2 Jan; restaurant closed Mon, most
Tues in autumn and winter ('best to
book in advance').
FACILITIES: bar, lounge, restaurant,
private dining rooms, in-room TV
(Freeview), wedding facilities, 3-acre
garden, parking, EV charging.
BACKGROUND MUSIC: in bar, restaurant.
LOCATION: 'a tree's length' from town.
CHILDREN: all ages welcomed.
DOGS: allowed in kennels in converted
stables.
CREDIT CARDS: Amex, MC, Visa.
PRICES: B&B doubles from €180,
singles from €90. À la carte €57.50
(4-course), €49.50 (3-course), tasting
menu from €49.50.

Prices may change – check with hotel.

CORK
THE MONTENOTTE HOTEL

In tiered gardens, an impressive panorama
spreads over the city and harbour from this large,
modern hotel with an artistic bent. Colourful
china dogs greet visitors; the plushly furnished
public spaces have a stylish sense of fun. Diners
gather in curving booths in the bistro or on
sofas on the spacious heated terrace for Modern
Irish dishes off the all-day menu: salads, sharing
platters and heartier options. A glass bridge leads
to a rooftop bar for botanical cocktails, inspired
by the Victorian sunken garden below. Brightly
decorated bedrooms, some suitable for a family,
are equipped with bathrobes and slippers, bottled
waters and hot drinks. There are nightly cinema
screenings, and treatments in the spa.

MAP 6:D5
Middle Glanmire Road
Cork T23 E9DX
T: 00 353 21 453 0050
W: themontenottehotel.com

BEDROOMS: 107. Some suitable
for disabled, plus 26 self-catering
apartments.
OPEN: all year except 24–26 Dec.
FACILITIES: lobby, bistro, in-room TV
(Sky), wedding facilities, room service,
gym, spa (20-metre heated indoor
swimming pool, sauna, steam room,
hot tub, treatments), cinema, terrace,
Victorian gardens, woodland.
BACKGROUND MUSIC: in lobby and
bistro.
LOCATION: St Luke's Cross district.
CHILDREN: all ages welcomed.
DOGS: only assistance dogs allowed.
CREDIT CARDS: Amex, MC, Visa.
PRICES: per room €210–€330. Breakfast
€15, à la carte €55.

Prices may change – check with hotel.

NEW

DINGLE Co. Kerry

PAX HOUSE

'A haven of peace', John O'Farrell's 'terrific' contemporary B&B sits on a hilltop with 180-degree views over the harbour and Dingle peninsula. The large sitting room has interesting artwork, books, comfortable seating, and sensational scenery through floor-to-ceiling windows. In the evening, a drink and cheese platter can be enjoyed on the surrounding terrace. Among many thoughtful touches, there are fresh flowers and binoculars in the softly toned bedrooms. 'Delicious, beautifully presented' breakfasts have the feel of 'a special afternoon tea'; perhaps soft eggs in panko crumb on asparagus or home-made potato cake with smoked salmon and crème fraîche. The town is a 12-minute downhill walk.

MAP 6:D4
Upper John Street
Dingle V92 NX45
T: 00 353 66 915 1518
W: pax-house.com

BEDROOMS: 16.
OPEN: all year, except Nov–Mar.
FACILITIES: lounge, in-room TV, terrace, garden, parking.
BACKGROUND MUSIC: none.
LOCATION: 1 km from Dingle.
CHILDREN: over 12 welcomed.
DOGS: allowed in 1 bedroom, not in lounge, breakfast room. Resident dog and cat.
CREDIT CARDS: MC, Visa.
PRICES: per room €140–€265.

Prices may change – check with hotel.

INIS MEAIN Co. Galway

INIS MEAIN RESTAURANT AND SUITES

Remote and remarkable, Ruairí and Marie-Thérèse de Blacam's sustainably run restaurant-with-suites blends into the rugged Aran Islands landscape. Wood, glass, stone and wool define the large, architectural suites; each has vast views through panoramic windows and from outdoor seating areas. In the Michelin green-starred restaurant, short menus use prime produce from their greenhouse, farm and surrounding waters: think oyster and scallop tartare, monkfish with tzatziki, rhubarb soufflé. Breakfasts (freshly baked breads, eggs, fruit, cured meats) are delivered to suites. 'Hotpot' lunches and exploration kits (bikes, fishing rods, swimming towels, binoculars, maps, nature guides) are included.

MAP 6:C4
Inis Meáin
Aran Islands H91 NX86
T: 00 353 86 826 6026
W: inismeain.com

BEDROOMS: 5 suites.
OPEN: Wed–Sat, Apr–Aug (2-night min.); Mon–Thurs, Sept, Oct and Mar (4-night min).
FACILITIES: restaurant, 3-acre grounds.
BACKGROUND MUSIC: none.
LOCATION: centre of a small island, 15 miles off the Galway coast; 40-min. ferry from Ros a' Mhíl or 7-min. flight from Connemara airport.
CHILDREN: not under 12.
DOGS: not allowed.
CREDIT CARDS: MC, Visa.
PRICES: doubles €300–€650 per night includes lunch, exploration kit, transport to/from ferry/airport. Set 4-course dinner €75.

Prices may change – check with hotel.

LISDOONVARNA Co. Clare
WILD HONEY INN

Within the Burren and Cliffs of Moher Geopark, Ireland's only Michelin-starred pub attracts discerning diners with its refined bistro cooking and country-cosy accommodation. It is owned and run by chef/patron Aidan McGrath and his partner, Kate Sweeney. In the informal bar and dining room, Aidan's frequently changing menus are based on sustainable gastronomy, and feature flavourful Irish produce – organic vegetables, freshly picked berries, seasonal game, wild fish straight off the day boat. Uncluttered bedrooms, some with views of the surrounding countryside, some snug, have traditional charm and many fine touches: duck-down duvets, hand-woven throws, glossy magazines. Bespoke nature walks can be organised.

MAP 6:C4
Kincora Road
Lisdoonvarna V95 P234
T: 00 353 65 707 4300
W: wildhoneyinn.com

BEDROOMS: 13. 3 on ground floor.
OPEN: Mar–Oct, closed Sun, Mon, Tues.
FACILITIES: bar, lounge/drawing room, restaurant, in-room TV, courtyard garden.
BACKGROUND MUSIC: classical music in reception and at breakfast, 'an eclectic playlist' in bar.
LOCATION: on the edge of town.
CHILDREN: not allowed.
DOGS: not allowed.
CREDIT CARDS: MC, Visa.
PRICES: per room B&B €190–€270. Prix fixe menu €85.

Prices may change – check with hotel.

RAMELTON Co. Donegal
FREWIN

Peaceful, old-fashioned charm is found at Regina Gibson and Thomas Coyle's relaxing B&B in a Victorian rectory on the outskirts of a Georgian port town on the Wild Atlantic Way. Set in a large garden, the creeper-covered house has been sympathetically restored. There are stained-glass windows, interesting pictures and antiques, plus shelves of books to peruse. Upstairs, spacious, traditionally decorated bedrooms, each with a compact bathroom, might have a four-poster bed, roll-top bath or separate sitting area. Breakfasts are taken communally in a sunny dining room with a view of the mature wooded grounds. The congenial hosts can help arrange golf, fishing and guided hikes in the Bluestack mountains.

MAP 6:B5
Rectory Road
Ramelton F92 DW77
T: 00 353 74 915 1246
W: frewinhouse.com

BEDROOMS: 3. Plus 1-bedroom cottage in grounds.
OPEN: Mar–end Oct, by special arrangement for small groups in Feb and Nov.
FACILITIES: sitting room, library, dining room, 2-acre garden.
BACKGROUND MUSIC: none.
LOCATION: on the outskirts of town.
CHILDREN: not under 16.
DOGS: not allowed.
CREDIT CARDS: MC, Visa.
PRICES: per room B&B single €125–€130, double €170–€180.

Prices may change – check with hotel.

RATHNEW Co. Wicklow

HUNTER'S

Enveloped in old-world charm, with 'staff who really make an effort', this rambling, 'extremely comfy' hotel in 'lovely' grounds by the River Vartry has been owned by the same family for almost 200 years. Said to be Ireland's oldest coaching inn, the current stewards, the Gelletlie brothers, run it with 'acceptable eccentricity': antiques, old prints and floral fabrics decorate the rooms; most of the chintz-filled bedrooms overlook the 'inspiring' garden. 'Delicious' classic cuisine is served on crisp table linens in the dining room. 'Well worth a stop-over from the Rosslare ferry.' Gardens, golf courses and mountain scenery are close by.

MAP 6:C6
Newrath Bridge
Rathnew A67 TN30
T: 00 353 404 40106
w: hunters.ie

BEDROOMS: 16. 1 on ground floor.
OPEN: all year except 24–26, 31 Dec.
FACILITIES: drawing room, lounge, bar, dining room, private dining room, in-room TV (Freeview), 5-acre grounds, golf, tennis, fishing nearby.
BACKGROUND MUSIC: none.
LOCATION: 1 mile SE of Ashford.
CHILDREN: all ages welcomed.
DOGS: allowed in garden, not in bedrooms.
CREDIT CARDS: MC, Visa.
PRICES: B&B €150–€190. Lunch from €30. À la carte from €30. Set dinner from €45.

Prices may change – check with hotel.

ALPHABETICAL LIST OF HOTELS

(S) indicates a Shortlist entry

INDEX OF HOTELS BY COUNTY
(S) indicates a Shortlist entry

BRITISH ISLES MAPS

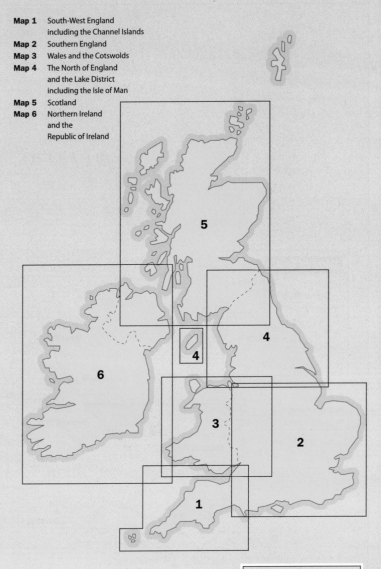

Channel Islands

1

Not to scale

MAP 1 • SOUTH-WEST ENGLAND

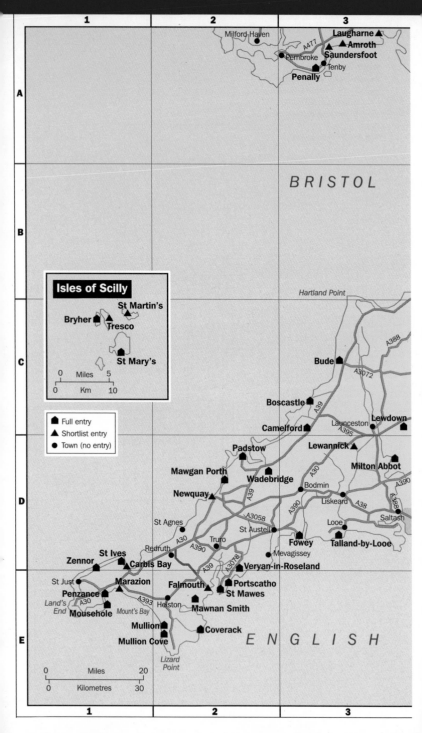

1   **2**   **3**

Milford-Haven

A477

Laugharne ▲

▲ Amroth

Pembroke

Saundersfoot

Tenby

Penally

A

BRISTOL

B

Isles of Scilly

St Martin's ▲

Bryher ■

Tresco

St Mary's

0   Miles   5

0   Km   10

Hartland Point

C

A388

Bude ■

A3072

■ Full entry

▲ Shortlist entry

● Town (no entry)

Boscastle ▲

A39

Lewdown ■

Camelford ■

Launceston

Lewannick ▲

Padstow ■

Milton Abbot ■

Mawgan Porth ■

Wadebridge ■

A30

Bodmin

A390

A388

Newquay ▲

D

A3058

Liskeard

A38

A390

St Agnes ●

St Austell ●

Saltash

Looe ●

Redruth ●

Truro ●

Fowey ■

Talland-by-Looe ■

A390

A39

Mevagissey ●

St Ives ▲

Zennor ■

Carbis Bay ▲

A3078

Veryan-in-Roseland ■

St Just ●

Marazion ▲

Falmouth ■

Portscatho ▲

Penzance ■

A393

St Mawes ■

Land's End

A30

Helston ●

Mawnan Smith ■

Mousehole ■

Mount's Bay

Mullion ■

Coverack ■

E

Mullion Cove ■

E N G L I S H

Lizard Point

0   Miles   20

0   Kilometres   30

1   **2**   **3**

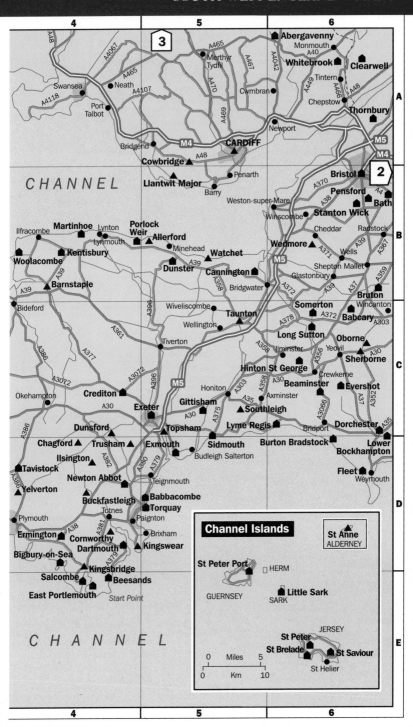

4 · **5** · **6**

3

Swansea · Neath · A48 · A4118 · Port Talbot · A4067 · A465 · A4107 · A4107 · A410 · A467 · Merthyr Tydfil · A469 · A465 · A4042 · Cwmbran

Abergavenny · Monmouth · A40 · **Whitebrook** · Tintern · **Clearwell** · A449 · A466 · A48

Newport · Chepstow · **Thornbury** · M5 · M4 · **A**

Bridgend · M4 · **CARDIFF** · A48

Cowbridge · Penarth · **Bristol** · A370 · A4 · **Pensford** · A38 · **Bath** · **2**

Llantwit Major · Barry · Weston-super-Mare · **Stanton Wick** · A367

CHANNEL

Martinhoe · Lynton · **Porlock Weir** · **Allerford** · Minehead · Cheddar · Radstock · **B**

Ilfracombe · Lynmouth · **Watchet** · **Wedmore** · A371 · Wells · A39 · A367

Kentisbury · **Dunster** · A39 · **Cannington** · Shepton Mallet · A359 · A372 · **Bruton** · A359

Woolacombe · Bridgwater · Glastonbury · A37 · Wincanton

Barnstaple · A39 · Wiveliscombe · **Somerton** · A372 · **Babcary** · A303

Bideford · A396 · **Taunton** · A378 · **Long Sutton** · **Oborne** · A30

A361 · Wellington · Ilminster · A356 · Yeovil · **Sherborne** · A30

Okehampton · A3072 · Tiverton · A358 · **Hinton St George** · Crewkerne · **Evershot** · A37 · **C**

A377 · A3072 · M5 · Honiton · A303 · **Beaminster** · A3066

Crediton · A30 · A35 · Axminster · A356 · **Dorchester** · A35

A386 · **Exeter** · **Gittisham** · A30 · A375 · **Southleigh** · Bridport · **Lower Bockhampton**

Dunsford · **Topsham** · **Lyme Regis**

Chagford · **Trusham** · **Exmouth** · **Sidmouth** · **Burton Bradstock** · **D**

Tavistock · **Ilsington** · A382 · Budleigh Salterton · **Fleet** · Weymouth

Yelverton · **Newton Abbot** · Teignmouth

A386 · **Buckfastleigh** · **Babbacombe**

Plymouth · Totnes · **Torquay**

A38 · Paignton

Ermington · **Cornworthy** · Brixham

A381 · **Dartmouth**

Bigbury-on-Sea · **Kingsbridge** · **Kingswear**

Salcombe · **Beesands**

East Portlemouth · *Start Point*

CHANNEL

Channel Islands

St Anne
ALDERNEY

St Peter Port · □ HERM

GUERNSEY · **Little Sark**

SARK

JERSEY

St Peter
St Brelade · **St Saviour**
St Helier

| 0 | Miles | 5 |
| 0 | Km | 10 |

MAP 2 · SOUTHERN ENGLAND

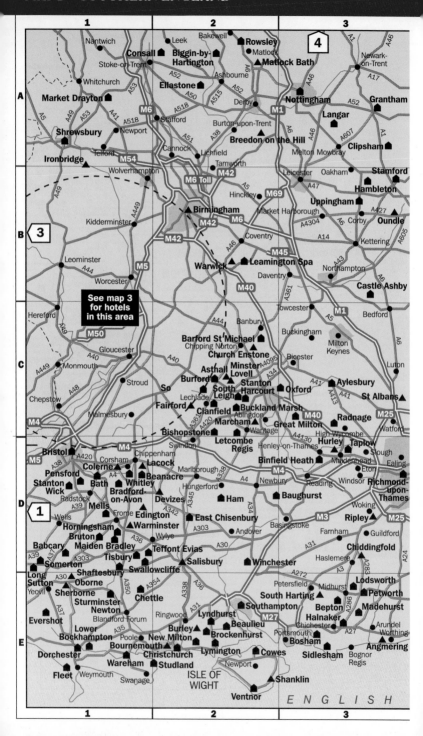

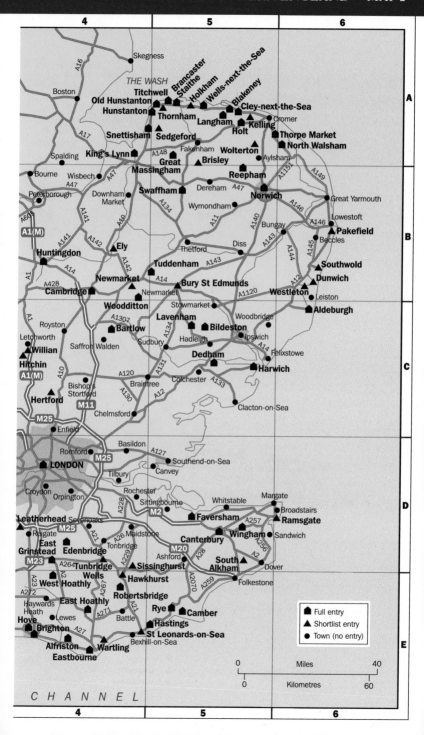

4 **5** **6**

THE WASH

Skegness

Boston

Brancaster
Staithe
Titchwell Holkham Wells-next-the-Sea
Old Hunstanton Blakeney
Hunstanton Thornham Cley-next-the-Sea
Langham Cromer
Snettisham Sedgeford Holt Kelling
Fakenham Wolterton Thorpe Market
Spalding King's Lynn Great Brisley North Walsham
A148 Massingham Aylsham
Bourne Wisbech A47 Reepham A149 Great Yarmouth
A16 Swaffham Dereham Norwich
Peterborough Downham A134 A47
A605 Market Wymondham A146 Lowestoft
A1(M) A141 A10 A11 Bungay A146 Pakefield
Huntingdon A142 Ely Thetford Diss A143 Beccles
A1 A14 Tuddenham A143 Southwold
A428 Newmarket A14 Bury St Edmunds Dunwich
Cambridge Newmarket A1120 Westleton
Royston A1307 Stowmarket Leiston
Wooddton Lavenham Woodbridge Aldeburgh
Letchworth Bartlow A134 Bildeston
Willian Saffron Walden Sudbury Hadleigh Ipswich
Hitchin A10 Dedham A14 Felixstowe
A1(M) A120 A331 Colchester Harwich
Hertford Bishop's A133
M25 Stortford A130 A12 Clacton-on-Sea
Enfield Chelmsford
Basildon A127
Romford M25 Southend-on-Sea
LONDON Tilbury Canvey
Croydon Rochester Whitstable Margate
Orpington Sittingbourne Broadstairs
Leatherhead Sevenoaks M2 Faversham Ramsgate
Reigate M25 A257 Wingham Sandwich
East Edenbridge Maidstone Canterbury A256
Grinstead Tonbridge M20 A2
M23 A264 Ashford South Dover
West Tunbridge Sissinghurst Alkham
Hoathly Wells Hawkhurst A20 Folkestone
East Hoathly Robertsbridge A259
Haywards A21 Rye Camber
Heath Lewes Battle Hastings
Hove Brighton A27 St Leonards-on-Sea
Alfriston Wartling Bexhill-on-Sea
Eastbourne

■ Full entry
▲ Shortlist entry
● Town (no entry)

0 ———— Miles ———— 40
0 ———— Kilometres ———— 60

C H A N N E L

4 **5** **6**

MAP 3 · WALES AND THE COTSWOLDS

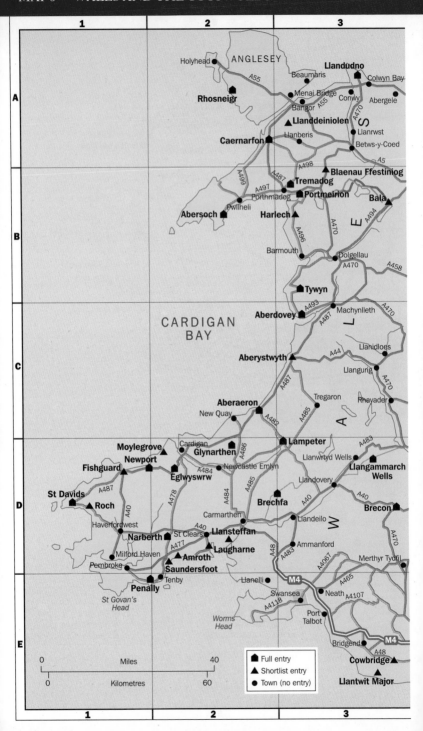

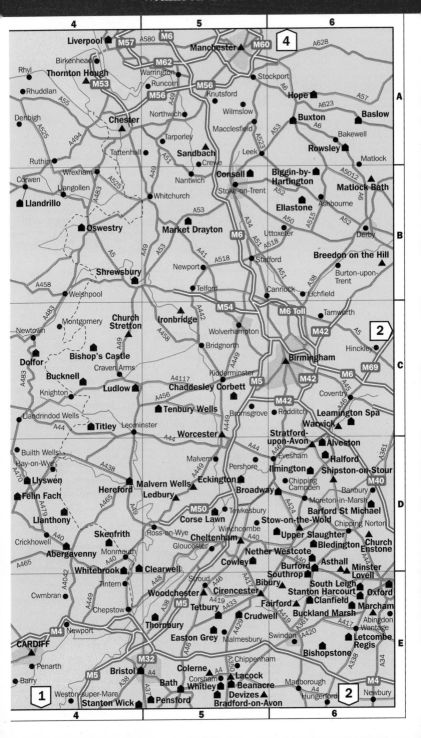

MAP 4 · THE NORTH OF ENGLAND AND THE LAKE DISTRICT

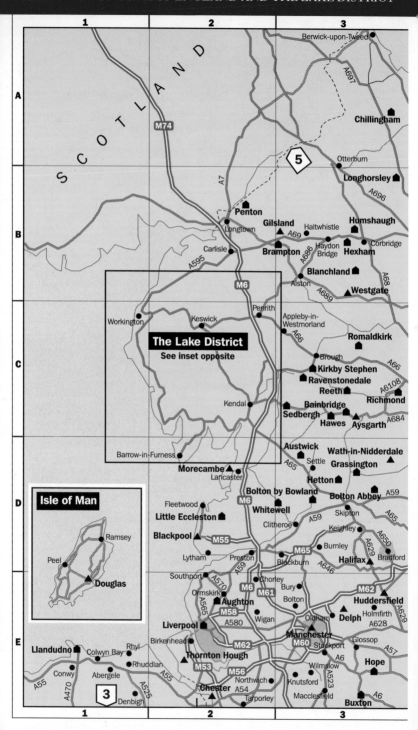

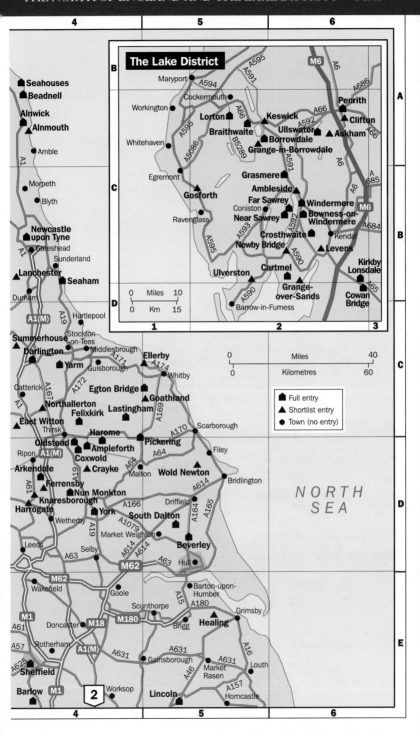

The Lake District

Maryport
Workington
Whitehaven
Egremont
Ravenglass
Cockermouth
Lorton
Braithwaite
Keswick
Ullswater
Borrowdale
Grange-in-Borrowdale
Grasmere
Ambleside
Gosforth
Far Sawrey
Coniston
Near Sawrey
Windermere
Bowness-on-Windermere
Crosthwaite
Newby Bridge
Kendal
Levens
Ulverston
Cartmel
Grange-over-Sands
Kirkby Lonsdale
Cowan Bridge
Barrow-in-Furness
Penrith
Clifton
Askham

0 Miles 10
0 Km 15

Seahouses
Beadnell
Alnwick
Alnmouth
Amble
Morpeth
Blyth
Newcastle upon Tyne
Gateshead
Sunderland
Lanchester
Seaham
Durham
Hartlepool

Summerhouse
Darlington
Yarm
Stockton-on-Tees
Middlesbrough
Guisborough
Ellerby
Whitby
Catterick
Egton Bridge
Goathland
Northallerton
Felixkirk
Lastingham
Thirsk
East Witton
Harome
Scarborough
Oldstead
Ampleforth
Coxwold
Pickering
Filey
Ripon
Arkendale
Crayke
Malton
Wold Newton
Ferrensby
Nun Monkton
Bridlington
Knaresborough
Harrogate
York
Wetherby
South Dalton
Driffield
Leeds
Selby
Market Weighton
Beverley
Hull

Wakefield
Goole
Barton-upon-Humber
Scunthorpe
Grimsby
Doncaster
Brigg
Healing
Rotherham
Sheffield
Gainsborough
Market Rasen
Louth
Barlow
Worksop
Lincoln
Horncastle

NORTH SEA

Miles 40
Kilometres 60

■ Full entry
▲ Shortlist entry
● Town (no entry)

MAP 5 • SCOTLAND

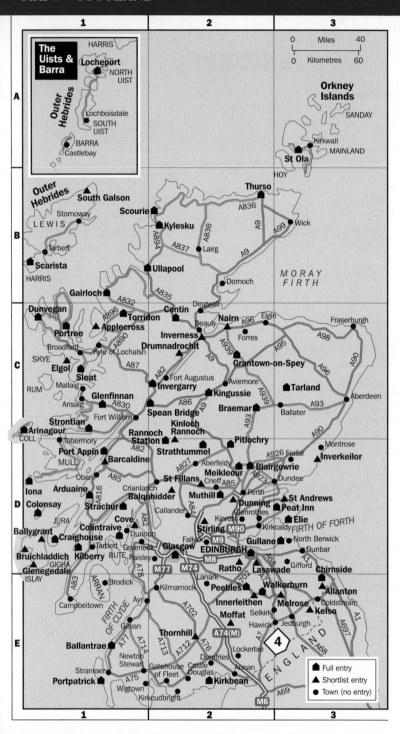

The Uists & Barra

HARRIS
Locheport
NORTH UIST
Outer Hebrides
Lochboisdale
SOUTH UIST
BARRA
Castlebay

0 Miles 40
0 Kilometres 60

Orkney Islands

SANDAY
Kirkwall
MAINLAND
St Ola
HOY

Outer Hebrides
South Galson
Stornoway
LEWIS
Tarbert
Scarista
HARRIS

Thurso
A836
Scourie
Kylesku
A894 A837 A836 A9 A99 Wick
Lairg
Ullapool
Dornoch
MORAY FIRTH

A835
Gairloch A832
Dingwall
Dunvegan Contin Nairn A96 Elgin Fraserburgh
Torridon A896 Beauly A98
Portree Applecross Inverness Forres A95
Broadford A890 Drumnadrochit A96 A90
SKYE Kyle of Lochalsh Grantown-on-Spey
Elgol A87 A9 Aviemore A939
Sleat A82 Fort Augustus Tarland
RUM Mallaig Invergarry Kingussie Aberdeen
Glenfinnan A830 A86 Braemar A93 Ballater A90
Arisaig Fort William Spean Bridge A9
Strontian Kinloch Rannoch A93 Montrose
COLL Arinagour Rannoch Station Pitlochry
Tobermory A82 Strathtummel Inverkeilor
Port Appin Barcaldine Aberfeldy A926 Forfar
MULL Oban A85 St Fillans Meikleour Blairgowrie
Iona Arduaine Crianlarich Crieff A85 A923 Dundee
Colonsay Strachur Balquhidder Muthill Perth
JURA A816 Cove Callander A84 Dunning St Andrews
Ballygrant Colintraive Kinross Glenrothes Peat Inn
Craighouse Dunoon Kirkcaldy Elie
Bruichladdich Kilberry Tarbert Greenock Stirling FIRTH OF FORTH
GIGHA BUTE Paisley Glasgow M9 M90 Gullane
Glenegedale Brodick Falkirk North Berwick
ISLAY A83 ARRAN EDINBURGH Dunbar
Campbeltown Kilmarnock M77 M74 M8 Ratho Lasswade Gifford Chirnside
FIRTH OF CLYDE Ayr Lanark A702 A68 Walkerburn Allanton
Ballantrae Girvan Peebles Melrose Coldstream
A77 A713 Innerleithen Selkirk Kelso
Stranraer Newton Stewart Thornhill Moffat A7 Jedburgh A697 A1
Portpatrick A75 Gatehouse A76 A74(M) Hawick A68
of Fleet Castle Lockerbie
Wigtown Douglas Dumfries Annan
Kirkbean ENGLAND
Kirkcudbright A69 M6

■ Full entry
▲ Shortlist entry
● Town (no entry)

1   2   3
A
B
C
D
E

4

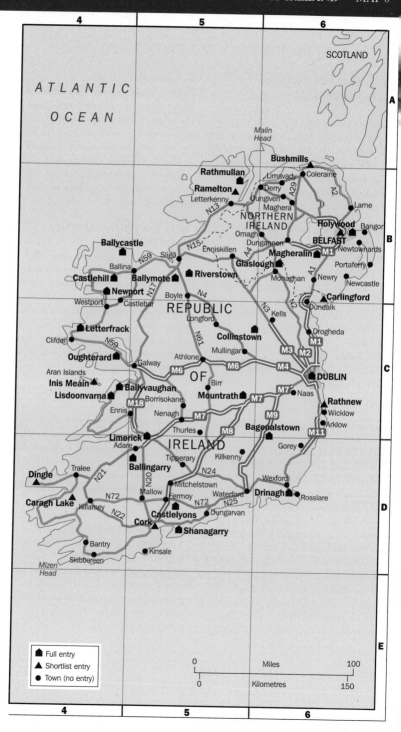

SCOTLAND

ATLANTIC

OCEAN

Malin
Head

Bushmills

Rathmullan
Limavady
Coleraine

Ramelton
Derry
Larne

Letterkenny
Dungiven
A29
A2

N13
Maghera

NORTHERN
Holywood
Bangor

IRELAND
Omagh
Dungannon
BELFAST
Newtownards

Ballycastle
N15
Enniskillen
Magheralin
M1
Portaferry

Sligo
N59
Glaslough
A1
Newcastle

Ballina
Riverstown
Monaghan
Newry

Castlehill
Ballymote
N2
Carlingford

Newport
Boyle
N4
Dundalk

Westport
Castlebar
REPUBLIC
N3
Kells
Drogheda

Letterfrack
Longford
M3
M1

Clifden
N61
Collinstown
M2

N59
Athlone
Mullingar
M4
DUBLIN

Oughterard
M6
M6
OF

Aran Islands
Birr
M7
Naas

Inis Meáin
Ballyvaughan
Borrisokane
Mountrath
M7
Rathnew

Lisdoonvarna
M18
Nenagh
M7
M9
Wicklow

Ennis
IRELAND
Thurles
M8
Bagenalstown
Arklow

Limerick
M11

Adare
Tipperary
Kilkenny
Gorey

Dingle
Tralee
Ballingarry
N24
Wexford

Caragh Lake
N21
Mitchelstown
Drinagh
Rosslare

Killarney
N72
Mallow
Waterford

N22
Fermoy
N72

N20
Castlelyons
Dungarvan

Cork
N25

Shanagarry

Bantry
Kinsale

Skibbereen

Mizen
Head

Legend:
- ⬟ Full entry
- ▲ Shortlist entry
- ● Town (no entry)

0   Miles   100

0   Kilometres   150

FREQUENTLY ASKED QUESTIONS

HOW DO YOU CHOOSE A GOOD HOTEL?

The hotels we like are relaxed, unstuffy and personally run. We do not have a specific template: our choices vary greatly in style and size. Most of the hotels in the Guide are family owned and family run. These are places where the needs and comfort of the guest are put ahead of the convenience of the management.

WHAT ARE YOUR LIKES AND DISLIKES?

We like
* Flexible times for meals.
* Two decent armchairs in the bedroom.
* Good bedside lighting.
* Proper hangers in the wardrobe.
* Fresh milk with the tea tray in the room.

We dislike
* Intrusive background music.
* Stuffy dress codes.
* Bossy notices and house rules.
* Hidden service charges.
* Packaged fruit juices at breakfast.

YOU ARE A HOTEL GUIDE – WHY DO YOU INCLUDE SO MANY PUBS AND B&BS?

Attitudes and expectations have changed considerably since the Guide was founded in the 1970s. Today's guests expect more informality, less deference. There has been a noticeable rise in the standards of food and accommodation in pubs and restaurants. This is demonstrated by the number of such places suggested to us by our readers. While pubs may have a more relaxed attitude than some traditional hotels, we ensure that only those that maintain high standards of service are included in our selections. The best B&Bs have always combined a high standard of accommodation with excellent value for money. Expect the bedrooms in a pub or B&B listed in the Guide to be well equipped, with thoughtful extras. B&B owners invariably know how to serve a good breakfast.

WHY DO YOU SOMETIMES DROP HOTELS?

Readers don't hesitate to tell us if they think standards have slipped at a hotel. If the evidence is overwhelming, we drop the hotel from the Guide or perhaps downgrade it to the Shortlist. Sometimes we send inspectors just to be sure. When a hotel is sold, we look for reports since the new owners took over, otherwise we inspect or omit it.

WHAT SHOULD I TELL YOU IN A REPORT?

How you enjoyed your stay. We welcome reports of any length. We want to know what you think about the welcome, the service, the building and the facilities. Even a short report can tell us a great deal about the owners, the staff and the atmosphere.

HOW SHOULD I SEND YOU A REPORT?

You can email us at editor@goodhotelguide.com. Or you can write to us at the address given on the report form opposite, or send a report via the GHG's website: goodhotelguide.com.

Please send your reports to:
The Good Hotel Guide, 94 Church Lane, London N2 0TB, England.

Unless asked not to, we assume that we may publish your name. If you would like more report forms please tick ☐ Alternatively, you can either photostat this form or submit a review on our website: goodhotelguide.com

NAME OF HOTEL: _____

ADDRESS: _____

_____

Date of most recent visit: _____ Duration of stay: _____

☐ New recommendation   ☐ Comment on existing entry

Report:

Please continue overleaf

I am not connected directly or indirectly with the management or proprietors

Signed: _____

Name: (CAPITALS PLEASE) _____

Address: _____

_____

Email address: _____